12-10-64

37724
1608

D1269188

INTERNATIONAL SERIES OF MONOGRAPHS IN

PURE AND APPLIED MATHEMATICS

GENERAL EDITORS: I. N. SNEDDON, M. STARK AND S. ULAM

VOLUME 63

LINEAR REPRESENTATIONS OF THE LORENTZ GROUP

LINEAR REPRESENTATIONS OF THE LORENTZ GROUP

M. A. NAIMARK

Translated by

ANN SWINFEN

and

O. J. MARSTRAND

Translation edited by

H. K. FARAHAT
DEPARTMENT OF MATHEMATICS
THE UNIVERSITY OF SHEFFIELD

A Pergamon Press Book

THE MACMILLAN COMPANY
NEW YORK
1964

THE MACMILLAN COMPANY
60 Fifth Avenue
New York 11, N.Y.

This book is distributed by
THE MACMILLAN COMPANY
pursuant to a special arrangement with
PERGAMON PRESS LIMITED
Oxford, England

Copyright © 1964
Pergamon Press Ltd.

This translation has been made from M. A. Naimark's book entitled ЛИНЕЙНЫЕ ПРЕДСТАВЛЕНИЯ ГРУППЫ ЛОРЕНЦА (Lineinyye predstavleniya gruppy Lorentsa) published in 1958 by Fizmatgiz, Moscow

Library of Congress Catalog Card Number 63-10025

QA171
.N15
1964

PRINTED IN POLAND
PWN–DRP

CONTENTS

PREFACE

THE study of the linear representations of a given group is one of the most important problems of the theory of groups; it has a great number of applications in various branches of mathematics and of theoretical physics. A specially important part in theoretical physics is played by the representations of the three-dimensional rotation group and of the Lorentz group. The importance of the former is bound up with the fact that a knowledge of the representations of the three-dimensional rotation group enables us to describe in invariant form the physical magnitudes and equations of non-relativistic mechanics. This invariance is the mathematical expression of the independence of the laws of non-relativistic mechanics of the choice of the coordinate system. The representations of the Lorentz group play an analogous part in relativistic mechanics; in this case the invariance is with respect to the transformations of the Lorentz group, and this is the mathematical expression of the independence of the laws of relativistic mechanics of the choice of inertial system of reference (see §§ 2, 17 and 18).

The finite-dimensional irreducible representations of the complete Lorentz group and proper Lorentz group are well known (see, e.g. Ref. [7a]) and are widely used in quantum mechanics; it is known that none of these representations is unitary, with the exception of the trivial unity representation. The study of the infinite-dimensional representations of the Lorentz group may prove useful for the further development of quantum theory.

Apart from this, the study of the infinite-dimensional representations of the proper Lorentz group is a good introduction to the general theory of infinite-dimensional representations of semi-simple Lie groups. Indeed, it was this simplest example of the proper Lorentz group, which elucidated the characteristic properties of the representations of complex semi-simple Lie groups.

For example the representations of the so-called complementary series are not included in the decomposition of the regular representation into irreducible components; while for commutative and compact groups, the decomposition of the regular representation yields all the irreducible representations of the group. Moreover, many methods of the general theory of infinite-dimensional representations of semi-simple Lie groups were originally worked out for the simplest case of the proper Lorentz group.

A complete description of all the irreducible unitary representations of the Lorentz group, to within equivalence, has been given in papers by I. M. Gelfand and the author(see Refs. [12a] and [12b]). It was found that the formulae obtained for the operators of the representations retain a definite meaning also for those values of the parameters for which these representations cease to be unitary (see Ref. [12b]). The question thus arises as to whether the resulting formulae determine, in some sense, *all* irreducible representations and not only the unitary ones. This problem was solved by the author in Ref. [28c], where all the completely irreducible representations of the proper Lorentz group were found, to within equivalence. The definition of equivalence of two representations of the Lorentz group given there seems to us to be the most natural one in the theory of representations; from the point of view of this definition the spaces of two equivalent representations need not be isometric, so that it is the formulae which are essential for the representations and not the norm of the space.

The method of investigation is a development of the method, previously applied by the author in Ref. [28b] for the description of all irreducible unitary representations of the complex classical groups. It is to be noted that this method can also be applied to the description of all completely irreducible linear representations of semi-simple Lie groups (not only the unitary ones†).

The author recently used his method in Ref. [28f] for the exact formulation and solution of the problem of describing all completely

† F. A. Berezin recently developed another method of describing the irreducible representations of complex semi-simple Lie groups. Ref. [5b].

irreducible representations of the complete Lorentz group to within equivalence.

In connection with these results, the problem of finding all the representations (not only the completely irreducible ones) of the proper Lorentz group and the complete Lorentz group, remains unsolved.†

The solution of this problem has important applications especially to the theory of relativistically invariant equations, which still lacks a conclusive treatment.

The present book is devoted to a systematic exposition of the theory of linear representations of the proper Lorentz group and the complete Lorentz group. Having in mind physicist readers, the author has endeavoured to make the exposition as elementary as possible, so that the reader is not expected to have any special mathematical knowledge beyond what is acquired in university courses on analysis and analytical geometry. The necessary supplementary information is given in the text itself or in the appendices.

The book consists of four chapters. The first two chapters are of an introductory nature; they contain an exposition of the basic material on the three-dimensional rotation group, on the complete Lorentz group and the proper Lorentz group, as well as the theory of representations of the three-dimensional rotation group in the form in which it will be needed in the chapters that follow. In addition, the second chapter contains an exposition of the necessary basic information from the general theory of group representations. Chapter III is devoted to the representations of the proper Lorentz group and the complete Lorentz group. The first three sections are of a more elementary nature and contain a description of the completely irreducible representations of the proper Lorentz group in infinitesimal form and of spinor representations. In order to make the exposition simple the author has imposed on the representations some supplementary conditions; later on (in §§ 13 and 15) it is proved that these conditions in fact hold for any

† Added in proof. This problem was recently discussed by Zhelobenko.

completely irreducible representation of the proper Lorentz group. Then, in §§ 10–14, we give the theory of infinite-dimensional representations of the proper Lorentz group in integral form, the theory of characters (traces) and Plancherel's formula for the proper Lorentz group.

Finally, §§ 15 and 16 contain the formulation and solution of the problem of describing all completely irreducible representations of the proper Lorentz group and complete Lorentz group to within equivalence; the detailed exposition of these matters is here given for the first time.

The last chapter (Chapter IV) deals with the theory of invariant equations. As mentioned above, this theory cannot yet be considered complete; nevertheless, in view of the important applications of the theory, the author considered the inclusion of this chapter to be justified.

The author expresses his sincere thanks to I. M Gelfand, M. I. Grayev, D. P. Zhelobenko and S. V. Fomin who have read through the manuscript of the book and made many valuable suggestions.

M. A. NAIMARK

CHAPTER I†

THE THREE-DIMENSIONAL ROTATION GROUP AND THE LORENTZ GROUP

§ 1. The Three-dimensional Rotation Group

1. General definition of a group

An aggregate G of elements $g, h, \ldots$ is called a *group*, if

(1) in G there is defined the product gh of any two elements $g, h \in G$ in such a way that the product of these two elements g, $h \in G$ also belongs to G;

(2) $(g_1 g_2)g_3 = g_1(g_2 g_3)$ for any three elements $g_1, g_2, g_3 \in G$;

(3) G has an element e satisfying the conditions

$$eg = ge = g \tag{1}$$

for all $g \in G$; the element e is called the *unit element* of the group G;

(4) for any element $g \in G$ there exists an element $h \in G$ such that

$$hg = gh = e. \tag{2}$$

The element h is called the inverse of the element g and is denoted by g^{-1}. Thus, from the definition of the inverse element,

$$g^{-1}g = gg^{-1} = e. \tag{3}$$

We note that the group G has only one unit element. For, if we suppose that there is another unit element e_1 in G, then $ee_1 = e$ and at the same time $ee_1 = e_1$; therefore $e = e_1$.

Further, for every element g there exists only one inverse g^{-1}. For, supposing that the element g, besides having the inverse

---

† *Publisher's note*: §§ 1–9 were translated by O. J. Marstrand.

$g^{-1} = h$, also has another inverse h_1, then $h_1 g = e$; by multiplying both sides of this equation by h we get:

$$h_1(gh) = h,$$

i.e. $h_1 = h$.

Equation (3) shows that the element g is the inverse of g^{-1}, so that

$$(g^{-1})^{-1} = g. \tag{4}$$

Let us note also that the product gh need not be commutative, i.e. in general $gh \neq hg$; the group G is called *commutative* (or Abelian) if $gh = hg$ for all g, $h \in G$.†

2. Definition of the three-dimensional rotation group

We shall use the above definitions in the case when the elements $g, h, \ldots$ are all the possible rotations of 3-dimensional space about a fixed point. Let G_0 denote the aggregate of all such rotations. We shall then define the product gh of two rotations g, h to be the rotation obtained by successive applications first of the rotation h and then of the rotation g.

It is easy to verify that all the conditions of the general definition of a group are satisfied, so that, with this definition of the product of rotations, G_0 becomes a group; the unit element of the group G_0 will be the rotation through zero angle, while the inverse of a given rotation g is the rotation that returns the space into the initial position.

The group G_0 is called the *three-dimensional rotation group.*

3. Description of rotations by means of orthogonal matrices

Take a fixed orthogonal system of coordinates with origin O; let e_1, e_2, e_3 be unit vectors along the coordinate axes. A rotation g takes these vectors into three mutually orthogonal vectors which we denote respectively by g_1, g_2, g_3. These vectors are completely

---

† We confine ourselves here only to those facts about the theory of groups which we shall need; the reader, if interested in the general theory of groups, is referred to one of the text-books on that theory (see, for example, Ref. [23]).

determined by their projections on the axes of coordinates; therefore, denoting the projection of the vector g_k on the ith-axis by g_{ik}, we see that the vectors g_1, g_2, g_3 are completely determined by the matrix

$$\begin{Vmatrix} g_{11} & g_{12} & g_{13} \\ g_{21} & g_{22} & g_{23} \\ g_{31} & g_{32} & g_{33} \end{Vmatrix}. \tag{1}$$

We shall also denote the matrix (1) by the letter g and call it the *matrix of the rotation* g.

I. *The rotation g is completely determined by the vectors g_1, g_2, g_3 and therefore by its matrix g.* In fact, every vector x in 3-dimensional space may be represented in the form

$$x = x_1 e_1 + x_2 e_2 + x_3 e_3,$$

where x_1, x_2, x_3 are the projections of x on the respective coordinate axes. The rotation g takes the vectors e_1, e_2, e_3 into vectors g_1, g_2, g_3 and consequently the vector x into the vector $x' = x_1 g_1 + x_2 g_2 + x_3 g_3$, completely determined by the numbers x_1, x_2, x_3 and the vectors g_1, g_2, g_3.

It is easy to express the projections x'_1, x'_2, x'_3 of the vector x' on the coordinate axes in terms of the projections of the vector x. In fact, from the equations

$$\begin{aligned} x' &= x'_1 e_1 + x'_2 e_2 + x'_3 e_3 = x_1 g_1 + x_2 g_2 + x_3 g_3 \\ &= x_1(g_{11}e_1 + g_{21}e_2 + g_{31}e_3) + x_2(g_{12}e_1 + g_{22}e_2 + g_{32}e_3) \\ &\qquad + x_3(g_{13}e_1 + g_{23}e_2 + g_{33}e_3) \end{aligned}$$

it follows that

$$\left.\begin{aligned} x'_1 &= g_{11}x_1 + g_{12}x_2 + g_{13}x_3, \\ x'_2 &= g_{21}x_1 + g_{22}x_2 + g_{23}x_3, \\ x'_3 &= g_{31}x_1 + g_{32}x_2 + g_{33}x_3. \end{aligned}\right\} \tag{2}$$

Consequently, *the rotation g is determined by the linear transformation of the projections x_1, x_2, x_3* with matrix g. The successive application, first of a rotation h and then of a rotation g corresponds to the successive application of the linear transformation with matrix h and the linear transformation with matrix g. The result is the linear transformation whose matrix is the product gh of the matrices g and h. Thus:

II. *The product gh of two rotations g, h corresponds to the product of their matrices.* Let us now determine which matrices g are the matrices of rotations. The vectors e_1, e_2, e_3 can be transformed into the vectors g_1, g_2, g_3 by a rotation if and only if the latter three vectors are mutually orthogonal, normalized and have the same orientation as the vectors e_1, e_2, e_3, that is if

$$\sum_{k=1}^{3} g_{ki} g_{kj} = \begin{cases} 1 & \text{if} \quad i = j, \\ 0 & \text{if} \quad i \neq j \end{cases} \tag{3}$$

$$(i, j = 1, 2, 3)$$

and†

$$\begin{vmatrix} g_{11} & g_{12} & g_{13} \\ g_{21} & g_{22} & g_{23} \\ g_{31} & g_{32} & g_{33} \end{vmatrix} = 1. \tag{4}$$

A matrix g satisfying conditions (3) is called *orthogonal.*

Our reasoning shows that a *matrix g is the matrix of a rotation if and only if it is an orthogonal matrix with determinant unity.*

From this and from Proposition II we conclude that *the group G_0 can be realized as the group of all orthogonal matrices of order three with determinant unity.*

Conditions (3) mean that

$$g'g = 1, \tag{5}$$

where

$$1 = \begin{Vmatrix} 1 & 0 & 0 \\ 0 & 1 & 0 \\ 0 & 0 & 1 \end{Vmatrix}$$

is the unit matrix, while

$$g' = \begin{Vmatrix} g_{11} & g_{21} & g_{31} \\ g_{12} & g_{22} & g_{32} \\ g_{13} & g_{23} & g_{33} \end{Vmatrix}$$

is the transposed matrix of g.

† See for example Ref. [20], § 60–61.

But then g' is the inverse matrix of g, that is $g' = g^{-1}$ and so

$$gg' = gg^{-1} = 1;$$

consequently, also

$$\sum_{k=1}^{3} g_{ik} g_{jk} = \begin{cases} 1 & \text{if} \quad i = j, \\ 0 & \text{if} \quad i \neq j \end{cases} \tag{6}$$

$$(i, j = 1, 2, 3).$$

4. Eulerian angles

The above results show that the rotation g may be specified by nine parameters, namely the elements g_{ik} of the matrix of this rotation; however these parameters are not independent, but are connected by the relations (3) and (4) of Subsection 3.

Among a number of problems that arise, an important one is that of describing rotations by independent parameters. An example of such parameters is furnished by the Eulerian angles.

Let the rotation g take the coordinate axes Ox, Oy, Oz into the axes Ox', Oy', Oz' (Fig. 1).†

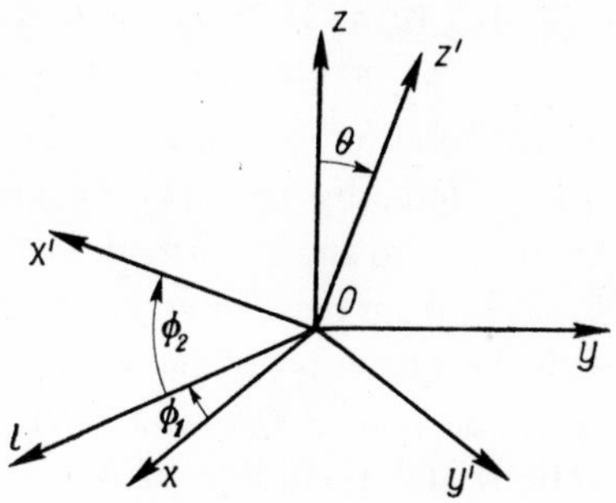

FIG. 1.

Let Ol be the line of intersection of the planes xOy and $x'Oy'$ and assign to this line such a direction that, to an observer looking in that direction, the rotation through an angle $\leqslant \pi$ taking the

† In Subsections 4 and 5, it will be more convenient to denote the coordinates of a point by the letters x, y, z instead of x_1, x_2, x_3.

axis Oz into the axis Oz' would appear to be anti-clockwise. This condition determines the direction of Ol uniquely, except when Oz and Oz' coincide or make an angle equal to π.

Further, let us denote by ϕ_1 the angle between the axis Ox and the line Ol and by ϕ_2 the angle between the line Ol and the axis Ox' and by θ the angle between Oz and Oz'. Finally, let g_ϕ and g_θ denote the rotations about Oz and Ox through angles ϕ and θ respectively. The rotation g can be represented as a product $g = \tilde{g}_{\phi_2}\tilde{g}_\theta g_{\phi_1}$ of three rotations g_{ϕ_1}, $\tilde{g}_\theta$, $\tilde{g}_{\phi_2}$ about the axes Oz, Ol, Oz' respectively.† In fact, as a result of the rotation g_{ϕ_1}, the axis Ox coincides with Ol, after which, as a result of the rotation $\tilde{g}_\theta$, the axis Oz will coincide with Oz' and then, as a result of the rotation $\tilde{g}_{\phi_2}$, the axes Ox and Oy will coincide with Ox' and Oy'.

The rotations $\tilde{g}_\theta$ and $\tilde{g}_{\phi_2}$ were made about the auxiliary axes Ol and Oz'; they can be expressed in terms of rotations about the initial axes Ox and Oz.

In fact, $\tilde{g}_\theta$ is the rotation g_θ of the *new* system of coordinate axes obtained from the initial system by the rotation g_{ϕ_1}; therefore $\tilde{g}_\theta = g_{\phi_1} g_\theta g_{\phi_1}^{-1}$. Similarly, $\tilde{g}_{\phi_2} = (\tilde{g}_\theta g_{\phi_1}) g_{\phi_2} (\tilde{g}_\theta g_{\phi_1})^{-1}$ and therefore $g = \tilde{g}_{\phi_2}\tilde{g}_\theta g_{\phi_1} = (\tilde{g}_\theta g_{\phi_1}) g_{\phi_2} (\tilde{g}_\theta g_{\phi_1})^{-1} \tilde{g}_\theta g_{\phi_1} = \tilde{g}_\theta g_{\phi_1} g_{\phi_2} = g_{\phi_1} g_\theta g_{\phi_2}$.

Thus, the angles ϕ_1, ϕ_2, θ are independent parameters fully determining the given rotation g; they are called the *Eulerian angles of the rotation.* Here, by the very definition of Eulerian angles, $0 \leqslant \phi_1 \leqslant 2\pi$, $0 \leqslant \phi_2 \leqslant 2\pi$, $0 \leqslant \theta \leqslant \pi$. Different sets of three numbers ϕ_1, ϕ_2, θ, taken from these intervals, correspond to different rotations g, with the exception of the cases $\theta = 0$ and $\theta = \pi$. In these special cases the planes xOy and $x'Oy'$ coincide (except possibly in orientation) and their line of intersection Ol is indeterminate. By taking this line in various ways as the initial line for measuring the angles ϕ_1 and ϕ_2 we conclude that in the first case the pairs (ϕ_1, ϕ_2) and $(\phi_1+\alpha, \phi_2-\alpha)$ determine one and the same rotation; similarly, in the second case the pairs $(\phi_1+\alpha, \phi_2+\alpha)$ are equivalent for any α.

It is easy to express the elements g_{ik} of a matrix of a rotation

† The directions of rotation are shown on the figure by arrows.

in terms of its Eulerian angles. Indeed, from the definition of the rotations g_{ϕ_1}, g_θ, g_{ϕ_2}, it follows that their matrices have the forms

$$\left.\begin{aligned} g_{\phi_1} &= \begin{Vmatrix} \cos\phi_1 & -\sin\phi_1 & 0 \\ \sin\phi_1 & \cos\phi_1 & 0 \\ 0 & 0 & 1 \end{Vmatrix}; \quad g_\theta = \begin{Vmatrix} 1 & 0 & 0 \\ 0 & \cos\theta & -\sin\theta \\ 0 & \sin\theta & \cos\theta \end{Vmatrix}; \\ g_{\phi_2} &= \begin{Vmatrix} \cos\phi_2 & -\sin\phi_2 & 0 \\ \sin\phi_2 & \cos\phi_2 & 0 \\ 0 & 0 & 1 \end{Vmatrix}. \end{aligned}\right\} \tag{1}$$

But when the rotations g_{ϕ_1}, g_θ, g_{ϕ_2} are multiplied, their matrices have to be multiplied; therefore

$$g = g_{\phi_1} g_\theta g_{\phi_2} = \begin{Vmatrix} \cos\phi_1\cos\phi_2 - \cos\theta\sin\phi_1\sin\phi_2 & -\cos\phi_1\sin\phi_2 - \cos\theta\sin\phi_1\cos\phi_2 & \sin\phi_1\sin\theta \\ \sin\phi_1\cos\phi_2 + \cos\theta\cos\phi_1\sin\phi_2 & -\sin\phi_1\sin\phi_2 + \cos\theta\cos\phi_1\cos\phi_2 & -\cos\phi_1\sin\theta \\ \sin\phi_2\sin\theta & \cos\phi_2\sin\theta & \cos\theta \end{Vmatrix}. \tag{2}$$

From this formula it follows that, *if the rotation g is given by the angles ϕ_1, ϕ_2, θ, then the rotation g^{-1} is given by the angles $\pi-\phi_2$, $\pi-\phi_1$, θ.*

In fact, direct substitution in formula (2) shows that if ϕ_1, ϕ_2, θ are replaced by $\pi-\phi_2$, $\pi-\phi_1$, θ the matrix g changes into the transposed matrix $g' = g^{-1}$. (See (5) Subsection 3.)

5. The description of rotations by means of unitary matrices

We shall now show that rotations can also be specified by unitary matrices of order two. With this end in view we consider a fixed sphere S with centre at O. Every rotation g results in a rotation of the sphere, and is evidently fully determined by that rotation of the sphere. On the other hand, the points of the sphere correspond, under stereographic projection, to points of the complex plane; consequently, the rotations g correspond to transformations of the complex plane. Let us find these transformations.

To be definite, let the diameter of the sphere S be unity. Stereographic projection maps the point P of the sphere S to the point ζ of the plane $\xi\eta$ on the ray joining the point N (the "north pole" of the sphere S) to the point P (Fig. 2). Denote by x, y, z the coordinates of the point P, and put $\zeta = \xi + i\eta$.

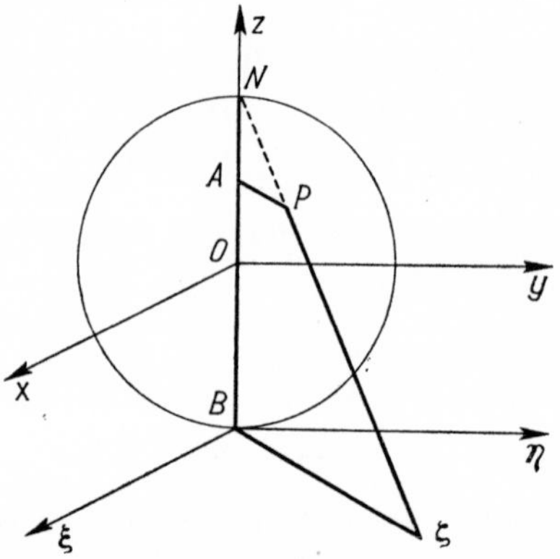

FIG. 2.

From the similarity of the triangles NAP and $NB\zeta$ it readily follows that $\xi = \dfrac{x}{\frac{1}{2}-z}$, $\eta = \dfrac{y}{\frac{1}{2}-z}$, and therefore

$$\zeta = \xi + i\eta = \frac{x+iy}{\frac{1}{2}-z}. \tag{1}$$

It then also follows from the relation $x^2+y^2 = \frac{1}{4}-z^2$ that

$$\zeta = \frac{x^2+y^2}{(\frac{1}{2}-z)(x-iy)} = \frac{\frac{1}{2}+z}{x-iy}. \tag{2}$$

We have to find how ζ is transformed by an arbitrary rotation g. Since any rotation can be given in the form of a product $g = g_{\phi_1} g_\theta g_{\phi_2}$, it is sufficient to answer this question for the rotations g_{ϕ_2}, g_θ, g_{ϕ_1}. But, under a rotation g_ϕ, the coordinates x, y, z are transformed according to the formulae

$$x' = x\cos\phi - y\sin\phi, \quad y' = x\sin\phi + y\cos\phi, \quad z' = z,$$

and therefore ζ goes into

$$\zeta' = \frac{x'+iy'}{\frac{1}{2}-z'} = \frac{e^{i\phi}(x+iy)}{\frac{1}{2}-z} = e^{i\phi}\zeta.$$

Consequently, the rotation g_ϕ corresponds to the transformation

$$\zeta' = e^{i\phi}\zeta. \tag{3}$$

Similarly, under the rotation g_θ the expression $w = \dfrac{y+iz}{\frac{1}{2}-x}$ goes into

$$w' = e^{i\theta}w. \tag{4}$$

But by virtue of formulae (1) and (2)

$$\frac{w+i}{w-i} = \frac{\dfrac{y+iz}{\frac{1}{2}-x}+i}{\dfrac{y+iz}{\frac{1}{2}-x}-i} = \frac{-(x+iy)+(\frac{1}{2}+z)}{(x-iy)-(\frac{1}{2}-z)}$$

$$= \frac{-\zeta(\frac{1}{2}-z)+(\frac{1}{2}+z)}{\dfrac{1}{\zeta}(\frac{1}{2}+z)-(\frac{1}{2}-z)} = \zeta,$$

whence

$$w = i\frac{\zeta+1}{\zeta-1}.$$

Similarly

$$w' = i\frac{\zeta'+1}{\zeta'-1}.$$

Therefore formula (4) means that

$$\frac{\zeta'+1}{\zeta'-1} = e^{i\theta}\frac{\zeta+1}{\zeta-1}.$$

Solving this equation for ζ' we obtain that the rotation g_θ corresponds to the transformation

$$\zeta' = \frac{\zeta(e^{i\theta}+1)+(e^{i\theta}-1)}{\zeta(e^{i\theta}-1)+(e^{i\theta}+1)} = \frac{\zeta\cos\dfrac{\theta}{2}+i\sin\dfrac{\theta}{2}}{i\zeta\sin\dfrac{\theta}{2}+\cos\dfrac{\theta}{2}}. \tag{5}$$

Each of the transformations (3) and (5) is a bilinear transformation of the form

$$\zeta' = \frac{\alpha\zeta+\beta}{\gamma\zeta+\delta}. \tag{6}$$

Multiplication of rotations corresponds to the successive application of the corresponding transformations (6) as a result of which a transformation of the form (6) is again obtained. Consequently, to every rotation g *corresponds a bilinear transformation of the variable* ζ. The determinant $\alpha\delta-\beta\gamma$ of the transformation (6) can be taken to be equal to unity; if it is not already unity, we can divide all the coefficients α, β, γ, δ by $\pm\sqrt{(\alpha\delta-\beta\gamma)}$. It is evident that the coefficients α, β, γ, δ, that is the matrix $\left\|\begin{matrix}\alpha & \beta\\ \gamma & \delta\end{matrix}\right\|$, of the bilinear transformation are thereby determined uniquely to within a factor ± 1.

In particular, to the transformation (3) correspond the two matrices

$$\left\|\begin{matrix} e^{\frac{i\phi}{2}} & 0 \\ 0 & e^{-\frac{i\phi}{2}} \end{matrix}\right\|, \quad \left\|\begin{matrix} -e^{\frac{i\phi}{2}} & 0 \\ 0 & -e^{-\frac{i\phi}{2}} \end{matrix}\right\|, \tag{7}$$

while the transformation (5) corresponds to the matrices

$$\left\|\begin{matrix} \cos\frac{\theta}{2} & i\sin\frac{\theta}{2} \\ i\sin\frac{\theta}{2} & \cos\frac{\theta}{2} \end{matrix}\right\|, \quad \left\|\begin{matrix} -\cos\frac{\theta}{2} & -i\sin\frac{\theta}{2} \\ -i\sin\frac{\theta}{2} & -\cos\frac{\theta}{2} \end{matrix}\right\|, \tag{8}$$

with determinant unity. It is easy to find the matrix of the bilinear transformation corresponding to an arbitrary rotation $g=g_{\phi_1}g_\theta g_{\phi_2}$. In fact, for the consecutive application of the bilinear transformations corresponding to rotations g_{ϕ_1}, g_θ, g_{ϕ_2}, the matrices of these rotations must be multiplied; therefore the rotation g corresponds to the matrix

$$\pm\left\|\begin{matrix} e^{\frac{i\phi_1}{2}} & 0 \\ 0 & e^{-\frac{i\phi_1}{2}} \end{matrix}\right\| \left\|\begin{matrix} \cos\frac{\theta}{2} & i\sin\frac{\theta}{2} \\ i\sin\frac{\theta}{2} & \cos\frac{\theta}{2} \end{matrix}\right\| \left\|\begin{matrix} e^{\frac{i\phi_2}{2}} & 0 \\ 0 & e^{-\frac{i\phi_2}{2}} \end{matrix}\right\|$$

$$= \pm \begin{Vmatrix} \cos\frac{\theta}{2} e^{\frac{i(\phi_1+\phi_2)}{2}} & i\sin\frac{\theta}{2} e^{-\frac{i(\phi_2-\phi_1)}{2}} \\ i\sin\frac{\theta}{2} e^{\frac{i(\phi_2-\phi_1)}{2}} & \cos\frac{\theta}{2} e^{-\frac{i(\phi_1+\phi_2)}{2}} \end{Vmatrix}. \tag{9}$$

Each matrix of the left hand side of (9) is a unitary matrix† with determinant unity:

$$\alpha\delta - \beta\gamma = 1, \tag{10}$$

and therefore the product of these matrices, that is the matrix on the right hand side of (9), is a unitary matrix with determinant unity (this may also be verified directly).

Thus, *to each rotation g there correspond two unitary matrices* $u(g)$ and $-u(g)$ *with determinant unity, differing only by the factor* -1, *such that the product of the rotations g_1 and g_2 corresponds the product $u(g_1)u(g_2)$ of the corresponding matrices.*

Conversely, to each unitary matrix $\begin{Vmatrix} \alpha & \beta \\ \gamma & \delta \end{Vmatrix}$ with determinant unity, there corresponds some rotation g. In fact‡ from the conditions required to make this matrix unitary, viz:

$$\alpha\bar{\gamma} + \beta\bar{\delta} = 0, \quad \alpha\bar{\alpha} + \beta\bar{\beta} = 1, \quad \gamma\bar{\gamma} + \delta\bar{\delta} = 1$$

and, from the condition $\alpha\delta - \beta\gamma = 1$, it follows that

$$\bar{\beta} = \alpha\delta\bar{\beta} - \beta\bar{\beta}\gamma = -\alpha(\bar{\alpha}\gamma) - \beta\bar{\beta}\gamma = -(\alpha\bar{\alpha} + \beta\bar{\beta})\gamma = -\gamma,$$
$$\bar{\delta} = \alpha\delta\bar{\delta} - \beta\gamma\bar{\delta} = \alpha\delta\bar{\delta} + \gamma \cdot \alpha\bar{\gamma} = \alpha(\delta\bar{\delta} + \gamma\bar{\gamma}) = \alpha;$$

consequently, every unitary matrix u with determinant unity, can be represented in the form

---

† A matrix is said to be unitary, if $\overline{a}'a = a\overline{a}' = 1$ where a' is the transpose of a and $\overline{a}'$ is the matrix whose elements are the complex-conjugates of the elements of a'. It follows therefore that the statement that a matrix a is unitary is equivalent to the relations

$$\sum_\nu \overline{a}_{\nu j} a_{\nu k} = \sum_\nu a_{j\nu} \overline{a}_{k\nu} = \begin{cases} 1 & \text{if } j = k, \\ 0 & \text{if } j \neq k. \end{cases}$$

Incidentally a bar over a complex number will henceforth indicate its conjugate.

‡ See the preceding footnote.

$$u = \begin{Vmatrix} \alpha & \beta \\ -\bar{\beta} & \bar{\alpha} \end{Vmatrix}, \quad \text{where} \quad |\alpha|^2 + |\beta|^2 = 1. \tag{11}$$

Therefore there exists a real number θ, $0 \leqslant \theta \leqslant \pi$, for which

$$\cos\frac{\theta}{2} = |\alpha|, \quad \sin\frac{\theta}{2} = |\beta|; \tag{12}$$

further, putting

$$\frac{\phi_1 + \phi_2}{2} = \arg\alpha, \quad \frac{\phi_1 - \phi_2}{2} + \frac{\pi}{2} = \arg\beta, \tag{13}$$

we reduce the matrix u to the form (9). This means that the matrix u corresponds to the rotation $g = g_{\phi_1} g_\theta g_{\phi_2}$. Changing the angle ϕ_1 or ϕ_2 by adding or subtracting 2π does not alter the corresponding matrix g, but the matrix u changes into $-u$. Consequently, *to each rotation g there correspond two unitary matrices with determinant unity, differing only by a factor* -1, *and conversely, to every such unitary matrix there corresponds some rotation g.*

We note that it is impossible to avoid this ambiguity in the matrices of the rotation g, if we require that the elements of a matrix should be continuous functions of θ, ϕ_1, ϕ_2. In fact, if the angle ϕ_1 is increased continuously to $\phi_1 + 2\pi$, each of the matrices (9) changes continuously into the other, i.e. is multiplied by -1; the same thing happens if the angle ϕ_2 is increased continuously to $\phi_2 + 2\pi$. If, therefore, we wish to preserve the continuity of the elements of the matrix u, we must take it that to every rotation g there correspond two matrices (9).

Let us denote by $\mathfrak{U}$ the aggregate of all unitary matrices u with determinant unity; it is evident that $\mathfrak{U}$ forms a group, if in $\mathfrak{U}$ we define multiplication as multiplication of matrices. The group $\mathfrak{U}$ is called the *unitary group*.† The results obtained above signify that, under the correspondence $g \to u$ which we have set up between the elements of the groups G_0 and $\mathfrak{U}$, the product of elements

† [Editor's note.] This term is used to describe the group of all unitary matrices in the English literature. The group $\mathfrak{U}$ is usually called the special unitary group.

of the group G_0 corresponds to the product of the corresponding elements of the group $\mathfrak{U}$.

The matrix of a rotation g may be expressed in terms of the elements α, β of the corresponding matrix u as follows:

$$g = \begin{Vmatrix} \frac{1}{2}(\alpha^2-\beta^2+\bar{\alpha}^2-\bar{\beta}^2) & \frac{i}{2}(\alpha^2+\beta^2-\bar{\alpha}^2-\bar{\beta}^2) & -\alpha\beta-\bar{\alpha}\bar{\beta} \\ \frac{i}{2}(-\alpha^2+\beta^2+\bar{\alpha}^2-\bar{\beta}^2) & \frac{1}{2}(\alpha^2+\beta^2+\bar{\alpha}^2+\bar{\beta}^2) & i(\alpha\beta-\bar{\alpha}\bar{\beta}) \\ \alpha\bar{\beta}+\bar{\alpha}\beta & i(\alpha\bar{\beta}-\bar{\alpha}\beta) & \alpha\bar{\alpha}-\beta\bar{\beta} \end{Vmatrix}. \quad (14)$$

In order to verify this, it is sufficient to substitute for α, β the expressions for them given by formula (9); after a simple manipulation we arrive at the expression (2) of Subsection 4 for the matrix g in terms of the Eulerian angles.

6. The invariant integral over the rotation group

We shall say that a function $w = f(g)$ is defined over the group G_0 if to each rotation $g \in G_0$ there corresponds some number w. If the rotation g is given by the Eulerian angles ϕ_1, ϕ_2, θ then $f(g)$ becomes simply the following function of ϕ_1, ϕ_2, θ:

$$f(g) = f(\phi_1, \phi_2, \theta),$$

where

$$f(\phi_1+2\pi, \phi_2, \theta) = f(\phi_1, \phi_2, \theta), \quad f(\phi_1, \phi_2+2\pi, \theta) = f(\phi_1, \phi_2, \theta).$$

The integral

$$\int_0^{2\pi}\int_0^{2\pi}\int_0^{\pi} f(g)\omega(g)\mathrm{d}\phi_1\mathrm{d}\phi_2\mathrm{d}\theta = \int_0^{2\pi}\int_0^{2\pi}\int_0^{\pi} f(\phi_1, \phi_2, \theta)\omega(\phi_1, \phi_2, \theta)\mathrm{d}\phi_1\mathrm{d}\phi_2\mathrm{d}\theta,$$

is called the *invariant integral* of the function $f(g)$ over the group G_0, if the factor $\omega(g)$ is so chosen that, for any function $f(g) = f(\phi_1, \phi_2, \theta)$, continuous with respect to ϕ_1, ϕ_2, θ, the following condition is satisfied:

$$\int_0^{2\pi}\int_0^{2\pi}\int_0^{\pi} f(gg_0)\omega(g)\mathrm{d}\phi_1\mathrm{d}\phi_2\mathrm{d}\theta = \int_0^{2\pi}\int_0^{2\pi}\int_0^{\pi} f(g)\omega(g)\mathrm{d}\phi_1\mathrm{d}\phi_2\mathrm{d}\theta. \quad (1)$$

By direct calculation it is possible to show that the factor $\omega(g)$ is determined uniquely (by the above condition) except for a numerical factor.† However, we shall nowhere be obliged to make use of this fact; therefore we shall confine ourselves simply to proving the existence of the factor $\omega(g)$ and to a direct verification that it satisfies condition (1). In other words, we prove that the function

$$\omega(g) = \sin\theta \quad \text{for} \quad g = g_{\phi_1} g_\theta g_{\phi_2} \tag{2}$$

satisfies condition (1), i.e. that the expression

$$\int_0^{2\pi}\int_0^{2\pi}\int_0^{\pi} f(g)\sin\theta\,\mathrm{d}\phi_1\,\mathrm{d}\phi_2\,\mathrm{d}\theta \tag{3}$$

is an invariant integral over the group G_0. For this purpose put $\tilde{g} = gg_0$ and let $\tilde{\phi}_1, \tilde{\phi}_2, \tilde{\theta}$ be the Eulerian angles of the rotation $\tilde{g}$; it is evident that $\tilde{\phi}_1, \tilde{\phi}_2, \tilde{\theta}$ are functions of the Eulerian angles ϕ_1, ϕ_2, θ of the rotation g and condition (1) for the integral (3) means that we must have

$$\int_0^{2\pi}\int_0^{2\pi}\int_0^{\pi} f(\tilde{\phi}_1, \tilde{\phi}_2, \tilde{\theta})\sin\theta\,\mathrm{d}\phi_1\,\mathrm{d}\phi_2\,\mathrm{d}\theta = \int_0^{2\pi}\int_0^{2\pi}\int_0^{\pi} f(\phi_1, \phi_2, \theta)\sin\theta\,\mathrm{d}\phi_1\,\mathrm{d}\phi_2\,\mathrm{d}\theta. \tag{4}$$

If in the integral on the left, we change the variables of integration ϕ_1, ϕ_2, θ to the variables $\tilde{\phi}_1, \tilde{\phi}_2, \tilde{\theta}$, we see that it will be equal to the integral on the right hand side provided that this change of variable takes $\sin\theta\,\mathrm{d}\phi_1\,\mathrm{d}\phi_2\mathrm{d}\theta$ into $\sin\tilde{\theta}\,\mathrm{d}\tilde{\phi}_1\,\mathrm{d}\tilde{\phi}_2\,\mathrm{d}\tilde{\theta}$, that is, provided that

$$\sin\tilde{\theta}\,\mathrm{d}\tilde{\phi}_1\,\mathrm{d}\tilde{\phi}_2\,\mathrm{d}\tilde{\theta} = \sin\theta\,\mathrm{d}\phi_1\,\mathrm{d}\phi_2\,\mathrm{d}\theta. \tag{5}$$

To prove relation (5) let P be the point on the unit sphere to which the point $N(0,0,1)$ is carried as a result of the rotation $g^{-1} = g'$ (see Fig. 3), and denote by Q the point on the same sphere to which the point (1,0,0) is carried as a result of the rotation g'. It is evident that the points P,Q completely determine the rota-

† This result also follows without any computation, from the general theory of integration on topological groups (see, for instance. Ref, [8] Chap. II.)

tion g; the point P can be chosen arbitrarily on the sphere, and then the point Q arbitrarily on the great circle K, whose plane is perpendicular to the radius OP. But, as a result of the application of the matrix g', the vector (0,0,1) goes into the vector (g_{31}, g_{32}, g_{33}),

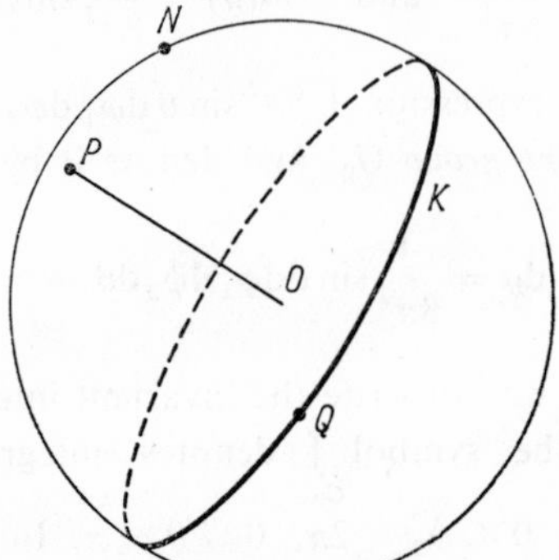

FIG. 3.

so that g_{31}, g_{32}, g_{33} are the Cartesian coordinates of P. It follows by formula (2), Subsection 4, that the spherical coordinates of this point are $\pi/2-\phi_2$, θ; consequently $\sin\theta d\phi_2\, d\theta$ is a spherical surface element at the point P. On the other hand $d\phi_1$, is an element of arc of the circle K. In fact, an increment $d\phi_1$ in ϕ_1, with fixed ϕ_2 and θ, corresponds to a rotation through $d\phi_1$ about OP, that is, a displacement of $d\phi_1$ of the point Q.

But the points $\tilde{P}$ and $\tilde{Q}$, corresponding to the rotation $\tilde{g} = gg_0$, are obtained from the points P and Q by the rotation g_0'. This rotation leaves both the surface element $\sin\theta d\phi_2\, d\theta$ and the element of arc $d\phi_1$ of the circle K invariant; it follows that their product $\sin\theta d\phi_1 d\phi_2 d\theta$ also remains invariant, which proves formula (5).

It is evident that, for any positive constant c, the multiple $\dot{\omega}(g) = c\sin\theta$ also satisfies condition (1). Let us choose c so that the following condition is satisfied:

$$\int_0^{2\pi}\int_0^{2\pi}\int_0^{\pi} c\sin\theta\, d\phi_1 d\phi_2 d\theta = 1, \tag{6}$$

that is

$$8\pi^2 c = 1.$$

Hence

$$c = \frac{1}{8\pi^2} \quad \text{and} \quad \omega(g) = \frac{1}{8\pi^2}\sin\theta.$$

We shall call the expression $1/8\pi^2 \sin\theta \, d\phi_1 \, d\phi_2 \, d\theta$ *the invariant volume element of the group* G_0 and denote it by dg, so that

$$dg = \frac{1}{8\pi^2}\sin\theta d\phi_1 d\phi_2 d\theta. \tag{7}$$

Using this notation we can write the invariant integral in the form $\int\limits_{G_0} f(g) dg$, where the symbol $\int\limits_{G_0}$ denotes integration over the range $0 \leqslant \phi_1 \leqslant 2\pi$, $0 \leqslant \phi_2 \leqslant 2\pi$, $0 \leqslant \theta \leqslant \pi$. In future we shall drop the letter G_0 and denote the invariant integral over the whole group G_0 by $\int f(g)\,dg$. The condition (1) of invariance will then become

$$\int f(gg_0)dg = \int f(g)dg. \tag{8}$$

We note that furthermore

$$\int f(g^{-1})dg = \int f(g)dg \tag{9}$$

and

$$\int f(g_0 g)dg = \int f(g)dg. \tag{10}$$

In fact, the passage from g to g^{-1} corresponds to the passage from ϕ_1, ϕ_2, θ to $\pi-\phi_2, \pi-\phi_1, \theta$ (see Subsection 4) and, as a result, the expression $\sin\theta d\phi_1 d\phi_2 d\theta$ does not alter; formula (9) follows from this; further, putting $f_1(g) = f(g^{-1})$ and using formulae (8) and (9), we have:

$$\begin{aligned}\int f(g_0 g)dg &= \int f(g_0 g^{-1})dg = \int f_1(g g_0^{-1})dg \\ &= \int f_1(g)dg = \int f(g^{-1})dg = \int f(g)dg.\end{aligned}$$

Finally, we note that by virtue of condition (6)

$$\int dg = 1. \tag{11}$$

7. The invariant integral on the unitary group

The preceding reasoning carries over easily to the group $\mathfrak{U}$. From formula (9) of Subsection 5, every function $f(u)$ on the group $\mathfrak{U}$ can be considered as a function of ϕ_1, ϕ_2, θ,

i.e.
$$f(u) = f(\phi_1, \phi_2, \theta),$$

where, in contrast with the case of group G_0, we have

$$f(\phi_1+4\pi, \phi_2, \theta) = f(\phi_1, \phi_2+4\pi, \theta) = f(\phi_1+2\pi, \phi_2+2\pi, \theta) = f(\phi_1, \phi_2, \theta) \quad (1)$$

(see (13) of Subsection 5).

The reasoning in Subsection 6 shows that the integral

$$\frac{1}{16\pi^2}\int_0^{4\pi}\int_0^{2\pi}\int_0^{\pi} f(\phi_1, \phi_2, \theta)\sin\theta\, d\phi_1\, d\phi_2\, d\theta \quad (2)$$

remains invariant when $f(u)$ is replaced by $f(u\, u_0)$; it is called the *invariant integral* of the function $f(u)$ over the group $\mathfrak{U}$ and is briefly denoted by $\int f(u)du$, so that du is an abbreviation for

$$du = \frac{1}{16\pi^2}\sin\theta\, d\phi_1\, d\phi_2\, d\theta. \quad (3)$$

Here

$$\int du = 1, \quad (4)$$

and, by the definition of the invariant integral,

$$\int f(uu_0)du = \int f(u)du; \quad (5)$$

in addition we have the formulae

$$\int f(u_0 u)du = \int f(u)du, \quad \int f(u^{-1})du = \int f(u)du, \quad (6)$$

analogous to formulae (9) and (10) of Subsection 6.

Later on we shall need still another expression for du in terms of other parameters. It will be recalled that every matrix $u \in \mathfrak{U}$ has the form

$$u = \begin{Vmatrix} \alpha & \beta \\ -\bar{\beta} & \bar{\alpha} \end{Vmatrix},$$

where $|\alpha|^2+|\beta|^2 = 1$. From this it is seen that the matrix u is uniquely determined by the parameters

$$t = |\alpha|^2, \quad \phi = \arg\alpha, \quad \psi = \arg\beta. \tag{7}$$

Here, by (12) and (13) of Subsection 5

$$t = \cos^2\frac{\theta}{2}, \quad \phi = \frac{\phi_1+\phi_2}{2}, \quad \psi = \frac{\phi_1-\phi_2}{2}+\frac{\pi}{2}.$$

From this it readily follows that in terms of the new parameters

$$\int f(u)\,\mathrm{d}u = \frac{1}{4\pi^2}\int_0^1 \mathrm{d}t \int_0^{2\pi} \mathrm{d}\phi \int_0^{2\pi} f(u)\,\mathrm{d}\psi, \tag{8}$$

so that

$$\mathrm{d}u = \frac{1}{4\pi^2}\mathrm{d}t\,\mathrm{d}\phi\,\mathrm{d}\psi. \tag{9}$$

Remark. Put $\alpha = a_1+ia_2, \beta = a_3+ia_4$; then the relation $|\alpha|^2+|\beta|^2 = 1$ means that $a_1^2+a_2^2+a_3^2+a_4^2 = 1$, i.e. that the point (a_1, a_2, a_3, a_4) of four-dimensional space lies on the surface of the unit sphere S_4 in that space. Thus we arrive at a one-to-one correspondence $u \to (a_1, a_2, a_3, a_4)$ between the matrices $u \in \mathfrak{U}$ and the points of the unit sphere S_4 in four-dimensional space. The expression $\frac{1}{2}\mathrm{d}t\mathrm{d}\phi\mathrm{d}\psi$ has a simple geometrical meaning: it is the surface element of the sphere S_4. This can be verified by a simple calculation, which we leave to the reader. (See in this connection subsection 2 of § 6 in [28d].) The invariance of the expression $\frac{1}{2}\mathrm{d}t\mathrm{d}\phi\mathrm{d}\psi$ under displacements $u \to uu_0$ means simply that the element $\frac{1}{2}\mathrm{d}t\mathrm{d}\phi\mathrm{d}\psi$ remains invariant under rotations of the sphere S_4.

§ 2. The Lorentz Group

1. The general Lorentz group

It is well-known that the laws of classical mechanics do not depend upon the choice of any particular fixed coordinate system, with reference to which, motion is considered to take place; moreover, the laws of classical mechanics are not altered by going over from one reference system to another which has uniform, rectilinear, translational motion relative to the first.

The first fact means that the laws of classical mechanics are invariant with respect to orthogonal transformations of the coordinates $x_i' = \sum_{k=1}^{3} a_{ik}x_k$, $i = 1, 2, 3$, with constant coefficients a_{ik}; the second fact can be most simply represented by choosing both coordinate systems so that corresponding axes are parallel. If v_x, v_y, v_z are the projections of the velocity of the second system, x', y', z' on the coordinate axes Ox, Oy, Oz of the first system, then

$$x' = x+v_x t, \quad y' = y+v_y t, \quad z' = z+v_z t. \tag{1}$$

A transformation of the form (1) is called a *Galilean transformation*. The laws of classical mechanics must therefore be invariant with respect to Galilean transformations.

A coordinate system is said to be *inertial* if the movement of bodies in it is rectilinear and uniform in the absence of external forces. Classical mechanics asserts that Galilean transformations give the formulae for passing from one inertial system of coordinates to another inertial system of coordinates with corresponding axes parallel.

In this, classical mechanics proceeds from the assumption that the time t may be taken to be the same for both coordinate systems.

The theory of relativity rejects this assumption and assigns to each inertial system x, y, z its own time t; the passage from an inertial system x, y, z, whose time is t, to an inertial system x', y', z', whose time is t' is accomplished by a linear transformation of the variables x, y, z, t, which leaves invariant the quadratic form:

$$x^2+y^2+z^2-c^2t^2, \tag{2}$$

where c is the velocity of light in vacuum: $c = 2{\cdot}99776\times 10^{10}$ cm/sec.

The invariance of the form (2) is a mathematical expression of the fact, established by experiment, that the velocity of light in vacuum is the same for any inertial system whatever.†

† For a detailed treatment of the physical aspects of this matter see, for instance, Ref. [24a].

A linear transformation of the variables x, y, z, t which leaves the form $x^2+y^2+z^2-c^2t^2$ invariant is called a general Lorentz transformation.

It will be convenient in what follows to use, instead of the variable t, a new variable

$$x_4 = ct. \tag{3}$$

A general Lorentz transformation can then be described as a linear transformation

$$x_i' = \sum_{j=1}^{4} g_{ij}x_j, \quad i = 1, 2, 3, 4, \tag{4}$$

of the variables x_1, x_2, x_3, x_4, leaving invariant the form

$$x_1^2+x_2^2+x_3^2-x_4^2. \tag{5}$$

We denote by x and x' the vectors in four-dimensional space whose projections are x_1, x_2, x_3, x_4 and x_1', x_2', x_3', x_4' respectively, and by g the matrix of the transformation (4). The relations (4) can then be written in the form

$$x' = gx. \tag{6}$$

In what follows the letter g will also serve as the symbol denoting the transformation (4) itself.

Let us find the conditions that must be satisfied by the matrix g of a Lorentz transformation. From the definition of a Lorentz transformation it follows that we must have

$$x_1'^2+x_2'^2+x_3'^2-x_4'^2 = x_1^2+x_2^2+x_3^2-x_4^2. \tag{7}$$

Substituting in this for the x_i' their values from (4) we get:

$$\sum_{i=1}^{3}\left(\sum_{j=1}^{4} g_{ij}x_j\right)^2 - \left(\sum_{j=1}^{4} g_{4j}x_j\right)^2 = \sum_{i=1}^{3} x_i^2 - x_4^2; \tag{8}$$

Equating the coefficients of the products $x_j\,x_k$ gives

$$\sum_{i=1}^{3} g_{ij}g_{ik} - g_{4j}g_{4k} = \begin{cases} 0 & \text{if} \quad j \neq k, \\ 1 & \text{if} \quad j = k \leqslant 3, \\ -1 & \text{if} \quad\;\; = k = 4. \end{cases} \tag{9}$$

The conditions (9) can also be written in matrix form. For this purpose, with every matrix

$$g = \begin{Vmatrix} g_{11} & g_{12} & g_{13} & g_{14} \\ g_{21} & g_{22} & g_{23} & g_{24} \\ g_{31} & g_{32} & g_{33} & g_{34} \\ g_{41} & g_{42} & g_{43} & g_{44} \end{Vmatrix} \tag{10}$$

we associate the matrix

$$g^+ = \begin{Vmatrix} g_{11} & g_{21} & g_{31} & -g_{41} \\ g_{12} & g_{22} & g_{32} & -g_{42} \\ g_{13} & g_{23} & g_{33} & -g_{43} \\ g_{14} & g_{24} & g_{34} & -g_{44} \end{Vmatrix}. \tag{11}$$

Further, we denote by I^+ the matrix

$$I^+ = \begin{Vmatrix} 1 & 0 & 0 & 0 \\ 0 & 1 & 0 & 0 \\ 0 & 0 & 1 & 0 \\ 0 & 0 & 0 & -1 \end{Vmatrix}. \tag{12}$$

Then it is easily seen that the relations (9) are equivalent to the matrix equation

$$g^+ g = I^+; \tag{13}$$

thus:

I. *Condition* (9) *or the equivalent condition* (13) *is necessary and sufficient for the transformation g to be a general Lorentz transformation.* Let us find det g. For this purpose we note that det $g^+ = -\det g$, det $I^+ = -1$; hence it follows from (13) that

$$-\det g \det g = -1, \quad \text{i.e. that} \quad (\det g)^2 = 1;$$

consequently,

$$\det g = \pm 1. \tag{14}$$

II. *The determinant of every general Lorentz transformation is equal to* ± 1. From this it follows that

III. *Every general Lorentz transformation has an inverse transformation.* Of course, this inverse transformation is also a general Lorentz transformation, since it also leaves invariant the form

$$x_1^2 + x_2^2 + x_3^2 - x_4^2.$$

It is easily seen that $I^{+2} = 1$, where 1 stands for the unit matrix; therefore, multiplying both sides of (13) on the left by I^+, we get

$$I^+g^+ \cdot g = 1.$$

This relation means that

$$g^{-1} = I^+g^+, \tag{15}$$

consequently, also

$$gI^+g^+ = 1.$$

Writing the last in terms of the matrix elements, we get:

$$\sum_{j=1}^{3} g_{ij}g_{kj} - g_{i4}g_{k4} = \begin{cases} 0 & \text{if} \quad i \neq k, \\ 1 & \text{if} \quad i = k \leqslant 3, \\ -1 & \text{if} \quad i = k = 4. \end{cases} \tag{16}$$

As in the case of rotations, the *product* g_1g_2 of the transformations g_1 and g_2 is defined as the transformation obtained by the successive application of g_2 and g_1. Evidently, the multiplication of transformations corresponds to the multiplication of matrices.

IV. *The product of two general Lorentz transformations is also a general Lorentz transformation.* In fact, the successive application of two transformations which do not change the form (5), also leaves the form invariant.

We denote by $\mathfrak{G}$ the aggregate of all general Lorentz transformations. Propositions III and IV show that this aggregate is a group. Further, the unit element e of the group $\mathfrak{G}$ is the unit transformation.

$$x_1' = x_1, \quad x_2' = x_2, \quad x_3' = x_3, \quad x_4' = x_4. \tag{17}$$

The group $\mathfrak{G}$ is called the *general Lorentz group.*

From relation (9) for $j = k = 4$

$$g_{14}^2 + g_{24}^2 + g_{34}^2 - g_{44}^2 = -1 \tag{18}$$

it follows that

$$g_{44}^2 = 1 + g_{14}^2 + g_{24}^2 + g_{34}^2 \geqslant 1.$$

Consequently,

$$g_{44} \geqslant 1 \quad \text{or} \quad g_{44} \leqslant -1. \tag{19}$$

A general Lorentz transformation satisfying the condition

$$g_{44} \geqslant 1$$

is called a *Lorentz transformation.*

2. The complete Lorentz group and the proper Lorentz group

A vector (x_1, x_2, x_3, x_4) is called *time-like* if

$$x_1^2+x_2^2+x_3^2-x_4^2 < 0. \tag{1}$$

Time-like vectors characterize the displacements of material particles having real motion; in fact, if in some inertial system $\Delta x_1, \Delta x_2, \Delta x_3$ are increments in the coordinates of a material particle, and Δt is the time which has elapsed, the vector $(\Delta x_1, \Delta x_2, \Delta x_3, \Delta x_4)$, where $\Delta x_4 = c\Delta t$, will be time-like, and

$$\Delta x_1^2+\Delta x_2^2+\Delta x_3^2-c^2\Delta t^2 < 0,$$

since the motion of a material particle can only take place with a velocity less than the velocity of light. A time-like vector (x_1, x_2, x_3, x_4) is said to be *positive* if $x_4 > 0$ and *negative* if $x_4 < 0$. Evidently, time-like vectors $(\Delta x_1, \Delta x_2, \Delta x_3, \Delta x_4)$, characterizing the motion of a material particle during a positive time interval $\Delta t = t''-t'(t'' > t')$ will be positive.

I. *A general Lorentz transformation satisfies the condition* $g_{44} \geqslant 1$ *if and only if it converts every positive time-like vector into another positive (time-like) vector.*

Proof. Let $x = (x_1, x_2, x_3, x_4,)$ be a positive, time-like vector; a general Lorentz transformation takes it into a vector $x' = (x_1', x_2', x_3', x_4')$, where

$$x_4' = g_{41}x_1+g_{42}x_2+g_{43}x_3+g_{44}x_4.$$

Applying the Cauchy–Bunyakovskii inequality† and making use of relations (18) of Subsection 1 and (1), we have:

$$\begin{aligned}(g_{41}x_1+g_{42}x_2+g_{43}x_3)^2 &\leqslant (g_{41}^2+g_{42}^2+g_{43}^2)(x_1^2+x_2^2+x_3^2)\\ &\leqslant (g_{44}^2-1)x_4^2 = g_{44}^2x_4^2-x_4^2 < g_{44}^2x_4^2.\end{aligned}$$

From this it follows that the sum $g_{41}\, x_1+g_{42}x_2+g_{43}x_3+g_{44}x_4 = x_4'$ has the same sign as g_{44}, since, by hypothesis, $x_4 > 0$. In

---

† We recall that the inequality $\left(\sum_{k=1}^{n} x_k y_k\right)^2 < \sum_{k=1}^{n} x_k^2 \sum_{k=1}^{n} y_k^2$, valid for any real numbers $x_1, \dots x_n$; $y_1, \dots y_n$, is known as the Cauchy–Bunyakovskii inequality (see, for instance, Ref. [35], Vol. III, part 1; see also below (2), Subsection 7, § 6).

other words, if $g_{44} > 0$, the transformation g takes every positive time-like vector into another such vector. In this case, from (19) of Subsection 1, $g_{44} \geqslant 1$.

It follows from Proposition I that the *aggregate of all Lorentz transformations* (that is of general Lorentz transformations satisfying the condition $g_{44} \geqslant 1$) forms a group; this group is called the *complete Lorentz group* and is denoted by $\mathfrak{G}_0$.

The passage from one inertial system to another must take every positive, time-like vector (characterizing actual motion) into another such vector; consequently, this passage must be described by transformations belonging to the group $\mathfrak{G}_0$.

A Lorentz transformation is said to be *proper*, if its determinant is equal to unity.

Evidently, the aggregate of all proper Lorentz transformations also forms a group; this group is called the *proper Lorentz group* and is denoted by $\mathfrak{G}_+$. An example of an improper Lorentz transformation is furnished by a reflection s relative to the three space axes:

$$x_1' = -x_1, \quad x_2' = -x_2, \quad x_3' = -x_3, \quad x_4' = x_4.$$

If g is an arbitrary improper Lorentz transformation, then the transformation $g_1 = sg$ will be proper, since $\det g_1 = \det s \det g = (-1)(-1) = 1$. Hence $g = s^2 g = ssg = sg_1$, so that:

II. *Every improper Lorentz transformation has the form $g = sg_1$, where g_1 is a proper Lorentz transformation.*

CHAPTER II

THE REPRESENTATIONS OF THE THREE-DIMENSIONAL ROTATION GROUP

§ 3. The Basic Concepts of the Theory of Finite-dimensional Representations

1. Linear spaces

A set R of elements $x, y, z, \ldots$ is called a *linear space* if the sum $x+y$ of any two elements $x, y \in R$ and the product αx of any element $x \in R$ with any complex number α are defined in R and have the following properties:

(a) if $x, y \in R$, then $x+y \in R$;

(b) $x+y = y+x$;

(c) $(x+y)+z = x+(y+z)$;

(d) there exists in R a "zero" element 0 such that $x+0 = x$ for all $x \in R$;

(e) if $x \in R$, then $\alpha x \in R$;

(f) $\alpha(\beta x) = (\alpha\beta)x$;

(g) $1 \cdot x = x$;

(h) $0 \cdot x = 0$ (the number zero appears on the left, the zero element on the right);

(j) $\alpha(x+y) = \alpha x+\alpha y$;

(k) $(\alpha+\beta)x = \alpha x+\beta x$.

The element $(-1)x$ is then usually denoted by $-x$; by properties (g), (k), (h),

$$x+(-x) = (1+(-1))\,x = 0x = 0.$$

The elements x, y, z of the space R are called *vectors*. A set M in the linear space R is called a *sub-space* of R if M is a linear space under the same definitions of the operations of addition and multiplication by a number as given for R, i.e. if it follows from $x, y \in M$ that $\alpha x \in M$ and $x+y \in M$.

An expression of the form $\alpha_1 x_1 + \alpha_2 x_2 + \ldots + \alpha_n x_n$ is called a *linear combination* of the vectors $x_1, x_2, \ldots, x_n$; the vectors $x_1, x_2, \ldots, x_n$ are said to be *linearly dependent* if there exist numbers $\alpha_1, \alpha_2, \ldots, \alpha_n$, not all zero, for which $\alpha_1 x_1 + \alpha_2 x_2 + \ldots \alpha_n x_n = 0$. If the equation $\alpha_1 x_1 + \alpha_2 x_2 + \ldots + \alpha_n x_n = 0$ holds only for $\alpha_1 = \alpha_2 = \ldots = \alpha_n = 0$, then the vectors $x_1, x_2, \ldots, x_n$ are called *linearly independent*. A space R is said to be finite-dimensional and, more precisely, *n-dimensional* if there are n and not more than n linearly independent vectors in R. If the number of linearly independent vectors in R is arbitrarily great, then R is said to be *infinite-dimensional*. Every system of n linearly independent vectors in an n-dimensional space R is called a *basis* for R. If $e_1, e_2, \ldots, e_n$ is a basis for an n-dimensional space R and x is an arbitrary vector in R, then $x, e_1, e_2, \ldots, e_n$ are linearly dependent, so that

$$\alpha x + \alpha_1 e_1 + \alpha_2 e_2 + \ldots + \alpha_n e_n = 0 \tag{1}$$

for some $\alpha, \alpha_1, \alpha_2, \ldots, \alpha_n$ not all zero. Then $\alpha \neq 0$, for otherwise we should have $\alpha_1 e_1 + \ldots + \alpha_n e_n = 0$, where $\alpha_1, \ldots, \alpha_n$ are not all zero, which contradicts the supposition that the vectors $e_1, \ldots, e_n$ are linearly independent. But, if $\alpha \neq 0$, it follows from (1) that $x = \xi_1 e_1 + \ldots + \xi_n e_n$, where $\xi_k = -\alpha_k/\alpha$. This representation of the element x is unique. In fact, if also $x = \xi'_1 e_1 + \ldots + \xi'_n e_n$, then $0 = (\xi_1 - \xi'_1) e_1 + \ldots + (\xi_n - \xi'_n) e_n$ and, since $e_1, \ldots, e_n$ are linearly independent, it follows from this that $\xi_1 = \xi'_1, \ldots, \xi_n = \xi'_n$. Thus:

Every vector x of an n-dimensional space R can be uniquely represented in the form $x = \xi_1 e_1 + \ldots + \xi_n e_n$, where $e_1, e_2, \ldots, e_n$ is a basis for R. The numbers $\xi_1, \ldots, \xi_n$ are called the *coordinates* of the vector x relative to the basis $e_1, \ldots, e_n$.

Evidently, when vectors are added, their corresponding coordinates relative to a fixed basis are added and, when a vector is multiplied by any number, all the coordinates are multiplied by that number.

2. Linear operators

Let R be a linear space. Every function A, which makes a vector $y = A(x)$ of the same space R correspond to every vector $x \in R$ is called an *operator*† in R. Often, when there can be no ambiguity, Ax is written instead of $A(x)$. An operator A in R is called *linear* if

$$A(x+y) = Ax+Ay, \quad A(\alpha x) = \alpha Ax \tag{1}$$

for all $x, y \in R$ and all numbers α. Linear operators in a finite-dimensional space R can be represented by means of matrices. For this purpose we choose a fixed basis $e_1, \ldots, e_n$ for R. Every vector $x \in R$ and, in particular, the vectors Ae_k may be expressed as linear combinations of the elements of the basis. Put

$$Ae_k = \sum_{j=1}^{n} a_{jk} e_j, \quad k = 1, 2, \ldots, n. \tag{2}$$

The numbers a_{jk} form a matrix of order n, which is called *the matrix of the operator A relative to the basis $e_1, \ldots, e_n$*.

The operator A is completely determined by its matrix $\|a_{jk}\|$. In fact, putting $x = \xi_1 e_1 + \ldots + \xi_n e_n$ and $Ax = \xi'_1 e_1 + \ldots + \xi'_n e_n$, we have:

$$\begin{aligned}\xi' e_1 + \ldots + \xi'_n e_n &= A(\xi_1 e_1 + \ldots + \xi_n e_n) = \xi_1 Ae_1 + \ldots + \xi_n Ae_n \\ &= \xi_1(a_{11} e_1 + \ldots + a_{n1} e_n) + \ldots + \xi_n(a_{1n} e_1 + \ldots + a_{nn} e_n),\end{aligned}$$

whence

$$\left.\begin{aligned}\xi'_1 &= a_{11}\xi_1 + \ldots + a_{1n}\xi_n, \\ &\ldots\ldots\ldots\ldots\ldots\ldots \\ \xi'_n &= a_{n1}\xi_1 + \ldots + a_{nn}\xi_n.\end{aligned}\right\} \tag{3}$$

Consequently, the vector $Ax = \xi'_1 e_1 + \ldots + \xi'_n e_n$ is completely determined by the vector x and the matrix $\|a_{jk}\|$. At the same time we see that the linear transformation (3) of the variables $\xi_1, \ldots, \xi_n$ by the matrix $\|a_{jk}\|$ corresponds to the application of a linear operator to the vector $x = \xi_1 e_1 + \ldots + \xi_n e_n$.

† This definition of "operator" will be generalized later (see p. 239).

It is possible to define the operations of addition, multiplication by a number and multiplication of operators in R. In fact, by $A+B$, αB, AB we shall understand the operators defined by the formulae:

$$\left.\begin{aligned} (A+B)x = Ax+Bx, \quad (\alpha A)x = \alpha(Ax), \\ (AB)x = A(Bx) \end{aligned}\right\} \tag{4}$$

for all $x \in R$. It is easily verified that $A+B$, αA, AB are linear operators, if A, B are linear operators. In addition, it is easy to verify that the operations of addition, multiplication by a number and multiplication together of operators correspond to the addition, multiplication by a number and multiplication of their matrices relative to a fixed basis. We leave it as an exercise to the reader to verify the validity of these statements in detail.

3. Definition of a finite-dimensional representation of a group

Let G be an arbitrary group. We shall say that there is set up a *representation*† $g \to T_g$ of the group G in a *finite-dimensional space* R if, corresponding to every element $g \in G$ there is assigned a linear operator T_g in R in such a way that the following conditions are satisfied:

(1) $T_{g_1 g_2} = T_{g_1} T_{g_2}$;

(2) $T_e = 1$, where 1 is the unit operator, that is the operator which leaves every vector in R unchanged.

The space R is called the *space of the representation*, and the dimension of the space R the *dimension of the representation*. Two finite-dimensional representations $g \to T_g$, $g \to T'_g$ in spaces R and R' of the same dimension are said to be *equivalent*, if bases for R and R' can be so chosen that the matrices of the operators T_g and T'_g relative to these bases coincide for all $g \in G$. Equivalent representations are regarded as not essentially different. A subspace M of R is said to be *invariant with respect to the representation* $g \to T_g$ if it follows from $x \in M$ that $T_g x \in M$ for all $g \in G$, that

† This definition of a representation will be generalized later (see § 6, Subsection 3 below).

is if the operators T_g take the vectors of the subspace M into vectors of the same subspace M. Evidently, in this case the operators T_g, regarded only as affecting M, will be operators in M, forming a representation in the space M. This representation is called the *part* of the original representation in the invariant subspace M.

A representation $g \to T_g$ in a space R is said to be *irreducible* if there are in R no subspaces other than (0) and the whole space R, which are invariant with respect to this representation.

4. Continuous finite-dimensional representations of the three-dimensional rotation group

We shall apply the above definitions to the case in which the group G is the three-dimensional rotation group G_0. Every element $g \in G_0$ may be regarded as an orthogonal matrix $g = \|g_{jk}\|$ of order three; consequently, it may be represented as a point of nine-dimensional space. The aggregate of all those points, corresponding to all possible rotations $g \in G_0$, forms a set Γ in nine-dimensional space. Every function $f(g)$ on the group G_0 may also be regarded as a function of a point of the set Γ; the function $f(g)$ is said to be *continuous on* G_0 if it is a continuous function on the set Γ.

Given a representation $g \to T_g$ of the group G_0, this representation is called *continuous*, if T_g is a continuous operator function on the group G_0. Here we call an operator function T_g continuous on G_0 if the elements of the matrix of T_g relative to a fixed basis are continuous functions on G_0. The definition of continuity of a function T_g does not in fact depend on the choice of basis, since the matrix elements relative to another basis are linear combinations with constant coefficients of the matrix elements relative to the original basis.

We note that the definitions we have given of a continuous function and a continuous representation carry over to any group of real or complex matrices of a fixed order, in particular to the representations of the complete Lorentz group and the proper Lorentz group. The only thing which changes is the dimension of the space whose points represent the elements of the group under consideration.†

In what follows we shall only consider continuous representations of the three-dimensional rotation group and the Lorentz group without having to say so.

5. Unitary representations

A linear space is called *Euclidean*, if in it a function (x, y) is defined, having the following properties:

(1) $(x, x) \geqslant 0$, $(x, x) = 0$ if and only if $x = 0$;

(2) $(y, x) = \overline{(x, y)}$;

(3) $(\alpha x, y) = \alpha(x, y)$;

(4) $(x_1 + x_2, y) = (x_1, y) + (x_2, y)$.

This function is called the *scalar product* of the elements x and y.

Such a scalar product can be introduced in every fiinte-dimensional space; thus, if $e_1, \ldots, e_n$ is a basis for R and $x = \xi_1 e_1 + \ldots + \xi_n e_n$, $y = \eta_1 e_1 + \ldots + \eta_n e_n$, then, putting, for example,

$$(x, y) = \xi_1 \overline{\eta}_1 + \ldots + \xi_n \overline{\eta}_n, \tag{1}$$

we get a function (x, y) satisfying conditions (1) to (4).

An operator A in a finite-dimensional Euclidean space R is said to be *unitary*, if it preserves the scalar product, i.e. if $(Ax, Ay) = (x, y)$ for all $x, y \in R$.

A representation $g \to T_g$ in such a space is said to be *unitary*, if all the operators T_g are unitary.

Every finite-dimensional representation $g \to T_g$ *of the three-dimensional rotation group* G_0 *may be considered unitary, i.e. a scalar product can be introduced in the space* R *of the representation in such a way that all the operators* T_g *become unitary operators.*

For proof we start with some scalar product $(x, y)_1$ in R, and we then put

† Actually, the definitions of a continuous function and a continuous representation can be given for an even wider class of groups (see in this connection Ref. [32] § 28). However, such a general definition is not required for our purpose.

$$(x, y) = \int (T_g x, T_g y)_1 \, dg. \tag{2}$$

It is easy to see that (x, y) satisfies conditions (1) to (4) and is therefore a scalar product; since the right-hand side of (2) is an invariant integral over G_0, we have

$$(T_{g_0} x, T_{g_0} y) = \int (T_{g_0} T_g x, T_{g_0} T_g y)_1 \, dg$$
$$= \int (T_{g_0 g} x, T_{g_0 g} y)_1 \, dg = \int (T_g x, T_g y)_1 \, dg = (x, y),$$

that is, every operator T_g is unitary relative to the scalar product (x, y).

§ 4. Irreducible Representations of the Three-dimensional Rotation Group in Infinitesimal Form

1. Differentiability of representations of the group G_0

We will again represent the elements of the group G_0 as points of nine-dimensional space and, consequently, the group G_0 in the form of some set Γ in this space (see § 3, Subsection 4). A function $f(g)$ on G_0 is said to be *differentiable*, if it is a differentiable function on the set Γ.†

The differential of the function $f(g)$ at a point of the set Γ is called the differential of this function at the corresponding point g of the group G_0 and is denoted by $df(g)$. A function $f(g)$ on G_0

---

† This means that, in a neighbourhood of every point of the set Γ, local coordinates can be introduced with reference to which $f(g)$ is differentiable. Thus making use of the parametrization of § 1, Subsection 5 of the group G_0 by means of unitary matrices, in a neighbourhood of a point $g_0 \in \Gamma$ we can take for the coordinates of the element g three independent parameters of the unitary matrix $\left\| \begin{matrix} \alpha & \beta \\ -\bar{\beta} & \bar{\alpha} \end{matrix} \right\|$, corresponding to the rotation gg_0^{-1}; for example we can take $a_1 = \operatorname{Re} \alpha$, $a_2 = \operatorname{Im} \alpha$, $a_3 = \operatorname{Re} \beta$. Ambiguity in the choice of this unitary matrix can be avoided by choosing a_1 near to $+1$ and not -1. Then the correspondence $g \to (a_1, a_2, a_3)$ in a neighbourhood of the point g_0 is one-to-one and differentiable, and differentiability of the function $f(g) = f(a_1, a_2, a_3)$ at the point g_0 means that it is differentiable in the parameters a_1, a_2, a_3 for corresponding values of these parameters.

is said to be *continuously differentiable* on G_0 if it is differentiable on G_0 and $df(g)$ is a continuous function on G_0.

Further, an operator function $A(g)$ on G_0 is said to be differentiable, if all the elements of its matrix relative to a fixed basis are differentiable functions.†

In particular, a representation $g \to T_g$ of the group G_0 will be said to be *differentiable*, if T_g is a differentiable operator function. Evidently, the concept of a differentiable function and a differentiable representation can be applied to any group of real or complex matrices.

THEOREM 1. *Every continuous finite-dimensional representation of the group G_0 is differentiable.*

Proof. Consider all possible vectors of the form

$$y = \int f(g)\, T_g x\, dg, \tag{1}$$

where x runs through all vectors of the space of the representation R, and the $f(g)$ are continuously differentiable functions on G_0. Here, by the integral of the vector $f(g)T_g x$ is understood the vector resulting from the integration of each coordinate of the vector $f(g)T_g x$ relative to a fixed basis.

Let us show that $T_{g_0} y$ is a differentiable vector-function of $g_0 \in G_0$. For this purpose we note that

$$T_{g_0} y = T_{g_0} \int f(g)\, T_g x\, dg = \int f(g)\, T_{g_0} T_g x\, dg = \int f(g)\, T_{g_0 g} x\, dg.$$

Consequently, by the invariance of the integral

$$T_{g_0} y = \int f(g_0^{-1} g)\, T_g x\, dg. \tag{2}$$

Since $f(g)$ is continuously differentiable on G_0, $f(g_0^{-1} g)$ is differentiable in g_0, uniformly‡ with respect to all $g \in G_0$; it follows from this and (2) that $T_{g_0} y$ is a differentiable function of g_0.

---

† Evidently in this definition the choice of basis is immaterial.

‡ Using the parametrization $g_0 \to (\alpha_1, \alpha_2, \alpha_3)$, described in the footnote on page 31, this means that

$$\Delta_{g_0} f(g_0^{-1} g) = d_{g_0} f(g_0^{-1} g) + \mu \sum_{i=1}^{3} |\Delta \alpha_i|,$$

where $\mu \to 0$ as $\sum_{i=1}^{3} |\Delta \alpha_i| \to 0$ uniformly with respect to all $g \in G_0$; this uniformity follows easily from the uniform continuity of the differential $df(g)$ on Γ.

But if $T_{g_0}y_1$ and $T_{g_0}y_2$ are differentiable vector-functions, then also $T_{g_0}(\alpha_1 y_1+\alpha_2 y_2) = \alpha_1 T_{g_0}y_1+\alpha_2 T_{g_0}y_2$ is a differentiable vector-function. Therefore $T_{g_0}z$ is differentiable for all vectors z which are linear combinations of vectors y of the form (1), and it suffices to prove that such vectors z fill the whole space R. Suppose not; then the vectors z form a subspace M of R, not coinciding with R. Choose in M a basis $e_1, \ldots, e_m$ and complete it by the vectors $e_{m+1}, e_{m+2}, \ldots, e_n$ to form a basis for the whole space R. We can determine a scalar product in R by putting

$$(x, y) = \xi_1\bar{\eta}_1 + \ldots + \xi_n\bar{\eta}_n$$

for $x = \xi_1 e_1 + \ldots + \xi_n e_n, \quad y = \eta_1 e_1 + \ldots + \eta_n e_n.$

Then, evidently, $(z, e_n) = 0$ for all $z \in M$, and in particular $(y, e_n) = 0$ for all vectors y of the form (1). But, written in full, this relation means that $\int f(g)(T_g x, e_n)\mathrm{d}g = 0$ for an arbitrary continuously differentiable function $f(g)$; this last is only possible when $(T_g x, e_n) = 0$ for all $g \in G_0$. Putting here $g = e$ and $x = e_n$, we arrive at the contradictory relation $(e_n, e_n) = 0$. Consequently, M coincides with R and the theorem is proved.

2. Basic infinitesimal matrices of the group G_0

Let us consider a rotation of three-dimensional space about a fixed axis, for example the axis Ox_3. If t is the angle of rotation about the axis Ox_3, then the corresponding transformation of the coordinates has the form

$$x_1' = x_1 \cos t - x_2 \sin t, \quad x_2' = x_1 \sin t + x_2 \cos t, \quad x_3' = x_3. \tag{1}$$

Denoting by $a_3(t)$ the matrix of this transformation, we have

$$a_3(t) = \begin{Vmatrix} \cos t & -\sin t & 0 \\ \sin t & \cos t & 0 \\ 0 & 0 & 1 \end{Vmatrix}. \tag{2}$$

The matrix $a_3(t)$ satisfies the relation

$$a_3(t_1+t_2) = a_3(t_1)a_3(t_2). \tag{3}$$

In fact, a rotation through the angle t_1+t_2 about the axis Ox_3 can be obtained as the result of two successive rotations about the same axis through the angles t_2 and t_1; the validity of relation (3) can also be verified directly by multiplication of the matrices $a_3(t_1)$, $a_3(t_2)$.

Expanding the matrix $a_3(t)$ as a power series in t,† we get

$$a_3(t) = 1 + a_3 t + \dots, \tag{4}$$

where

$$a_3 = \begin{Vmatrix} 0 & -1 & 0 \\ 1 & 0 & 0 \\ 0 & 0 & 0 \end{Vmatrix}. \tag{5}$$

The matrix a_3 is called the *infinitesimal matrix corresponding to a rotation about the axis* Ox_3; it is uniquely determined by the condition that $1+a_3 t$ is, neglecting small quantities of higher order, the matrix of a rotation through the small angle t about the axis Ox_3.

In an exactly similar way we determine the infinitesimal matrices

$$a_1 = \begin{Vmatrix} 0 & 0 & 0 \\ 0 & 0 & -1 \\ 0 & 1 & 0 \end{Vmatrix}, \quad a_2 = \begin{Vmatrix} 0 & 0 & 1 \\ 0 & 0 & 0 \\ -1 & 0 & 0 \end{Vmatrix}, \tag{6}$$

corresponding to rotations

$$a_1(t)\colon\ x_1' = x_1,\ x_2' = x_2 \cos t - x_3 \sin t,\ x_3' = x_2 \sin t + x_3 \cos t, \tag{7}$$

$$a_2(t)\colon\ x_1' = x_3 \sin t + x_1 \cos t,\ x_2' = x_2,\ x_3' = x_3 \cos t - x_1 \sin t \tag{8}$$

about the axes Ox_1 and Ox_2 respectively.

It is easily seen that‡

$$a_k = \left[\frac{\mathrm{d}}{\mathrm{d}t} a_k(t)\right]_{t=0}, \quad k = 1, 2, 3. \tag{9}$$

---

† A series $A^{(1)} + A^{(2)} + \dots$ of matrices $A^{(n)} = \|a_{jk}^{(n)}\|$ is said to be *convergent* if each of the series $s_{jk} = a_{jk}^{(1)} + a_{jk}^{(2)} + \dots$ converges; the matrix $\|s_{jk}\|$ of the sums of these series is called the *sum* of the matrix series.

‡ The derivative of a matrix $a(t) = \|a_{jk}(t)\|$ is the matrix $\|a_{jk}'(t)\|$ obtained by differentiating every element $a_{jk}(t)$ of the matrix $a(t)$.

Conversely, the matrices $a_k(t)$ may be expressed in terms of the infinitesimal matrices a_k by the formulae

$$a_k(t) = e^{ta_k} = 1+ta_k+\frac{1}{2!}t^2a_k^2+\frac{1}{3!}t^3a_k^3+\ldots, \qquad (10)$$

as may be directly verified. Thus, for example,

$$1+ta_3+\frac{1}{2!}t^2a_3^2+\ldots = \begin{Vmatrix} 1 & 0 & 0 \\ 0 & 1 & 0 \\ 0 & 0 & 1 \end{Vmatrix} + t\begin{Vmatrix} 0 & -1 & 0 \\ 1 & 0 & 0 \\ 0 & 0 & 0 \end{Vmatrix} +$$

$$+\frac{1}{2}t^2\begin{Vmatrix} -1 & 0 & 0 \\ 0 & -1 & 0 \\ 0 & 0 & 0 \end{Vmatrix} + \frac{1}{3!}t^3\begin{Vmatrix} 0 & 1 & 0 \\ -1 & 0 & 0 \\ 0 & 0 & 0 \end{Vmatrix} + \ldots$$

$$= \begin{Vmatrix} \left(1-\frac{1}{2!}t^2+\ldots\right) & -\left(t-\frac{1}{3!}t^3+\ldots\right) & 0 \\ \left(t-\frac{1}{3!}t^3+\ldots\right) & \left(1-\frac{1}{2!}t^2+\ldots\right) & 0 \\ 0 & 0 & 1 \end{Vmatrix}$$

$$= \begin{Vmatrix} \cos t & -\sin t & 0 \\ \sin t & \cos t & 0 \\ 0 & 0 & 1 \end{Vmatrix} = a_3(t).$$

It can be verified directly in exactly the same way that

$$a_1a_2-a_2a_3 = a_3, \quad a_2a_3-a_3a_2 = a_1, \quad a_3a_1-a_1a_3 = a_2. \qquad (11)$$

If a, b are two matrices of the same order, then the matrix $ab-ba$ is called the *commutator* of the matrices a, b and is denoted by $[a, b]$. With this notation relations (11) may be written in the form

$$[a_1, a_2] = a_3, \quad [a_2, a_3] = a_1, \quad [a_3, a_1] = a_2. \qquad (12)$$

3. Basic infinitesimal operators of a representation of the group G_0

Consider a representation $g \to T_g$ of the group G_0 in an n-dimensional space R, and put

$$A_3(t) = T_{a_3(t)}. \qquad (1)$$

From (3), Subsection 2 we have,

$$A_3(t_1+t_2) = T_{a_3(t_1+t_2)} = T_{a_3(t_1)a_3(t_2)} = T_{a_3(t_1)}T_{a_3(t_2)} = A_3(t_1)\,A_3(t_2),$$

so that

$$A_3(t_1+t_2) = A_3(t_1)\,A_3(t_2). \tag{2}$$

Similarly, putting

$$A_1(t) = T_{a_1(t)} \qquad A_2(t) = T_{a_2(t)}, \tag{3}$$

we obtain operator functions satisfying the relations

$$A_1(t_1+t_2) = A_1(t_1)\,A_1(t_2), \qquad A_2(t_1+t_2) = A_2(t_1)\,A_2(t_2). \tag{4}$$

We note that $A_1(t)$, $A_2(t)$, $A_3(t)$ are continuous operator functions of t; this follows from the fact that T_g is a continuous function on G_0, and $a_1(t)$, $a_2(t)$, $a_3(t)$ are continuous functions of t. Every continuous operator function $A(t)$ of the parameter t, satisfying the condition $A(t_1+t_2) = A(t_1)A(t_2)$, is called a *one-parameter group of operators*. Relations (2) and (4) mean that $A_1(t)$, $A_2(t)$, $A_3(t)$ are one-parameter groups of operators. We shall call them the *basic one-parameter groups* of the given representation $g \to T_g$.

I. *The representation $g \to T_g$ is uniquely determined by its one-parameter groups $A_1(t)$, $A_2(t)$, $A_3(t)$.*

Proof. From (2) in § 1, Subsection 4, every rotation g may be represented in the form of a product $g = a_3(t_3)a_1(t_2)a_3(t_1)$ for certain t_1, t_2, t_3 (these t_1, t_2, t_3 are the Eulerian angles of the rotation g). Hence

$$T_g = T_{a_3(t_3)}T_{a_1(t_2)}T_{a_3(t_1)} = A_3(t_3)\,A_1(t_2)\,A_3(t_1).$$

Remark. From the above reasoning it follows that in reality the representation $g \to T_g$ is completely determined by *only two* one-parameter groups $A_1(t)$, $A_3(t)$. This is so because in reality the one-parameter groups $A_1(t)$, $A_2(t)$, $A_3(t)$ are not independent and any one of them, for instance $A_2(t)$, can be expressed by means of the other two: $A_1(t)$, $A_3(t)$ (see Subsection 4 Theorem 2, below).

II. *The basic one-parameter groups are differentiable functions of the parameter t.*

Proof. By Theorem 1 of Subsection 1, T_g is a differentiable function on G_0; on the other hand, $a_1(t)$, $a_2(t)$, $a_3(t)$ are differentiable functions of t. Therefore $A_k(t) = T_{a_k(t)}$, $k = 1, 2, 3$ are differentiable functions of t.

Now put

$$A_k = \left[\frac{\mathrm{d}}{\mathrm{d}t} A_k(t)\right]_{t=0}, \quad k = 1, 2, 3; \tag{5}$$

by proposition 2 these derivatives exist.

The operators A_k are called the *basic infinitesimal operators* of the representation $g \to T_g$.

The definition of these operators is similar to formulae (9) Subsection 2 for the infinitesimal matrices a_k. We shall now see that this analogy extends still further.

III. *The basic one-parameter group* $A_k(t)$, $k = 1, 2, 3$ *satisfies the differential equation*

$$\frac{\mathrm{d}A_k(t)}{\mathrm{d}t} = A_k(t)\, A_k = A_k A_k(t) \tag{6}$$

and the initial condition

$$A_k(0) = 1. \tag{7}$$

Proof. Differentiating with respect to t_1 both sides in the relation $A_k(t+t_1) = A_k(t)A_k(t_1) = A_k(t_1)A_k(t)$ and putting $t_1 = 0$, we get (6). Further, $A_k(0) = T_{a_k(0)} = T_e = 1$.

IV. *The basic one-parameter group* $A_k(t), k = 1, 2, 3$ *can be expressed in terms of the infinitesimal operator* A_k *by the formula*

$$A_k(t) = 1 + tA_k + \frac{t^2}{2!} A_k^2 + \ldots = e^{tA_k}. \tag{8}$$

Proof. It follows from (6) that $A_k(t)$ has derivatives of all orders, with

$$\frac{\mathrm{d}^p A_k(t)}{\mathrm{d}t^p} = A_k^p A_k(t), \qquad \left[\frac{\mathrm{d}^p A_k(t)}{\mathrm{d}t^p}\right]_{t=0} = A_k^p. \tag{9}$$

Consequently, from Maclaurin's series and (7) we get:

$$A_k(t) = 1+tA_k+\frac{t^2}{2!}A_k^2+ \dots + \frac{t^{p-1}}{(p-1)!}A_k^{p-1}+R_p(t), \qquad (10)$$

where

$$R_p(t) = \frac{1}{(p-1)!}\int_0^t (t-\tau)^{p-1}\frac{\mathrm{d}^p A_k(\tau)}{\mathrm{d}\tau^p}\mathrm{d}\tau$$

$$= \frac{1}{(p-1)!}\int_0^t (t-\tau)^{p-1}A_k^p A_k(\tau)\,\mathrm{d}\tau. \qquad (11)$$

We shall prove that $R_p(t) \to 0$ as $p \to \infty$ (i.e. that every element of the matrix $R_p(t)$ tends to zero as $p \to \infty$); formula (8) will then follow from (10).

Let c be the largest of the moduli of the elements of the matrix A_k; then every element of the matrix A_k^2 is not larger than nc^2 in modulus and every element of the matrix A_k^3 is not larger than n^2c^3 in modulus. Generally, the modulus of every element of the matrix A_k^p is not larger than $n^{p-1}c^p$. Further, let every element of the matrix $A_k(\tau)$ be less than $M(t)$ in modulus for $0 \leqslant \tau \leqslant t$. Then from (11) every element of the matrix $R_p(t)$ has modulus less than

$$\frac{1}{(p-1)!}\int_0^t (t-\tau)^{p-1}n^{p-1}c^p M(t)\,n\,\mathrm{d}\tau = M(t)\frac{(nc)^p}{(p-1)!}\int_0^t (t-\tau)^{p-1}\,\mathrm{d}\tau$$

$$= M(t)\frac{(nct)^p}{p!} \to 0 \quad \text{as} \quad p \to \infty,$$

and formula (8) is proved.

V. *A representation $g \to T_g$ of the group G_0 is uniquely determined by its basic infinitesimal operators A_1, A_2, A_3.*

Proof. From (8) the operators A_k, $k = 1, 2, 3$ uniquely determine the basic one-parameter groups $A_k(t)$, $k = 1, 2, 3$, which in their turn uniquely determine the representation $g \to T_g$ (see I).

Thus, for the determination of a representation $g \to T_g$, it is sufficient to determine its basic infinitesimal operators A_1, A_2, A_3.

4. Relations between the basic infinitesimal operators of a representation of the group G_0

The determination of all the finite-dimensional representations of the group G_0 is based on the fact that, among the operators A_k, $k = 1, 2, 3$, the same relations exist as among the infinitesimal matrices a_k. To derive these relations we consider an arbitrary matrix function $g = g(t) = \|g_{jk}(t)\|$ of the real parameter t, all of whose values belong to G_0. We suppose that $g(0) = e$ and that $g(t)$ is a differentiable function of t at $t = 0$. This means that the local coordinates $\alpha_j(t), j = 1, 2, 3$ (see footnote on page 31) are differentiable with respect to t at $t = 0$. Put $\lambda_j = \alpha_j'(0)$, $a_{jk} = g_{jk}'(0)$. From (14) in § 1, Subsection 5 it easily follows that the numbers λ_j are uniquely determined by the numbers a_{jk}.

By Theorem 1 of Subsection 1, the function T_g is differentiable; we put

$$(\mathrm{d}T_g)_{g=e} = \sum_{j=1}^{3} \mathrm{d}\alpha_j T_j,$$

where the T_j are some operators; applying the rule for the differentiation of a function, we conclude that

$$\left[\frac{\mathrm{d}}{\mathrm{d}t} T_{g(t)}\right]_{t=0} = \sum_{j=1}^{3} \lambda_j T_j.$$

We see that the derivative $\left[\frac{\mathrm{d}}{\mathrm{d}t} T_{g(t)}\right]_{t=0}$ depends only on the numbers λ_j, and consequently only on the numbers a_{jk}; it does not change when $T_{g(t)}$ is replaced by $T_{h(t)}$, if also $h_{jk}'(0) = a_{jk}$.

We make use of this remark in the proof of the following theorem:

THEOREM 2. *The basic infinitesimal operators of a representation of the group G_0 satisfy the relations*

$$[A_1, A_2] = A_3, \quad [A_2, A_3] = A_1, \quad [A_3, A_1] = A_2. \tag{1}$$

Proof. We denote by a, b, c the matrices a_1, a_2, a_3, written in another order, and by A, B, C the operators A_1, A_2, A_3, written in the same order as a, b, c.

By formulae (12) of Subsection 2 it is sufficient to prove that, if $[a, b] = c$, then also $[A, B] = C$.

So, let $[a, b] = c$ and let $a(t), b(t), c(t)$ be the corresponding one-parameter groups, so that

$$a'(0) = a, \quad b'(0) = b, \quad c'(0) = c.$$

We consider the function

$$g(t) = a(\sqrt{t})b(\sqrt{t})a(-\sqrt{t})b(-\sqrt{t}); \tag{2}$$

expanding in order of powers of $\sqrt{t}$ and applying (10) of Subsection 2, we see that

$$g(t) = \left(1+\sqrt{t}\cdot a+\frac{t}{2}a^2+\ldots\right)\left(1+\sqrt{t}\cdot b+\frac{t}{2}b^2+\ldots\right)\times$$
$$\times\left(1-\sqrt{t}\cdot a+\frac{t}{2}a^2-\ldots\right)\left(1-\sqrt{t}\cdot b+\frac{t}{2}b^2-\ldots\right)$$
$$= 1+t(ab-ba)+\ldots = 1+tc+\ldots;$$

consequently

$$g'(0) = c. \tag{3}$$

On the other hand also $c'(0) = c$; hence, by the remark made above, we conclude that

$$\left[\frac{\mathrm{d}}{\mathrm{d}t}T_{c(t)}\right]_{t=0} = \left[\frac{\mathrm{d}}{\mathrm{d}t}T_{g(t)}\right]_{t=0}. \tag{4}$$

But the left-hand side of this equation is C. We shall prove that the right-hand side is $AB-BA$; the theorem will then be proved. For this purpose we put

$$A(t) = T_{a(t)}, \quad B(t) = T_{b(t)}, \quad C(t) = T_{c(t)}, \tag{5}$$

so that

$$A = A'(0), \quad B = B'(0), \quad C = C'(0). \tag{6}$$

Since the correspondence $g \to T_g$ is a representation, it follows from (2) that

$$T_{g(t)} = A(\sqrt{t})B(\sqrt{t})A(-\sqrt{t})B(-\sqrt{t}).$$

Expanding in powers of $\sqrt{t}$ and making use of formula (8) of Subsection 3, we conclude that

$$T_{g(t)} = \left(1+\sqrt{t}\cdot A+\frac{t}{2}A^2+\ldots\right)\left(1+\sqrt{t}\cdot B+\frac{t}{2}B^2+\ldots\right)\times$$
$$\times\left(1-\sqrt{t}\cdot A+\frac{t}{2}A^2-\ldots\right)\left(1-\sqrt{t}\cdot B+\frac{t}{2}B^2-\ldots\right)$$
$$= 1+t(AB-BA)+\ldots .$$

Hence

$$\left[\frac{\mathrm{d}}{\mathrm{d}t}T_{g(t)}\right]_{t=0} = AB-BA,$$

and the theorem is proved.

5. The condition for a representation to be unitary

We saw above that, without loss of generality, a finite-dimensional representation of the group G_0 can be considered to be unitary (see § 3, Subsection 5). Let us see how this affects the operators A_k, $k = 1, 2, 3$.

For this purpose we introduce the following definition. An operator B in a finite-dimensional Euclidean space R is said to be adjoint to the operator A in the same space, if

$$(Ax, y) = (x, By) \quad \text{for all} \quad x, y \in R.$$

The adjoint of A is denoted by A^*. Thus, from the definition of the adjoint operator,

$$(Ax, y) = (x, A^* y) \quad \text{for all} \quad x, y \in R. \tag{1}$$

It is easily shown that, for every linear operator A, there exists one and only one adjoint operator A^*.

It can be seen from (1) that A is the adjoint operator to A^*, i.e.

$$A^{**} = A. \tag{2}$$

Further, it is easily verified that

$$1^* = 1, \quad (\alpha A)^* = \bar{\alpha}A, \quad (A+B)^* = A^*+B^*, \quad (AB)^* = B^*A^*. \tag{3}$$

The operator A is called *Hermitian*, if $A^* = A$.

I. *An operator A is unitary if and only if* $A^*A = 1$. In fact, $(Ax, Ay) = (A^*Ax, y)$, therefore the relation $(Ax, Ay) = (x, y)$ is equivalent to the relation $(A^*Ax, y) = (x, y) = (1 \cdot x, y)$, that is to the relation $A^*A = 1$.

II. *If the representation* $g \to T_g$ *is unitary, then*

$$A_k^* = -A_k, \quad k = 1, 2, 3. \tag{4}$$

Proof. Let the representation $g \to T_g$ be unitary. Then, for any t, the operators $A_k(t) = T_{a_k(t)}$ are unitary, i.e.

$$(A_k(t)x, A_k(t)y) = (x, y) \tag{5}$$

for all $x, y \in R$ and all real t.

Differentiating both sides with respect to t, we get

$$\left(\frac{dA_k(t)}{dt}x, A_k(t)y\right) + \left(A_k(t)x, \frac{dA_k(t)}{dt}y\right) = 0;$$

hence, for $t = 0$,

$$(A_k x, y) + (x, A_k y) = 0,$$

or

$$(A_k x, y) = -(x, A_k y).$$

This means that $A_k^* = -A_k$.

Remark. We note that the converse is also true. In fact, let $A_k^* = -A_k$. From the formula

$$A_k(t) = 1 + \frac{t}{1!}A_k + \frac{t^2}{2!}A_k^2 + \dots$$

it follows that†

$$(A_k(t))^* = 1 + \frac{t}{1!}A_k^* + \frac{t^2}{2!}A_k^{*2} + \dots$$

$$= 1 - \frac{t}{1!}A_k + \frac{t^2}{2!}A_k^2 - \dots = A_k(-t),$$

and therefore $A_k(t)^*A_k(t) = A_k(-t)A_k(t) = A_k(0) = 1$.

---

† We leave it to the reader to prove that the passage to the adjoint operator can be carried out for the series for $A_k(t)$ *term by term*.

Thus, the operators $A_k(t)$, and therefore all possible products of them, are unitary. Since every operator T_g can be represented in the form of a product $A_3(t_3)A_1(t_2)A_3(t_1)$ (see the proof of proposition I, Subsection 3), all the operators are unitary and the representation $g \to T_g$ is unitary.

6. General form of the basic infinitesimal operators of the irreducible representations of the group G_0

We now make use of the relations

$$[A_1, A_2] = A_3, \quad [A_2, A_3] = A_1, \quad [A_3, A_1] = A_2, \tag{1}$$

$$A_k^* = -A_k, \quad k = 1, 2, 3, \tag{2}$$

which we have obtained, in order to determine the general form of the operators A_k in the case of an irreducible finite-dimensional representation of the group G_0.

We put

$$H_+ = iA_1 - A_2, \quad H_- = iA_1 + A_2, \quad H_3 = iA_3; \tag{3}$$

it will be more convenient to look for the general form of the operators H_+, H_-, H_3 by means of which A_1, A_2, A_3 may be easily expressed. It is easy to find the commutators of the operators H_+, H_-, H_3. Thus, by (1),

$$\begin{aligned}[H_+, H_3] &= [iA_1 - A_2, iA_3] = -[A_1, A_3] - i[A_2, A_3] \\ &= A_2 - iA_1 = -H_+.\end{aligned}$$

By similar calculations we get:

$$[H_+, H_3] = -H_+, \quad [H_-, H_3] = H_-, \quad [H_+, H_-] = 2H_3. \tag{4}$$

Further, from (2),

$$H_+^* = (iA_1 - A_2)^* = -iA_1^* - A_2^* = iA_1 + A_2 = H_-,$$

$$H_3^* = (iA_3)^* = -iA_3^* = iA_3 = H_3,$$

so that

$$H_+^* = H_-, \quad H_3^* = H_3. \tag{5}$$

Our problem reduces to the determination of the operators H_+, H_-, H_3 satisfying conditions (4) and (5).

For the solution of this problem we consider the eigenvalues and eigenvectors† of the operator H_3.

I. *If f is an eigenvector of the operator H_3, corresponding to the eigenvalue λ, then the vector $f_1 = H_+ f$ is either zero, or it is an eigenvector of the operator H_3, corresponding to the eigenvalue $\lambda+1$. Further, the vector $f_2 = H_- f$ is either zero, or it is an eigenvector of the operator H_3 corresponding to the eigenvalue $\lambda-1$.*

---

† The number λ is called an *eigenvalue* of the operator A if there exists a vector $x \neq 0$, for which $Ax = \lambda x$.

The vector x itself is called an *eigenvector* corresponding to the eigenvalue λ. *Every linear operator in a finite-dimensional space has at least one eigenvalue.* In fact, choosing a fixed basis $e_1, e_2, \ldots, e_n$, we see that, for $x = \xi_1 e_1 + \ldots + \xi_n e_n$, the condition $Ax = \lambda x$ is equivalent to the homogeneous system of equations.

$$\begin{aligned} (a_{11}-\lambda)\,\xi_1 + a_{12}\xi_2 + \cdots + a_{1n}\xi_n &= 0, \\ a_{21}\xi_1 + (a_{22}-\lambda)\,\xi_2 + \cdots + a_{2n}\xi_n &= 0, \\ \cdots\cdots\cdots\cdots\cdots\cdots\cdots\cdots \\ a_{n1}\xi_1 + a_{n2}\xi_2 + \cdots + (a_{nn}-\lambda)\,\xi_n &= 0, \end{aligned} \tag{A}$$

which has a non-trivial solution if and only if

$$\begin{vmatrix} a_{11}-\lambda & a_{12} & \cdots & a_{1n} \\ a_{21} & a_{22}-\lambda & \cdots & a_{2n} \\ \cdot & \cdot & \cdot & \cdot \\ a_{n1} & a_{n2} & \cdots & a_{nn}-\lambda \end{vmatrix} = 0. \tag{B}$$

Consequently, every root of equation (B) will be an eigenvalue of the operator A.

Evidently, if x is a eigenvector corresponding to the eigenvalue λ, then the vector cx will have the same property if $c \neq 0$; therefore the number c can be so chosen that $(x, x) = 1$. A vector x, for which $(x, x) = 1$, is said to be *normalized*.

If the operator A is Hermitian, then all its eigenvalues are real and eigenvectors x, y, corresponding to different eigenvalues, are orthogonal, i.e. $(x, y) = 0$.

In fact, if A is Hermitian, then, for any $x, y \in R$, $(Ax, y) = (x, Ay)$.

In particular, $(Ax, x) = (x, Ax) = \overline{(Ax, x)}$, so that (Ax, x) is a real number. But then, for $Ax = \lambda x$, $x \neq 0$, we get: $(Ax, x) = (\lambda x, x) = \lambda(x, x)$, and therefore $\lambda = \dfrac{(Ax, x)}{(x, x)}$ is a real number. Further, if $Ax = \lambda x$, $Ay = \mu y$ and $\lambda \neq \mu$, then $(\lambda x, y) = (Ax, y) = (x, Ay) = (x, \mu y)$, whence $(\lambda - \mu)(x, y) = 0$ i.e. $(x, y) = 0$. The eigenvectors of the Hermitian operator H_3 are also called its *weight vectors* and the corresponding eigenvalues are called *weights.*

Proof. By hypothesis, $H_3 f = \lambda f$. Hence, from (4),

$$H_3 f_1 = H_3 H_+ f = [H_3, H_+]f + H_+ H_3 f$$
$$= H_+ f + H_+(\lambda f) = f_1 + \lambda f_1 = (\lambda+1) f_1,$$

so that either $f_1 = 0$ or f_1 is an eigenvector of the operator H_3 corresponding to the eigenvalue $\lambda+1$.

It can be proved similarly that $H_3 f_2 = (\lambda-1) f_2$, from which the second statement follows.

Let us now consider all the eigenvalues of the operator H_3. They are all real and, since their number is finite (not larger than n), there is among them a largest eigenvalue; we denote this largest eigenvalue by k, and let f_k be some normalized eigenvector corresponding to the eigenvalue k, so that

$$H_3 f_k = k f_k, \quad (f_k, f_k) = 1. \tag{6}$$

Here we have

$$H_+ f_k = 0, \tag{7}$$

for otherwise the operator H_3 would have the eigenvalue $k+1$, which is impossible, since k is the largest eigenvalue of the operator H_3.

Consider the vector $H_- f_k$; if the vector $H_- f_k \neq 0$, then it is an eigenvector of the operator H_3 corresponding to the eigenvalue $k-1$.

Putting

$$\alpha_k = \sqrt{(H_- f_k, H_- f_k)} \quad \text{and} \quad f_{k-1} = \frac{1}{\alpha_k} H_- f_k,$$

we get

$$H_3 f_{k-1} = (k-1) f_{k-1}, \quad (f_{k-1}, f_{k-1}) = 1, \quad H_- f_k = \alpha_k f_{k-1}. \tag{8}$$

Similarly, either $H_- f_{k-1} = 0$ or $H_- f_{k-1} = \alpha_{k-1} f_{k-2}$, where $H_3 f_{k-2} = (k-2) f_{k-2}$, $(f_{k-2}, f_{k-2}) = 1$.

Repeating this argument, we obtain a sequence of vectors $f_k, f_{k-1}, f_{k-2}, \ldots$, satisfying the conditions

$$H_3 f_p = p f_p, \quad H_- f_p = \alpha_p f_{p-1}, \quad (f_p, f_p) = 1,$$
$$\alpha_p > 0, \quad p = k,\ k-1, \ldots . \tag{9}$$

These vectors $f_k, f_{k-1}, \ldots$ are eigenvectors of the Hermitian operator H_3, corresponding to the distinct eigenvalues $k, k-1, \ldots,$ and therefore they are mutually orthogonal. But in a finite-dimensional space there is only a finite number of mutually orthogonal vectors, and therefore the sequence $f_k, f_{k-1}, \ldots$ must terminate. This means that for some $l = k-v$ we must have

$$H_- f_l = 0. \tag{10}$$

As in (9) we can write:

$$H_3 f_l = l f_l, \quad H_- f_l = \alpha_l f_{l-1}, \quad \text{where} \quad \alpha_l = 0;$$

here the symbol f_{l-1} is undefined and $\alpha_l f_{l-1}$ is understood to be the zero vector 0.

We shall now consider the effect of the operator H_+ on the vectors f_p. We saw above (see (7)) that $H_+ f_k = 0$; let us find $H_+ f_{k-1}$. From the relation $[H_+, H_-] = 2H_3$, we get

$$H_+ f_{k-1} = \frac{1}{\alpha_k} H_+ H_- f_k = \frac{1}{\alpha_k}[H_+, H_-] f_k + \frac{1}{\alpha_k} H_- H_+ f_k$$
$$= \frac{2}{\alpha_k} H_3 f_k = \frac{2k}{\alpha_k} f_k,$$

i.e.

$$H_+ f_{k-1} = \beta_k f_k, \quad \text{where} \quad \beta_k = \frac{2k}{\alpha_k}.$$

We prove that in general

$$H_+ f_p = \beta_{p+1} f_{p+1} \quad \text{for} \quad p = k-1, k-2, \ldots, l, \tag{11}$$

where the β_{p+1} are real numbers. For $p = k-1$ this formula has just been proved; we suppose that the formula (11) has already been proved for the vector f_p and we prove its validity for the vector f_{p-1}. We have:

$$H_+ f_{p-1} = \frac{1}{\alpha_p} H_+ H_- f_p = \frac{1}{\alpha_p}[H_+, H_-] f_p + \frac{1}{\alpha_p} H_- H_+ f_p$$
$$= \frac{2}{\alpha_p} H_3 f_p + \frac{\beta_{p+1}}{\alpha_p} H_- f_{p+1} = \left(\frac{2p}{\alpha_p} + \frac{\beta_{p+1}\alpha_{p+1}}{\alpha_p}\right) f_p,$$

consequently, also $H_+ f_{p-1} = \beta_p f_p$, where

$$\beta_p = \frac{2p}{\alpha_p} + \frac{\beta_{p+1}\alpha_{p+1}}{\alpha_p}. \tag{12}$$

Thus, we have

$$H_3 f_p = p f_p, \quad H_- f_p = \alpha_p f_{p-1}, \quad H_+ f_p = \beta_{p+1} f_{p+1} \tag{13}$$

$$\text{for} \quad p = k,\ k-1, \ldots, l.$$

Here $\alpha_l = 0$, $\beta_{k+1} = 0$, the symbols f_{k+1}, f_{l-1} are undefined and $\alpha_l f_{l-1}$, $\beta_{k+1} f_{k+1}$ are understood to be the zero vector.

We now make use of the relation $H_+^* = H_-$, from which it follows that

$$(H_+ f_{p-1}, f_p) = (f_{p-1}, H_- f_p).$$

By (13) this means that

$$(\beta_p f_p, f_p) = (f_{p-1}, \alpha_p f_{p-1});$$

since $(f_p, f_p) = (f_{p-1}, f_{p-1}) = 1$, we conclude that $\beta_p = \alpha_p$. Putting α_p and α_{p+1} in place of β_p and β_{p+1} in formula (12), we arrive at the relation

$$\alpha_p = \frac{2p}{\alpha_p} + \frac{\alpha_{p+1}^2}{\alpha_p},$$

whence

$$\alpha_p^2 - \alpha_{p+1}^2 = 2p. \tag{14}$$

It is now easy to find the numbers α_p. In (14) we give p the values $k, k-1, \ldots$ down to an arbitrary value of p; adding the resulting equations, we find:

$$\alpha_p^2 - \alpha_{k+1}^2 = 2p + 2(p+1) + \ldots + 2k = (k+p)(k-p+1).$$

But $\alpha_{k+1} = \beta_{k+1} = 0$; consequently,

$$\alpha_p = \sqrt{[(k+p)(k-p+1)]}. \tag{15}$$

On the other hand, also $\alpha_l = 0$, i.e. $(k+l)(k-l+1) = 0$. Since $l < k$, this is only possible if $l = -k$; consequently the chain of vectors f_p which we have constructed has the form

$$f_{-k}, f_{-k+1}, \ldots, f_{k-1}, f_k,$$

and the number of vectors in this chain is equal to $k-(-k)+1 = 2k+1$. From this we conclude that $2k$ is a whole number and therefore that k is a non-negative integer or semi-integer.†

Up to now the given representation $g \to T_g$ could be either reducible or irreducible. We shall now suppose that this representation is irreducible, and show that in that case the vectors $f_{-k}, f_{-k+1}, \ldots, f_k$ form a basis for the space R. We denote by R' the subspace of R generated by all the vectors $f_{-k}, f_{-k+1}, \ldots, f_k$, (i.e. the aggregate of all possible linear combinations of these vectors). It is shown by (13) that R' is invariant with respect to the operators H_3, H_+, H_- and so also with respect to the operators A_1, A_2, A_3. But it is then also invariant with respect to the operators

$$A_j(t) = 1+tA_j+\frac{t^2}{2!}A_j^2+\ldots, \quad j = 1, 2, 3,$$

and so also with respect to all the operators T_g since they are products of the operators $A_j(t)$, $j = 1, 2, 3$.

Since the representation $g \to T_g$ is irreducible, this is possible only if $R' = R$, i.e. if the vectors $f_{-k}, f_{-k+1}, \ldots, f_k$ form a basis for the space R.

We have now proved the following theorem:

THEOREM 3. *Every finite-dimensional irreducible representation of the three-dimensional rotation group is uniquely determined by a non-negative integer or semi-integer* k. *The space of the representation corresponding to such a number* k *has the dimension* $2k+1$, *while the operators* H_3, H_+, H_- *of this representation are given relative to some orthogonal normalized basis* $f_{-k}, f_{-k+1}, \ldots, f_k$ *by the formulae:*

$$H_3 f_\nu = \nu f_\nu, \quad H_+ f_\nu = \alpha_{\nu+1} f_{\nu+1}, \quad H_- f_\nu = \alpha_\nu f_{\nu-1}, \qquad (16)$$
$$\nu = -k, \; -k+1, \ldots, k,$$

where

$$\alpha_\nu = \sqrt{[(k+\nu)(k-\nu+1)]}. \qquad (17)$$

The number k is called the *weight* of this representation, while the basis $f_{-k}, f_{-k+1}, \ldots, f_k$ is called its *canonical basis.*

† By a semi-integer we mean half of an odd integer.

We note that for the moment the question remains open whether to each non-negative integer or semi-integer k there really corresponds an irreducible representation of the group G_0, i.e. whether, for any such k, the operators H_3, H_+, H_-, defined by (16), (17), are really the linear combinations $H_+ = iA_1-A_2$, $H_- = iA_1+A_2$, $H_3 = iA_3$ of the basic infinitesimal operators of some irreducible representation of the group G_0.

In the next section we shall answer this question in the affirmative; indeed, for every non-negative integer or semi-integer k, we shall in fact construct an irreducible representation of the group G_0 with weight k. Meanwhile we take note of the following proposition:

II. *If the operators* H_+, H_-, H_3 *of a representation* $g \to T_g$ *of the group* G_0 *in a* $(2k+1)$*-dimensional space are given relative to some basis* $f_{-k}, f_{-k+1}, \ldots, f_k$ *by the formulae* (16), (17), *then that representation is irreducible.*

Proof. Let R' be a subspace of R distinct from (0) and invariant with respect to the representation $g \to T_g$. Then it is also invariant with respect to the operators $A_j(t) = T_{a_j(t)}$, and therefore also with respect to the operators $A_j = \lim\limits_{t\to 0} \dfrac{A_j(t)-1}{t}$. But then R' is also invariant with respect to the operators $H_+ = iA_1-A_2$, $H_- = iA_1+A_2$, $H_3 = iA_3$. The operator H_3, regarded as an operator in R', has a greatest eigenvalue k'; let $f' = \sum\limits_{p=-k}^{k} c_p f_p$ be a vector of R', which is an eigenvector of the operator H_3, corresponding to the eigenvalue k'. Then, by *I*, we have $H_+ f' = 0$, i.e.†

$$\sum_{p=-k}^{k-1} c_p \alpha_{p+1} f_{p+1} = 0.$$

Since the vectors f_p are linearly independent, $c_p \alpha_{p+1} = 0$ for $p = -k, -k+1, \ldots, k-1$, and therefore also $c_p = 0$ for $p = -k, -k+1, \ldots, k-1$. From this we conclude that $f' = c_k f_k$; consequently,‡ $f_k = \dfrac{1}{c_k} f' \in R'$. But then also all the vectors

† Remembering that $H_+ f_k = 0$.

‡ $c_k \neq 0$, as f' is an eigenvector, and therefore $f' \neq 0$.

$f_{k-1} = \dfrac{1}{\alpha_k} H_- f_k, f_{k-2} = \dfrac{1}{\alpha_{k-1}} H_- f_{k-1}, \ldots$ belong to R'; consequently $R' = R$.

Thus, every subspace $R' \neq (0)$, invariant with respect to the representation $g \to T_g$, coincides with the whole space R; this means that the representation $g \to T_g$ is irreducible.

§ 5. The Realization of Finite-dimensional Irreducible Representations of the Three-dimensional Rotation Group

1. The connection between the representations of the group G_0 and the representations of the unitary group $\mathfrak{U}$

We recall that every rotation g of three-dimensional space is given by a unitary matrix

$$u = \begin{Vmatrix} \alpha & \beta \\ -\bar{\beta} & \bar{\alpha} \end{Vmatrix}, \quad |\alpha|^2 + |\beta|^2 = 1 \tag{1}$$

with determinant unity (see Section 1, Subsection 5); here the product of matrices u corresponds to the product of the corresponding rotations g, and two different matrices u_1, u_2 determine one and the same rotation g if and only if $u_2 = -u_1$.

Let $g \to T_g$ be a representation of the group G_0. We put $T_u = T_g$ if the rotation g corresponds to the matrix $u \in \mathfrak{U}$; since the product of rotations g corresponds to the product of matrices u, the correspondence $u \to T_u$ is a representation of the group $\mathfrak{U}$. Here we have

$$T_{-u} = T_u, \tag{2}$$

for to the matrices $-u$ and u there corresponds one and the same rotation g, which means one and the same operator $T_g = T_u = T_{-u}$.

Conversely, to every representation $u \to T_u$ of the group $\mathfrak{U}$ satisfying condition (2), there corresponds a representation $g \to T_g$ of the group G_0; it is obtained by putting $T_g = T_u$ if the rotation g corresponds to the matrix u. The representation $g \to T_g$ is continuous if and only if the corresponding representation $u \to T_u$ of the group $\mathfrak{U}$ is continuous. This follows directly from (12) and (13) of § 1, Subsection 5, which establish the correspondence between the matrices $u \in \mathfrak{U}$ and the rotations g.

Thus, *the description of the representations of the group* G_0 *is equivalent to the description of the representations of the group* $\mathfrak{U}$ *which satisfy condition* (2), and it will be convenient to realize the irreducible representations of the group G_0 as representations of the group $\mathfrak{U}$. It turns out to be a matter of some interest to consider arbitrary representations of the group $\mathfrak{U}$, and not only those satisfying condition (2). If this condition is satisfied, the corresponding representation $g \to T_g$ of the group G_0 will be single-valued, but if it is not satisfied, the representation $g \to T_g$ will be *two-valued.*

2. Spinor representations of the group $\mathfrak{U}$

We shall now write the matrices $u \in \mathfrak{U}$ in the form

$$u = \begin{Vmatrix} u_{11} & u_{12} \\ u_{21} & u_{22} \end{Vmatrix}, \tag{1}$$

so that $u_{11} = \alpha, u_{12} = \beta, u_{21} = -\bar{\beta}, u_{22} = \bar{\alpha}$. Every such matrix may be considered as the matrix of the linear transformation†

$$\xi^{1\prime} = u_{11}\xi^1 + u_{12}\xi^2, \quad \xi^{2\prime} = u_{21}\xi^1 + u_{22}\xi^2 \tag{2}$$

of the linear space of all pairs (ξ^1, ξ^2) of complex numbers ξ^1, ξ^2. If $T_u^{(1)}$, denotes this linear transformation, then, evidently, $T_{u_1u_2}^{(1)} = T_{u_1}^{(1)}T_{u_2}^{(1)}$, so that the correspondence $u \to T_u^{(1)}$ is a representation of the group $\mathfrak{U}$.

We get a less trivial representation of the group $\mathfrak{U}$ if we consider several pairs

$$(\xi_1^1, \xi_1^2), (\xi_2^1, \xi_2^2), \dots, (\xi_m^1, \xi_m^2) \tag{3}$$

and form all possible products

$$\xi_1^{p_1}\xi_2^{p_2} \dots \xi_m^{p_m}, \tag{4}$$

† Throughout this section we shall write the indices 1, 2 of the transformed variables above, not below.

where the indices $p_1, p_2, \ldots, p_m$ run through the values 1, 2 independently of one another. If every one of the pairs (3) undergoes the linear transformation (2), then the product $\xi_1^{p_1}\xi_2^{p_2}\ldots\xi_m^{p_m}$ becomes

$$\xi_1'^{p_1}\xi_2'^{p_2}\ldots\xi_m'^{p_m} = \sum_{q_1,\ldots,q_m=1}^{2} u_{p_1q_1}u_{p_2q_2}\ldots u_{p_mq_m}\xi_1^{q_1}\xi_2^{q_2}\ldots\xi_m^{q_m}, \tag{5}$$

$$p_1, p_2, \ldots, p_m = 1, 2.$$

For every choice of fixed pairs (3), the aggregate of all possible products $\xi_1^{p_1}\xi_2^{p_2}\ldots\xi_m^{p_m}$, can be considered as a vector in a 2^m-dimensional linear space, namely the space of all possible systems of 2^m complex numbers $\xi^{p_1p_2\cdots p_m}$, where the indices $p_1, p_2, \cdots, p_m$ run through the values 1, 2 independently of one another. Here the addition of vectors $\xi = \{\xi^{p_1p_2\cdots p_m}\}$ and their multiplication by a number α are defined by the addition of the corresponding components $\xi^{p_1p_2\cdots p_m}$, and the multiplication of all these components by the number α. We denote this linear space by R_m.

If in (5) we replace the products $\xi_1^{p_1}\xi_2^{p_2}\ldots\xi_m^{p_m}$ by the components $\xi^{p_1p_2\cdots p_m}$ of an arbitrary vector $\xi \in R_m$, then we get the linear transformation

$$\xi'^{p_1p_2\ldots p_m} = \sum_{q_1,q_2,\ldots q_m=1}^{2} u_{p_1q_1}u_{p_2q_2}\ldots u_{p_mq_m}\xi^{q_1q_2\ldots q_m} \tag{6}$$

of the space R_m; we denote this linear transformation by $T_u^{(m)}$.

I. *The correspondence* $u \to T_u^{(m)}$ *is a representation of the group* $\mathfrak{U}$. In fact, the product u_1u_2 of the matrices u_1, u_2, corresponds to the successive application, first of the transformation $T_{u_2}^{(1)}$, and then of $T_{u_1}^{(1)}$ to each of the pairs $(\xi_1^1, \xi_1^2), \ldots, (\xi_m^1, \xi_m^2)$; but this means that the product u_1u_2 corresponds to the successive application to the vector $\xi = \{\xi_1^{p_1}\xi_2^{p_2}\ldots\xi_m^{p_m}\}$, which means also to any arbitrary vector $\xi = \{\xi^{p_1p_2\cdots p_m}\}$, first of the transformation $T_{u_2}^{(m)}$, and then of the transformation $T_{u_1}^{(m)}$, so that $T_{u_1u_2}^{(m)} = T_{u_1}^{(m)}T_{u_2}^{(m)}$.

The representation $u \to T_u^{(m)}$ just constructed is closely connected with the spinors of rank m and is therefore called the *spinor representation* of rank m.

By *a contravariant spinor of rank m* in three-dimensional space we understand a system $\xi = \{\xi^{p_1p_2\cdots p_m}\}$ of numbers, defined relative to each system of coordinates in three-dimensional space, and having the following properties:

(1) the numbers $\xi^{p_1 p_2 \cdots p_m}$ of the system ξ are uniquely defined except for a common multiple $(-1)^m$;

(2) on transition to another system of coordinates by a rotation g the components are transformed according to the formula (6), where $u = \|u_{pq}\|_{pq = 1,2}$ is the unitary matrix corresponding to the rotation g. Here, by condition (1), it is immaterial which matrix is chosen of the two matrices u $-u$, corresponding to the rotation g.

If the system of coordinates in three-dimensional space is fixed, then formula (6) can be considered as a transformation of the spinor $\xi = \{\xi^{p_1 p_2 \cdots p_m}\}$ into the spinor $\xi' = \{\xi'^{p_1 p_2 \cdots p_m}\}$. However, such a transformation of spinors determines a linear representation of the group $\mathfrak{U}$ only if m is even, for, by condition (1), the spinors of an odd rank m do not form a linear space.

Therefore, it will be more convenient to consider the linear space R_m, instead of considering the aggregate of all spinors of rank m.

The spinor representation $u \to T_u^{(m)}$ is not irreducible. In order to see this, we consider all those vectors $\xi = \{\xi^{p_1 p_2 \cdots p_m}\} \in R_m$, whose components are not changed under any permutation of the indices $p_1, p_2, \ldots, p_m$; we shall call such vectors ξ *symmetrical*. It is evident that the symmetrical vectors form a subspace S_m of R_m.

II. *The subspace S_m is invariant with respect to all the operators $T_u^{(m)}$.* This assertion follows immediately from (6), for every permutation of the indices $p_1, p_2, \ldots, p_m$ in $\xi'^{p_1 p_2 \cdots p_m}$ may be obtained by the same permutation of the factors $u_{p_1 q_1}, \ldots, u_{p_m q_m}$ and the indices $q_1, q_2, \ldots, q_m$ in $\xi^{q_1 q_2 \cdots q_m}$. Therefore, if ξ is a symmetrical vector, then also ξ' is a symmetrical vector.

Thus, the operators $T_u^{(m)}$ can be considered as operators in the space S_m, and in that case the correspondence $u \to T_u^{(m)}$ will be a representation of the group $\mathfrak{U}$ in the space S_m. We shall call this representation the *spinor representation of the group* $\mathfrak{U}$ *in the space* S_m, and we shall denote it by $\mathfrak{S}_m$.

We shall see below (see Subsection 4, I) that all the representations $\mathfrak{S}_m$ are irreducible, $\mathfrak{S}_m$ being an irreducible representation of weight $m/2$. Consequently, with the aid of the representations $\mathfrak{S}_m$, $m = 1, 2, 3, \ldots$, we shall be able to realize representations having any non-negative integral or semi-integral weight $k = m/2$.

This would prove that for any such k, the formulae (16), (17) of § 4, Subsection 6 do in fact determine the infinitesimal operators of an irreducible representation of the group $\mathfrak{U}$.

Let us determine the dimension of the space S_m of the representation $\mathfrak{S}_m$. From the symmetry of the vector $\xi = \{\xi^{p_1 p_2 \dots p_m}\} \in S_m$, a suitable permutation of the indices will carry its components into one of the following $m+1$ components:

$$\xi^{\overbrace{11\dots1}^{m}}, \quad \xi^{\overbrace{1\dots1}^{m-1},2}, \quad \dots, \quad \xi^{\overbrace{1\dots1}^{m-s}\ \overbrace{2\dots2}^{s}}, \quad \dots, \quad \xi^{\overbrace{2\dots2}^{m}};$$

consequently, the dimension of the space S_m is equal to $m+1$.

3. Realization of the representations $\mathfrak{S}_m$ in a space of polynomials

In the sequel we shall also require the following realization of the representations $\mathfrak{S}_m$, completely equivalent to the original one. We place in correspondence with every vector $\xi = \{\xi^{p_1 p_2 \dots p_m}\} \in S_m$ the homogeneous polynomial

$$p(z, z_2) = \sum_{p_1, p_2, \dots, p_m = 1}^{2} \xi^{p_1 p_2 \dots p_m} z_{p_1} z_{p_2} \dots z_{p_m} \tag{1}$$

of degree m in two complex variables z_1, z_2. These polynomials also form a linear space of dimension $m+1$, for the monomials $z_1^m, z_1^{m-1} z_2, z_1^{m-2} z_2^2, \dots, z_2^m$ form a basis of that space. The correspondence thus set up between the vectors $\xi \in S_m$ and the polynomials $p(z_1, z_2)$ is one-to-one, and the addition of vectors $\xi \in S_m$ and their multiplication by a number correspond to the addition of polynomials and their multiplication by a number. Therefore the space S_m may be identified with the space of homogeneous polynomials $p(z_1, z_2)$ of degree m. Let us see what form is assumed by the operator $T_u^{(m)}$, for this new realization of the space S_m. From formula (6), Subsection 2,

$$\begin{aligned} T_u^{(m)} p(z_1, z_2) &= \sum_{p_1 p_2 \dots p_m = 1}^{2} \xi'^{p_1 p_2 \dots p_m} z_{p_1} z_{p_2} \dots z_{p_m} \\ &= \sum_{p_1 p_2 \dots p_m = 1}^{2} \sum_{q_1 q_2 \dots q_m = 1}^{2} u_{p_1 q_1} u_{p_2 q_2} \dots u_{p_m q_m} \xi^{q_1 q_2 \dots q_m} z_{p_1} z_{p_2} \dots z_{p_m} \\ &= \sum_{q_1 q_2 \dots q_m = 1}^{2} \xi^{q_1 q_2 \dots q_m} z'_{q_1} z'_{q_2} \dots z'_{q_m} = p(z'_1, z'_2), \end{aligned} \tag{2}$$

where

$$z'_q = \sum_{p=1}^{2} u_{pq} z_p, \quad q = 1, 2, \tag{3}$$

i.e.

$$z'_1 = u_{11} z_1 + u_{21} z_2, \quad z'_2 = u_{12} z_1 + u_{22} z_2. \tag{4}$$

Thus, *the operator $T_u^{(m)}$ in the space of homogeneous polynomials $p(z_1, z_2)$ of degree m* is given by the formula

$$T_u^{(m)} p(z_1, z_2) = p(u_{11} z_1 + u_{21} z_2, \quad u_{12} z_1 + u_{22} z_2). \tag{5}$$

The space S_m can be realized in still another way, namely as the aggregate of all polynomials $p(z)$ in the complex variable z of degree not exceeding m. In fact, the quotient $p(z_1, z_2)/z_2^m$ is a polynomial $p(z_1/z_2)$ in the ratio (z_1/z_2), of degree not exceeding m; putting z in place of z_1/z_2, we get the polynomial $p(z)$. Consequently, the correspondence between the polynomials $p(z_1, z_2)$ and $p(z)$ will be given by the formula

$$p(z_1, z_2) = z_2^m p\left(\frac{z_1}{z_2}\right). \tag{6}$$

Let us see what form is taken by the operator $T_u^{(m)}$ for this realization of the space S_m. Let $T_u^{(m)} p(z) = q(z)$; then, by (5) and (6):

$$z_2^m q\left(\frac{z_1}{z_2}\right) = p(u_{11} z_1 + u_{21} z_2, \quad u_{12} z_1 + u_{22} z_2)$$
$$= (u_{12} z_1 + u_{22} z_2)^m p\left(\frac{u_{11} z_1 + u_{21} z_2}{u_{12} z_1 + u_{22} z_2}\right).$$

Hence

$$q\left(\frac{z_1}{z_2}\right) = \left(u_{12} \frac{z_1}{z_2} + u_{22}\right)^m p\left(\frac{u_{11} \dfrac{z_1}{z_2} + u_{21}}{u_{12} \dfrac{z_1}{z_2} + u_{22}}\right),$$

i.e.

$$q(z) = (u_{12} z + u_{22})^m p\left(\frac{u_{11} z + u_{21}}{u_{12} z + u_{22}}\right).$$

Consequently, for the realization of the space S_m in the form of the space of polynomials $p(z)$ of degree not exceeding m, the operators $T_u^{(m)}$ of the representation $\mathfrak{S}_m$ are given by the formula

$$T_u^{(m)} p(z) = (u_{12} z + u_{22})^m p\left(\frac{u_{11} z + u_{21}}{u_{12} z + u_{22}}\right). \tag{7}$$

In what follows we shall consider the representation $\mathfrak{S}_m$ chiefly in this last realization.

4. Basic infinitesimal operators of the representation $\mathfrak{S}_m$

We shall find the operators H_+, H_-, H_3, corresponding to the representation $\mathfrak{S}_m$. For this purpose we determine the unitary matrices $u_1(t), u_2(t), u_3(t)$, corresponding to the rotations $a_1(t)$, $a_2(t), a_3(t)$.

From (9), § 1, Subsection 5 (see also (7) and (8), Section 1 Subsection 5) it follows that

$$u_1(t) = \pm \begin{Vmatrix} \cos\frac{t}{2} & i\sin\frac{t}{2} \\ i\sin\frac{t}{2} & \cos\frac{t}{2} \end{Vmatrix}, \quad u_2(t) = \pm \begin{Vmatrix} \cos\frac{t}{2} & -\sin\frac{t}{2} \\ \sin\frac{t}{2} & \cos\frac{t}{2} \end{Vmatrix},$$

$$u_3(t) = \pm \begin{Vmatrix} e^{\frac{it}{2}} & 0 \\ 0 & e^{-\frac{it}{2}} \end{Vmatrix}. \tag{1}$$

But, for the determination of the operators A_1, A_2, A_3, we only require $u_1(t), u_2(t), u_3(t)$ for small values of t, and then the signs in the formulae (1) are uniquely determined by the condition $\lim_{t\to 0} u_q(t) = 1$, $q = 1, 2, 3$; from this condition we conclude that in the formulae (1) the + sign must be taken. Thus, putting $A_q(t) = T_{u_q(t)}^{(m)}$, and making use of formula (7) Subsection 3, we get:

$$A_1(t) p(z) = \left(i\sin\frac{t}{2} z + \cos\frac{t}{2}\right)^m p\left(\frac{\cos\frac{t}{2} z + i\sin\frac{t}{2}}{i\sin\frac{t}{2} z + \cos\frac{t}{2}}\right), \tag{2a}$$

$$A_2(t)p(z) = \left(-\sin\frac{t}{2}z+\cos\frac{t}{2}\right)^m p\left(\frac{\cos\frac{t}{2}z+\sin\frac{t}{2}}{-\sin\frac{t}{2}z+\cos\frac{t}{2}}\right), \tag{2b}$$

$$A_3(t)p(z) = e^{-\frac{imt}{2}}p(e^{it}z). \tag{2c}$$

Differentiating both sides of these equations with respect to t, and putting $t = 0$ we get:

$$A_1 p = \frac{1}{2}i(1-z^2)\frac{\partial p}{\partial z}+\frac{1}{2}imzp, \tag{3a}$$

$$A_2 p = \frac{1}{2}(1+z^2)\frac{\partial p}{\partial z}-\frac{1}{2}mzp, \tag{3b}$$

$$A_3 p = iz\frac{\partial p}{\partial z}-\frac{1}{2}imp. \tag{3c}$$

Hence, remembering that $H_+ = iA_1 - A_2$, $H_- = iA_1 + A_2$, $H_3 = iA_3$ (see (3), § 4, Subsection 6), we conclude that

$$H_+ p = -\frac{\partial p}{\partial z}, \tag{4a}$$

$$H_- p = z^2\frac{\partial p}{\partial z}-mzp, \tag{4b}$$

$$H_3 p = -z\frac{\partial p}{\partial z}+\frac{1}{2}mp. \tag{4c}$$

Let us apply the operator H_3 to the monomials z^ν, $\nu = 0, 1, \ldots, m$. We get:

$$H_3 z^\nu = -z\nu z^{\nu-1}+\tfrac{1}{2}mz^\nu = (\tfrac{1}{2}m-\nu)z^\nu; \tag{5}$$

consequently, the z^ν form a basis from the weight vectors of the operator H_3 of weights $\frac{1}{2}m-\nu$. In particular, we get a vector of the highest weight for $\nu = 0$ and this highest weight will be $\frac{1}{2}m$.

I. $\mathfrak{S}_m$ *is an irreducible representation of the group* $\mathfrak{U}$.

Proof. Let $\mathfrak{M}$ be a subspace of S_m other than (0), invariant with respect to all operators T_u of the representation $\mathfrak{S}_m$ and hence also with respect to the infinitesimal operators H_+, H_-, H_3 of that representation (see the proof of II, Section 4 Subsection 6). We have to prove that $\mathfrak{M} = S_m$.

Let $p(z) \in \mathfrak{M}$, $p(z) \neq 0$. Applying to it the operator $H_+ = -\partial/\partial z$ repeatedly, we get a constant $c \neq 0$, belonging to $\mathfrak{M}$; consequently, $\mathfrak{M}$ contains all constants. From this it readily follows that $\mathfrak{M}$ contains all the powers z^ν, $\nu = 0, 1, 2, \ldots, m$.

In fact, if $z^\nu \in \mathfrak{M}$, where $0 \leqslant \nu < m$, then also $H_- z^\nu \in \mathfrak{M}$. But, by (4b)

$$H_- z^\nu = z^2 \frac{\partial}{\partial z} z^\nu - mzz^\nu = (\nu - m) z^{\nu+1};$$

consequently, $(\nu - m)z^{\nu+1} \in \mathfrak{M}$, and $z^{\nu+1} \in \mathfrak{M}$. Since $z^0 = 1 \in \mathfrak{M}$, it follows from this that $\mathfrak{M}$ contains all z^ν, $\nu = 0, 1, \ldots, m$, and therefore $\mathfrak{M} = S_m$.

In accordance with Theorem 3 § 4, Subsection 6, the representation $\mathfrak{S}_m$ must be given by the formulae (16), (17), § 4, Subsection 6. According to (5) the vector of highest weight will be $z^0 = 1$, the weight of this vector being $\frac{1}{2}m$; consequently, $\mathfrak{S}_m$ realizes an irreducible representation of the group $\mathfrak{U}$ of weight $k = \frac{1}{2}m$. But m is here any non-negative whole number, and therefore $\frac{1}{2}m$ is any non-negative integer or semi-integer.

Combining these remarks with Theorem 3 § 4, Subsection 6, we arrive at the following result:

THEOREM 4. *Every irreducible finite-dimensional representation of the group* $\mathfrak{U}$ *is uniquely determined by some non-negative integer or semi-integer* k, *the weight of this representation; conversely, for any non-negative integer or semi-integer* k, *there exists an irreducible representation of the group* $\mathfrak{U}$ *of weight* k.

A representation of weight k *can be realized as the representation* $\mathfrak{S}_m$, *where* $m = 2k$; *consequently, every finite-dimensional irreducible representation of the group* $\mathfrak{U}$ *is equivalent to one of the representations* $\mathfrak{S}_m$.

Putting

$$f_\nu(z) = (-1)^{k-\nu}\frac{z^{k-\nu}}{\sqrt{[(k-\nu)!(k+\nu)!]}}, \quad \nu = -k, \ -k+1, \ldots, k; \quad (6)$$

it follows from (4a, 4c) that $H_3 f_\nu$, $H_- f_\nu$, $H_+ f_\nu$ are given by the formulae (16), (17), of Section 4, Subsection 6; consequently, *the functions $f_\nu(z)$ form a canonical basis for the representation $\mathfrak{S}_m$ in the space S_m.*

From this it is easy to find the matrix elements of the irreducible representation of weight k, relative to the canonical basis. Indeed, from formula (7) Subsection 3,

$$T_u^{(m)} f_\nu(z) = \frac{(-1)^{k-\nu}}{\sqrt{[(k-\nu)!(k+\nu)!]}}(u_{12}z+u_{22})^{2k}\left(\frac{u_{11}z+u_{21}}{u_{12}z+u_{22}}\right)^{k-\nu}$$

$$= \frac{(-1)^{k-\nu}}{\sqrt{[(k-\nu)!(k+\nu)!]}}(u_{11}z+u_{21})^{k-\nu}(u_{12}z+u_{22})^{k+\nu}$$

$$= \frac{(-1)^{k-\nu}}{\sqrt{[(k-\nu)!(k+\nu)!]}}\sum_{\mu=-k}^{k} z^{k-\mu}\sum_{\alpha=\max(0,-\mu-\nu)}^{\min(k-\mu,k-\nu)} C_\alpha^{k-\nu}C_{k-\mu-\alpha}^{k+\nu}\times$$

$$\times\, u_{11}^{\alpha}u_{12}^{k-\mu-\alpha}u_{21}^{k-\nu-\alpha}u_{22}^{\mu+\nu+\alpha}$$

$$= \frac{(-1)^{k-\nu}}{\sqrt{[(k-\nu)!(k+\nu)!]}}\sum_{\mu=-k}^{k}(-1)^{k-\mu}\sqrt{[(k-\mu)!(k+\mu)!]}\times$$

$$\times f_\mu(z)\sum_{\alpha=\max(0,-\mu-\nu)}^{\min(k-\mu,k-\nu)} C_\alpha^{k-\nu}C_{k-\mu-\alpha}^{k+\nu}u_{11}^{\alpha}u_{12}^{k-\mu-\alpha}u_{21}^{k-\nu-\alpha}u_{22}^{\mu+\nu+\alpha},$$

where C_m^n denotes the number of combinations of m elements from n.

Consequently we have

II. *The matrix elements $c_{\mu\nu}^k(u)$ of an operator T_u of the irreducible representation of weight k relative to the canonical basis* are *given by the formula*†

---

† We remark that these functions are related to the Jacobi polynomials (see [13]).

$$c^k_{\mu\nu}(u) = (-1)^{2k-\mu-\nu} \frac{\sqrt{[(k-\mu)!(k+\mu)!]}}{\sqrt{[(k-\nu)!\,(k+\nu)!]}} \times$$

$$\times \sum_{\alpha=\max(0,-\mu-\nu)}^{\min(k-\mu,k-\nu)} C^{k-\nu}_{\alpha} C^{k+\nu}_{k-\mu-\alpha} u^{\alpha}_{11}\, u^{k-\mu-\alpha}_{12}\, u^{k-\nu-\alpha}_{21}\, u^{\mu+\nu+\alpha}_{22}. \quad (7)$$

5. Orthogonality relations

We shall consider some properties of the matrices $c^k(u) = \|c^k_{\mu\nu}(u)\|$. Firstly, these matrices are unitary; and the correspondence $u \to c^k(u)$ is a representation of the group $\mathfrak{U}$, and therefore $c^k(u_1u_2) = c^k(u_1)c^k(u_2)$; this means that

$$c^k_{\mu\nu}(u_1 u_2) = \sum_{j=-k}^{k} c^k_{\mu j}(u_1) c^k_{j\nu}(u_2). \quad (1)$$

Finally, we note that

$$c^k(u^{-1}) = c^k(u)^{-1} = c^k(u)^*; \quad (2)$$

this means that

$$c^k_{\mu\nu}(u^{-1}) = \overline{c^k_{\nu\mu}(u)}. \quad (3)$$

We now denote by Γ the aggregate of all diagonal matrices

$$\gamma = \begin{Vmatrix} e^{-\frac{it}{2}} & 0 \\ 0 & e^{\frac{it}{2}} \end{Vmatrix}, \quad (4)$$

where t is a real number. Let us find the matrix elements $c^k_{\mu\nu}(\gamma)$. To do this we apply formulae (7) Subsection 3 and (6) Subsection 4; we get:

$$T_\gamma f_\nu(z) = (-1)^{k-\nu} e^{ikt} \frac{(e^{-it}z)^{k-\nu}}{\sqrt{[(k-\nu)!(k+\nu)!]}} = e^{i\nu t} f_\nu(z);$$

consequently:

I. *The matrix* $\|c^k_{\mu\nu}(\gamma)\|$ *is diagonal and*

$$c^k_{\nu\nu}(\gamma) = e^{i\nu t}. \quad (5)$$

Hence we conclude from (1) that

$$c^k_{\mu\nu}(\gamma u) = e^{i\mu t}\, c^k_{\mu\nu}(u), \quad c^k_{\mu\nu}(u\gamma) = e^{i\nu t} c^k_{\mu\nu}(u). \quad (6)$$

II. *The functions $c^k_{\mu\nu}(u)$ satisfy the relations*

$$\int c^k_{\mu\nu}(u)\overline{c^l_{\mu_1\nu_1}(u)}du = \begin{cases} 0 \text{ if } \mu \neq \mu_1, \text{ or } \nu \neq \nu_1, \text{ or } k \neq l, \\ \dfrac{1}{2k+1} \text{ if } \mu = \mu_1, \ \nu = \nu_1, \ k = l. \end{cases} \tag{7}$$

Proof. From the invariance of the integral with respect to du and from the formulae (6), we have

$$\int c^k_{\mu\nu}(u)\overline{c^l_{\mu_1\nu_1}(u)}du = \int c^k_{\mu\nu}(\gamma u)\overline{c^l_{\mu_1\nu_1}(\gamma u)}du$$
$$= e^{i(\mu-\mu_1)t}\int c^k_{\mu\nu}(u)\overline{c^l_{\mu_1\nu_1}(u)}du;$$

for $\mu \neq \mu_1$, this is only possible if

$$\int c^k_{\mu\nu}(u)\overline{c^l_{\mu_1\nu_1}(u)}du = 0. \tag{8}$$

Similarly it can be proved that (8) holds for $\nu \neq \nu_1$.

We now consider the case of $k \neq l$. To be definite, let $k > l$; applying (1) and (8), we get:

$$\int c^k_{\mu k}(u)\overline{c^l_{\mu_1\nu_1}(uu_0^{-1})}du = \sum_{j=-l}^{l}\left[\int c^k_{\mu k}(u)\overline{c^l_{\mu_1 j}(u)}du\right]\overline{c^l_{j\nu_1}(u_0^{-1})} = 0$$

(since $k \neq j$), i.e.

$$0 = \int c^k_{\mu k}(uu_0)\overline{c^l_{\mu_1\nu_1}(u)}du = \sum_{\nu=-k}^{k}\left[\int c^k_{\mu\nu}(u)\overline{c^l_{\mu_1\nu_1}(u)}du\right]c^k_{\nu k}(u_0). \tag{9}$$

But by (8) the functions $c^k_{\nu k}(u_0)$, $\nu = -k, -k+1, \ldots, k$, are mutually orthogonal; therefore from (9) it follows that $\int c^k_{\mu\nu}(u)\overline{c^l_{\mu_1\nu_1}(u)}du = 0$ for $k \neq l$.

It remains to be proved that $\int |c^k_{\mu\nu}(u)|^2 du = \dfrac{1}{2k+1}$. If we put, for fixed k,

$$\int |c^k_{\mu\nu}(u)|^2 du = \kappa_{\mu\nu}; \tag{10}$$

then we have

$$\int c^k_{\mu j}(u_1)c^k_{j\nu}(u_1^{-1}u)du_1 = \kappa_{\mu j}c^k_{\mu\nu}(u). \tag{11}$$

In fact, by (1), (3), (8) and (10) we have

$$\int c^k_{\mu j}(u_1)c^k_{j\nu}(u_1^{-1}u)du_1$$
$$= \sum_{\alpha=-k}^{k}\left[\int c^k_{\mu j}(u_1)\overline{c^k_{\alpha j}(u_1)}du_1\right]c^k_{\alpha\nu}(u) = \kappa_{\mu j}c^k_{\mu\nu}(u).$$

From (10) and (11) it follows that

$$\kappa_{\mu\nu} = \int c^k_{\mu\nu}(u)\overline{c^k_{\mu\nu}(u)}\,du$$

$$= \frac{1}{\kappa^2_{\mu j}}\iiint c^k_{\mu j}(u_1)\,c^k_{j\nu}(u_1^{-1}u)\,\overline{c^k_{\mu j}(u_2)}\,\overline{c^k_{j\nu}(u_2^{-1}u)}\,du_1\,du_2\,du. \qquad (12)$$

But, by (3) and (11):

$$\int c^k_{j\nu}(u_1^{-1}u)\overline{c^k_{j\nu}(u_2^{-1}u)}\,du = \int c^k_{j\nu}(u)\overline{c^k_{j\nu}(u_2^{-1}u_1u)}\,du$$

$$= \int c^k_{j\nu}(u)\,c^k_{\nu j}(u^{-1}u_1^{-1}u_2)\,du = \kappa_{j\nu}\,c^k_{jj}(u_1^{-1}u_2);$$

therefore from (12) it follows that

$$\kappa_{\mu\nu} = \frac{\kappa_{j\nu}}{\kappa^2_{\mu j}}\iint c^k_{\mu j}(u_1)\,\overline{c^k_{\mu j}(u_2)}\,c^k_{jj}(u_1^{-1}\,u_2)\,du_1\,du_2$$

$$= \frac{\kappa_{j\nu}}{\kappa_{\mu j}}\int c^k_{\mu j}(u_2)\overline{c^k_{\mu j}(u_2)}\,du_2 = \kappa_{j\nu},$$

i.e. $\kappa_{\mu\nu}$ does not depend on μ. Consequently, integrating with respect to u both sides of the equation

$$\sum_{\mu=-k}^{k} |c^k_{\mu\nu}(u)|^2 = 1,$$

we get $(2k+1)\kappa_{\mu\nu} = 1$, i.e. $\kappa_{\mu\nu} = \dfrac{1}{2k+1}$ and the proof of the relations (7) is complete.

The relations (7) are called the *orthogonality relations*.† Replacing $\kappa_{\mu\nu}$ in (11) by its value (as above), we conclude that

$$\int c^k_{\mu j}(u_1)\,c^k_{j\nu}(u_1^{-1}u)\,du_1 = \frac{1}{2k+1}\,c^k_{\mu\nu}(u). \qquad (13)$$

---

† We remark that similar relations hold for any compact group (see, for example, Ref. [32] § 32 or Ref. [28e] § 32).

§ 6. The Decomposition of a Given Representation of the Three-dimensional Rotation Group into Irreducible Representations

1. The case of a finite-dimensional unitary representation

We recall that two vectors x, y in a Euclidean space R are called *orthogonal* if their scalar product $(x, y) = 0$. Two sets in R are called *orthogonal*, if each vector of one set is orthogonal to each vector of the other set; the concept of several mutually orthogonal sets is defined similarly. In particular, we may speak of mutually orthogonal subspaces of a Euclidean space R.

If $R_1, R_2, \ldots, R_n$ are mutually orthogonal subspaces of R, then the aggregate of all vectors $x = x_1+x_2+ \ldots +x_n$, $x_k \in R_k$ is also a subspace of R; it is called the *orthogonal sum of the subspaces* R_k and is denoted by $R_1 \oplus R_2 \oplus \ldots \oplus R_n$.

Let $\mathfrak{S}$ be an arbitrary set in R. The aggregate of all vectors in R orthogonal to $\mathfrak{S}$ is evidently a subspace of R; it is called the *orthogonal complement of the set* $\mathfrak{S}$ in R and is denoted by $R-\mathfrak{S}$. In particular, we can speak of the orthogonal complement $R-R_1$ of a subspace R_1 of R.

I. *If $R_1 \neq R$, then $R-R_1 \neq (0)$.*

Proof. Let $e_1, e_2, \ldots, e_n$ be a basis for R, and $f_1, \ldots, f_m$ a basis for R_1; by hypothesis $m < n$. We choose a vector

$$x = \xi_1 e_1 + \cdots + \xi_n e_n$$

so that

$$(x, f_1) = \ldots = (x, f_m) = 0; \qquad (1)$$

this means that $x \perp R_1$, i.e. $x \in R-R_1$. But the conditions (1) represent a system of m linear homogeneous equations

$$(e_1, f_1)\xi_1 + \cdots + (e_n, f_1)\xi_n = 0,$$

$$\cdots\cdots\cdots\cdots\cdots\cdots$$

$$(e_1, f_m)\xi_1 + \cdots + (e_n, f_m)\xi_n = 0$$

in $n (n > m)$ unknowns $\xi_1, \ldots, \xi_n$. This system has a non-trivial solution in $\xi_1, \ldots, \xi_n$; the corresponding vector x will be a non-zero vector in $R-R_1$, so that $R-R_1 \neq (0)$.

II. *If* $R_2 = R - R_1$, *then* $R = R_1 \oplus R_2$.

Proof. Put $R' = R_1 \oplus R_2$; we have to prove that $R' = R$. If $R' \neq R$, then, from I, there exists a vector $x \neq 0$, orthogonal to R'. Then also $x \perp R_1, x \perp R_2$. But if $x \perp R_1$, then $x \in R_2$. On the other hand, $x \perp R_2$, implies in particular $x \perp x$, which is impossible for $x \neq 0$.

III. *Let* $g \to T_g$ *be a unitary representation in the space* R, *and* R_1 *a subspace, invariant with respect to the operators* T_g, *then the orthogonal complement* $R - R_1$ *is also invariant with respect to the operators* T_g.

Proof. If $x \in R_1$, then also $T_g x \in R_1$; replacing g by g^{-1}, we see that also $T_g^* x = T_g^{-1} x = T_{g^{-1}} x \in R_1$.
Hence, if $y \in R - R_1$,

$$0 = (T_g^* x, y) = (x, T_g y);$$

consequently, $T_g y \in R - R_1$.

Let $R = R_1 \oplus R_2 \oplus \dots \oplus R_m$. A linear operator A in R is called the *orthogonal sum of the linear operators* A_k in R_k and is denoted by $A_1 \oplus A_2 \oplus \dots \oplus A_m$, if

$$A(x_1 + x_2 + \dots + x_m) = A_1 x_1 + A_2 x_2 + \dots + A_m x_m. \tag{2}$$

This definition has the following matrix interpretation. We choose an orthonormal (i.e. orthogonal and normalized) basis $e_1, e_2, \dots, e_n$ for R so that the vectors $e_1, \dots, e_{n_1}$ form a basis for R_1, the vectors $e_{n_1+1}, \dots, e_{n_2}$ form a basis for R_2 and so on. Then the matrix of the operator $A = A_1 \oplus \dots \oplus A_m$ relative to the basis $e_1, \dots, e_n$ will take the form

$$a = \begin{Vmatrix} a_1 & & & \\ & a_2 & & \\ & & \ddots & \\ & & & a_m \end{Vmatrix}, \tag{3}$$

where $a_1, a_2, \dots$ are the matrices of the operators $A_1, A_2, \dots$ relative to the bases $\{e_1, \dots, e_{n_1}\}, \{e_{n_1+1}, \dots, e_{n_2}\}, \dots$. All non-diagonal constituents of a are zero.

A representation $g \to T_g$ in a space R is called the *orthogonal sum of the representations* $g \to T_g^{(k)}$ in the spaces R_k, $k = 1, 2, \ldots, m$, if $R = R_1 \oplus \ldots \oplus R_m$ and $T_g = T_g^{(1)} \oplus \ldots \oplus T_g^{(m)}$ for all $g \in G$.

THEOREM 5. *Every finite-dimensional unitary representation $g \to T_g$ is an orthogonal sum of irreducible unitary representations.*

Proof. If the representation $g \to T_g$ is not irreducible, then in the space R of the representation there exists a subspace R', distinct from (0) and from the whole space space R, which is invariant with respect to the operators T_g. By III, the orthogonal complement $R'' = R - R'$ is also invariant with respect to the operators T_g.

Let T_g', T_g'' be the operators T_g, considered only in R' and R'' respectively; then $g \to T_g'$, $g \to T_g''$ are unitary representations in the spaces R', R'', and $T_g = T_g' \oplus T_g''$. To each of the representations $g \to T_g'$, $g \to T_g''$, if it is not irreducible, we apply the same process; because of the finite dimensionality of the initial space R, after a finite number of such steps we get a decomposition $T_g = T_g^{(1)} \oplus \ldots \oplus T_g^{(n)}$, where all the representations $g \to T_g^{(1)}, \ldots, g \to T_g^{(n)}$ are irreducible.

COROLLARY. *Every homogeneous polynomial* in u_{11}, u_{12}, u_{21}, u_{22} *is a linear combination of the functions* $c_{\mu\nu}^k(u)$.

Proof. We denote by R the aggregate of all homogeneous polynomials in u_{11}, u_{12}, u_{21}, u_{22} of fixed degree n; evidently R is a finite-dimensional linear space if the addition of polynomials and their multiplication by a number are defined in the natural way. Further, we define a scalar product in R, putting

$$(p_1, p_2) = \int p_1(u)\overline{p_2(u)}\,du \tag{4}$$

for $p_1, p_2 \in R$; then R becomes a Euclidean space.

If $p(u) \in R$, then for any fixed $v \in \mathfrak{U}$, $p(uv) \in R$ also; in fact, when u is replaced by uv, the elements u_{jk} are replaced by $u_{j1}v_{1k} + u_{j2}v_{2k}$, $j, k = 1, 2$, and therefore $p(uv)$ is also a homogeneous polynomial in the u_{jk} of degree n.

We put $T_v p(u) = p(uv)$; then T_v is a unitary operator in R, since by the invariance of the integral with respect to du,

$$(T_v p_1, T_v p_2) = \int p_1(uv)\overline{p_2(uv)}\,du = \int p_1(u)\overline{p_2(u)}\,du = (p_1, p_2).$$

Besides, the correspondence $u \to T_u$ is a representation, consequently a unitary representation of the group $\mathfrak{U}$; in fact,

$$T_e p(u) = p(ue) = p(u),$$

$$T_{u_1} T_{u_2} p(u) = T_{u_1} p(uu_2) = p((uu_1)u_2) = p(u(u_1 u_2)) = T_{u_1 u_2} p(u).$$

By Theorem (5) this representation $u \to T_u$ can be decomposed into an orthogonal sum of irreducible representations, so that

$$R = R_1 \oplus \dots \oplus R_\nu, \tag{5}$$

$$T_u = T_u^{(1)} \oplus \dots \oplus T_u^{(\nu)}, \tag{6}$$

the $u \to T_u^{(\alpha)}$ being irreducible representations in the space R_α.

Let k_α be the weight† of the representation $u \to T_u^{(\alpha)}$, and $f_{j\alpha}(u)$, $j = -k_\alpha, -k_\alpha+1, \dots, k_\alpha$ a canonical basis for R_α. Relations (5) and (6) mean that every polynomial $p \in R$ can be represented in the form

$$p(u) = \sum_{j,\alpha} \lambda_{j\alpha} f_{j\alpha}(u),$$

where the $\lambda_{j\alpha}$ are constants, and that

$$p(uv) = T_v p(u) = \sum_{j,\alpha} \lambda_{j\alpha} T_v^{(\alpha)} f_{j\alpha}(u) = \sum_{j,\alpha,l} \lambda_{j\alpha} c_{lj}^{k_\alpha}(v) f_{l\alpha}(u). \tag{7}$$

Putting $u = e$, we get

$$p(v) = \sum_{j,\alpha,l} \lambda_{j\alpha} f_{l\alpha}(e) c_{lj}^{k_\alpha}(v), \tag{8}$$

i.e. $p(v)$ is a linear combination of the functions $c_{lj}^{k_\alpha}(v)$.

2. The theorem of completeness

THEOREM 6.‡ *Every continuous function $f(u)$ in the group $\mathfrak{U}$ is the limit of a uniformly convergent sequence of finite linear combinations of the functions $c_{jl}^k(u)$.*

Proof. Putting

† Among the weights k_α, $\alpha = 1, 2, \dots, \nu$, there may be repetitions.

‡ Theorem 6 can be generalized to a wider class of groups (the so called compact groups); see, for instance Ref. [32] § 33 or Ref. [28e] § 30.

$$u = \begin{Vmatrix} \alpha & \beta \\ -\bar{\beta} & \bar{\alpha} \end{Vmatrix}, \qquad \alpha = \alpha_1 + i\alpha_2, \qquad \beta = \alpha_3 + i\alpha_4,$$

we see that

$$\alpha_1^2 + \alpha_2^2 + \alpha_3^2 + \alpha_4^2 = |\alpha|^2 + |\beta|^2 = 1;$$

consequently, a continuous function $f(u)$ can be considered as a continuous function $f(\alpha_1, \alpha_2, \alpha_3, \alpha_4)$ on the unit sphere S_4 in four-dimensional space. In accordance with the theorem of Weierstrass,† there exists a sequence of polynomials $p_n = p_n(\alpha_1, \alpha_2, \alpha_3, \alpha_4)$ uniformly converging to f on S_4. By the relations

$$\alpha_1 = \frac{1}{2}(\alpha + \bar{\alpha}) = \frac{1}{2}(u_{11} + u_{22}), \quad \alpha_2 = \frac{1}{2i}(\alpha - \bar{\alpha}) = \frac{1}{2i}(u_{11} - u_{22}),$$

$$\alpha_3 = \frac{1}{2}(\beta + \bar{\beta}) = \frac{1}{2}(u_{12} - u_{21}), \quad \alpha_4 = \frac{1}{2i}(\beta - \bar{\beta}) = \frac{1}{2i}(u_{12} + u_{21}),$$

the polynomials p_n are also polynomials in $u_{11}, u_{12}, u_{21}, u_{22}$ and can therefore be represented in the form of linear combinations of the functions $c_{jl}^k(u)$. This completes the proof of Theorem 6.

This theorem means that the functions $c_{jl}^k(u)$ form a complete orthogonal system for the aggregate of all functions $f(u)$ whose modulus square is integrable with respect to du. Further on we shall need the following corollary of this property of completeness.

COROLLARY. *If a continuous function $f(u)$ satisfies the condition*

$$\int f(u) c_{jl}^k(u) \mathrm{d}u = 0 \tag{1}$$

for all $c_{jl}^k(u)$, then $f(u) \equiv 0$.

Proof. From (8) it follows that

$$\int f(u) \phi(u) \mathrm{d}u = 0 \tag{2}$$

for any function $\phi(u)$, which is a linear combination of the functions $c_{jl}^k(u)$, and hence also for any function $\phi(u)$, which is the uniform limit of such linear combinations. But, according to Theorem 6, any continuous function is such a limit; consequently, (2) holds for any continuous function $\phi(u)$. Putting $\phi(u) = \overline{f(u)}$ in (2), we get $\int |f(u)|^2 \mathrm{d}u = 0$; this is possible only if $f(u) \equiv 0$.

† See for example Ref. [22] Chap. II § 4.

3. General definition of a representation

So far we have discussed only finite-dimensional representations. We shall now give the general definition of a representation. In this the space of the representation will be what is called a complete normed space. Therefore we commence with the definition of such a space.

A linear space R is said to be *normed*, if a function, denoted by $|x|$, is defined in it, satisfying the conditions:

(1) $|x| \geqslant 0$, $|x| = 0$ if and only if $x = 0$;

(2) $|\alpha x| = |\alpha||x|$ for any number α and any $x \in R$;

(3) $|x+y| \leqslant |x|+|y|$ for any $x, y \in R$. Such a function $|x|$ is called a *norm*.

The simplest example of a normed space is furnished by the aggregate C of all complex numbers x, if the modulus of a complex number is taken as its norm. We get a less trivial example if we take R to be the set of all sequences $x = \{\xi_1, \xi_2, \xi_3, ...\}$ of complex numbers $\xi_1, \xi_2, ...$, for which the series $|\xi_1|^2+|\xi_2|^2+|\xi_3|^2 + ...$ is convergent; here the operations and the norm in R are defined by the formulae

$$\alpha x = \{\alpha\xi_1, \alpha\xi_2, \alpha\xi_3, ...\}, \quad x+y = \{\xi_1+\eta_1, \xi_2+\eta_2, \xi_3+\eta_3, ...\},$$
$$|x| = \sqrt{[|\xi_1|^2+|\xi_2|^2+|\xi_3|^2+ ...]}$$

for $x = \{\xi_1, \xi_2, \xi_3, ...\}$, $y = \{\eta_1, \eta_2, \eta_3, ...\}$. We leave it to the reader to prove that all the axioms for a linear space, and also axioms (1) to (3) for the norm are satisfied (see also Subsection 7 below). This space is usually denoted by l^2.

A sequence of elements x_n of a normed space R is said to be *convergent in norm* to the element $x \in R$, if $|x-x_n| \to 0$ as $n \to \infty$; the sequence $x_n \in R$ is said to be *fundamental*, if it satisfies the Cauchy condition, i.e. if for every $\varepsilon > 0$ there exists a number $N = N(\varepsilon)$, such that $|x_n-x_m| < \varepsilon$ for $n, m > N$. The space R is said to be *complete* if every fundamental sequence in R converges in norm to some element $x \in R$.

Thus, the space C of all complex numbers, considered above as an example, is complete; this is Cauchy's criterion of convergence. It can be shown that the space l^2 defined above is also complete, and we leave the proof of this to the reader as a useful exercise. An example of a non-complete normed space is furnished by the set of all sequences $x = \{\xi_1, \xi_2, \ldots, \xi_n, \ldots\}$, in which only finitely many of the numbers ξ_n are non-zero, with the same definition of the operations and the norm as in l^2.

A complete normed space is usually called a *Banach space*.†

Let S be an arbitrary set in a Banach space R; the *closure* of the set S is the name given to the set obtained by augmenting S by all the limits in norm of sequences of elements $x_n \in S$. In what follows we shall denote the closure of a set S by $\bar{S}$. A set S is said to be *dense in R* if $\bar{S} = R$. A set S is said to be *closed*‡ if $\bar{S} = S$; in particular we can speak of a *closed subspace* of R. Evidently, *a closed subspace of a Banach space is also a Banach space.*

A series $x_1 + x_2 + x_3 + \ldots$ of elements $x_n \in R$ is said to be *convergent*, and the element $x \in R$ is called the *sum* of the series, if $x_1 + x_2 + \ldots + x_n \to x$ as $n \to \infty$ in the sense of the norm in R. A series $x_1 + x_2 + x_3 + \ldots$ is said to be *absolutely convergent* if the series $|x_1| + |x_2| + |x_3| + \ldots$ of real numbers is convergent.

From the inequality $|x_{n+1} + \ldots + x_{n+p}| \leqslant |x_{n+1}| + \ldots + |x_{n+p}|$ and the fact that the space is complete, it follows that *in a Banach space every absolutely convergent series converges.*

A linear operator A in a Banach space R is called *bounded* if there exists a constant $c \geqslant 0$ such that

$$|Ax| \leqslant c|x| \quad \text{for all} \quad x \in R. \tag{1}$$

It is easily seen that among the numbers $c \geqslant 0$ satisfying condition (1), there exists a least number; it is called the *norm* of the bounded operator A and is denoted by $|A|$. Thus, from the definition of the norm:

$$|Ax| \leqslant |A|\,|x|, \tag{2}$$

and for an arbitrary $\varepsilon > 0$ there exists a vector x such that

$$|Ax| \geqslant (|A| - \varepsilon)|x|. \tag{3}$$

† After the Polish mathematician S. Banach, who brought to notice and investigated such spaces.

‡ It is easy to prove that $s = S$, hence s is always closed.

Furthermore, it is easy to verify that if A, B are bounded operators, then also αA, $A+B$, AB are bounded operators and

$$|\alpha A| = |\alpha|\,|A|; \quad |A+B| \leqslant |A|+|B|, \quad |AB| \leqslant |A|\,|B|. \qquad (4)$$

Thus, by virtue of (2), $|ABx| \leqslant |A||Bx| \leqslant |A||B||x|$, but $|AB|$ is the least of the numbers c, for which $|ABx| \leqslant c|x|$; consequently $|AB| \leqslant |A|\|B|$.

I. *Every bounded linear operator A is continuous.*

Proof. If $x_n \to x$, then from the inequality $|Ax-Ax_n| = |A(x-x_n)| \leqslant |A||x-x_n|$ it follows that $Ax_n \to Ax$; this means that A is continuous.

II. *If two bounded operators A, B coincide on a set S which is dense in R, then they coincide on the whole of R.*

Proof. For any $x \in R$ there exists a sequence $x_n \in S$, convergent to x. Proceeding to the limit in the relation $Ax_n = Bx_n$ and taking into account the continuity of the operators A and B, we get $Ax = Bx$.

We can now give the general definition of a representation.

We shall say that we have a representation $g \to T_g$ of a group G in a Banach space R, if to every element $g \in G$ there corresponds a bounded linear operator T_g in R such that

$$(1)\quad T_e = 1; \qquad (2)\quad T_{g_1 g_2} = T_{g_1} T_{g_2}.$$

A representation $g \to T_g$ in a Banach space R is called *irreducible*, if R contains no *closed* subspace $\mathfrak{M}$, other than (0) and R, which is invariant with respect to all operators T_g.

In the case of a finite-dimensional representation this definition coincides with the definition of irreducibility in § 3, Subsection 3 since every finite-dimensional subspace is closed.

4. Continuous representations

In order to give a definition of a continuous representation, we introduce the concept of a bounded linear functional.

A *linear functional* $f(x)$ in a linear space R is the name given to every numerical function $f(x)$ in R, satisfying the conditions

$$f(\alpha x) = \alpha f(x), \quad f(x+y)f = f(x)+(y) \qquad (1)$$

for all numbers α and all $x, y \in R$. A linear functional in a normed space R is said to be *bounded*, if there exists a constant $c \geqslant 0$ such that

$$|f(x)| \leqslant c|x| \quad \text{for all} \quad x \in R. \tag{2}$$

The smallest of the numbers $c \geqslant 0$ satisfying (2) is called the *norm* of the functional $f(x)$ and is denoted by $|f|$. Thus, from the definition of the norm of a functional,

$$|f(x)| \leqslant |f|\,|x|, \tag{3}$$

and for any $\varepsilon > 0$ there exists an element $x \in R$, such that

$$|f(x)| \geqslant (|f|-\varepsilon)|x|. \tag{4}$$

The bounded linear functionals in R form a normed linear space if the sum of two functional and the product of a functional with a number are defined by the formulae

$$(f_1+f_2)(x) = f_1(x)+f_2(x), \quad (\alpha f)(x) = \bar{\alpha} f(x). \tag{5}$$

This space of functionals is called the *conjugate* of R and is denoted by R'.

I. *The conjugate space R' is complete.* Let f_n be a fundamental sequence in R', and let $|f_n - f_m| < \varepsilon$ for $n, m > N(\varepsilon)$. From the inequalities

$$|f_n(x)-f_m(x)| = |(f_n-f_m)(x)| \leqslant |f_n-f_m|\,|x| < \varepsilon|x| \tag{6}$$

it follows that $f_n(x)$ is a fundamental numerical sequence, and therefore the limit $\lim\limits_{n\to\infty} f_n(x)$, which we denote by $f(x)$, exists. Evidently $f(x)$ is a linear functional. Proceeding in (6) to the limit as $m \to \infty$, we obtain

$$|f(x)-f_n(x)| \leqslant \varepsilon|x|, \tag{7}$$

consequently $|f-f_n| \leqslant \varepsilon$ for $n > N(\varepsilon)$. Therefore, the functional $f = f_n + (f-f_n)$ is bounded and $|f_n - f| \to 0$ as $n \to \infty$.

We further take note of the following propositions, which are given without proof.†

† For the proofs of these propositions see Ref. [26] § 21.

II. *For every element $x \in R$ there exists a functional $f \in R'$ such that $f(x) = |x|$ and $|f| = 1$.* Hence follows

III. *If $f(x) = 0$ for all $f \in R'$ then $x = 0$.*

Further:

IV. *If $\mathfrak{M}$ is a closed subspace of a Banach space R, and x_0 is a vector in R, not belonging to $\mathfrak{M}$, then there exists a functional $f \in R'$, satisfying the conditions*

$$f(x_0) \neq 0, \quad f(x) = 0 \quad \text{for all} \quad x \in \mathfrak{M}.$$

Since R' is a normed space, it is also possible to consider the linear bounded functionals $F(f)$ in R'. Such functionals are obtained for example if, having fixed an element $x \in R$, we put

$$F_x(f) = \overline{f(x)}. \tag{8}$$

In fact,

$$F_x(f_1+f_2) = \overline{(f_1+f_2)(x)} = \overline{f_1(x)}+\overline{f_2(x)} = F_x(f_1)+F_x(f_2),$$

$$F_x(\alpha f) = \overline{(\alpha f)(x)} = \overline{\alpha}\overline{f(x)} = \alpha F_x(f)$$

and

$$|F_x(f)| = |f(x)| \leqslant |f|\,|x|,$$

so that $F_x(f)$ is a bounded linear functional in R'.

A space R is called *reflexive* if the functionals $F_x(f)$ for all possible $x \in R$ exhaust all the bounded linear functionals in R', i.e. if every bounded linear functional $F(f)$ in R' is given by a formula $F(f) = f(x)$ for some $x \in R$. We observe that, by virtue of III, the element $x \in R$ is uniquely defined by this condition; in fact, if also $F(f) = f(x')$ then $f(x-x') = 0$ for all $f \in R'$, and so by III, $x-x' = 0$.

In what follows we shall only consider representations in reflexive Banach spaces, and accordingly all Banach spaces will be supposed to be reflexive.†

Now let $x(t) = x(t_1, t_2, \ldots, t_m)$ be a vector function of a point $t = (t_1, t_2, \ldots, t_m)$ of m-dimensional space with values in R. A vector function $x(t)$ is called *continuous* in a set D in m-dimen-

† In this connection there arises the interesting question of the application of the results given below to representations in non-reflexive Banach spaces, and more generally, in topological linear spaces without norm.

sional space, if for any functional $f \in R'$ the numerical function $f[x(t)]$ is continuous in D. Further, let A_t be an operator function, every value of which is a bounded linear operator in R; the function A_t is called *continuous* in D, if for any $x \in R, f \in R'$, the numerical function $f(A_t x)$ is continuous in D.

If G is a group of matrices (for instance, the group $\mathfrak{U}$ or the proper Lorentz group), then G may be regarded as a subset of m-dimensional space for a sufficiently large m; therefore we may speak of a vector-function $x(g)$ or an operator function A_g, being continuous in the group G.

In particular, a representation $g \to T_g$ of a group of matrices is called *continuous*, if T_g is a continuous operator function.

In what follows we shall only consider continuous representations, so that, unless otherwise stated, the term representation will mean a continuous representation.

We note further, without proof,† the following property of continuous vector and operator functions:

V. *If* $x(t)$, and A_t *are vector and operator functions, respectively, which are continuous in a closed bounded set* D, *then the numerical functions* $|x(t)|$, $|A_t|$ *are bounded in that set.*

5. The integrals of vector and operator functions

As before, let R be a reflexive Banach space, and $x(t) = x(t_1, t_2, ..., t_m)$ a function of a point $t = (t_1, t_2, ..., t_m)$ in m-dimensional space with values in R, continuous in some closed bounded region D of that space. By definition, this means that $f(x(t))$ is a continuous numerical function in D; consequently, $\int_D f(x(t))dt$ exists, where dt denotes an m-dimensional element of volume.

We put

$$F(f) = \int_D f(x(t))dt; \tag{1}$$

† The proof of this proposition follows from the fact that, if $f(x_n)$ is convergent for every $f \in R'$, then the sequence $|x_n|$ is bounded, and if $f(A_n x)$ is convergent for every $f \in R'$ and every $x \in R$, then the sequence $|A_n|$ is bounded (see Ref. [26] § 24).

it is easily seen that $F(f)$ is a linear functional in R'. This functional is bounded. In fact, by virtue of V, Subsection 4, the function $|x(t)|$ is bounded in D. Let $|x(t)| \leqslant c$ for $t \in D$. Then $|f(x(t))| \leqslant |f||x(t)| \leqslant c|f|$, and therefore

$$|F(f)| \leqslant c|f| \int_D dt = cV|f|, \tag{2}$$

where V is the volume of the region D. But, by hypothesis, R is reflexive; consequently, there exists one and only one element $y \in R$ such that $F(f) = f(y)$; we shall call this element y the *integral of the function $x(t)$ over the region D* and denote it by $\int_D x(t)dt$.

Here, by definition:

$$f(\int_D x(t)dt) = \int_D f(x(t))dt. \tag{3}$$

Also, from II Subsection 4, and (2), we conclude that

$$|\int_D x(t)dt| \leqslant cV, \tag{4}$$

if $|x(t)| \leqslant c$ for $t \in D$.

Next, it is easily verified that

$$\begin{gathered}\int_D \alpha x(t)dt = \alpha \int_D x(t)dt, \\ \int_D [x_1(t)+x_2(t)]dt = \int_D x_1(t)dt + \int_D x_2(t)dt\end{gathered} \tag{5}$$

for any continuous functions $x(t)$, $x_1(t)$, $x_2(t)$ and any number α.

Finally,

$$A \int_D x(t)dt = \int_D Ax(t)dt \tag{6}$$

for any continuous function $x(t)$ and any bounded linear operator A.

In fact, putting for any functional $f \in R'$,

$$f_1(x) = f(Ax);$$

then $f_1(x)$ is a bounded linear functional, since $|f_1(x)| \leqslant |f||Ax| \leqslant |f||A||x|$. Consequently, by virtue of (3):

$$f_1(\int_D x(t)dt) = \int_D f_1(x(t))dt,$$

i.e.

$$f(A\int_D x(t)\mathrm{d}t) = \int_D f(Ax(t))\mathrm{d}t = f(\int_D Ax(t)\mathrm{d}t).$$

By virtue of III, Subsection 4, (6) now follows.

Now let A_t be an operator function, continuous in the region D; then $A_t x$ is a continuous vector-function for any $x \in R$. We define an operator B in R, putting

$$Bx = \int_D A_t x\,\mathrm{d}t. \tag{7}$$

Evidently B is linear; we shall prove that B is bounded. By virtue of V, Subsection 4, the numerical function $|A_t|$ is bounded in D; let $|A_t| \leqslant c$ for $t \in D$. Then $|A_t x| \leqslant c|x|$; consequently, by virtue of (4) (where $c|x|$ plays the part of c):

$$|Bx| = |\int_D A_t x\,\mathrm{d}t| \leqslant cV|x|. \tag{8}$$

The operator B is called the *integral of the operator function* over the region D and is denoted by $\int_D A_t\mathrm{d}t$.

Thus, from the definition:

$$(\int_D A_t\mathrm{d}t)x = \int_D A_t x\,\mathrm{d}t; \tag{9}$$

also, by virtue of (8):

$$|\int_D A_t\mathrm{d}t| \leqslant cV, \quad \text{if} \quad |A_t| \leqslant c \quad \text{for} \quad t \in D. \tag{10}$$

It is evident furthermore that

$$\int_D \alpha A_t\mathrm{d}t = \alpha\int_D A_t\mathrm{d}t, \quad \int_D (A_t+B_t)\mathrm{d}t = \int_D A_t\mathrm{d}t + \int_D B_t\mathrm{d}t \tag{11}$$

for any operator functions A_t, B_t, continuous in D and for any number α.

We also have

$$B\int_D A_t\mathrm{d}t = \int_D BA_t\mathrm{d}t \tag{12}$$

for any continuous operator function A_t and any bounded linear operator B. In fact, by virtue of (6) and (9), for any vector $x \in R$

$$B\int_D A_t x\mathrm{d}t = \int_D BA_t x\mathrm{d}t, \quad \text{i.e.} \quad (\mathrm{B}\int_D A_t\mathrm{d}t)x = (\int_D BA_t\mathrm{d}t)x.$$

The inequalities (4) and (10) admit the following generalization:

If $|x(t)| \leqslant \alpha(t)$ *and* $|A_t| \leqslant \alpha(t)$, *where* $\alpha(t)$ *is a numerical function integrable over D, then*

$$\left| \int_D x(t) \mathrm{d}t \right| \leqslant \int_D \alpha(t) \mathrm{d}t, \tag{13}$$

and

$$\left| \int_D A_t \mathrm{d}t \right| \leqslant \int_D \alpha(t) \mathrm{d}t.$$

In fact, if $|x(t)| \leqslant \alpha(t)$, then $|f(x(t))| \leqslant |f| |x(t)| \leqslant |f| \alpha(t)$, and therefore

$$\left| f\left(\int_D x(t) \mathrm{d}t\right) \right| = \left| \int_D f(x(t)) \mathrm{d}t \right| \leqslant \int_D |f(x(t))| \, \mathrm{d}t \leqslant \left(\int_D \alpha(t) \mathrm{d}t \right) |f|;$$

by proposition II, Subsection 4 we conclude from this that

$$\left| \int_D x(t) \mathrm{d}t \right| \leqslant \int_D \alpha(t) \mathrm{d}t.$$

If now $|A_t| \leqslant \alpha(t)$, then $|A_t x| \leqslant \alpha(t) |x|$, and so

$$\left| \left(\int_D A_t \mathrm{d}t \right) x \right| = \left| \int_D A_t x \mathrm{d}t \right| \leqslant \left(\int_D \alpha(t) \mathrm{d}t \right) |x|;$$

hence, from the definition of the norm of an operator,

$$\left| \int_D A_t \mathrm{d}t \right| \leqslant \int_D \alpha(t) \mathrm{d}t.$$

Improper integrals of vector and operator functions can also be defined; from the inequality (13) and the completeness of the space it follows that if $|x(t)| \leqslant \alpha(t)$ and $|A_t| \leqslant \alpha(t)$, and if the integral $\int_D \alpha(t) \mathrm{d}t$ converges, then $\int_D x(t) \mathrm{d}t$ and $\int_D A_t \mathrm{d}t$ also converge. Here, the convergence of the integral $\int_D x(t) \mathrm{d}t$ is in the sense of the norm in R and the convergence of $\int_D A_t \, \mathrm{d}t$ is in the sense of the operator norm.

The above definition of the integral and its properties are easily applied to the case of a vector function $x(u)$ or an operator function A_u on the group $\mathfrak{U}$; here $\mathrm{d}t$ has to be replaced by the element $\mathrm{d}u$ of invariant volume, and $V = \int \mathrm{d}u = 1$. In particular the property (10) takes the form

$$\left| \int A_u \mathrm{d}u \right| \leqslant c, \quad \text{if} \quad |A_u| \leqslant c \quad \text{for all} \quad u \in \mathfrak{U}. \tag{14}$$

6. Decomposition of a representation of the group $\mathfrak{U}$ into irreducible representations

Let $u \to T_u$ be an arbitrary continuous representation of the group $\mathfrak{U}$ in a reflexive Banach space R. We put

$$E_{jl}^k = (2k+1) \int \overline{c_{jl}^k(u)} T_u \mathrm{d}u; \tag{1}$$

since $\overline{c_{jl}^k(u)} T_u$ is a continuous operator function in $\mathfrak{U}$, the integral on the right hand side exists, and E_{jl}^k is a bounded operator in R. In what follows, the operators E_{jl}^k will play an important part. We note the basic properties of these operators.

I. *The operators* E_{jl}^k *satisfy the relations*:

$$T_u E_{jl}^k = \sum_{\nu=-k}^{k} c_{\nu j}^k(u) E_{\nu l}^k, \tag{2a}$$

$$E_{jl}^k T_u = \sum_{\nu=-k}^{k} c_{l\nu}^k(u) E_{j\nu}^k, \tag{2b}$$

$$E_{jl}^k E_{\mu\nu}^{k'} = \begin{cases} 0 & \text{for} \quad k' \neq k, \quad \text{or} \quad l \neq \mu, \\ E_{j\nu}^k & \text{for} \quad k' = k \quad \text{and} \quad l = \mu; \end{cases} \tag{3}$$

in particular,

$$T_\gamma E_{jl}^k = \mathrm{e}^{ij\omega} E_{jl}^k, \quad E_{jl}^k T_\gamma = \mathrm{e}^{il\omega} E_{jl}^k \tag{4}$$

for

$$\gamma = \begin{Vmatrix} \mathrm{e}^{-\frac{i\omega}{2}} & 0 \\ 0 & \mathrm{e}^{\frac{i\omega}{2}} \end{Vmatrix} \tag{5}$$

and

$$E_{jj}^k E_{ll}^{k'} = 0 \quad \text{for} \quad k \neq k' \quad \text{or} \quad j \neq l, \tag{6}$$

$$E_{jj}^k E_{jj}^k = E_{jj}^k. \tag{7}$$

Proof. By virtue of (1), and (3), § 5, Subsection 5 we have

$$T_u E_{jl}^k = T_u\left((2k+1)\int \overline{c_{jl}^k(u')} T_{u'} \mathrm{d}u'\right) = (2k+1)\int \overline{c_{jl}^k(u')} T_{uu'} \mathrm{d}u'$$

$$= (2k+1)\int \overline{c_{jl}^k(u^{-1}u')} T_{u'} \mathrm{d}u' = (2k+1) \sum_{\nu=-k}^{k} \int \overline{c_{j\nu}^k(u^{-1})}\, \overline{c_{\nu l}^k(u')} T_{u'} \mathrm{d}u'$$

$$= \sum_{\nu=-k}^{k} \overline{c_{j\nu}^k(u^{-1})} E_{\nu l}^k = \sum_{\nu=-k}^{k} c_{\nu j}^k(u) E_{\nu l}^k,$$

and (2a) is proved; (2b) is proved in similar fashion. Applying (2a), we have

$$E^k_{jl}E^{k'}_{\mu\nu} = ((2k+1)\int \overline{c^k_{jl}(u)}\, T_u \mathrm{d}u)E^{k'}_{\mu\nu} = (2k+1)\int \overline{c^k_{jl}(u)}\, T_u E^{k'}_{\mu\nu}\,\mathrm{d}u$$
$$= (2k+1)\int \overline{c^k_{jl}(u)} \sum_{\tau=-k'}^{k'} c^{k'}_{\tau\mu}(u) E^{k'}_{\tau\nu}\,\mathrm{d}u;$$

combining this result with the orthogonality relations (see (7) § 5, Subsection 5), we obtain (3). Relations (6) and (7) are a special case of relation (3); relations (4) are obtained by the combination of relations (2a), (2b) with I, § 5, Subsection 5.

Let us now write

$$E^k = \sum_{j=-k}^{k} E^k_{jj}. \tag{8}$$

II. *The operators E^k satisfy the relations*:

$$E^{k'}E^k = \begin{cases} 0 & \text{for} \quad k' \neq k, \\ E^k & \text{for} \quad k' = k, \end{cases} \tag{9}$$

$$T_u E^k = E^k T_u \quad \text{for all} \quad u \in \mathfrak{U}. \tag{10}$$

Proof. Relations (9) follow immediately from (6) and (7). Further, by virtue of (2a) and (2b) we have,

$$T_u E^k = \sum_{\nu,j=-k}^{k} c^k_{\nu j}(u) E^k_{\nu j}, \quad E^k T_u = \sum_{\nu,j=-k}^{k} c^k_{j\nu}(u) E^k_{j\nu},$$

consequently, $T_u E^k = E^k T_u$, and the proof is complete.

We denote by $\mathfrak{M}^k_j$ the aggregate of all vectors $x \in R$ satisfying the condition $E^k_{jj}x = x$, and by $\mathfrak{M}^k$ the aggregate of all vectors $x \in R$ satisfying the condition $E^k x = x$.

III. $\mathfrak{M}^k_j$ *and* $\mathfrak{M}^k$ *are closed subspaces of* R.

Proof. If $E^k_{jj}x_1 = x_1$, $E^k_{jj}x_2 = x_2$, then also $E^k_{jj}(\alpha_1 x_1 + \alpha_2 x_2) = \alpha_1 x_1 + \alpha_2 x_2$ for any numbers α_1, α_2; consequently, $\mathfrak{M}^k_j$ is a subspace of R. Further, if $E^k_{jj}x_n = x_n$ and $|x_n - x| \to 0$ as $n \to \infty$, then, proceeding to the limit and making use of the continuity of the operator E^k_{jj}, we obtain $E^k_{jj}x = x$; consequently, $\mathfrak{M}^k_j$ is closed. It can be proved similarly that $\mathfrak{M}^k$ is a closed subspace of R.

Subspaces $\mathfrak{M}_1, \mathfrak{M}_2, \ldots$ are said to be linearly independent if an equation of the form $x_1+x_2+\ldots+x_n = 0$, where $x_j \in \mathfrak{M}_j$, is valid only for $x_1 = x_2 = \ldots = x_n = 0$.

IV. *The subspaces $\mathfrak{M}_j^k$ for all possible j and k, and also the subspaces $\mathfrak{M}^k$ for all possible k, are linearly independent.*

Proof. From (6) and (7) it follows that

$$\text{if } x \in \mathfrak{M}_v^{k'}, \quad \text{then} \quad E_{jj}^k x = \begin{cases} 0 & \text{for} \quad k \neq k' \quad \text{or} \quad j \neq v; \\ x & \text{for} \quad k = k' \quad \text{and} \quad j = v; \end{cases} \tag{11}$$

similarly:

$$\text{if} \quad x \in \mathfrak{M}^{k'}, \quad \text{then} \quad E^k x = \begin{cases} 0 & \text{for} \quad k \neq k', \\ x & \text{for} \quad k = k'. \end{cases} \tag{12}$$

In fact, if $x \in \mathfrak{M}_v^{k'}$, then $E_{jj}^k x = E_{jj}^k E_{vv}^{k'} x$; (11) follows from this; relations (12) can be proved in a similar way.

Now let

$$x_1+x_2+\ldots+x_n = 0, \tag{13}$$

where $x_1 \in \mathfrak{M}_{j_1}^{k_1}, \ldots, x_n \in \mathfrak{M}_{j_n}^{k_n}$ and all pairs of indices $(j_1, k_1), \ldots, (j_n, k_n)$ are different. Applying $E_{j_1 j_1}^{k_1}$ to both sides of (13) and making use of the relations (11), we obtain $x_1 = 0$: similarly, applying $E_{j_2 j_2}^{k_2}, \ldots, E_{j_n j_n}^{k_n}$, we obtain $x_2 = 0, \ldots, x_n = 0$; consequently, the $\mathfrak{M}_j^k$ are linearly independent. Similarly it can be proved that the $\mathfrak{M}^k$ are linearly independent.

A subspace $\mathfrak{M}$ is called the *direct sum* of the linearly independent subspaces $\mathfrak{M}_1, \mathfrak{M}_2, \ldots, \mathfrak{M}_n$ and is denoted by $\mathfrak{M}_1+\mathfrak{M}_2+\ldots+\mathfrak{M}_n$, if $\mathfrak{M}$ is the aggregate of all sums $x_1+x_2+\ldots+x_n$, $x_j \in \mathfrak{M}_j$.

A closed subspace $\mathfrak{M}$ will be called the *closed direct sum* of the finite or infinite (possibly non-denumerable) number of closed subspaces $\mathfrak{M}_1, \mathfrak{M}_2, \mathfrak{M}_3 \ldots$ and will be denoted by $\mathfrak{M}_1 \dot{+} \mathfrak{M}_2 \dot{+} \mathfrak{M}_3 \dot{+} \ldots$, if the following conditions are satisfied:

(1) $\mathfrak{M}$ is the closure of the aggregate of all finite sums of the form

$$x_1+x_2+\ldots+x_n, \quad x_j \in \mathfrak{M}_j, \quad n = 1, 2, \ldots;$$

(2) If the sequence $x^{(m)} = x_1^{(m)}+x_2^{(m)}+\ldots+x_{n_m}^{(m)}$, $x_j^{(m)} \in \mathfrak{M}_j$, converges in norm to zero, while for a fixed j the sequence $x_j^{(m)}$,

$m = 1, 2, 3, \ldots$, converges in norm, then that sequence $x_j^{(m)}$, converges in norm to zero.

Evidently, these concepts of a direct sum are generalizations of the concept given in Subsection 1, of the orthogonal sum of a finite number of subspaces.

V. $\mathfrak{M}^k$ *is the direct sum of the subspaces* $\mathfrak{M}_j^k$, $j = -k, -k+1, \ldots, k$:

$$\mathfrak{M}^k = \mathfrak{M}_{-k}^k + \mathfrak{M}_{-k+1}^k + \ldots + \mathfrak{M}_k^k. \tag{14}$$

Proof. If $x_j \in \mathfrak{M}_j^k$ then, by (11),

$$E^k x_j = (E_{-k,-k}^k + \ldots + E_{kk}^k) x_j = x_j,$$

consequently, $x_j \in \mathfrak{M}^k$; hence we conclude that $\mathfrak{M}^k$ contains all sums $x_{-k} + \ldots + x_k$, $x_j \in \mathfrak{M}_j^k$.

Conversely, let $x \in \mathfrak{M}^k$; putting $x_j = E_{jj}^k x$, we have: $E_{jj}^k x_j = E_{jj}^k E_{jj}^k x = E_{jj}^k x = x_j$; consequently, $x_j \in \mathfrak{M}_j^k$. Also,

$$\sum_{j=-k}^{k} x_j = \left(\sum_{j=-k}^{k} E_{jj}^k \right) x = E^k x = x,$$

so that $\mathfrak{M}^k$ is the aggregate of all sums $\sum_{j=-k}^{k} x_j$, $x_j \in \mathfrak{M}_j^k$.

VI. *The space R is the closed direct sum of all the subspaces* $\mathfrak{M}_j^k$, *and consequently, of all the subspaces* $\mathfrak{M}^k$.

Proof. We denote by R_1 the closure of the aggregate of all finite sums of elements $x_j^k \in \mathfrak{M}_j^k$. If $R_1 \neq R$, then there exists a functional $f \in R'$, other than zero, which is equal to zero† on R_1. In particular, it is equal to zero on all the $\mathfrak{M}_j^k$. But, by virtue of (3),

$$E_{jj}^k E_{jl}^k x = E_{jl}^k x$$

for all $x \in R$, and therefore $E_{jl}^k x \in \mathfrak{M}_j^k$; consequently, $f(E_{jl}^k x) = 0$, i.e.

$$(2k+1) \int \overline{c_{jl}^k(u)} f(T_u x) du = 0$$

for all $c_{jl}^k(u)$. Since the functions $c_{jl}^k(u)$ form a complete system (see the corollary in Subsection 2), $f(T_u x) = 0$ for all $u \in \mathfrak{U}$. Putting

† See IV, Subsection 4.

$u = e$, we obtain $f(x) = 0$ for all $x \in R$, i.e. $f = 0$, and we arrive at a contradiction; consequently, $R_1 = R$.

This shows that condition (1) of the definition of a closed direct sum is satisfied.

Suppose now that the sequence $x^{(m)} = \sum_{j,k} x_{jk}^{(m)}$, $x_{jk}^{(m)} \in \mathfrak{M}_j^k$, of finite sums converges in norm to zero; then also every sequence $x_{jk}^{(m)} = E_{jj}^k x^{(m)}$ converges in norm to zero; consequently, conditions (2) are also satisfied (and in a stronger form, since the convergence of the sequence $x_{jk}^{(m)}$, $m = 1, 2, \ldots$ is not assumed beforehand), and the proof of proposition VI is complete.

A representation $u \to T_u$ in a Banach space R is called a *multiple of the irreducible representation* $u \to T_u^{(k)}$ *of weight* k, if R is the direct sum of closed subspaces R_j, $j = -k, -k+1, \ldots, k$, having the following property: for any R_p and any $x \in R_p$ there exist vectors $x_j \in R_j$, $j = -k, -k+1, \ldots, k$, such that $x_p = x$ and

$$T_u x_j = \sum_{\nu=-k}^{k} c_{\nu j}^k(u) x_\nu. \tag{15}$$

In order to make this definition clear, let us consider, for example that case in which one of the subspaces R_j, namely R_ν, is two-dimensional. Let x, y be linearly independent vectors in R_ν; by definition, there exist $x_j, y_j \in R_j$, for which $x_\nu = x$, $y_\nu = y$, such that (15) is satisfied. Here the vectors x_j, y_j in every R_j are linearly independent. In fact, if for some j

$$\alpha x_j + \beta y_j = 0,$$

then, from (15) it follows that $\sum_{\mu=-k}^{k} c_{\mu j}^k(u)(\alpha x_\mu + \beta y_\mu) = 0$; hence $\alpha x_\mu + \beta y_\mu = 0$, since the functions $c_{\mu j}^k(u)$ are linearly independent. In particular, $\alpha x + \beta y = \alpha x_\nu + \beta y_\nu = 0$, which is possible only for $\alpha = \beta = 0$.

These considerations also show that R_j is two-dimensional, so that x_j, y_j is a basis of R_j for every $j = -k, -k+1, \ldots, k$.

Let $\mathfrak{M}$ be the subspace generated by the elements x_j, and $\mathfrak{N}$ the subspace generated by the elements y_j. Evidently, $R = \mathfrak{M} + \mathfrak{N}$.

Further, from (15) it follows that $\mathfrak{M}, \mathfrak{N}$ are invariant with respect to the operators T_u and that in each of these subspaces the representation $u \to T_u$ coincides with the representation $u \to T_u^{(k)}$. We may therefore say that, in the case under consideration, the representation $u \to T_u$ is a double multiple of the representation $u = T_u^{(k)}$.

In the general case the multiplicity of the irreducible representation $u \to T_u^{(k)}$, in the representation $u \to T_u$ depends upon the dimension of the space R_j.

If, in particular, R_j is one-dimensional, then the representation $u \to T_u$ coincides with $u \to T_u^{(k)}$.

VII. *Every subspace $\mathfrak{M}^k$ is invariant with respect to the representation $u \to T_u$, and if $\mathfrak{M}^k \neq (0)$, then the representation $u \to T_u$, considered only on $\mathfrak{M}^k$, is a multiple of the irreducible representation $u \to T_u^{(k)}$ of weight k.*

Proof. By virtue of V, $\mathfrak{M}^k$ is the direct sum of the subspaces $\mathfrak{M}_j^k$. Further let $x \in \mathfrak{M}_l^k$ for some l. Put $x_j = E_{jl}^k x$, $j = -k, -k+1, \ldots, k$; by virtue of (3), $E_{jj}^k x_j = E_{jj}^k E_{jl}^k x = E_{jl}^k x = x_j$; consequently $x_j \in \mathfrak{M}_j^k$ and $x_l = E_{ll}^k x = x$, since $x \in \mathfrak{M}_l^k$. Finally, applying formula (2a), we obtain:

$$T_u x_j = T_u E_{jl}^k x = \sum_{\nu=-k}^{k} c_{\nu j}^k(u) E_{\nu l}^k x = \sum_{\nu=-k}^{k} c_{\nu j}^k(u) x_\nu .$$

Hence we conclude that $\mathfrak{M}^k$ is invariant with respect to the operators T_u and that, for the operator T_u, considered only on $\mathfrak{M}^k$, condition (15) is satisfied. This means that the representation $u \to T_u$, considered only on $\mathfrak{M}^k$, is a multiple of the representation $u \to T_u^{(k)}$.

A bounded linear operator A in a Banach space R is called the *direct sum of the bounded linear operators A_j* in the closed subspaces R_j and is denoted by $A_1 \dot{+} A_2 \dot{+} A_3 \dot{+} \ldots$, if $R = R_1 \dot{+} R_2 \dot{+} R_3 \dot{+} \ldots$ and $A(x_1 + x_2 + \ldots + x_n) = A_1 x_1 + A_2 x_2 + \ldots + A_n x_n$ for any vectors $x_j \in R_j$ finite in number.

A representation $g \to T_g$ of a group G in a Banach space R is called the *direct sum of the representations* $g \to T_g^{(j)}$ in the subspaces R_j if $T_g = T_g^{(1)} \dot{+} T_g^{(2)} \dot{+} T_g^{(3)} \dot{+} \ldots$ for all $g \in G$.

Propositions VI and VII taken in conjunction lead to the following theorem:

THEOREM 7. *Every representation $u \to T_u$ of the group $\mathfrak{U}$ is the direct sum of representations which are multiples of irreducible representations $u \to T_u^{(\alpha)}$.*

Going from the representation $u \to T_u$ to the corresponding representation $g \to T_g$ of the three-dimensional rotation group, we conclude that Theorem 7 is also valid for the one-valued and two-valued representations of this group.

7. The case of a unitary representation

The concept of a unitary representation, introduced above in the finite-dimiensional case (see § 3, Subsection 5), may be generalized to infinite-dimensional representations.

Let R be a Euclidean space, not necessarily finite-dimensional. Then, in R, a norm can be defined by putting

$$|x| = \sqrt{(x, x)}. \tag{1}$$

The axioms for a norm will be satisfied; in fact, the first two axioms are satisfied trivially. To prove the triangle inequality we need:

$$|(x, y)| \leqslant |x|\,|y|. \tag{2}$$

This is the so-called *Cauchy–Buniakovsky inequality*, and it holds since the form

$$\alpha\bar{\alpha}(x, x) + (x, y)\alpha\bar{\beta} + \overline{(x, y)}\bar{\alpha}\beta + (y, y)\beta\bar{\beta}$$
$$= (\alpha x + \beta y, \alpha x + \beta y) \geqslant 0,$$

is non-negative, and therefore so is its discriminant $(x, x)(y, y) - (x, y)\overline{(x, y)} \geqslant 0$. From the inequality (2) we conclude that

$$|x+y|^2 = (x+y, x+y) = (x, x) + (x, y) + \overline{(x, y)} + (y, y)$$
$$\leqslant |x|^2 + 2|x|\,|y| + |y|^2 = (|x| + |y|)^2;$$

consequently, $|x+y| \leqslant |x| + |y|$.

A Euclidean space R, complete with respect to the norm $|x| = \sqrt{(x, x)}$, is called a *Hilbert space.*

The space l^2 constructed in Subsection 3 is a Hilbert space if the scalar product is defined by the formula $(x, y) = \sum_{k=1}^{\infty} \xi_k \bar{\eta}_k$ for $x = \{\xi_1, \xi_2, \ldots\}$, $y = \{\eta_1, \eta_2, \ldots\}$.

Another important example of a Hilbert space is the aggregate of all functions $f(x)$, measurable in a fixed interval (a, b), which satisfy the condition $\int_a^b |f(x)|^2 dx < \infty$, if the operations of addition and multiplication by a number are defined in the usual way, while the scalar product is defined by the formula† $(f_1, f_2) = \int_a^b f_1(x)\overline{f_2(x)}dx$; this Hilbert space is denoted by $L^2(a, b)$.

We define in the same way the Hilbert space $L^2(\mathfrak{U})$ of all measurable functions $f(u)$ (i.e. measurable functions $f(t, \phi, \psi)$ of the parameters t, ϕ, ψ, see § 1, Subsection 7), satisfying the condition $\int |f(u)|^2 du < \infty$, the scalar product in $L^2(\mathfrak{U})$ being defined by the formula $(f_1, f_2) = \int f_1(u)\overline{f_2(u)}du$.

The proof of the completeness of the space $L^2(\mathfrak{U})$ is similar to that of the completeness of the space $L^2(a, b)$.

In a Hilbert space R every bounded linear functional $f(x)$ is represented in the form

$$f(x) = (x, y),$$

where $y \in R$, and $|f| = |y|$ (see, for example [2]). This means that the space conjugate to a Hilbert space R may be identified with R:

$$R' = R.$$

Two Hilbert spaces R_1, R_2 are called *isometric* if there exists a linear operator U, mapping R_1 onto R_2 and preserving the scalar product, i.e.

$$(Ux, Uy) = (x, y) \quad \text{for all} \quad x, y \in R_1; \tag{3}$$

in this case the operator U itself is said to be *isometric*. Isometric Hilbert spaces are usually regarded as not essentially different. We note that, for a linear operator U to be isometric, it is sufficient

---

† The completeness of this space is the subject of the Riesz–Fischer theorem (see, for example, Ref. [26] § 4).

that the condition $|Ux| = |x|$ should be satisfied for all $x \in R_1$. In fact, from the easily verified identity

$$(x, y) = \tfrac{1}{4}[(x+y, x+y)-(x-y, x-y) + i(x+iy, x+iy)-i(x-iy, x-iy)]$$

it follows that in this case also $(Ux, Uy) = (x, y)$ for all $x, y \in R_1$. If, in particular, U is an isometric operator mapping R onto R (so that $R_1 = R_2 = R$), then U is called a *unitary operator* in R. A representation $g \to T_g$ of a group G in a space R is said to be *unitary* if R is a Hilbert space and T_g is a unitary operator for all $g \in G$.

I. *A representation $g \to T_g$ in a Hilbert space R is unitary if*

$$(T_g x, T_g y) = (x, y) \quad \text{for all} \quad g \in G \quad \text{and all} \quad x, y \in R. \tag{4}$$

Proof. We only have to prove that T_g maps R *onto* R; but this is obvious, since, for any $x \in R$,

$$T_g T_{g^{-1}} x = T_e x = 1 \cdot x = x.$$

Unitary operators may also be defined by means of the concept of an *adjoint operator.*

Let A be a bounded operator in a Hilbert space R. An operator B is said to be *adjoint* to the operator A, if

$$(Ax, y) = (x, By) \quad \text{for all} \quad x, y \in R. \tag{5}$$

The operator adjoint to A is denoted by A^*, so that, by definition:†

$$(Ax, y) = (x, A^*y) \quad \text{for all} \quad x, y \in R. \tag{6}$$

It is easily proved that

$$A^{**} = A,\ (\alpha A)^* = \bar{\alpha} A^*,\ (A+B)^* = A^*+B^*,\ (AB)^* = B^*A^* \tag{7}$$

and that

$$|A^*| = |A|. \tag{8}$$

From (8) it follows that A^* is a continuous function of A (in the sense of the operator norm).

† It can be shown (see, for example Ref. [26] § 30) that for every bounded operator A, there is an adjoint operator A^*, which is also bounded.

It is now easy to verify that an *operator U is unitary if and only if*

$$U^*U = UU^* = \mathbf{1}. \tag{9}$$

An operator B is called the *inverse* of A and is denoted by A^{-1}, if $AB = BA = \mathbf{1}$. The relation (9) means that

$$U^* = U^{-1}. \tag{10}$$

We shall now describe what properties the operators E^k_{jl} will have in the case of a unitary representation. For this purpose we shall need the following definitions.

An operator A is said to be *Hermitian*, if $A^* = A$. A Hermitian operator P is called an *operator of projection*, if $P^2 = P$. If P is an operator of projection, then the aggregate $\mathfrak{M}$ of all the vectors $x \in R$ for which $Px = x$ (forming a closed subspace of R), is called the subspace onto which P projects.

We note that $Px \in \mathfrak{M}$, while $(\mathbf{1}-P)x \perp \mathfrak{M}$ *for* any $x \in R$, since $PPx = Px$ and $((\mathbf{1}-P)x, y) = ((\mathbf{1}-P)x, Py) = (P(\mathbf{1}-P)x, y) = ((P-P^2)x, y) = (0, y) = 0$ for all $y \in \mathfrak{M}$. Consequently, the equation $x = Px + (\mathbf{1}-P)x$ is a decomposition of the vector x into the sum of the vector $Px \in \mathfrak{M}$ and $(\mathbf{1}-P)x \perp \mathfrak{M}$; the vector Px is therefore called the *projection of the vector x onto the subspace* $\mathfrak{M}$ (this explains the name given to the operator P).

It can be shown (see, for example, Ref. [26] § 33) that, for any closed subspace $\mathfrak{M}$ of a Hilbert space R, there exists an operator of projection onto $\mathfrak{M}$, which means that, for every vector $x \in R$, there exists one and only one decomposition into the sum of vectors $x_1 \in \mathfrak{M}$, $x_2 \perp \mathfrak{M}$.

If R is three-dimensional space and $\mathfrak{M}$ is a plane in it, passing through the origin, then Px is the ordinary projection of the vector x on the plane $\mathfrak{M}$ (Fig. 4).

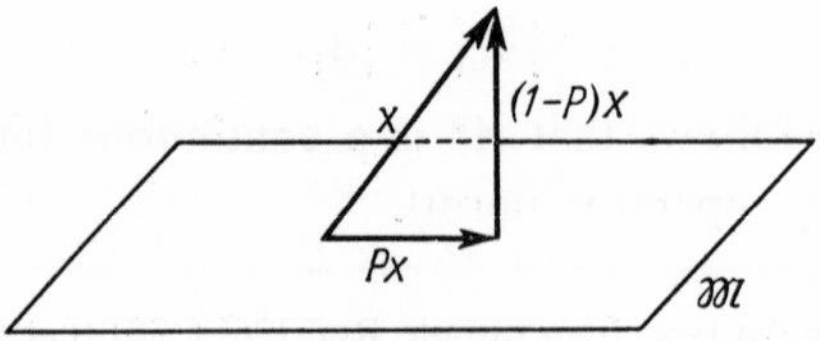

FIG. 4.

II. *If a representation* $g \to T_g$ *of the group* G_0 *is unitary, then*:

(1) E^k_{jj} *and* E^k *are operators of projection*;

(2) *The subspaces* $\mathfrak{M}^k_j$ *are mutually orthogonal*;

(3) *The subspaces* $\mathfrak{M}^k$ *are mutually orthogonal.*

Proof. By virtue of (7), (10) and the fact that the operator T_u is unitary,

$$\begin{aligned}(E^k_{jj})^* &= ((2k+1)\int \overline{c^k_{jj}(u)\, T_u du})^* = (2k+1)\int c^k_{jj}(u)\, T^*_u du\\ &= (2k+1)\int c^k_{jj}(u)\, T_u^{-1} du = (2k+1)\int c^k_{jj}(u)\, T_{u^{-1}} du\\ &= (2k+1)\int c^k_{jj}(u^{-1})\, T_u du = (2k+1)\int \overline{c^k_{jj}(u)}\, T_u du = E^k_{jj},\end{aligned}$$

since, owing to the continuity of the transition from A to A^*, it is possible to go over to the adjoint operators under the integral sign; hence

$$(E^k)^* = \left(\sum_{j=-k}^{k} E^k_{jj}\right)^* = \sum_{j=-k}^{k} E^{k*}_{jj} = \sum_{j=-k}^{k} E^k_{jj} = E^k.$$

Further, it was proved earlier (see (7) and (9) Subsection 6) that $E^k_{jj}E^k_{jj} = E^k_{jj}$, $E^kE^k = E^k$; consequently, E^k_{jj} and E^k are operators of projection in R. Here the subspaces $\mathfrak{M}^k_j$ and $\mathfrak{M}^k$, from their definition, are the subspaces onto which E^k_{jj} and E^k project. If $x \in \mathfrak{M}^k_j$, $y \in \mathfrak{M}^{k'}_{j'}$, then, for $j \neq j'$ or $k \neq k'$,

$$(x, y) = (E^k_{jj}x, E^{k'}_{j'j'}y) = (E^{k'}_{j'j'}E^k_{jj}x, y) = (0, y) = 0$$

(see (6) Subsection 6); consequently $\mathfrak{M}^k_j \perp \mathfrak{M}^{k'}_{j'}$ for $j \neq j'$ or $k \neq k'$. It is proved similarly that $\mathfrak{M}^k \perp \mathfrak{M}^{k'}$ for $k \neq k'$.

Let $R_1, R_2, R_3, \ldots$ be closed mutually orthogonal subspaces of a Hilbert space R. The *orthogonal sum* $R_1 \oplus R_2 \oplus R_3 \oplus \ldots$ of these subspaces is the name given to the aggregate of all sums $x = x_1+x_2+x_3+\ldots$ of convergent series of elements $x_k \in R_k$; it is easy to show that $R_1 \oplus R_2 \oplus R_3 \oplus \ldots$ is also a closed subspace of R, and we leave the detailed proof to the reader (in this connection see also [2], Chapter I). If E_n is an operator of projection in R onto $R_1 \oplus R_2 \oplus \ldots \oplus R_n$, then for any vector x of R

$$E_n x = x_1 + \ldots + x_n \quad \text{for} \quad x = x_1+x_2+\ldots,\ x_k \in R_k,$$

and therefore

$$|x-E_n x| = |x_{n+1}+x_{n+2}+ \dots | \to 0 \quad \text{as} \quad n \to \infty. \qquad (11)$$

Further, the bounded linear operator A in R is called *the orthogonal sum of the operators* A_k in R_k and is denoted by $A_1 \oplus A_2 \oplus \dots$, if $R = R_1 \oplus R_2 \oplus \dots$ and $Ax = A_1x_1 + A_2x_2 + \dots$ wherever $x = x_1 + x_2 + \dots$.

Finally, a unitary representation $g \to T_g$ of a group G in a Hilbert space R is called the *orthogonal sum of the representations* $g \to T_g^{(k)}$ in the closed subspaces R_k, if $T_g = T_g^{(1)} \oplus T_g^{(2)} \oplus T_g^{(3)} \oplus \dots$ for all $g \in G$.

THEOREM 8. *Every unitary representation* $u \to T_u$ *of the group* $\mathfrak{U}$ *(and hence also of the group* G_0*) is the orthogonal sum of unitary representations of that group which are multiples of irreducible representations* $u \to T_u^{(k)}$.

Proof. We denote by R the space of the representation $u \to T_u$, and by $\mathfrak{M}$ the orthogonal sum of all the subspaces $\mathfrak{M}^k$ corresponding to this representation. By virtue of Theorem 7, Subsection 6, it is sufficient to show that $\mathfrak{M} = R$. But $\mathfrak{M}$ is a closed subspace of R, dense in R by virtue of that theorem; therefore $R = \overline{\mathfrak{M}} = \mathfrak{M}$.

CHAPTER III

IRREDUCIBLE LINEAR REPRESENTATIONS OF THE PROPER AND COMPLETE LORENTZ GROUPS

§ 7. The Infinitesimal Operators of a Linear Representation of the Proper Lorentz Group

1. The infinitesimal Lorentz matrices

Consider the linear transformations g, defined by the formulae:

$$x'_i = \sum_{i=1}^{3} g_{ij} x_j, \quad i = 1, 2, 3, \quad x'_4 = x_4, \tag{1}$$

where $\|g_{ij}\|$, $i, j = 1, 2, 3$ is an orthogonal matrix of order 3 with determinant unity. These transformations leave the forms $x_1^2+x_2^2+x_3^2$ and x_4 separately invariant and are therefore proper Lorentz transformations. Evidently, the transformation (1) is simply a rotation of the coordinate axes Ox_1, Ox_2, Ox_3 of three-dimensional space, with the time left unchanged.

Two successive such rotations of the coordinate axes Ox_1, Ox_2, Ox_3 are equivalent to a single rotation of the coordinate axes Ox_1, Ox_2, Ox_3; consequently, the aggregate of all transformations of the form (1) is a subgroup† of the proper Lorentz group $\mathfrak{G}_+$. Denote this subgroup by G_0. Clearly, G_0 is simply the three-dimensional rotation group.‡

† A set G_1 in a group G is called a *subgroup* of the group G if from $g, h \in G_1$ it follows that g^{-1}, $gh \in G_1$. Obviously, a subgroup of G, itself forms a group with the same definition of multiplication as in G.

‡ More precisely, G_0 and the three-dimensional rotation group are isomorphic. Two groups G and G' are called *isomorphic* if a one-to-one correspon-

Let us find the infinitesimal matrices of the group G_0, in this interpretation, corresponding to rotations about the coordinate axes Ox_1, Ox_2, Ox_3. We consider in detail a rotation about the axis Ox_3. If t is the angle of this rotation, the corresponding transformation formulae are:

$$x_1' = x_1 \cos t - x_2 \sin t, \quad x_2' = x_1 \sin t + x_2 \cos t,$$
$$x_3' = x_3, \quad x_4' = x_4. \tag{2}$$

Denoting by $a_3(t)$ the matrix of this transformation, we have

$$a_3(t) = \begin{Vmatrix} \cos t & -\sin t & 0 & 0 \\ \sin t & \cos t & 0 & 0 \\ 0 & 0 & 1 & 0 \\ 0 & 0 & 0 & 1 \end{Vmatrix}. \tag{3}$$

Expanding the matrix (3) in a power series in t, we obtain

$$a_3(t) = 1 + a_3 t + \ldots, \tag{4}$$

where

$$a_3 = \begin{Vmatrix} 0 & -1 & 0 & 0 \\ 1 & 0 & 0 & 0 \\ 0 & 0 & 0 & 0 \\ 0 & 0 & 0 & 0 \end{Vmatrix}. \tag{5}$$

Consequently, a_3 is *the infinitesimal matrix corresponding to a rotation about the axis* Ox_3 (see § 4 Subsection 2).

In a completely analogous manner we determine the infinitesimal matrices

$$a_1 = \begin{Vmatrix} 0 & 0 & 0 & 0 \\ 0 & 0 & -1 & 0 \\ 0 & 1 & 0 & 0 \\ 0 & 0 & 0 & 0 \end{Vmatrix} \tag{6}$$

and

$$a_2 = \begin{Vmatrix} 0 & 0 & 1 & 0 \\ 0 & 0 & 0 & 0 \\ -1 & 0 & 0 & 0 \\ 0 & 0 & 0 & 0 \end{Vmatrix}, \tag{7}$$

---

dence $g \leftrightarrow g'$ can be set up between their elements in such a way that if $g_1 \leftrightarrow g_1'$, $g_2 \leftrightarrow g_2'$, then $g_1 g_2 \leftrightarrow g_1' g_2'$. In the theory of groups two isomorphic groups are not considered as essentially distinct.

corresponding to rotations

$$a_1(t):\begin{cases} x_1' = x_1, \quad x_2' = x_2 \cos t - x_3 \sin t, \\ x_3' = x_2 \sin t + x_3 \cos t, \quad x_4' = x_4, \end{cases} \tag{8}$$

$$a_2(t):\begin{cases} x_3' = x_3 \cos t - x_1 \sin t, \quad x_1' = x_3 \sin t + x_1 \cos t, \\ x_2' = x_2, \quad x_4' = x_4 \end{cases} \tag{9}$$

about the respective axes Ox_1 and Ox_2.

Let us now pass on to a consideration of the Lorentz transformations under which the variable x_4 is also transformed. To begin with we find the general form of a proper Lorentz transformation which leaves x_2 and x_3 unchanged and transforms only the variables x_1, x_4, i.e. a transformation

$$\begin{aligned} x_1' &= g_{11}x_1 + g_{14}x_4, \quad x_2' = x_2, \\ x_3' &= x_3, \quad x_4' = g_{41}x_1 + g_{44}x_4, \end{aligned} \tag{10}$$

so that $g_{22} = g_{33} = 1$, $g_{i2} = g_{2i} = 0$, for $i \neq 2$, $g_{i3} = g_{3i} = 0$ for $i \neq 3$.

Applying conditions (9) of § 2, Subsection 1, we conclude that

$$g_{11}^2 - g_{41}^2 = 1, \quad g_{14}^2 - g_{44}^2 = -1, \quad g_{11}g_{14} - g_{44}g_{41} = 0. \tag{11}$$

The last equation is equivalent to the relations

$$g_{44} = \lambda g_{11}, \quad g_{14} = \lambda g_{41};$$

substituting these expressions in the second equation in (11) and taking account of the first, we find that $\lambda = \pm 1$. But the condition $\det g = 1$ excludes the value $\lambda = -1$, and so finally

$$g_{44} = g_{11} \geqslant 1. \tag{12}$$

From these conditions we conclude that we may put

$$g_{11} = g_{44} = \cosh t, \quad g_{14} = g_{41} = \sinh t.$$

The transformation (10) then assumes the form

$$\begin{aligned} x_1' &= x_1 \cosh t + x_4 \sinh t, \quad x_2' = x_2, \\ x_3' &= x_3, \quad x_4' = x_1 \sinh t + x_4 \cosh t. \end{aligned} \tag{13}$$

Let us denote by $b_1(t)$ the matrix of this transformation, so that

$$b_1(t) = \begin{Vmatrix} \cosh t & 0 & 0 & \sinh t \\ 0 & 1 & 0 & 0 \\ 0 & 0 & 1 & 0 \\ \sinh t & 0 & 0 & \cosh t \end{Vmatrix}, \tag{14}$$

again taking the parameter t small and expanding the matrix $b_1(t)$ in powers of t, we obtain

$$b_1(t) = 1 + b_1 t + \dots, \tag{15}$$

where

$$b_1 = \begin{Vmatrix} 0 & 0 & 0 & 1 \\ 0 & 0 & 0 & 0 \\ 0 & 0 & 0 & 0 \\ 1 & 0 & 0 & 0 \end{Vmatrix}. \tag{16}$$

The matrix b_1 is called the *infinitesimal matrix corresponding to the transformation* $b_1(t)$ of the variables x_1, x_4. Similarly one can construct the infinitesimal matrices†

$$b_2 = \begin{Vmatrix} 0 & 0 & 0 & 0 \\ 0 & 0 & 0 & 1 \\ 0 & 0 & 0 & 0 \\ 0 & 1 & 0 & 0 \end{Vmatrix}, \tag{17}$$

$$b_3 = \begin{Vmatrix} 0 & 0 & 0 & 0 \\ 0 & 0 & 0 & 0 \\ 0 & 0 & 0 & 1 \\ 0 & 0 & 1 & 0 \end{Vmatrix}, \tag{18}$$

corresponding to the proper Lorentz transformations $b_2(t)$, $b_3(t)$ of the variables x_2, x_4 and x_3, x_4 respectively.

We remark that the infinitesimal matrices a_i, b_i may also be considered as the derivatives at $t = 0$ of the corresponding matrices $a_i(t)$, $b_i(t)$.

---

† This enumeration of the matrices b_1, b_2, b_3 will in fact be convenient for future use.

I. *The matrices* $a_i(t)$, $b_i(t)$ *satisfy the relations*

$$\begin{aligned} a_i(t_1+t_2) &= a_i(t_1)a_i(t_2), \\ b_i(t_1+t_2) &= b_i(t_1)b_i(t_2), \qquad i = 1, 2, 3. \end{aligned} \tag{19}$$

The validity of these relations may be verified by direct multiplication of the matrices. We remark that we have already established the first relation in § 4, Subsection 2. We note also that the relations (19) follow from the following proposition:

II. *The matrices* $a_i(t)$, $b_i(t)$ *may be expressed in terms of the infinitesimal matrices* a_i, b_i *by means of the formulae*

$$a_i(t) = e^{ta_i} = 1 + ta_i + \frac{1}{2!}t^2a_i^2 + \ldots, \tag{20}$$

$$b_i(t) = e^{tb_i} = 1 + tb_i + \frac{1}{2!}t^2b_i^2 + \ldots. \tag{21}$$

The validity of these formulae may also be verified directly (compare p. 35).

III. *Every proper Lorentz matrix* g *may be represented in the form*

$$g = ub_1(t)v, \tag{22}$$

where $u, v \in G_0$.

Proof. Let $g \in \mathfrak{G}_+$. Consider in three-dimensional space R_3 the vector $x = (g_{14}, g_{24}, g_{34})$; if this vector is equal to zero then the matrix g has the form

$$g = \begin{Vmatrix} g_{11} & g_{12} & g_{13} & 0 \\ g_{21} & g_{22} & g_{23} & 0 \\ g_{31} & g_{32} & g_{33} & 0 \\ g_{41} & g_{42} & g_{43} & g_{44} \end{Vmatrix}. \tag{23}$$

Condition (9) of § 2, Subsection 1 for $j = k = 4$, namely

$$g_{14}^2 + g_{24}^2 + g_{34}^2 - g_{44}^2 = -1 \tag{24}$$

reduces in this case to $-g_{44}^2 = -1$, i.e. $g_{44} = \pm 1$; by I of § 2, Subsection 2, $g_{44} = 1$.

Further, applying relations (16) of § 2, Subsection 1 for $i=k=4$, we obtain

$$g_{41}^2+g_{42}^2+g_{43}^2-1 = -1.$$

Hence

$$g_{41} = g_{42} = g_{43} = 0,$$

and formula (23) assumes the form

$$g = \begin{Vmatrix} g_{11} & g_{12} & g_{13} & 0 \\ g_{21} & g_{22} & g_{23} & 0 \\ g_{31} & g_{32} & g_{33} & 0 \\ 0 & 0 & 0 & 1 \end{Vmatrix}.$$

But by relations (9) of § 2, Subsection 1

$$\begin{Vmatrix} g_{11} & g_{12} & g_{13} \\ g_{21} & g_{22} & g_{23} \\ g_{31} & g_{32} & g_{33} \end{Vmatrix}$$

is an orthogonal matrix with determinant unity, i.e. $g \in G_0$. Therefore equation (22) will be satisfied in our particular case with $u = g$, $t = 0$, $v = e$.

Thus the existence of a decomposition of the form (22) is proved for $x = 0$. Now assume that $x = (g_{14}, g_{24}, g_{34}) \neq 0$. We shall show that we may choose matrices $u_1, v_1 \in G_0$ such that the product $u_1 g v_1$ has the form corresponding to formulae (10), i.e. is the transformation $b_1(t)$ for some t. Normalizing x, we obtain a vector $e_1 = \lambda x = (\alpha_1, \alpha_2, \alpha_3)$ of unit length; let

$$e_2 = (\beta_1, \beta_2, \beta_3), \quad e_3 = (\gamma_1, \gamma_2, \gamma_3)$$

be two mutually orthogonal vectors of unit length, both orthogonal to the vector e_1, and so also to the vector x. Then for a proper orientation of the vectors e_1, e_2, e_3 the matrix

$$u_1 = \begin{Vmatrix} \alpha_1 & \alpha_2 & \alpha_3 & 0 \\ \beta_1 & \beta_2 & \beta_3 & 0 \\ \gamma_1 & \gamma_2 & \gamma_3 & 0 \\ 0 & 0 & 0 & 1 \end{Vmatrix}$$

is an element of the group G_0, and so also of $\mathfrak{G}_+$; therefore $u_1 g \in \mathfrak{G}_+$. On the other hand, from the orthogonality of the vectors e_2 and e_3 to the vector x it follows that $u_1 g$ has the form

$$u_1 g = \begin{Vmatrix} a_{11} & a_{12} & a_{13} & a_{14} \\ a_{21} & a_{22} & a_{23} & 0 \\ a_{31} & a_{32} & a_{33} & 0 \\ g_{41} & g_{42} & g_{43} & g_{44} \end{Vmatrix}. \tag{25}$$

Consider now the vectors $f_2 = (a_{21}, a_{22}, a_{23}), f_3 = (a_{31}, a_{32}, a_{33})$; relations (16) of § 2, Subsection 1 show that f_2, f_3 are mutually orthogonal vectors of unit length. Let $f_1 = (c_1, c_2, c_3)$ be a vector of unit length orthogonal to f_2 and f_3; then with a proper choice of orientation for the vector f_1 the matrix

$$v_1 = \begin{Vmatrix} c_1 & a_{21} & a_{31} & 0 \\ c_2 & a_{22} & a_{32} & 0 \\ c_3 & a_{23} & a_{33} & 0 \\ 0 & 0 & 0 & 1 \end{Vmatrix} \tag{26}$$

belongs to the group G_0, and so also to the group $\mathfrak{G}_+$; therefore $u_1 g v_1 \in \mathfrak{G}_+$. Put $b = u_1 g v_1$; actually carrying out the multiplication of the matrices (25), (26) and taking account of relations (16) of § 2, Subsection 1, we find that the matrix b has the form

$$b = \begin{Vmatrix} b_{11} & 0 & 0 & b_{14} \\ 0 & 1 & 0 & 0 \\ 0 & 0 & 1 & 0 \\ b_{41} & 0 & 0 & b_{44} \end{Vmatrix}, \quad b_{14} = a_{14}, \quad b_{44} = g_{44},$$

where, by I of § 2, Subsection 2, $b_{44} \geqslant 1$.

The argument of p. 91 shows that $b = b_1(t)$ for some value of t. Thus $u_1 g v_1 = b_1(t)$; hence, putting $u = u_1^{-1}$, $v = v_1^{-1}$, we obtain $g = u_1^{-1} b_1(t) v_1^{-1} = u b_1(t)\, v$.

IV. *Every proper Lorentz transformation may be represented in the form of a product of transformations of the form* $a_1(t)$, $a_3(t)$ *and* $b_1(t)$. In fact, every transformation u in the group G_0 is a rotation in three-dimensional space and therefore is a product of three rotations $a_3(t_3)$, $a_1(t_2)$, $a_3(t_1)$ (see § 1, Subsection 4).

Writing the matrices u and v in (22) as products of rotations in this way, we deduce that proposition IV is valid.

2. Relations between the infinitesimal Lorentz matrices

The following proposition will play an important role in the sequel.

I. *The infinitesimal Lorentz matrices satisfy the relations*

$$[a_1, a_2] = a_3, \quad [a_2, a_3] = a_1, \quad [a_3, a_1] = a_2; \tag{1}$$

$$[b_1, b_2] = -a_3, \quad [b_2, b_3] = -a_1, \quad [b_3, b_1] = -a_2; \tag{2}$$

$$[a_1, b_1] = 0, \quad [a_2, b_2] = 0, \quad [a_3, b_3] = 0; \tag{3}$$

$$[a_1, b_2] = b_3, \quad [a_1, b_3] = -b_2; \tag{4}$$

$$[a_2, b_3] = b_1, \quad [a_2, b_1] = -b_3; \tag{5}$$

$$[a_3, b_1] = b_2, \quad [a_3, b_2] = -b_1. \tag{6}$$

Here, as before (cf. § 4, Subsection 2) $[a, b]$ denotes the commutator of the matrices a, b, i.e. $[a, b] = ab - ba$. One can satisfy oneself of the validity of these relations by direct verification.

3. The infinitesimal operators of a representation of the proper Lorentz group

Now suppose we are given an arbitrary linear representation $g \to T_g$ of the group $\mathfrak{G}_+$ in a Banach space R. As the rotation $a_i(t)$ is an element of the group $\mathfrak{G}_+$, there corresponds to it an operator $T_{ai(t)}$; for brevity we shall denote this operator by $A_i(t)$, so that $A_i(t) = T_{ai(t)}$. Similarly, let us put $B_i(t) = T_{bi(t)}$. From relations (19) of Subsection 1 it follows that

$$\begin{aligned} A_i(t_1+t_2) &= A_i(t_1)A_i(t_2), \\ B_i(t_1+t_2) &= B_i(t_1)B_i(t_2), \quad i = 1, 2, 3; \end{aligned} \tag{1}$$

furthermore, we obviously have

$$A_i(0) = T_e = \mathbf{1}, \quad B_i(0) = T_e = \mathbf{1}, \quad i = 1, 2, 3. \tag{2}$$

By virtue of the continuity of the representation $g \to T_g$, the operator functions $A_j(t)$, $B_j(t)$ are continuous. Every continuous operator function $A(t)$ of a real parameter t, satisfying the conditions

$$A(t_1+t_2) = A(t_1)A(t_2), \quad A(0) = \mathbf{1}, \tag{3}$$

is called a *one-parameter group of operators.*

Thus, the functions $A_j(t)$, $B_j(t)$ are one-parameter groups of operators.

If the representation $g \to T_g$ is finite-dimensional, then, as we have seen (cf. II and III of § 4, Subsection 3), the $A_j(t)$ are differentiable functions of t, satisfying the equations

$$\frac{\mathrm{d}A_j(t)}{\mathrm{d}t} = A_j(t)A_j = A_jA_j(t), \quad j = 1, 2, 3,$$

and the condition $A_j(0) = \mathbf{1}$, $j = 1, 2, 3$, where

$$A_j = \left[\frac{\mathrm{d}}{\mathrm{d}t}A_j(t)\right]_{t=0}$$

is the infinitesimal operator of the one-parameter group $A_j(t)$; and in fact

$$A_j(t) = e^{tA_j} = \mathbf{1} + \frac{t}{1!}A_j + \frac{t^2}{2!}A_j^2 + \dots. \tag{4}$$

It can be shown that in the case of a finite-dimensional representation, analogous properties are also possessed by the one-parameter groups $B_j(t)$, $j = 1, 2, 3$.

In the case of an *infinite-dimensional* representation $g \to T_g$ the situation becomes more complicated. In this case the operator functions $A_j(t)$, $B_j(t)$ may prove to be non-differentiable, but there may exist vectors x, for which $A_j(t)x$, $B_j(t)x$ are differentiable vector-functions. In general let $A(t)$ be some continuous one-parameter group of operators in R. Denote by $\mathfrak{D}_A$ the aggregate of all vectors $x \in R$ for which the limit

$$\lim_{t\to 0} \frac{A(t)x - x}{t} \tag{5}$$

exists in the sense of the norm in R; in every case $\mathfrak{D}_A$ contains the vector $x = 0$. Define an operator A by putting

$$Ax = \lim_{t \to 0} \frac{A(t)x - x}{t}. \tag{6}$$

Thus the operator A is defined only for vectors $x \in \mathfrak{D}_A$ (or, as we sometimes say, applies to vectors $x \in \mathfrak{D}_A$); therefore $\mathfrak{D}_A$ is called *the domain of definition of the operator A*. It is easy to see that $\mathfrak{D}_A$ is a subspace of R (not in general closed), and that the operator A is linear in the following sense: $A(\lambda_1 x_1 + \lambda_2 x_2) = \lambda_1 A x_1 + \lambda_2 A x_2$ for all $x_1, x_2 \in \mathfrak{D}_A$. The operator A is called the *infinitesimal operator* of the one-parameter group $A(t)$.

Now let us suppose that $A(t)$ is not an arbitrary one-parameter group of operators, but the group of operators $A(t) = T_{a(t)}$ of our representation $g \to T_g$, corresponding to a one-parameter subgroup $a(t)$ of the group $\mathfrak{G}_+$; the corresponding operator is then called an *infinitesimal operator of the representation* $g \to T_g$. Choosing all possible one-parameter subgroups $a(t)$ of the group $\mathfrak{G}_+$, we obtain all possible infinitesimal operators of the representation $g \to T_g$.

We shall assume that the irreducible representation $g \to T_g$ of the group $\mathfrak{G}_+$ which is under consideration possesses the following properties:

A. *In the space R of the representation there exists a dense subspace* $\mathfrak{D}$, *invariant relative to all the operators* T_g, *such that:*

(1) *All the infinitesimal operators of the representation, and also all finite products of them, apply to the vectors* $x \in \mathfrak{D}$.

(2) *For any vector* $x \in \mathfrak{D}$ *the vector* $T_g x$ *is an infinitely differentiable function*† *on* $\mathfrak{G}_+$.

(3) *For any vector* $x \in \mathfrak{D}$ *and any one-parameter group* $a(t) \in \mathfrak{G}_+$ *the vector* $A(t)x = T_{a(t)}x$ *satisfies the condition*

$$\frac{\mathrm{d}A(t)x}{\mathrm{d}t} = A \cdot A(t)x = A(t)\,Ax \tag{7}$$

† Here, local coordinates in $\mathfrak{G}_+$ may be introduced, for example, in accordance with the footnote on p. 31; cf. also formula (11) on p. 122.

and the relations:

$$A(t)x = x + tAx + \frac{t^2}{2!}A^2x + \frac{t^3}{3!}\tilde{A}(t)A^3x, \tag{8a}$$

$$A(t)x = x + tAx + \frac{t^2}{2!}A^2x + \dots + \frac{t^n}{n!}A^nx + \dots, \tag{8b}$$

where $\tilde{A}(t) = \frac{3}{t^2}\int_0^t (t-\tau)A^2(\tau)d\tau$ *is bounded in norm in any finite interval, while the series on the right hand side of* (8b) *converges in norm, absolutely.* (3) *If* $D(t)$ *is a finite product of terms* $A_i(t)$ *and* A_j and *if* $x \in D$, *then* $|D(t)x|$ *is a bounded function of* t *in any finite interval.*† From (8b) it follows that, on the vectors $x \in \mathfrak{D}$, the operator $A(t)$ is uniquely determined by the infinitesimal operator A; as these vectors form a set dense in R and $A(t)$ is bounded, $A(t)$ is uniquely determined by continuity on the whole space R (cf. II of § 6, Subsection 3).

Thus it follows from (3) that

(4) *The one-parameter group* $A(t)$ *is uniquely determined on the whole space* R *by the infinitesimal operator* A.

In order to formulate further assumptions concerning the representation $g \to T_g$, let us consider this representation only for $g \in G_0$. We then obtain a representation $g \to T_g$ of the group G_0. According to Theorem 7 of § 6, Subsection 6, R is the closed direct sum of the subspaces $\mathfrak{M}^k$, invariant relative to the operators T_g, $g \in G_0$; here, if $\mathfrak{M}^k \neq (0)$, the representation $g \to T_g$ of the subgroup G_0, considered only on $\mathfrak{M}^k$, is a multiple of the irreducible representation of weight k of the subgroup G_0.

We shall say that a given representation $g \to T_g$ of the group $\mathfrak{G}_+$ *does not contain* the irreducible representation of weight k of the group G_0 if $\mathfrak{M}^k = (0)$, and that it *contains it* μ *times* if the representation $g \to T_g$ for $g \in G_0$, considered only on $\mathfrak{M}^k$, is a μ-th multiple of the irreducible representation of weight k of the group G_0.

† In fact (3) and (3′) follow from (2) except for (8b) (see remark 1 in § 13, Subsection 5).

Our further assumptions concerning the irreducible representation $g \to T_g$ of the group $\mathfrak{G}_+$ are the following:

B. *Each irreducible representation of the subgroup G_0 is contained at most once in the representation $g \to T_g$ of the group $\mathfrak{G}_+$.*

C. *Each subspace $\mathfrak{M}^k$ is completely contained in the set $\mathfrak{D}$.*

In actual fact these assumptions *are unnecessary*. However, wishing to obtain as quickly as possible the formulae for the irreducible representations of the proper Lorentz group $\mathfrak{G}_+$, we shall look for representations for which these assumptions are fulfilled. Later (see § 15) we shall see that the formulae obtained are also true without these assumptions.

I. *If the infinitesimal operators A_i, B_i and A_i', B_i', $i = 1, 2, 3$, of two representations $g \to T_g$ and $g \to T_g'$ of the group $\mathfrak{G}_+$ in a space R coincide on a subspace $\mathfrak{D}' \subset \mathfrak{D}$, dense in R and invariant relative to A_i, B_i, A_i', B_i', $i = 1, 2, 3$, then these representations $g \to T_g$, $g \to T_g'$ coincide on the whole space R.*

Proof. From assumption **A**, (4) it follows that

$$A_i(t) = A_i'(t), \quad B_i(t) = B_i'(t), \quad i = 1, 2, 3$$

on the whole space R. On the other hand, every proper Lorentz transformation g is the product of matrices $a_i(t)$, $b_i(t)$ (see IV of Subsection 1); consequently the operators T_g and T_g' are the products of operators $A_i(t)$, $B_i(t)$ and $A_i'(t)$, $B_i'(t)$ respectively, and therefore coincide on the whole space R.

Proposition I signifies that *a representation $g \to T_g$ of the group $\mathfrak{G}_+$ is completely determined by its infinitesimal operators A_i, B_i, $i = 1, 2, 3$.*

II. *If a subspace $\mathfrak{D}' \subset \mathfrak{D}$, $\mathfrak{D}' \neq (0)$ is invariant relative to all the infinitesimal operators A_i, B_i, $i = 1, 2, 3$ of an irreducible representation $g \to T_g$ of the group $\mathfrak{G}_+$, then $\mathfrak{D}'$ is dense in R.*

Proof. Let $\overline{\mathfrak{D}'}$ be the closure of the set $\mathfrak{D}'$. From assumption **A**, (3) (see 8 (b)) it follows that $\overline{\mathfrak{D}'}$ is invariant relative to all the operators $A_i(t)$, $B_i(t)$, $i = 1, 2, 3$, and so also relative to all possible products of these operators, i.e. relative to all the operators T_g (see the proof of proposition I). Hence by virtue of the irreducibility of the representation $g \to T_g$ we conclude that $\overline{\mathfrak{D}'} = R$, i.e. $\mathfrak{D}'$ is dense in R.

4. Relations between the basic infinitesimal operators of a representation

The determination of the irreducible representations of the group $\mathfrak{G}_+$ is based on the fact that there exist simple relationships between the operators A_i, B_i. In order to derive them, let us consider a proper Lorentz matrix $g(t)$ which is a function of a real parameter t, and let us suppose that $g(0) = e$ and that the function $g(t)$ is differentiable at $t = 0$. The latter means that each matrix element $g_{ik}(t)$ is a differentiable function of t at $t = 0$. Put

$$g'_{ik}(0) = a_{ik}.$$

To the matrix $g(t)$ corresponds an operator $T_{g(t)}$ of our representation; let us apply to it the rule for differentiating a function of a function, using proposition **A**, (3). Repeating essentially the reasoning on p. 39, we conclude that for a fixed $x \in \mathfrak{D}$ the derivative $\mathrm{d}/\mathrm{d}t\ \{T_{g(t)}\, x\}_{t=0}$ depends only on the a_{ik}; it does not change when $T_{g(t)}$ is replaced by $T_{h(t)}$, if also $h'_{ik}(0) = a_{ik}$. We shall use this remark in the proof of the following theorem:

THEOREM 1. *The basic infinitesimal operators of a representation of the group* $\mathfrak{G}_+$ *satisfy the following relations*:†

$$[A_1, A_2] = A_3, \quad [A_2, A_3] = A_1, \quad [A_3, A_1] = A_2; \tag{1}$$

$$[B_1, B_2] = -A_3, \quad [B_2, B_3] = -A_1, \quad [B_3, B_1] = -A_2; \tag{2}$$

$$[A_1, B_1] = 0, \quad [A_2, B_2] = 0, \quad [A_3, B_3] = 0, \tag{3}$$

$$[A_1, B_2] = B_3, \quad [A_1, B_3] = -B_2; \tag{4}$$

$$[A_2, B_3] = B_1, \quad [A_2, B_1] = -B_3; \tag{5}$$

$$[A_3, B_1] = B_2, \quad [A_3, B_2] = -B_1. \tag{6}$$

Proof.‡ *Let* a, b, c be three arbitrary infinitesimal matrices from the a_i, b_i, and A, B, C the corresponding operators of the representation; by virtue of formulae (1–6) of Subsection 2 it is sufficient to establish that if $[a, b] = c$, then for $x \in \mathfrak{D}$ also $[A, B]x = Cx$.

† In the sequel we shall understand algebraic relations between the infinitesimal operators in the sense that the left and right hand sides are to be applied only to vectors of the set $\mathfrak{D}$.

‡ The given proof is a repetition with a few modifications of the proof of Theorem 2 of § 4, Subsection 4. We present it nevertheless for the sake of completeness of exposition.

So let $[a, b] = c$ and let $a(t)$, $b(t)$, $c(t)$ be the corresponding one-parameter groups, so that

$$a'(0) = a; \quad b'(0) = b; \quad c'(0) = c. \tag{7}$$

Consider the function

$$g(t) = a(\sqrt{t})b(\sqrt{t})a(-\sqrt{t})b(-\sqrt{t}); \tag{8}$$

expanding it in powers of $\sqrt{t}$ and applying formulae (20), (21) of Subsection 1, we see that

$$g(t) = \left(1+\sqrt{t}\cdot a+\frac{ta^2}{2}+\dots\right)\left(1+\sqrt{t}\cdot b+\frac{tb^2}{2}+\dots\right)\times$$
$$\times\left(1-\sqrt{t}\cdot a+\frac{ta^2}{2}-\dots\right)\left(1-\sqrt{t}\cdot b+\frac{tb^2}{2}-\dots\right)$$
$$= 1+t(ab-ba)+\dots = 1+tc+\dots,$$

consequently,

$$g'(0) = c. \tag{9}$$

On the other hand, also $c'(0) = c$; hence on the grounds of the remark made above we conclude that for $x \in \mathfrak{D}$

$$\left(\frac{\mathrm{d}}{\mathrm{d}t} T_{c(t)}x\right)_{t=0} = \left(\frac{\mathrm{d}}{\mathrm{d}t} T_{g(t)}x\right)_{t=0}. \tag{10}$$

But the left hand side of this equation is Cx. Let us prove that the right hand side is $(AB-BA)x$; the theorem will thereby be proved. For this purpose set

$$A(t) = T_{a(t)}, \quad B(t) = T_{b(t)}, \quad C(t) = T_{c(t)}. \tag{11}$$

As the correspondence $g \to T_g$ is a representation, equation (8) yields the relation

$$T_{g(t)}x = A(\sqrt{t})B(\sqrt{t})A(-\sqrt{t})B(-\sqrt{t})x, \quad x \in \mathfrak{D}. \tag{12}$$

Using formulae (8a) of Subsection 3, we conclude that

$$T_{g(t)}x = [\mathbf{1}+\sqrt{(t)}A+\tfrac{1}{2}tA^2+\dots][\mathbf{1}+\sqrt{(t)}B+\tfrac{1}{2}tB^2+\dots]\times$$
$$\times[\mathbf{1}-\sqrt{(t)}A+\tfrac{1}{2}tA^2+\dots][\mathbf{1}-\sqrt{(t)}B+\tfrac{1}{2}tB^2+\dots]x$$
$$= x+t(AB-BA)x+o(t).$$

Hence it follows that

$$\left(\frac{\mathrm{d}}{\mathrm{d}t} T_{g(t)}x\right)_{t=0} = (AB-BA)x,$$

and the theorem is proved.

§ 8. Determination of the Infinitesimal Operators of a Representation of the Group $\mathfrak{G}_+$

1. Statement of the problem

In connection with Theorem 1 of § 7, Subsection 4 the following problem arises:

To find the general form of the linear operators A_i, B_i, $i = 1, 2, 3$, *satisfying relations* (1–6) *of* § 7, Subsection 4.

By virtue of I of § 7, Subsection 3, the representation is completely determined by these operators.

In place of the operators A_i, B_i it will be convenient for us to seek the following linear combinations of them:

$$H_+ = iA_1 - A_2, \quad H_- = iA_1 + A_2, \tag{1}$$

$$F_+ = iB_1 - B_2, \quad F_- = iB_1 + B_2, \tag{2}$$

$$H_3 = iA_3, \quad F_3 = iB_3. \tag{3}$$

It is easy to find the commutators of these six operators. Thus, by virtue of (1), (3) and (1) of § 7, Subsection 4

$$[H_+, H_3] = [iA_1 - A_2, iA_3]$$
$$= -[A_1, A_3] - i[A_2, A_3] = A_2 - iA_1 = -H_+;$$

as the result of analogous calculations we obtain:

$$[H_+, H_3] = -H_+, [H_-, H_3] = H_-, [H_+, H_-] = 2H_3, \tag{4}$$

$$[H_+, F_+] = [H_-, F_-] = [H_3, F_3] = 0, \tag{5}$$

$$[F_+, F_3] = H_+, [F_-, F_3] = -H_-, [F_+, F_-] = -2H_3, \quad (6)$$

$$[H_+, F_3] = -F_+, [H_-, F_3] = F_-, \quad (7)$$

$$[H_+, F_-] = -[H_-, F_+] = 2F_3, \quad (8)$$

$$[F_+, H_3] = -F_+, [F_-, H_3] = F_-. \quad (9)$$

We arrive at the following problem:

To find the general form of the operators H_+, H_-, H_3, F_+, F_-, F_3 satisfying the relations (4–9).

2. Determination of the operators H_+, H_-, H_3

A given representation $g \to T_g$ of the group $\mathfrak{G}_+$ is also a representation of the group G_0. Let $\mathfrak{M}^k$ be the corresponding invariant subspaces, so that the space R of the representation $g \to T_g$ is the closed direct sum of the subspaces $\mathfrak{M}^k$. Here if $\mathfrak{M}^k \neq (0)$ then, by virtue of proposition **B** of § 7, Subsection 3, the representation $g \to T_g$ of the subgroup G_0, considered only on $\mathfrak{M}^k$, is irreducible. Let f_ν^k, $\nu = -k, -k+1, \ldots, k$ be a canonical basis for $\mathfrak{M}^k$ if $\mathfrak{M}^k \neq (0)$. The operators H_+, H_-, H_3 are also infinitesimal operators of the representation $g \to T_g$ of the subgroup G_0, and since $\mathfrak{M}^k$ is invariant relative to the operators of this representation, it is also invariant relative to the operators H_+, H_-, H_3. In this connection, it was proved in § 4, Subsection 6, that

$$H_+ f_\nu^k = \alpha_{\nu+1}^k f_{\nu+1}^k, \quad H_- f_\nu^k = \alpha_\nu^k f_{\nu-1}^k, \quad H_3 f_\nu^k = \nu f_\nu^k, \quad (1)$$

where

$$\alpha_\nu^k = \sqrt{[(k+\nu)(k-\nu+1)]}. \quad (2)$$

From these formulae it follows that

$$H_+ f_\nu^k = 0 \quad \text{for} \quad \nu = k, \quad (3)$$

$$H_+^2 f_\nu^k = \alpha_{\nu+1}^k H_+ f_{\nu+1}^k = 0 \quad \text{for} \quad \nu = k, k-1 \quad (4)$$

and in general

$$H_+^p f_\nu^k = 0 \quad \text{for} \quad \nu = k, k-1, \ldots, k-p+1. \quad (5)$$

Conversely we have

I. *If*

$$H^p_+ f^k_\nu = 0, \tag{6}$$

then

$$k \leqslant \nu + p - 1.$$

In fact, from formulae (1) and (2) it follows that equation (5) is only possible for $\nu = k, k-1, \ldots, k-p+1$, i.e. for $\nu \geqslant k-p+1$. Hence $k \leqslant \nu+p-1$.

Let us agree to call every vector $f \in R$, $f \neq 0$, satisfying the condition

$$H_3 f = \nu f; \tag{7}$$

a *weight vector* of our representation $g \to T_g$; we shall call the number ν the *weight* of the vector f.

II. *If f is a weight vector of weight ν, satisfying the condition*

$$H^p_+ f = 0, \tag{8}$$

then f is a linear combination of the vectors f^k_ν for which $k = \nu$, $\nu+1, \ldots, \nu+p-1$.

Proof. Put $f_k = E^k f$; from the relations $E^k T_u = T_u E^k$ (see II of § 6, Subsection 6) it follows that

$$H_3 f_k = H_3 E^k f = E^k H_3 f = \nu E^k f = \nu f_k, \tag{9}$$

$$H^p_+ f_k = H^p_+ E^k f = E^k H^p_+ f = 0. \tag{10}$$

From (9) we conclude that f_k differs from f^k_ν only by a numerical factor:

$$f_k = \lambda_k f^k_\nu,$$

and therefore also $H^p_+ f^k_\nu = 0$. Applying proposition I, we see that $k \leqslant \nu+p-1$, so that the possible values of k are $k = \nu$, $\nu+1$, $\ldots$, $\nu+p-1$; in other words, $E^k f = 0$ if k is not equal to one of the numbers ν, $\nu+1$, $\ldots$, $\nu+p-1$.

But then, putting

$$\phi = f - \sum_{k=\nu}^{\nu+p-1} f_k, \tag{11}$$

we obtain $E^k\phi = 0$ for all k. This is possible only for $\phi = 0$;† consequently, by virtue of (11):

$$f = \sum_{k=\nu}^{\nu+p-1} f_k = \sum_{k=\nu}^{\nu+p-1} \lambda_k f_\nu^k.$$

3. Determination of the operators F_+, F_-, F_3

Consider one of the subspaces $\mathfrak{M}^k \neq (0)$; by virtue of condition C of § 7, Subsection 3, the operators F_+, F_-, F_3 can be applied an unlimited number of times to the vectors of $\mathfrak{M}^k$; applying F_+ to the vector f_ν^k, we obtain some vector $\eta = F_+ f_\nu^k$. Let us elucidate the properties of this vector. Using the formulae

$$[F_+, H_3] = -F_+ \quad \text{and} \quad H_3 f_\nu^k = \nu f_\nu^k$$

(see (9) of Subsection 1 and (1) of Subsection 2), we have:

$$\begin{aligned} H_3\eta = H_3 F_+ f_\nu^k &= [H_3, F_+] f_\nu^k + F_+ H_3 f_\nu^k \\ &= F_+ f_\nu^k + \nu F_+ f_\nu^k = (\nu+1)\eta; \end{aligned}$$

consequently, if $\eta \neq 0$ then η is a weight vector of weight $\nu+1$. Now apply to η the operator $H_+^{k-\nu+1}$; by virtue of the commutability of this operator with the operator F_+ and by formula (5) of Subsection 2 we have

$$H_+^{k-\nu+1}\eta = H_+^{k-\nu+1} F_+ f_\nu^k = F_+ H_+^{k-\nu+1} f_\nu^k = 0;$$

consequently, by II of Subsection 2 the vector $\eta = F_+ f_\nu^k$ is a linear combination of the vectors

$$f_{\nu+1}^p, \; p = \nu+1, \nu+2, \ldots, k+1.$$

---

† In fact, if $E^k\phi = 0$ then also $E_{ll}^k\phi = E_{ll}^k E^k \phi = 0$, and therefore $E_{jl}^k\phi = E_{jl}^k E_{ll}^k \phi = 0$ for all j, l, k. Hence for any functional $f \in R'$

$$f(E_{jl}^k \phi) = (2k+1) \int \overline{c_{jl}^k(u)}\, f(T_u \phi)\, du = 0.$$

By virtue of the completeness of the system of functions $c_{jl}^k(u)$ (see the Corollary in § 6, Subsection 2), it follows from this that $f(T_u\phi) = 0$; putting $u = e$ we obtain that $f(\phi) = 0$ for all $f \in R'$, and consequently (see III of § 6, Subsection 4) $\phi = 0$.

Put

$$F_+f_\nu^k = \sum_{p=\nu+1}^{k+1} \beta_{\nu+1,p}^k f_{\nu+1}^p, \quad \nu = -k, -k+1, \ldots, k; \tag{1}$$

formula (1) may also be considered valid when $F_+f_\nu^k = 0$; in this case one must simply put $\beta_{\nu+1,p}^k = 0$.

Let us now find $F_3 f_\nu^k$. For this purpose we make use of the relation $2F_3 = -[H_-, F_+]$, by virtue of which

$$2F_3 f_\nu^k = -H_- F_+ f_\nu^k + F_+ H_- f_\nu^k.$$

Applying the formulae (1) of Subsection 2 and (1), we obtain

$$2F_3 f_\nu^k = -\sum_{p=\nu+1}^{k+1} \beta_{\nu+1,p}^k H_- f_{\nu+1}^p + \alpha_\nu^k F_+ f_{\nu-1}^k$$

$$= -\sum_{p=\nu+1}^{k+1} \beta_{\nu+1,p}^k \alpha_{\nu+1}^p f_\nu^p + \alpha_\nu^k \sum_{p=\nu}^{k+1} \beta_{\nu,p}^k f_\nu^p;$$

whence

$$F_3 f_\nu^k = \sum_{p=\nu}^{k+1} \gamma_{\nu p}^k f_\nu^p, \tag{2}$$

where

$$\gamma_{\nu\nu}^k = \tfrac{1}{2}\alpha_\nu^k \beta_{\nu\nu}^k, \quad \gamma_{\nu p}^k = -\tfrac{1}{2}(\beta_{\nu+1,p}^k \alpha_{\nu+1}^p - \alpha_\nu^k \beta_{\nu,p}^k), \tag{3}$$
$$p = \nu+1, \nu+2, \ldots, k+1.$$

Finally let us find $F_- f_\nu^k$, for which purpose we make use of the relation

$$F_- = [H_-, F_3].$$

We have

$$F_- f_\nu^k = H_- F_3 f_\nu^k - F_3 H_- f_\nu^k,$$

consequently, by virtue of the formulae (1) of Subsection 2 and by (2),

$$F_- f_\nu^k = \sum_{p=\nu}^{k+1} \gamma_{\nu p}^k H_- f_\nu^p - \alpha_\nu^k F_3 f_{\nu-1}^k$$

$$= \sum_{p=\nu}^{k+1} \gamma_{\nu p}^k \alpha_\nu^p f_{\nu-1}^p - \alpha_\nu^k \sum_{p=\nu-1}^{k+1} \gamma_{\nu-1,p}^k f_{\nu-1}^p;$$

whence

$$F_- f_\nu^k = \sum_{p=\nu-1}^{k+1} \delta_{\nu-1,p}^k f_{\nu-1}^p, \tag{4}$$

where

$$\delta^k_{\nu-1,\nu-1} = -\alpha^k_\nu \gamma^k_{\nu-1,\nu-1}, \tag{5a}$$

$$\delta^k_{\nu-1,p} = \gamma^k_{\nu p}\alpha^p_\nu - \alpha^k_\nu \gamma^k_{\nu-1,p}, \quad p = \nu, \nu+1, \ldots, k+1. \tag{5b}$$

Thus the vectors $F_+ f^k_\nu$, $F_3 f^k_\nu$ and $F_- f^k_\nu$ are determined by the formulae (1), (2) and (4) respectively; however the coefficients $\beta^k_{\nu+1,p}$, $\gamma^k_{\nu p}$ and $\delta^k_{\nu-1,p}$ will not be arbitrary, as the relations (5–9) of Subsection 1 have to be satisfied. It is easy to see that relation (9) of Subsection 1 is automatically satisfied; therefore only the fulfilling of relations (5–8) of Subsection 1 needs to be ensured.

The first of the relations (5) of Subsection 1 means that H_+ and F_+ commute; therefore

$$H_+ F_+ f^k_{\nu-1} = F_+ H_+ f^k_{\nu-1};$$

applying the formulae (1) of Subsection 2 and formula (1) we obtain

$$\sum_{p=\nu}^{k+1} \beta^k_{\nu p}\alpha^p_{\nu+1} f^p_{\nu+1} = \alpha^k_\nu \sum_{p=\nu+1}^{k+1} \beta^k_{\nu+1,p} f^p_{\nu+1}.$$

Hence

$$\beta^k_{\nu\nu}\alpha^\nu_{\nu+1} = 0, \quad \beta^k_{\nu p}\alpha^p_{\nu+1} = \alpha^k_\nu \beta^k_{\nu+1,p}$$

$$\text{for} \quad p = \nu+1, \nu+2, \ldots, k+1;$$

consequently,

$$\beta^k_{\nu p} = \frac{\alpha^k_\nu}{\alpha^p_{\nu+1}} \beta^k_{\nu+1,p} \quad \text{for} \quad p = \nu+1, \nu+2, \ldots, k+1. \tag{6}$$

Analogously, applying the relation $[H_-, F_-] = 0$ to $f^k_{\nu+1}$ we obtain

$$\alpha^k_{\nu+1}\delta^k_{\nu-1,\nu-1} = 0,$$

$$\delta^k_{\nu p}\alpha^p_\nu = \delta^k_{\nu-1,p}\alpha^k_{\nu+1} \quad \text{for} \quad p = \nu, \nu+1, \ldots, k+1; \tag{7}$$

as regards the relation $[H_3, F_3] = 0$, it is easily seen to be automatically satisfied.

From the first equation (7) it follows that $\delta^k_{\nu-1,\nu-1} = 0$ for $\alpha^k_{\nu+1} \neq 0$, and consequently, by formula (2) of Subsection 2, for $\nu < k$. Thus

$$\delta^k_{\nu-1,\nu-1} = 0 \quad \text{for} \quad \nu < k. \tag{8}$$

In particular, for $\nu = k-1$ we obtain

$$\delta^k_{k-2,k-2} = 0. \tag{9}$$

Further, putting $p = \nu$ in (7) we have

$$\delta^k_{\nu\nu}\alpha^\nu_\nu = \delta^k_{\nu-1,\nu}\alpha^k_{\nu+1}.$$

By (8) it follows from this that $\alpha^k_{\nu+1}\delta^k_{\nu-1,\nu} = 0$ for $\nu < k-1$. Thus $\delta^k_{\nu-1,\nu} = 0$ for $\alpha^k_{\nu+1} \neq 0$; consequently

$$\delta^k_{\nu-1,\nu} = 0 \quad \text{for} \quad \nu < k-1. \tag{10}$$

In particular, for $\nu = k-2$ it follows from (8) and (10) that

$$\delta^k_{k-3,k-3} = 0, \quad \delta^k_{k-3,k-2} = 0. \tag{11}$$

Repeating this reasoning, one easily satisfies oneself that generally

$$\delta^k_{\nu-1,\nu-1} = \delta^k_{\nu-1,\nu} = \ldots = \delta^k_{\nu-1,k-2} = 0 \quad \text{for} \quad \nu < k, \tag{12}$$

and now formula (4) becomes

$$F_- f^k_\nu = \delta^k_{\nu-1,k-1} f^{k-1}_{\nu-1} + \delta^k_{\nu-1,k} f^k_{\nu-1} + \delta^k_{\nu-1,k+1} f^{k+1}_{\nu-1}. \tag{13}$$

Formula (5a) now shows that $\alpha^k_\nu \gamma^k_{\nu-1,\nu-1} = 0$ for $\nu < k$, therefore also $\gamma^k_{\nu-1,\nu-1} = 0$ for $\alpha^k_\nu \neq 0$, i.e. for $\nu < k$. Thus

$$\gamma^k_{\nu,\nu} = 0 \quad \text{for} \quad \nu < k-1, \tag{14}$$

in particular

$$\gamma^k_{k-2,k-2} = 0. \tag{15}$$

Putting $p = \nu$ in (5b) and taking account of (10) and (14), we obtain $-\alpha^k_\nu \gamma^k_{\nu-1,\nu} = 0$. As $\alpha^k_\nu \neq 0$ for $\nu < k-1$, we have

$$\gamma^k_{\nu,\nu+1} = 0 \quad \text{for} \quad \nu < k-2. \tag{16}$$

In particular

$$\gamma^k_{k-3,k-3} = 0, \quad \gamma^k_{k-3,k-2} = 0.$$

Repeating this reasoning, we conclude that generally

$$\gamma^k_{\nu\nu} = \gamma^k_{\nu,\nu+1} = \ldots = \gamma^k_{\nu,k-2} = 0 \quad \text{for} \quad \nu < k-1, \tag{17}$$

and therefore equation (2) assumes the form

$$F_3 f^k_\nu = \gamma^k_{\nu,k-1} f^{k-1}_\nu + \gamma^k_{\nu k} f^k_\nu + \gamma^k_{\nu,k+1} f^{k+1}_\nu; \tag{18}$$

here one must consider $\gamma^k_{k,k-1} = 0$.

Applying analogous reasoning to the formula (3), we find that

$$\beta^k_{\nu+1,\nu+1} = \beta^k_{\nu+1,\nu+2} = \ldots = \beta^k_{\nu+1,k-2} = 0 \quad \text{for} \quad \nu < k-2, \tag{19}$$

so that formula (1) becomes

$$F_+ f^k_\nu = \beta^k_{\nu+1,k-1} f^{k-1}_{\nu+1} + \beta^k_{\nu+1,k} f^k_{\nu+1} + \beta^k_{\nu+1,k+1} f^{k+1}_{\nu+1}. \tag{20}$$

Here in formula (20) one must consider

$$\beta^k_{\nu+1,k-1} = 0 \quad \text{for} \quad \nu = k-1,\, k \tag{21}$$

and

$$\beta^k_{\nu+1,k} = 0 \quad \text{for} \quad \nu = k. \tag{22}$$

Now let us turn to formula (6); putting $p = k+1$ in it, we obtain

$$\beta^k_{\nu,k+1} = \frac{\alpha^k_\nu}{\alpha^{k+1}_{\nu+1}} \beta^k_{\nu+1,k+1}. \tag{23}$$

Further, putting $\nu = m,\ m+1,\ \ldots,\ k$ in (23) and multiplying together the resulting equations, we conclude that

$$\beta^k_{m,k+1} = \frac{\alpha^k_m \alpha^k_{m+1} \ldots \alpha^k_k}{\alpha^{k+1}_{m+1} \alpha^{k+1}_{m+2} \ldots \alpha^{k+1}_{k+1}} \beta^k_{k+1,k+1}$$

or, substituting in place of α^k_ν its expression from (2) of Subsection 2 and replacing m by ν,

$$\beta^k_{\nu,k+1} = \sqrt{\left[\frac{(\nu+k)(\nu+k+1)}{(2k+1)(2k+2)}\right]} \beta^k_{k+1,k+1}. \tag{24}$$

Now let us put $p = k$ in (6); we obtain

$$\beta^k_{\nu k} = \frac{\alpha^k_\nu}{\alpha^k_{\nu+1}} \beta^k_{\nu+1,k}.$$

Hence, repeating the previous reasoning, we conclude that

$$\beta^k_{\nu k} = \sqrt{\left[\frac{(k+\nu)(k-\nu+1)}{2k}\right]} \beta^k_{kk}, \tag{25}$$

and similarly, putting $p = k-1$ we find

$$\beta^k_{\nu,k-1} = \sqrt{\left[\frac{(k-\nu+1)(k-\nu)}{2}\right]} \beta^k_{k-1,k-1}. \tag{26}$$

Combining these formulae with (3), we obtain

$$\gamma^k_{\nu,k+1} = -\sqrt{\left[\frac{(\nu+k+1)(k-\nu+1)}{(2k+1)(2k+2)}\right]}\beta^k_{k+1,k+1}, \tag{27}$$

$$\gamma^k_{\nu,k} = \frac{\nu}{\sqrt{(2k)}}\beta^k_{kk}, \tag{28}$$

$$\gamma^k_{\nu,k-1} = \sqrt{\left[\frac{(k-\nu)(k+\nu)}{2}\right]}\beta^k_{k-1,k-1}. \tag{29}$$

Similarly, substituting the expressions (27–29) into the formulae (5), we find

$$\delta^k_{\nu-1,k+1} = -\sqrt{\left[\frac{(k-\nu+1)(k-\nu+2)}{(2k+1)(2k+2)}\right]}\beta^k_{k+1,k+1}, \tag{30}$$

$$\delta^k_{\nu-1,k} = \sqrt{\left[\frac{(k+\nu)(k-\nu+1)}{2k}\right]}\beta^k_{kk}, \tag{31}$$

$$\delta^k_{\nu-1,k-1} = -\sqrt{\left[\frac{(k+\nu)(k+\nu-1)}{2}\right]}\beta^k_{k-1,k-1}; \tag{32}$$

it is easy to verify that conditions (7) will then be automatically satisfied. Let us introduce the notation

$$A_k = -\frac{1}{\sqrt{(2k)}}\beta^k_{kk},$$

$$C_k = \frac{1}{\sqrt{2}}\beta^k_{k-1,k-1}, \quad D_{k+1} = \frac{1}{\sqrt{[(2k+1)(2k+2)]}}\beta^k_{k+1,k+1}. \tag{33}$$

Then, combining the formulae (13), (18) and (20) with (24–32), we obtain:

$$\begin{aligned} F_+f^k_\nu = {} & \sqrt{[(k-\nu)(k-\nu-1)]}\,C_k f^{k-1}_{\nu+1} \\ & -\sqrt{[(k-\nu)(k+\nu+1)]}\,A_k f^k_{\nu+1} \\ & +\sqrt{[(k+\nu+1)(k+\nu+2)]}\,D_{k+1} f^{k+1}_{\nu+1}, \end{aligned} \tag{34}$$

$$\begin{aligned} F_-f^k_\nu = {} & -\sqrt{[(k+\nu)(k+\nu-1)]}\,C_k f^{k-1}_{\nu-1} \\ & -\sqrt{[(k+\nu)(k-\nu+1)]}\,A_k f^k_{\nu-1} \\ & -\sqrt{[(k-\nu+1)(k-\nu+2)]}\,D_{k+1} f^{k+1}_{\nu-1}, \end{aligned} \tag{35}$$

$$F_3 f_\nu^k = \sqrt{[(k-\nu)(k+\nu)]}\, C_k f_\nu^{k-1} \\ -\nu A_k f_\nu^k - \sqrt{[(k+\nu+1)(k-\nu+1)]}\, D_{k+1} f_\nu^{k+1}. \quad (36)$$

We recall further the formulae (1) of Subsection 2:

$$\left.\begin{aligned} H_+ f_\nu^k &= \sqrt{[(k+\nu+1)(k-\nu)]} f_{\nu+1}^k, \\ H_- f_\nu^k &= \sqrt{[(k+\nu)(k-\nu+1)]} f_{\nu-1}^k, \quad H_3 f_\nu^k = \nu f_\nu^k. \end{aligned}\right\} \quad (37)$$

It remains to determine the coefficients A_k, C_k, D_k.

First of all we observe that in the definition of these coefficients there is an arbitrariness corresponding to a certain arbitrariness in the choice of the basis vectors f_ν^k. In fact, let us suppose that the basis vectors f_ν^k are replaced by vectors $\phi_\nu^k = \omega(k) f_\nu^k$, where $\omega(k)$ is an arbitrary numerical factor, depending only on k. Obviously the formulae (37) will have the same form in the new vectors ϕ_ν^k; to see this it is sufficient to multiply both sides of (37) by $\omega(k)$. If one multiplies both sides of (34–36) by $\omega(k)$ and goes over to the vectors ϕ_ν^k, then the coefficients A_k remain unchanged, while C_k and D_{k+1} go into

$$C_k' = \frac{\omega(k)}{\omega(k-1)} C_k, \quad D_{k+1}' = \frac{\omega(k)}{\omega(k+1)} D_{k+1}. \quad (38)$$

Consequently, we have

$$C_k' D_k' = \frac{\omega(k)}{\omega(k-1)} \frac{\omega(k-1)}{\omega(k)} C_k D_k = C_k D_k,$$

i.e. the product $C_k D_k$ remains unchanged. Let k_0 be the least of the weights k, for which $\mathfrak{M}^k \neq (0)$. The factor $\omega(k)$ may obviously be so chosen that $C_k' = D_k'$ for $k \geqslant k_0+1$; in fact, by (38) this equality is equivalent to

$$\frac{\omega(k)}{\omega(k-1)} C_k = \frac{\omega(k-1)}{\omega(k)} D_k.$$

Hence

$$\left[\frac{\omega(k)}{\omega(k-1)}\right]^2 = \frac{D_k}{C_k},$$

and so

$$\omega(k) = C\sqrt{\left[\prod_{\nu=k_0+1}^{k}\frac{D_\nu}{C_\nu}\right]}, \quad k \geqslant k_0+1,$$

where the argument of the root may be chosen in an arbitrary way.

We shall suppose that this replacement of the basis has already been carried out from the very beginning, so that $C_k = D_k$, and therefore D_{k+1} is to be replaced by C_{k+1} in formulae (34–37). It remains to determine A_k and C_k, for which purpose we shall use the remaining relations (6–8) of Subsection 1. It is easy, however, to verify directly that formulae (34–37) automatically satisfy relations (7) and (8) of Subsection 1; therefore we turn to relation (6) of Subsection 1. Let us apply both sides of the first of these relations

$$F_+F_3 - F_3F_+ = H_+$$

to the vector f_ν^k; taking account of the formulae (34), (36), (37) and then comparing coefficients of the same vectors $f_{\nu+1}^p$, we obtain

$$[A_k(k+1) - (k-1)A_{k-1}]C_k = 0; \tag{39}$$

$$[A_{k+1}(k+2) - kA_k]C_{k+1} = 0, \tag{40}$$

$$(2k-1)C_k^2 - (2k+3)C_{k+1}^2 - A_k^2 = 1. \tag{41}$$

It is easily seen that the remaining two of the relations (6) of Subsection 1 lead to the same formulae (39–41). We must take $C_{k_0} = 0$, since, by the very definition of the weight k_0, the weight k_0-1 cannot appear in the formulae (34–36) for $k = k_0$.

The following two cases are possible:

(1) C_k does not vanish for any of the values $k = k_0+n$, $n = 1$, 2, 3, ... ;

(2) C_k vanishes for some of the values $k = k_0+n$, $n = 1$, 2, 3, ...

Let us suppose first that case (1) occurs. Obviously, equations (39) and (40) then mean the same thing, namely that

$$A_k(k+1) - (k-1)A_{k-1} = 0 \quad \text{for} \quad k = k_0+n, \quad n = 1, 2, 3, \ldots \tag{42}$$

Multiplying both sides of (42) by k and introducing the notation

$$k(k+1)A_k = \rho_k, \tag{43}$$

we obtain

$$\rho_k - \rho_{k-1} = 0.$$

This means that ρ_k does not depend on k, i.e. is a constant. Let us denote this constant by ik_0c.

This notation is permissible for $k_0 \neq 0$; if $k_0 = 0$ then it is also permissible, as it follows easily from (42) that $A_k = 0$ for $k \geqslant 1$. In fact, putting $k = 1$ in (42), we obtain

$$A_1 = 0.$$

Further, putting $k = 2$, we obtain $3A_2 - A_1 = 0$; consequently $A_2 = 0$, and so on.

Thus

$$k(k+1)A_k = ik_0c,$$

or

$$A_k = \frac{ik_0c}{k(k+1)}. \tag{44}$$

Now let us turn to formula (41). Multiplying both sides of it by $2k+1$ and introducing the notation

$$\sigma_k = (2k-1)(2k+1)C_k^2, \tag{45}$$

we obtain

$$\sigma_k - \sigma_{k+1} - (2k+1)A_k^2 = (2k+1).$$

Hence, by (44)

$$\sigma_k - \sigma_{k+1} = (2k+1) - k_0^2c^2\left[\frac{1}{k^2} - \frac{1}{(k+1)^2}\right];$$

consequently,

$$\sigma_{k_0} - \sigma_k = \sum_{\nu=k_0}^{k-1}(\sigma_\nu - \sigma_{\nu+1}) = \sum_{\nu=k_0}^{k-1}(2\nu+1) - k_0^2c^2\sum_{\nu=k_0}^{k-1}\left[\frac{1}{\nu^2} - \frac{1}{(\nu+1)^2}\right]$$

$$= k^2 - k_0^2 - k_0^2c^2\left(\frac{1}{k_0^2} - \frac{1}{k^2}\right) = \frac{(k^2-k_0^2)(k^2-c^2)}{k^2}. \tag{46}$$

But $C_{k_0} = 0$, which means that also $\sigma_{k_0} = 0$; therefore we conclude from (46) that

$$\sigma_k = -\frac{(k^2-k_0^2)(k^2-c^2)}{k^2}.$$

Combining this result with (45), we obtain

$$C_k = \frac{i}{k}\sqrt{\left[\frac{(k^2-k_0^2)(k^2-c^2)}{4k^2-1}\right]}. \tag{47}$$

Here the argument of the root can be chosen for each value of k in an arbitrary way, as changing this argument is equivalent to multiplying the elements f_ν^k of the basis by a number with modulus unity.

Let us denote by $\mathfrak{K}$ the aggregate of all weights k for which $\mathfrak{M}^{(k)} \neq (0)$. Obviously, all the numbers C_k will be non-vanishing only in the case that $c^2 \neq k^2$, $k \in \mathfrak{K}$. Formulae (34–36) show that in this case, together with a weight k the set $\mathfrak{K}$ contains also the weight $k+1$; consequently, $\mathfrak{K}$ is the aggregate of all the numbers $k_0, k_0+1, k_0+2, \ldots$, and therefore R is infinite-dimensional. Here c^2 does not coincide with any of the numbers $(k_0+n)^2$, $n = 0, 1, 2, 3, \ldots$.

Let $\mathfrak{D}'$ be the aggregate of all finite linear combinations of the vectors f_ν^k, $\nu = -k, -k+1, \ldots, k$; $k = k_0, k_0+1, \ldots$; from formulae (34–37) it follows that $\mathfrak{D}'$ is invariant relative to all the operators $H_+, H_-, H_3, F_+, F_-, F_3$. In view of the assumed irreducibility of the given representation, $\mathfrak{D}'$ must be dense in R (see II of § 7, Subsection 3). Thus,

$$R = \mathfrak{M}^{k_0} \dot{+} \mathfrak{M}^{k_0+1} \dot{+} \ldots, \qquad \mathfrak{K} = \{k_0, k_0+1, \ldots\}.$$

Now suppose that case (2) occurs. Let us denote by k_1+1 the least of the numbers $k = k_0+n$, $n = 1, 2, 3, \ldots$, for which $C_k = 0$. Thus, $C_{k_1+1} = 0$, and $C_k \neq 0$ for $k = k_0+n$, $k_0 < k \leqslant k_1$; consequently, by virtue of (39),

$$A_k(k+1) - (k-1)A_{k-1} = 0 \quad \text{for} \quad k = k_0+n,\ k_0 < k \leqslant k_1.$$

Hence, as above, we find

$$A_k = \frac{ik_0c}{k(k+1)} \quad \text{for} \quad k = k_0+n,\ k_0 \leqslant k \leqslant k_1. \tag{48}$$

Applying now formula (41) and repeating the same reasoning as in the derivation of formula (47), we obtain:

$$C_k = \frac{i}{k}\sqrt{\left[\frac{(k^2-k_0^2)(k^2-c^2)}{4k^2-1}\right]} \text{ for } k = k_0+n,\ k_0 \leqslant k \leqslant k_1+1. \tag{49}$$

As we must have $C_{k_1+1} = 0$, it follows from this that

$$c^2 = (k_1+1)^2. \tag{50}$$

These formulae and formulae (34–36) show that $\mathfrak{K}$ contains all the weights $k_0, k_0+1, \ldots, k_1$. Denote by $\tilde{R}$ the direct sum of the subspaces $\mathfrak{M}^k$, $k = k_0, k_0+1, \ldots, k_1$. Let us prove that $\tilde{R}$ is invariant relative to all the operators $H_+, H_-, H_3, F_+, F_-, F_3$. As concerns H_+, H_-, H_3 this is obvious, as each subspace $\mathfrak{M}^k$ is invariant relative to these three operators; let us therefore consider the operators F_+, F_-, F_3. But formulae (34–36) show that for $k < k_1$ the vectors $F_+f_\nu^k$, $F_-f_\nu^k$, $F_3f_\nu^k$ are linear combinations of the vectors f_μ^p, where $p \leqslant k_1$, and therefore belong to $\tilde{R}$; for $k = k_1$ by virtue of the condition $C_{k_1+1} = 0$ the vectors $F_+f_\nu^{k_1}$, $F_-f_\nu^{k_1}$, $F_3f_\nu^{k_1}$ are also linear combinations of the vectors f_μ^p, where $p \leqslant k_1$, and therefore also belong to $\tilde{R}$. The assertion is thereby proved. Thus, $\tilde{R}$ is an invariant subspace of R; by virtue of the assumed irreducibility of the given representation $g \to T_g$, it follows from this that $\tilde{R} = R$ and $\mathfrak{K} = (k_0, k_0+1, \ldots, k_1)$.

Thus we arrive at the following theorem:

THEOREM 2. *Each irreducible representation of the proper Lorentz group $\mathfrak{G}_+$ is determined by a pair of numbers (k_0, c), where k_0 is an integral or semi-integral non-negative number, and c is a complex number. The irreducible representation corresponding to a given pair (k_0, c) is then, with a suitable choice of basis f_ν^k in the space of the representation, given by the formulae*

$$\left.\begin{aligned} H_+f_\nu^k &= \sqrt{[(k+\nu+1)(k-\nu)]}f_{\nu+1}^k, \\ H_-f_\nu^k &= \sqrt{[(k+\nu)(k-\nu+1)]}f_{\nu-1}^k,\ H_3f_\nu^k = \nu f_\nu^k, \end{aligned}\right\} \tag{51}$$

$$\begin{aligned} F_+f_\nu^k = \sqrt{[(k-\nu)(k-\nu-1)]}\,C_kf_{\nu+1}^{k-1} &- \sqrt{[(k-\nu)(k+\nu+1)]}\,A_kf_{\nu+1}^k \\ &+ \sqrt{[(k+\nu+1)(k+\nu+2)]}\,C_{k+1}f_{\nu+1}^{k+1}, \end{aligned} \tag{52}$$

$$F_-f_v^k = -\sqrt{[(k+v)(k+v-1)]}\,C_k f_{v-1}^{k-1} - \sqrt{[(k+v)(k-v+1)]}\,A_k f_{v-1}^k - \sqrt{[(k-v+1)(k-v+2)]}\,C_{k+1} f_{v-1}^{k+1}, \quad (53)$$

$$F_3 f_v^k = \sqrt{[(k-v)(k+v)]}\,C_k f_v^{k-1} - vA_k f_v^k - \sqrt{[(k+v+1)(k-v+1)]}\,C_{k+1} f_v^{k+1}, \quad (54)$$

where†

$$A_k = \frac{ik_0 c}{k(k+1)}, \qquad C_k = \frac{i}{k}\sqrt{\left[\frac{(k^2-k_0^2)(k^2-c^2)}{4k^2-1}\right]}. \quad (55)$$

If $c^2 = (k_0+n)^2$ *for some natural number* n, *then the representation is finite-dimensional and the possible values of the indices* v *and* k *are* $v = -k, -k+1, \ldots, k$; $k = k_0, k_0+1, \ldots, k_1$. *If, however,* $c^2 \neq (k_0+n)^2$ *for any natural number* n, *then the representation is infinite-dimensional and the possible values of the indices* v *and* k *are*

$$v = -k, -k+1, \ldots, k; \qquad k = k_0, k_0+1, k_0+2, \ldots .$$

We remark that at present we are leaving open the question whether to each pair of numbers (k_0, c) there really corresponds a representation $g \to T_g$ of the group $\mathfrak{G}_+$, i.e. whether the formulae (51–55) always define the infinitesimal operators of some representation. We shall give the answer to this question below in § 15, Subsection 16. At any rate the preceding arguments show that we have not left out any irreducible representation of the group $\mathfrak{G}_+$ which satisfies the conditions **A, B, C** of § 7, Subsection 3.

4. The conditions of being unitary

Let us now elucidate the conditions under which a given representation $g \to T_g$ is unitary, i.e. under what conditions all the

† Formulae (51–55) for unitary representations and under the assumptions **A, B, C** of Section 7, Subsection 3 were first obtained by I. M. GELFAND in 1944 (in this connection see Ref. [15]; subsequently these formulae were published (without rigorous justification) in HARISH-CHANDRA's paper Ref. [38] and in the paper Ref. [14a] of I. M. GELFAND and A. M. YAGLOM.

operators T_g are unitary. We shall use here the same notation as in condition **A** of § 7, Subsection 3.

I. *If the representation $g \to T_g$ is unitary, then the infinitesimal operators A of this representation satisfy the condition*

$$(Af, g) = -(f, Ag) \tag{1}$$

for all $f, g \in \mathfrak{D}$.

Proof. Since the representation is unitary.

$$A(t) = T_{a(t)}$$

is a unitary operator; hence

$$[A(t)]^* = [A(t)]^{-1} = A(-t),$$

and therefore for $f,\ g \in \mathfrak{D}$

$$(A(t)f, g) = (f, A(-t)g).$$

Differentiating both sides of this equation with respect to t, we obtain for $t = 0$:

$$(Af, g) = -(f, Ag).$$

II. *If the representation $g \to T_g$ of the group $\mathfrak{G}_+$ is unitary, then the operators $H_+, H_-, H_3, F_+, F_-, F_3$ satisfy the relations:*

$$(H_+f, g) = (f, H_-g), \quad (H_3 f, g) = (f, H_3 g), \tag{2}$$

$$(F_+f, g) = (f, F_-g), \quad (F_3 f, g) = (f, F_3 g), \tag{3}$$

for all $f,\ g \in \mathfrak{D}$.

Proof. By I, the operators A_k, B_k satisfy the relations

$$(A_k f, g) = -(f, A_k g), \quad (B_k f, g) = -(f, B_k g), \quad k = 1, 2, 3,$$

for $f,\ g \in \mathfrak{D}$; consequently,

$$(F_+f, g) = ((iB_1 - B_2)f, g) = (f, (iB_1 + B_2)g) = (f, F_-g).$$

The remaining relations (2), (3) are proved similarly.

THEOREM 3. *If the irreducible representation $g \to T_g$ of the group $\mathfrak{G}_+$ is unitary, then the pair of numbers (k_0, c) determining it satisfies one of the following conditions:*

(1) *c is purely imaginary, and k_0 is an arbitrary non-negative integral or semi-integral number;*

(2) *c is a real number in the interval $0 \leqslant c \leqslant 1$, $k_0 = 0$.*

Proof. Combining the relation

$$(F_3 f_\nu^k, f_\nu^k) = (f_\nu^k, F_3 f_\nu^k)$$

with formula (54) of Subsection 3, and taking account of the mutual orthogonality of the vectors f_ν^k, we obtain

$$-\nu A_k = -\nu \bar{A}_k;$$

consequently,†

$$A_k = \bar{A}_k, \tag{4}$$

i.e. A_k is a real number. From the first of the formulae (55) it follows that this is only possible in the following cases: (1) c pure imaginary, k_0 arbitrary; (2) c arbitrary, $k_0 = 0$. Similarly, combining the relation

$$(F_3 f_\nu^k, f_\nu^{k-1}) = (f_\nu^k, F_3 f_\nu^{k-1})$$

with the same formula (54) of Subsection 3, we obtain

$$\sqrt{[(k-\nu)(k+\nu)]}\, C_k = -\sqrt{[(k-\nu)(k+\nu)]}\, \bar{C}_k;$$

consequently,

$$C_k = -\bar{C}_k, \tag{5}$$

i.e. C_k is purely imaginary. Using the formulae (51–54) of Subsection 3, it is easy to see that, generally, all the relations (2), (3) as applied to the vectors $f = f_\nu^p$, $g = f_\mu^q$ are either satisfied identically, or else lead to (4) or (5).

By virtue of the second of the formulae (55) of Subsection 3 the relation (5) means that

$$\frac{1}{k}\sqrt{\left[\frac{(k^2-k_0^2)(k^2-c^2)}{4k^2-1}\right]} \tag{6}$$

must be a real number; consequently, the expression under the square root sign must be positive. Obviously this is possible only

† For $k = k_0 = 0$ the index ν takes only the single value $\nu = 0$, but in this case (see (55)) $A_k = 0$ also, i.e. (4) is satisfied.

when c^2 is real, i.e. when c is real or purely imaginary. In the second case $-c^2 \geqslant 0$, and therefore the expression under the square root sign will be positive. In the first case, i.e. in the case of real c, we must have $k_0 = 0$ (by virtue of what has been said above in connection with A_k). Therefore the expression (6) takes the form

$$\sqrt{\left[\frac{k^2-c^2}{4k^2-1}\right]},$$

where $c^2 \geqslant 0$. This latter expression must be $\geqslant 0$ for all $k = 0, 1, 2, \ldots$; obviously this is only possible if $c^2 \leqslant 1$. In order to see this it is sufficient to put $k = 1$. The theorem is thereby proved.

§ 9. The Finite-dimensional Representations of the Proper Lorentz Group

1. The Spinor description of the proper Lorentz group

We denote by $\mathfrak{A}$ the aggregate of all complex matrices

$$a = \begin{Vmatrix} \alpha & \beta \\ \gamma & \delta \end{Vmatrix} \tag{1}$$

of order two, whose determinant is equal to unity

$$\alpha\delta - \beta\gamma = 1. \tag{2}$$

Evidently, $\mathfrak{A}$ is a group with respect to matrix multiplication; it is called the *unimodular group of order two.*

In what follows we shall need the important fact that the elements of the proper Lorentz group $\mathfrak{G}_+$, can be given by means of the matrices $a \in \mathfrak{A}$, i.e. by means of complex parameters satisfying condition (2). This description of the group $\mathfrak{G}_+$ can be arrived at in the following way. Let

$$q = \begin{Vmatrix} q_{11} & q_{12} \\ q_{21} & q_{22} \end{Vmatrix} \tag{3}$$

be a Hermitian matrix, so that q_{11}, q_{22} are real numbers and

$q_{21} = \overline{q_{12}}$. We shall regard the q_{ik} as variables and define a linear transformation of these variables by putting

$$q' = aqa^*, \tag{4}$$

where

$$a^* = \begin{Vmatrix} \bar{\alpha} & \bar{\gamma} \\ \bar{\beta} & \bar{\delta} \end{Vmatrix} \tag{5}$$

is the conjugate transpose of a.

It is easy to write out this linear transformation; in fact, multiplying the matrices on the right hand side of (4), we obtain:

$$\left.\begin{aligned} q'_{12} &= q_{11}\alpha\bar{\gamma}+q_{12}\alpha\bar{\delta}+q_{21}\beta\bar{\gamma}+q_{22}\beta\bar{\delta}, \\ q'_{21} &= q_{11}\bar{\alpha}\gamma+q_{12}\gamma\bar{\beta}+q_{21}\delta\bar{\alpha}+q_{22}\delta\bar{\beta}, \\ q'_{11} &= q_{11}\alpha\bar{\alpha}+q_{12}\alpha\bar{\beta}+q_{21}\beta\bar{\alpha}+q_{22}\beta\bar{\beta}, \\ q'_{22} &= q_{11}\gamma\bar{\gamma}+q_{12}\gamma\bar{\delta}+q_{21}\delta\bar{\gamma}+q_{22}\delta\bar{\delta}. \end{aligned}\right\} \tag{6}$$

We denote this linear transformation by $\mathfrak{a}$ and write, symbolically, $q' = \mathfrak{a}q$, to indicate that the variables q'_{ik} arise from the variables q_{ik} as a result of the transformation $\mathfrak{a}$. We denote by Δ the determinant of the matrix q:

$$\Delta = \begin{vmatrix} q_{11} & q_{12} \\ \bar{q}_{12} & q_{22} \end{vmatrix} = q_{11}q_{22} - |q_{12}|^2. \tag{7}$$

It follows from the formula (4) that, as a result of the transformation $\mathfrak{a}$, the determinant Δ is multiplied by $\det a \cdot \det a^* = 1$, i.e. Δ remains invariant under the transformation $\mathfrak{a}$.

We now introduce new (real) variables x_1, x_2, x_3, x_4, putting

$$q_{12} = x_1+ix_2, \quad q_{21} = \bar{q}_{12} = x_1-ix_2, \quad x_3 = \frac{q_{11}-q_{22}}{2},$$

$$x_4 = \frac{q_{11}+q_{22}}{2}. \tag{8}$$

Expressed in terms of these variables, Δ takes the form

$$\Delta = x_4^2-x_3^2-x_2^2-x_1^2. \tag{9}$$

The transformation (6) may be regarded as a linear transformation of the variables x_1, x_2, x_3, x_4; from the preceding statement, Δ is not changed by this transformation of variables; consequently, this transformation is a general Lorentz transformation. Thus, *to every matrix* $a \in \mathfrak{A}$ *there corresponds a general Lorentz transformation*:

$$x'_i = \sum_{k=1}^{4} g_{ik} x_k, \qquad i = 1, 2, 3, 4, \tag{10}$$

of the variables x_1, x_2, x_3, x_4. It is easy to express the matrix $\|g_{ik}\|$ of this transformation directly in terms of the parameters $\alpha, \beta, \gamma, \delta$. In fact, substituting in (6) for q'_{ik}, q_{ik} their expressions in terms of x'_i, x_i, by the formulae (8), we obtain the formulae for the transformation of the variables x_i, from which it follows that†

$$\|g_{ik}\| =$$

$$= \left\| \begin{matrix} \operatorname{Re}(\alpha\bar{\delta}+\beta\bar{\gamma}) & -\operatorname{Im}(\alpha\bar{\delta}-\beta\bar{\gamma}) & \operatorname{Re}(\alpha\bar{\gamma}-\beta\bar{\delta}) & \operatorname{Re}(\alpha\bar{\gamma}+\beta\bar{\delta}) \\ \operatorname{Im}(\alpha\bar{\delta}+\beta\bar{\gamma}) & \operatorname{Re}(\alpha\bar{\delta}-\beta\bar{\gamma}) & \operatorname{Im}(\alpha\bar{\gamma}-\beta\bar{\delta}) & \operatorname{Im}(\alpha\bar{\gamma}+\beta\bar{\delta}) \\ \operatorname{Re}(\alpha\bar{\beta}-\gamma\bar{\delta}) & -\operatorname{Im}(\alpha\bar{\beta}-\gamma\bar{\delta}) & \frac{1}{2}(\alpha\bar{\alpha}-\beta\bar{\beta}- & \frac{1}{2}(\alpha\bar{\alpha}+\beta\bar{\beta} \\ & & -\gamma\bar{\gamma}+\delta\bar{\delta}) & -\gamma\bar{\gamma}-\delta\bar{\delta}) \\ \operatorname{Re}(\alpha\bar{\beta}+\gamma\bar{\delta}) & -\operatorname{Im}(\alpha\bar{\beta}+\gamma\bar{\delta}) & \frac{1}{2}(\alpha\bar{\alpha}-\beta\bar{\beta}+ & \frac{1}{2}(\alpha\bar{\alpha}+\beta\bar{\beta}+ \\ & & +\gamma\bar{\gamma}-\delta\bar{\delta}) & +\gamma\bar{\gamma}+\delta\bar{\delta}) \end{matrix} \right\|. \tag{11}$$

Evidently, in formula (11) $g_{44} \geqslant 1$ (see (19) § 2, Subsection 1), so that g is a *Lorentz transformation.*

We shall show that the determinant of this matrix is equal to unity, i.e. that the transformation (10), corresponding to the matrix $a \in \mathfrak{A}$ is a *proper Lorentz transformation.* Let b be the matrix of the substitution (8) from the q_{ik} to the x_i; on transition from the transformation (6) to the transformation (10) the matrix of (6) is multiplied on the left by b^{-1}, and on the right by b, and consequently, the determinant of the transformation is not changed.

† Re z and Im z denote respectively the real and imaginary parts of the complex number z.

Therefore the determinant of the matrix (11) is equal to the determinant of the matrix

$$\begin{Vmatrix} \alpha\bar{\delta} & \beta\bar{\gamma} & \alpha\bar{\gamma} & \beta\bar{\delta} \\ \gamma\bar{\beta} & \delta\bar{\alpha} & \bar{\alpha}\gamma & \bar{\beta}\delta \\ \alpha\bar{\beta} & \bar{\alpha}\beta & \alpha\bar{\alpha} & \beta\bar{\beta} \\ \gamma\bar{\delta} & \delta\bar{\gamma} & \gamma\bar{\gamma} & \delta\bar{\delta} \end{Vmatrix}$$

of transformation (6); evaluating this determinant by Laplace's theorem (making use of the minors of second order corresponding to the first and third, the second and fourth rows), it is easy to verify that it is in fact equal to unity.

The mapping $a \to g$ of the group $\mathfrak{A}$ into the group $\mathfrak{G}_+$, constructed in this way, is called the *spinor mapping*, and the description of the matrix $g \in \mathfrak{G}_+$ by means of the matrix $a \in \mathfrak{A}$ is called *its spinor description.*

I. *The multiplication of the matrices* $a \in \mathfrak{A}$ *corresponds to the multiplication of the corresponding Lorentz transformations.*

Proof. Let $\mathfrak{a}_1, \mathfrak{a}_2$ be the transformations of the variables q_{ik}, corresponding to the matrices $a_1, a_2 \in \mathfrak{A}$, and g_1, g_2 the corresponding Lorentz transformations. The consecutive application first of g_2, and then of g_1 is the same as the consecutive application first of $\mathfrak{a}_2$ and then of $\mathfrak{a}_1$, i.e. first of the transformation $q' = a_2 q a_2^*$, and then of the transformation $q'' = a_1 q' a_1^*$. As a result we obtain the transformation

$$q'' = a_1 a_2 q a_2^* a_1^* = (a_1 a_2) q (a_1 a_2)^*,$$

corresponding to the product $a_1 a_2$ of the matrices a_1, a_2.

The spinor mapping $a \to g$ of the group $\mathfrak{A}$ into the group $\mathfrak{G}_+$ is not one-to-one; thus, from formula (11) it is directly seen that the matrices

$$a = \begin{Vmatrix} \alpha & \beta \\ \gamma & \delta \end{Vmatrix} \quad \text{and} \quad -a = \begin{Vmatrix} -\alpha & -\beta \\ -\gamma & -\delta \end{Vmatrix}$$

correspond to one and the same Lorentz transformation.

We shall prove that this is the only ambiguity which can occur with the spinor description of a given Lorentz matrix by means of a matrix a. In fact, suppose that the matrices a_1 and a_2 correspond to one and the same Lorentz matrix g. Then, by virtue of I, the matrix $a = a_1 a_2^{-1}$ corresponds to the Lorentz unit matrix $g = e$. But then it follows from formula (11) that the elements $\alpha, \beta, \gamma, \delta$ of the matrix a must satisfy the conditions:

$$\alpha\bar{\delta}+\beta\bar{\gamma} = 1, \quad \alpha\bar{\delta}-\beta\bar{\gamma} = 1, \quad \alpha\bar{\alpha}-\beta\bar{\beta}-\gamma\bar{\gamma}+\delta\bar{\delta} = 2,$$
$$\alpha\bar{\alpha}+\beta\bar{\beta}+\gamma\bar{\gamma}+\delta\bar{\delta} = 2,$$

from which (taking into account the relation $\alpha\delta-\beta\gamma = 1$) it necessarily follows that

$$a = \begin{Vmatrix} 1 & 0 \\ 0 & 1 \end{Vmatrix}, \quad \text{on} \quad a = \begin{Vmatrix} -1 & 0 \\ 0 & -1 \end{Vmatrix}.$$

In the first case $a_1 = a_2$, in the second $a_1 = -a_2$.

Let us now suppose that the matrix a is unitary; this means that

$$\alpha\bar{\alpha}+\beta\bar{\beta} = 1, \quad \gamma\bar{\gamma}+\delta\bar{\delta} = 1, \quad \alpha\bar{\gamma}+\beta\bar{\delta} = 0;$$

hence, and from the relation $\alpha\delta-\beta\gamma = 1$, it follows (see § 1, Subsection 5) that

$$\delta = \bar{\alpha}, \quad \gamma = -\bar{\beta}.$$

Substituting in formula (11) we find that, in the case of a unitary matrix a,

$$\| g_{ik} \| = \begin{Vmatrix} \mathrm{Re}(\alpha^2-\beta^2) & -\mathrm{Im}(\alpha^2+\beta^2) & -2\mathrm{Re}(\alpha\beta) & 0 \\ \mathrm{Im}(\alpha^2-\beta^2) & \mathrm{Re}(\alpha^2+\beta^2) & -2\mathrm{Im}(\alpha\beta) & 0 \\ 2\mathrm{Re}(\alpha\bar{\beta}) & -2\mathrm{Im}(\alpha\bar{\beta}) & \alpha\bar{\alpha}-\beta\bar{\beta} & 0 \\ 0 & 0 & 0 & 1 \end{Vmatrix}, \quad (12)$$

i.e. *to unitary matrices a correspond transformations $g \in G_0$*. Consequently, in the spinor mapping, the elements of the unitary group $\mathfrak{U}$ correspond to the elements of the group G_0; formula (12), expressing this correspondence, is identical with the formula expressing a three-dimensional rotation matrix by means of the coefficients of a bilinear substitution

$$\zeta' = \frac{\alpha\zeta+\beta}{\gamma\zeta+\delta}$$

(see formula (14) § 1, Subsection 5). As was proved in § 1, Subsection 5, *under this correspondence* $u \to g$ *the whole group* G_0 *is obtained*; in other words, *every matrix* $g \in G_0$ *may be represented according to formula* (12) *by means of a unitary matrix* $u = \begin{Vmatrix} \alpha & \beta \\ \gamma & \delta \end{Vmatrix} \in \mathfrak{U}$, *there being exactly two matrices*, $u = \begin{Vmatrix} \alpha & \beta \\ \gamma & \delta \end{Vmatrix}$ *and* $-u = \begin{Vmatrix} -\alpha & -\beta \\ -\gamma & -\delta \end{Vmatrix}$, *representing a given matrix* $g \in G_0$.

We make use of this result in order to prove the following proposition.

II. *Every proper Lorentz matrix* g *may be represented by means of a matrix* $a \in \mathfrak{A}$ *according to formula* (11). *This representation is two-valued, and the two matrices of* $\mathfrak{A}$, *representing one and the same matrix* g, *have the form*

$$a = \begin{Vmatrix} \alpha & \beta \\ \gamma & \delta \end{Vmatrix}, \quad -a = \begin{Vmatrix} -\alpha & -\beta \\ -\gamma & -\delta \end{Vmatrix}. \tag{13}$$

Proof. In accordance with proposition III of § 7, Subsection 1, every matrix $g \in \mathfrak{G}_+$ can be represented in the form $g = ub_1(t)v$, where $u, v \in G_0$ and

$$b_1(t) = \begin{Vmatrix} \cosh t & 0 & 0 & \sinh t \\ 0 & 1 & 0 & 0 \\ 0 & 0 & 1 & 0 \\ \sinh t & 0 & 0 & \cosh t \end{Vmatrix}. \tag{14}$$

By virtue of this the unitary matrices u and v admit representations in the form (12), and therefore in the form (11). Applying I, we see that it is sufficient to prove the assertion for the matrix $b_1(t)$. But, if we put

$$a = \begin{Vmatrix} \cosh\frac{t}{2} & \sinh\frac{t}{2} \\ \sinh\frac{t}{2} & \cosh\frac{t}{2} \end{Vmatrix},$$

then, applying formula (11), it is easy to verify that the corresponding matrix g coincides with $b_1(t)$.

Proposition II, which we have just proved, means that the spinor mapping $a \to g$ is a two-fold mapping of the group $\mathfrak{A}$ on the whole group $\mathfrak{G}_+$.

2. The relation between the representations of the groups $\mathfrak{G}_+$ and $\mathfrak{A}$

Now, let a representation $g \to T_g$ of the group $\mathfrak{G}_+$ be given. We shall define a representation $a \to T_a$ of the group $\mathfrak{A}$ by putting $T_a = T_g$, if a goes into g under the spinor mapping. Since $-a$ also goes into g under the spinor mapping, then, necessarily, $T_{-a} = T_a$. Conversely, let a representation $a \to T_a$ of the group $\mathfrak{A}$ be given, satisfying the condition $T_{-a} = T_a$; we put $T_g = T_a$ if a goes into g under the spinor mapping. We then get a representation $g \to T_g$ of the group $\mathfrak{G}_+$. Thus, *the description of the representations of the group $\mathfrak{G}_+$ amounts to the same thing as the description of the representations of the group $\mathfrak{A}$, satisfying the condition $T_a = T_{-a}$*. Therefore, in what follows we shall consider the representations $a \to T_a$ of the group $\mathfrak{A}$. It turns out that it is relevant to consider an arbitrary representation of the group $\mathfrak{A}$, not necessarily satisfying the condition $T_a = T_{-a}$; if this condition is satisfied, then the corresponding representation $g \to T_g$ will be single-valued, and if it is not satisfied, then this representation will be two-valued.

3. The spinor representations of the group $\mathfrak{A}$

We proceed to a description of the irreducible finite-dimensional representations of the group $\mathfrak{A}$. We shall construct a certain class of finite-dimensional representations of the group $\mathfrak{A}$ analogous to the spinor representations of the group $\mathfrak{U}$ (see Section 5); this class, as we shall see below, contains all the irreducible finite-dimensional representations of this group. The class is constructed in the following way.

We denote by $R_{m,n}$ the aggregate of all polynomials $p(z, \bar{z})$ in the complex variables z and $\bar{z}$, of degree $\leqslant m$ in z, and of degree $\leqslant n$ in $\bar{z}$; here m and n are two fixed non-negative integers, determining the given representation. Evidently, $R_{m,n}$ becomes a linear vector space, if the operations of addition and multiplication by a number are defined in the natural way as the addition of polynomials and their multiplication by a number.

Now let

$$a = \begin{Vmatrix} \alpha & \beta \\ \gamma & \delta \end{Vmatrix}$$

be a matrix in $\mathfrak{A}$ and $p(z, \bar{z}) \in R_{m,n}$; consider the expression

$$(\beta z+\delta)^m \overline{(\beta z+\delta)}^n p\left(\frac{\alpha z+\gamma}{\beta z+\delta}, \frac{\bar{\alpha}\bar{z}+\bar{\gamma}}{\bar{\beta}\bar{z}+\bar{\delta}}\right). \tag{1}$$

Here, evidently, the denominators cancel out and, after their cancellation, a polynomial is obtained which also belongs to $R_{m,n}$. We define an operator T_a in $R_{m,n}$ by putting

$$T_a p(z, \bar{z}) = (\beta z+\delta)^m \overline{(\beta z+\delta)}^n p\left(\frac{\alpha z+\gamma}{\beta z+\delta}, \frac{\bar{\alpha}\bar{z}+\bar{\gamma}}{\bar{\beta}\bar{z}+\bar{\delta}}\right); \tag{2}$$

evidently, T_a is a linear operator; it can be directly verified that $T_{a_1} T_{a_2} = T_{a_1 a_2}$. Consequently, the correspondence $a \to T_a$ is a linear representation of the group $\mathfrak{A}$. We shall call this representation a *spinor representation of the group* $\mathfrak{A}$ (and thus also of the group $\mathfrak{G}_+$) and shall denote it by $S_{m,n}$. The dimension of the representation $S_{m,n}$, i.e. the dimension of the space $R_{m,n}$, is equal to the number of different products

$$z^p \bar{z}^q, \quad 0 \leqslant p \leqslant m, \quad 0 \leqslant q \leqslant n, \tag{3}$$

i.e. is equal to $(m+1)(n+1)$.

The spinor representation $S_{m,n}$ can also be defined in a some what different form; this is obtained in the following manner.

We consider all possible systems of numbers $a^{i_1 \dots i_m j_1 \dots j_n}$, symmetrical both in the indices $i_1, i_2, \dots i_m$, and in the indices $j_1, j_2, \dots, j_n$, each of which takes two values: 0 and 1; the aggregate of all such systems† forms a space of dimension $(m+1)(n+1)$,

† Every such system corresponds to a spinor $a^{i_1 \dots i_m j_1 \dots j_n}$ which is symmetrical in the indices $i_1, \dots, i_m$ and $j_1, \dots, j_n$; this explains the term "spinor representation" (see § 5, Subsection 2; it is convenient here not to denote the indices by 1 and 2, as in § 5, Subsection 2, but by 0 and 1).

which we denote by $\tilde{R}_{m,n}$. With each system $a^{i_1 i_2 \dots i_m j_1 j_2 \dots j_n}$ in $\tilde{R}_{m,n}$ we place in correspondence the polynomial

$$p(z,\bar{z}) = \sum_{i_1 i_2 \dots i_m, j_1 j_2 \dots j_n} a^{i_1 i_2 \dots i_m j_1 j_2 \dots j_n} z^{i_1+i_2+\dots+i_m} \bar{z}^{j_1+j_2+\dots+j_n}; \tag{4}$$

the degree of this polynomial in z does not exceed m, and that in $\bar{z}$ does not exceed n, and therefore $p(z,\bar{z}) \in R_{m,n}$. Consequently, this correspondence is a linear mapping of $\tilde{R}_{m,n}$ onto $R_{m,n}$. On the other hand, every polynomial

$$p(z,\bar{z}) = \sum_{p,q} a_{pq} z^p \bar{z}^q \tag{5}$$

in $R_{m,n}$ can be written in the form (4), for which purpose it is sufficient to put

$$a^{i_1 i_2 \dots i_m, j_1 \dots j_n} = \frac{1}{m!n!} a_{pq}$$

$$\text{for} \quad i_1+i_2+\dots+i_m = p, \quad j_1+j_2+\dots+j_n = q; \tag{6}$$

therefore our mapping is a one-to-one linear mapping of the space $\tilde{R}_{m,n}$ onto the whole space $R_{m,n}$. By virtue of this mapping, the operator T_a may also be regarded as an operator in $\tilde{R}_{m,n}$. We shall find an explicit expression for the operator T_a in $\tilde{R}_{m,n}$; and this expression will also define the second form of the spinor representation $S_{m,n}$. Here it is convenient to change the notation and to put

$$\alpha = a_{11}, \quad \beta = a_{10}, \quad \gamma = a_{01}, \quad \delta = a_{00}. \tag{7}$$

Applying the operator T_a to the polynomial $p(z,\bar{z})$ as given by (4), we obtain

$$T_a p(z,\bar{z}) = (a_{10}z+a_{00})^m(\bar{a}_{10}\bar{z}+\bar{a}_{00})^n \sum_{i_1 i_2 \dots i_m j_1 j_2 \dots j_n} \times$$

$$\times a^{i_1 i_2 \dots i_m j_1 \dots j_n} \left(\frac{a_{11}z+a_{01}}{a_{10}z+a_{00}}\right)^{i_1+i_2+\dots+i_m} \left(\frac{\bar{a}_{11}\bar{z}+\bar{a}_{01}}{\bar{a}_{10}\bar{z}+\bar{a}_{00}}\right)^{j_1+j_2+\dots+j_n}$$

$$= \sum_{i_1 i_2 \dots i_m, j_1 \dots j_n} a^{i_1 \dots i_m j_1 \dots j_n} (a_{1i_1}z+a_{0i_1}) \dots$$

$$\dots (a_{1i_m}z+a_{0i_m})(\bar{a}_{1j_1}\bar{z}+\bar{a}_{0j_1}) \dots (\bar{a}_{1j_n}\bar{z}+\bar{a}_{0j_n}). \tag{8}$$

Consequently, putting

$$T_a p(z, \bar{z}) = \sum_{i_1 \dots i_m j_1 \dots j_n} a'^{i_1 \dots i_m j_1 \dots j_n} z^{i_1 + \dots + i_m} \bar{z}^{j_1 + \dots + j_n}; \tag{9}$$

and comparing with (8), we see that

$$a'^{i_1 \dots i_m j_1 \dots j_n}$$

$$= \sum_{i'_1 \dots i'_m, j'_1 \dots j'_n} a^{i'_1 \dots i'_m j'_1 \dots j'_n} a_{i_1 i'_1} \dots a_{i_m i'_m} \bar{a}_{j_1 j'_1} \dots \bar{a}_{j_n j'_n}. \tag{10}$$

Thus, *the operator* T_a *of a spinor representation* $a \to T_a$ *in the space* $\tilde{R}_{m,n}$ *is a linear transformation, determined by formula* (10).

In theoretical physics the indices $i_1, \dots, i_m$ of the spinor $a^{i_1 \dots i_m j_1 \dots j_n}$ are called *undotted* and the indices $j_1, \dots, j_n$ *dotted*, so that m is the number of undotted and n the number of dotted indices of the spinors corresponding to the vectors of a given spinor representation.

4. The infinitesimal operators of a spinor representation

We shall find the infinitesimal operators H_+, H_-, H_3 and F_+, F_-, F_3 of the spinor representation $S_{m,n}$. For this purpose we shall first find the one-parameter subgroups of $\mathfrak{A}$, corresponding to the one-parameter subgroups $a_1(t), a_2(t), a_3(t)$ and $b_1(t)$, $b_2(t), b_3(t)$ in $\mathfrak{G}_+$. Applying formula (11) of Subsection 1, it is easy to verify that for these one-parameter groups,

$$\tilde{a}_1(t) = \begin{Vmatrix} \cos\frac{t}{2} & i\sin\frac{t}{2} \\ i\sin\frac{t}{2} & \cos\frac{t}{2} \end{Vmatrix}, \quad \tilde{a}_2(t) = \begin{Vmatrix} \cos\frac{t}{2} & -\sin\frac{t}{2} \\ \sin\frac{t}{2} & \cos\frac{t}{2} \end{Vmatrix},$$

$$\tilde{a}_3(t) = \begin{Vmatrix} e^{\frac{it}{2}} & 0 \\ 0 & e^{-\frac{it}{2}} \end{Vmatrix}; \tag{1}$$

$$\tilde{b}_1(t) = \begin{Vmatrix} \cosh\frac{t}{2} & \sinh\frac{t}{2} \\ \sinh\frac{t}{2} & \cosh\frac{t}{2} \end{Vmatrix}, \quad \tilde{b}_2(t) = \begin{Vmatrix} \cosh\frac{t}{2} & i\sinh\frac{t}{2} \\ -i\sinh\frac{t}{2} & \cosh\frac{t}{2} \end{Vmatrix},$$

$$\tilde{b}_3(t) = \begin{Vmatrix} e^{\frac{t}{2}} & 0 \\ 0 & e^{-\frac{t}{2}} \end{Vmatrix}; \tag{2}$$

(see also (1) § 5, Subsection 4). Hence, by virtue of (2) Subsection 3,

$$A_1(t)p(z,\bar{z}) = \left(i\sin\frac{t}{2}z+\cos\frac{t}{2}\right)^m \times$$

$$\times\left(-i\sin\frac{t}{2}\bar{z}+\cos\frac{t}{2}\right)^n p\left(\frac{\cos\frac{t}{2}z+i\sin\frac{t}{2}}{i\sin\frac{t}{2}z+\cos\frac{t}{2}}, \frac{\cos\frac{t}{2}\bar{z}-i\sin\frac{t}{2}}{-i\sin\frac{t}{2}\bar{z}+\cos\frac{t}{2}}\right),$$

$$A_2(t)p(z,\bar{z}) = \left(-\sin\frac{t}{2}z+\cos\frac{t}{2}\right)^m \times$$

$$\times\left(-\sin\frac{t}{2}\bar{z}+\cos\frac{t}{2}\right)^n p\left(\frac{\cos\frac{t}{2}z+\sin\frac{t}{2}}{-\sin\frac{t}{2}z+\cos\frac{t}{2}}, \frac{\cos\frac{t}{2}\bar{z}+\sin\frac{t}{2}}{-\sin\frac{t}{2}\bar{z}+\cos\frac{t}{2}}\right),$$

$$A_3(t)p(z,\bar{z}) = e^{-\frac{imt}{2}}e^{\frac{int}{2}}p(e^{it}z, e^{-it}\bar{z}),$$

$$B_1(t)p(z,\bar{z}) = \left(\sinh\frac{t}{2}z+\cosh\frac{t}{2}\right)^m \times$$

$$\times\left(\sinh\frac{t}{2}\bar{z}+\cosh\frac{t}{2}\right)^n p\left(\frac{\cosh\frac{t}{2}z+\sinh\frac{t}{2}}{\sinh\frac{t}{2}z+\cosh\frac{t}{2}}, \frac{\cosh\frac{t}{2}\bar{z}+\sinh\frac{t}{2}}{\sinh\frac{t}{2}\bar{z}+\cosh\frac{t}{2}}\right),$$

$$B_2(t)\,p(z,\bar{z}) = \left(i\sinh\frac{t}{2}z+\cosh\frac{t}{2}\right)^m \times$$

$$\times\left(-i\sinh\frac{t}{2}\bar{z}+\cosh\frac{t}{2}\right)^n p\left(\frac{\cosh\frac{t}{2}z-i\sinh\frac{t}{2}}{i\sinh\frac{t}{2}z+\cosh\frac{t}{2}},\ \frac{\cosh\frac{t}{2}\bar{z}+i\sinh\frac{t}{2}}{-i\sinh\frac{t}{2}\bar{z}+\cosh\frac{t}{2}}\right),$$

$$B_3(t)\,p(z,\bar{z}) = e^{-\frac{mt}{2}}e^{-\frac{nt}{2}}p(e^t z, e^t\bar{z}).$$

Differentiating both sides of these equations with respect to t, and putting $t = 0$, we obtain

$$A_1 p = \frac{i}{2}(1-z^2)\frac{\partial p}{\partial z} - \frac{i}{2}(1-\bar{z}^2)\frac{\partial p}{\partial \bar{z}} + \frac{i}{2}(mz-n\bar{z})p, \qquad (3)$$

$$A_2 p = \frac{1}{2}(1+z^2)\frac{\partial p}{\partial z} + \frac{1}{2}(1+\bar{z}^2)\frac{\partial p}{\partial \bar{z}} - \frac{1}{2}(mz+n\bar{z})p, \qquad (4)$$

$$A_3 p = iz\frac{\partial p}{\partial z} - i\bar{z}\frac{\partial p}{\partial \bar{z}} - \frac{i(m-n)}{2}p, \qquad (5)$$

$$B_1 p = \frac{1}{2}(1-z^2)\frac{\partial p}{\partial z} + \frac{1}{2}(1-\bar{z}^2)\frac{\partial p}{\partial \bar{z}} + \frac{1}{2}(mz+n\bar{z})p, \qquad (6)$$

$$B_2 p = -\frac{1}{2}i(1+z^2)\frac{\partial p}{\partial z} + \frac{1}{2}i(1+\bar{z}^2)\frac{\partial p}{\partial \bar{z}} + \frac{1}{2}i(mz-n\bar{z})p, \qquad (7)$$

$$B_3 p = z\frac{\partial p}{\partial z} + \bar{z}\frac{\partial p}{\partial \bar{z}} - \frac{1}{2}(m+n)p. \qquad (8)$$

Making use now of the definition of the operators H_+, H_-, H_3, F_+, F_-, F_3 (see (1–3) § 8, Subsection 1), we conclude that

$$H_+ p = -\frac{\partial p}{\partial z} - \bar{z}^2\frac{\partial p}{\partial \bar{z}} + n\bar{z}p, \qquad (9)$$

$$H_- p = z^2\frac{\partial p}{\partial z} + \frac{\partial p}{\partial \bar{z}} - mzp, \qquad (10)$$

$$H_3 p = -z\frac{\partial p}{\partial z} + \bar{z}\frac{\partial p}{\partial \bar{z}} + \frac{1}{2}(m-n)p, \tag{11}$$

$$F_+ p = i\frac{\partial p}{\partial z} - i\bar{z}^2\frac{\partial p}{\partial \bar{z}} + in\bar{z}p, \tag{12}$$

$$F_- p = -iz^2\frac{\partial p}{\partial z} + i\frac{\partial p}{\partial \bar{z}} + imzp, \tag{13}$$

$$F_3 p = iz\frac{\partial p}{\partial z} + i\bar{z}\frac{\partial p}{\partial \bar{z}} - \frac{1}{2}i(m+n)p. \tag{14}$$

We note that it would have been possible to obtain the formulae for the infinitesimal operators as operators in the spinor space $\tilde{R}_{m,n}$. These formulae may also be obtained from the formulae (9–14) by applying the differential operators $H_+, \ldots, F_3$ to the polynomial $p(z, \bar{z})$, written in the form (4) of Subsection 3. The application of these operators reduces to linear transformations on the coefficients of the polynomial $p(z, \bar{z})$, i.e. to linear transformations in the spinor space $\tilde{R}_{m,n}$.

5. The irreducibility of a spinor representation

THEOREM 4. *The spinor representations of the group $\mathfrak{A}$ are irreducible.*

Proof. We have to prove that a non-zero subspace $\mathfrak{M}$ of $R_{m,n}$, which is invariant with respect to all the operators of the representation, coincides with $R_{m,n}$.

Let $\mathfrak{M}$ be such a subspace; then $\mathfrak{M}$ is also invariant with respect to the operators $H_+, H_-, H_3, F_+, F_-, F_3$. Evidently, it is sufficient to show that $\mathfrak{M}$ contains all the products

$$z^\alpha \bar{z}^\beta, \quad 0 \leqslant \alpha \leqslant m, \quad 0 \leqslant \beta \leqslant n. \tag{1}$$

For this purpose we consider the operators

$$A = F_- + iH_-, \; B = F_+ - iH_+, \; C = F_- - iH_-, \; D = F_+ + iH_+. \tag{2}$$

$\mathfrak{M}$, being invariant with respect to F_-, F_+, H_-, H_+, is also invariant with respect to A, B, C, D; on the other hand, from formulae (9–14) of Subsection 4 it follows that

$$Ap = 2i\frac{\partial p}{\partial \bar{z}}, \qquad Bp = 2i\frac{\partial p}{\partial z}, \tag{3}$$

$$Cp = -2iz^2\frac{\partial p}{\partial z}+2imzp, \; Dp = -2i\bar{z}^2\frac{\partial p}{\partial \bar{z}}+2in\bar{z}p. \tag{4}$$

We shall first prove that $\mathfrak{M}$ contains a constant. Since by hypothesis $\mathfrak{M} \neq (0)$, there is in $\mathfrak{M}$ a polynomial $p \not\equiv 0$; if it is not a constant, then, applying to it several times in succession the operators A and B, we shall obtain polynomials of lower and lower degrees in z and $\bar{z}$, belonging to $\mathfrak{M}$, until we obtain a constant, also belonging to $\mathfrak{M}$. Applying the operator C to this constant, we obtain a monomial of the form az, and applying D, we obtain a monomial of the form $a\bar{z}$, $a \neq 0$. In general, applying to the constant the operator $C^\alpha D^\beta$, we obtain, for $\alpha \leqslant m, \beta \leqslant n$, a monomial of the form $az^\alpha\bar{z}^\beta$, $a \neq 0$, also belonging to $\mathfrak{M}$. For $\alpha = m+1$ or $\beta = n+1$, the result of the application of the operator $C^\alpha D^\beta$ to the constant is zero; it is thus proved that $\mathfrak{M}$ really contains all the products (1), which completes the proof of the theorem.

6. The infinitesimal operators of a spinor representation with respect to a canonical basis

We shall now show that, *for a suitable choice of basis* in $R_{m,n}$, the formulae for the infinitesimal operators of a spinor representation coincide with the formulae (51–55) of § 8, Subsection 3, it being possible, depending on the choice of m and n, to obtain any of the finite-dimensional representations defined by these formulae. Thus we shall give, for finite-dimensional representations, a positive answer to the question put at the end of § 8, Subsection 3.

To prove this assertion we shall show that the spinor representation $S_{m,n}$ of the group $\mathfrak{A}$ contains each irreducible representation of the group $\mathfrak{U}$ at most once. This implies that the reasoning of § 8, Subsection 3, applies to the representation $S_{m,n}$; consequently, the infinitesimal operators of this representation must necessarily be given by the formulae (51–55) of § 8, Subsection 3.

We consider the products

$$z^{\alpha}\bar{z}^{\beta}, \quad 0 \leqslant \alpha \leqslant m, \quad 0 \leqslant \beta \leqslant n; \tag{1}$$

evidently, they form a basis in $R_{m,n}$. Applying the operator H_3 to these products, we have:

$$H_3(z^{\alpha}\bar{z}^{\beta}) = \left[-z\frac{\partial}{\partial z}+\bar{z}\frac{\partial}{\partial \bar{z}}+\frac{1}{2}(m-n)\right](z^{\alpha}\bar{z}^{\beta})$$

$$=\left[\frac{1}{2}(m-n)+\beta-\alpha\right]z^{\alpha}\bar{z}^{\beta}, \tag{2}$$

so that $z^{\alpha}\bar{z}^{\beta}$ is a weight vector of weight $\frac{1}{2}(m-n)+\beta-\alpha$.

Therefore every weight vector of weight ν has the form

$$p = \sum a_{\alpha\beta} z^{\alpha}\bar{z}^{\beta}, \tag{3}$$

where the summation extends only over those indices α, β, for which

$$\tfrac{1}{2}(m-n)+\beta-\alpha = \nu. \tag{4}$$

We denote by S_ν the spinor representation of the group $\mathfrak{U}$ of weight ν, (so that $S_\nu = \mathfrak{S}_{2\nu}$; see § 5, Subsection 2); we shall consider all the irreducible representations S_ν of weight ν, contained in $S_{m,n}$, and we shall find the weight vectors of weight ν corresponding to them. The vectors, besides satisfying conditions (3) and (4), must satisfy the condition $H_{+}p = 0$, i.e., by virtue of (9) Subsection 4,

$$-\frac{\partial p}{\partial z}-\bar{z}^2\frac{\partial p}{\partial \bar{z}}+n\bar{z}p = 0. \tag{5}$$

Substituting in this the expression (3), we obtain:

$$-\sum a_{\alpha\beta}\alpha z^{\alpha-1}\bar{z}^{\beta}+\sum(n-\beta)a_{\alpha\beta}z^{\alpha}\bar{z}^{\beta+1} = 0;$$

hence

$$(n-\beta)a_{\alpha\beta}-(\alpha+1)a_{\alpha+1,\beta+1} = 0. \tag{6}$$

Here we agree to take $a_{\alpha\beta} = 0$, if $\alpha < 0$, or $\beta < 0$, or $\alpha > m$ or $\beta > n$. By virtue of (4), $a_{\alpha\beta}$ and $a_{\alpha+1, \beta+1}$ can differ from zero only if

$$\beta - \alpha = \nu - \tfrac{1}{2}(m-n). \tag{7}$$

Hence it follows that the weight ν must be an integer if $m-n$ is even, and a semi-integer if $m-n$ is odd. Consequently, a representation S_ν of the group $\mathfrak{U}$ can only be contained in $S_{m,n}$ if 2ν and $m-n$ are numbers of the same parity. In what follows we shall assume this condition to be satisfied.

We now put in (6) $\alpha = m, \beta < n$, then as $a_{m+1, \beta+1} = 0$ it follows from (6) that $a_{m,\beta} = 0$; the remaining coefficients corresponding to the same weight ν are expressed by (6) recursively in terms of the $a_{m,\beta}$ and are therefore also zero. Consequently, in this case the system (6) has only the trivial solution.

The corresponding weight ν is obtained from (7) for $\alpha = m$, so that

$$\beta - m = \nu - \tfrac{1}{2}(m-n),$$

from which

$$\nu = \beta - \tfrac{1}{2}(m+n) < n - \tfrac{1}{2}(m+n) = \tfrac{1}{2}(n-m).$$

Consequently, the system (6) can have a non-trivial solution only for

$$\nu \geqslant \tfrac{1}{2}(n-m). \tag{8}$$

Similarly, putting in (6) $\beta = -1$, $\alpha > -1$, we establish that the system (6) can have a non-trivial solution only for

$$\nu \geqslant \tfrac{1}{2}(m-n). \tag{9}$$

Combining (8) and (9), we see that the system (6) can have a non-trivial solution only for

$$\nu \geqslant \tfrac{1}{2}|m-n|. \tag{10}$$

Suppose now that the condition (10) is satisfied; the above reasoning shows that in this case each of the equations (6) will contain two unknown coefficients $a_{\alpha,\beta}$, differing from zero. Evidently, from equations (6), all the coefficients can be expressed by means of one of them, so that the system (6) has only one solution, to within a constant factor. This means that in $R_{m,n}$ there is, except for a numerical factor, only *one vector of leading weight* of the representation S_ν; that is, this representation occurs precisely once in the representation $S_{m,n}$. This shows that, in some basis, the infinitesimal operators of the representation $S_{m,n}$ must be given by the formulae (51–55) of § 8, Subsection 3.

We shall now find the connection between the parameters k_0, k_1 in these formulae and the numbers m, n.

For this purpose we note that k_1 is the highest of the weights k of the operator H_3; on the other hand, it follows from (2) that the product $z^\alpha \bar{z}^\beta$ is the vector of the highest weight for $\beta = n$, $\alpha = 0$. Consequently, this highest weight is $\frac{1}{2}(m+n)$. Thus

$$k_1 = \tfrac{1}{2}(m+n). \tag{11}$$

Further, k_0 is the lowest of the weights of the representation S_k, contained in $S_{m,n}$; but, as we saw above, the lowest weight is $\frac{1}{2}(m-n)$; consequently,

$$k_0 = \tfrac{1}{2}|m-n|. \tag{12}$$

We shall find still another expression for the parameter c. For this purpose we apply the operator F_3 to the vector of highest weight $f_{k_1}^{k_1} = \lambda \bar{z}^n$. From the formula (14), Subsection 4, we conclude that

$$F_3 f_{k_1}^{k_1} = i\frac{n-m}{2}\lambda \bar{z}^n = i\frac{n-m}{2} f_{k_1}^{k_1}.$$

On the other hand, formulae (54) and (55) § 8, Subsection 3, yield

$$F_3 f_{k_1}^{k_1} = -k_1 A_{k_1} f_{k_1}^{k_1} = -i\frac{k_0 c}{k_1+1} f_{k_1}^{k_1}.$$

Comparing these expressions, we see that

$$\frac{k_0 c}{k_1+1} = \frac{m-n}{2} = k_0 \operatorname{sign}(m-n);$$

consequently, for $m \neq n$, we have

$$c = \operatorname{sign}(m-n)(k_1+1) = \operatorname{sign}(m-n)[\tfrac{1}{2}(m+n)+1]. \tag{13}$$

If $m = n$ then, in formulae (52–55), § 8, Subsection 3, $A_k = 0$, and so the choice of sign of the parameter c is immaterial; consequently,

$$c = \pm[\tfrac{1}{2}(m+n)+1] \quad \text{for} \quad m = n. \tag{14}$$

Evidently, by choice of the numbers m and n, any two integers or semi-integers k_0 and c may be obtained, satisfying the condition $0 \leqslant k_0 < |c|$. Consequently, for any pair of integers or semi-integers $k_0, c, 0 \leqslant k_0 \leqslant |c|-1$, the formulae (51–55) § 8, Subsection 3, determine a finite-dimensional representation, in fact a spinor representation, of the group $\mathfrak{A}$ (which means also of $\mathfrak{G}_+$).

Hence, we conclude that *every finite-dimensional irreducible representation of the group $\mathfrak{A}$ is equivalent to some spinor representation of it, so that the spinor representations exhaust essentially all the finite-dimensional irreducible representations of the group $\mathfrak{A}$.* However, in the proof of this result, use was made of the assumption that the representations under consideration satisfy conditions **A**, **B**, **C**, of § 7, Subsection 3. We shall give another proof below (see § 15, Subsection 6) not depending upon any supplementary assumptions.

The simplest example of a spinor representation is given by $m = n = 0$. The space $R_{m,n}$ is in this case a one-dimensional space consisting of the constants. The formulae (2) Subsection 3, and (9) to (14) Subsection 4 show that, in this case, all the operators T_a are equal to the unit operator, and all the infinitesimal operators of the representation are equal to zero. This representation is called the *unit representation.*

Another simple example is obtained for $m = 1, n = 0$. The space $R_{m,n}$ is two-dimensional and consists of all linear functions a^0z+a^1. In this case formula (10) Subsection 3 takes the form

$$a'^i = \sum_{j=0}^{1} a_{ij}a^j, \quad i = 0, 1.$$

Consequently, the matrix of the operator T_a (for a suitable choice of basis) coincides with the matrix a and the representation $a \to T_a$ is the *identity* representation $a \to a$ (consequently, the spinor description $g \to a$ of the group $(\mathfrak{S}_+)$. By virtue of the formulae (12) and (13), the corresponding values of the parameters k_0 and c will be

$$k_0 = \tfrac{1}{2}, \quad c = \tfrac{3}{2}.$$

§ 10. Principal Series of Representations of the Group $\mathfrak{A}$†

We turn to the consideration of an important class of infinite dimensional representations of the group $\mathfrak{A}$, the so-called *principal series* of representations.

The purpose of this section is the construction of the principal series of representations; two subgroups of the group $\mathfrak{A}$ will play an essential part in this.

1. Some subgroups of the group $\mathfrak{A}$

(a) *The subgroup K.* Let us denote by K the set of all matrices of the form

$$k = \begin{Vmatrix} \lambda^{-1} & \mu \\ 0 & \lambda \end{Vmatrix}, \quad \lambda \neq 0. \tag{1}$$

From the relation

$$kk' = \begin{Vmatrix} \lambda^{-1} & \mu \\ 0 & \lambda \end{Vmatrix} \begin{Vmatrix} \lambda'^{-1} & \mu' \\ 0 & \lambda' \end{Vmatrix} = \begin{Vmatrix} \lambda^{-1}\lambda'^{-1} & \lambda^{-1}\mu' + \mu\lambda' \\ 0 & \lambda\lambda' \end{Vmatrix} \tag{2}$$

it follows that kk' is a matrix of this form; hence K is a subgroup of the group $\mathfrak{A}$.

(b) *The subgroup Z.* Let us denote by Z the set of all matrices z of the form‡

$$z = \begin{Vmatrix} 1 & 0 \\ z & 1 \end{Vmatrix}. \tag{3}$$

From the relation

$$zz' = \begin{Vmatrix} 1 & 0 \\ z & 1 \end{Vmatrix} \begin{Vmatrix} 1 & 0 \\ z' & 1 \end{Vmatrix} = \begin{Vmatrix} 1 & 0 \\ z+z' & 1 \end{Vmatrix} \tag{4}$$

---

† Publisher's note: §§ 10-end were translated by Ann Swinfen.

‡ We use one and the same letter z to denote the matrix z and its element at the intersection of the second row and first column; in what follows this never leads to misunderstanding.

if follows that zz' is a matrix of this form, so that Z is a subgroup of the group $\mathfrak{A}$.

2. Canonical decomposition of the elements of the group $\mathfrak{A}$

LEMMA. *Every element $a \in \mathfrak{A}$, satisfying the condition $a_{22} \neq 0$, may be represented uniquely in the form*

$$a = kz, \quad k \in K, \quad z \in Z. \tag{1}$$

Proof. Equation (1) means that

$$\begin{Vmatrix} a_{11} & a_{12} \\ a_{21} & a_{22} \end{Vmatrix} = \begin{Vmatrix} \lambda^{-1} & \mu \\ 0 & \lambda \end{Vmatrix} \begin{Vmatrix} 1 & 0 \\ z & 1 \end{Vmatrix} = \begin{Vmatrix} \lambda^{-1}+\mu z & \mu \\ \lambda z & \lambda \end{Vmatrix}, \tag{2}$$

i.e. that

$$\lambda = a_{22}, \quad \lambda z = a_{21}, \quad \mu = a_{12}, \quad \lambda^{-1}+\mu z = a_{11}. \tag{3}$$

The first three equations give

$$\lambda = a_{22}, \quad z = \frac{a_{21}}{a_{22}}, \quad \mu = a_{12}, \tag{4}$$

so that k and z are determined by equation (1) in a unique way. Conversely, if one chooses k and z according to formula (4), then the equation $\lambda^{-1}+\mu z = a_{11}$ in (3) will be satisfied automatically, since $a_{11}a_{22}-a_{12}a_{21} = 1$, and so

$$\lambda^{-1}+\mu z = \frac{1}{a_{22}}+a_{12}\frac{a_{21}}{a_{22}} = \frac{1+a_{12}a_{21}}{a_{22}} = \frac{a_{11}a_{22}}{a_{22}} = a_{11}.$$

Therefore all the equations in (3) will be satisfied, i.e. (1) will hold.

3. Residue classes with respect to K

Let G be any group, H a subgroup of G. A *right residue class of the group G with respect to the subgroup H* is any set Hg, i.e. the set of all products hg, in which the element g is fixed, and h goes through the whole group H; analogously, *a left residue class of the group G with respect to the subgroup H* is any set gH. In what follows we will consider only right residue classes.

Two residue classes Hg_1, Hg_2 are either non-intersecting or coincident. In fact, if $g \in Hg_1$ and $g \in Hg_2$, then $g = h_1 g_1 = h_2 g_2$. Hence, $g_1 = h_1^{-1} h_2 g_2$, $g_2 = h_2^{-1} h_1 g_1$, and so $Hg_1 = Hh_1^{-1} h_2 g_2 \subset Hg_2$, $Hg_2 = Hh_2^{-1} h_1 g_1 \subset Hg_1$; consequently, $Hg_1 = Hg_2$.

Thus every group G is decomposed into right residue classes, and every such class is completely defined by any of its elements; every element of a residue class is called a *representative* of that class. The set of all right residue classes of the group G with respect to the subgroup H is called *the space of residue classes of G with* respect to H; thus the "points" of the space of residue classes are the residue classes, each being considered as one element.

These concepts can be clarified in the following way. For example, let G be the group of transformations of a certain space X. The set H of all transformations $g \in G$, leaving invariant a fixed point $x_0 \in X$, is, as it is easy to see a subgroup of the group G, and the set of all transformations $g \in G$, carrying the point $x_0 \in X$ into a point $x_1 \in X$, is a right residue class of the group G with respect to the subgroup H, and the correspondence between the points $x \in X$ and the residue classes, thus established, is one-one. Therefore it is possible to replace the space X by the space of residue classes, and the points $x \in X$ are then residue classes.

Now let $G = \mathfrak{A}$, $H = K$. Let us denote by $\tilde{Z}$ the space of right residue classes of the group $\mathfrak{A}$ with respect to the subgroup K. Any such class (say $\tilde{z}$) is a set of all matrices ka, where a is fixed and k varies through the entire group K; the matrices ka are called the *representatives* of the class $\tilde{z}$.

By multiplication on the right of all representatives of the class $\tilde{z}$ by one and the same element a_0 of the group $\mathfrak{A}$ we obtain a new class, consisting of all elements kaa_0, $k \in K$; this new class we denote by $\tilde{z}\bar{a}_0$. The transition from $\tilde{z}$ to $\tilde{z}\bar{a}_0$ is a transformation in the space $\tilde{Z}$, so that the group $\mathfrak{A}$ generates a group of transformations in $\tilde{Z}$.

In what follows the representations of the principal series will be realized in the form of operators in the space of functions $f(\tilde{z})$ of classes $\tilde{z} \in \tilde{Z}$.

4. Parametrization of the space $\tilde{Z}$

We will call the class $\tilde{z}$ *non-singular* if its representatives a satisfy the condition $a_{22} \neq 0$, and *singular* in the contrary case. By multiplying on the right by the matrix

$$k = \begin{Vmatrix} \lambda^{-1} & \mu \\ 0 & \lambda \end{Vmatrix}$$

a_{22} is multiplied by λ; therefore, if one representative of the class satisfies the condition $a_{22} \neq 0$, then all remaining representatives satisfy it.

In $\tilde{Z}$ *there is exactly one singular class.* In fact, if $a_{22} = 0$, then from the condition $\det a = 1$ it follows that $a_{12}a_{21} = -1$. Therefore the equation

$$\begin{Vmatrix} a_{11} & a_{12} \\ a_{21} & 0 \end{Vmatrix} = \begin{Vmatrix} a_{21}^{-1} & a_{11} \\ 0 & a_{21} \end{Vmatrix} \begin{Vmatrix} 0 & -1 \\ 1 & 0 \end{Vmatrix},$$

holds, from which it follows that any singular class must contain the representative $\begin{Vmatrix} 0 & -1 \\ 1 & 0 \end{Vmatrix}$; hence, all singular classes coincide.

I. *Every non-singular class $\tilde{z}$ contains as a representative exactly one element z of the group Z.*

Proof. Let $\tilde{z}$ be a non-singular class and $a \in \tilde{z}$; then $a_{22} \neq 0$. By the fundamental lemma of Subsection 2, $a = kz$, $k \in K$, $z \in Z$; hence $z \in \tilde{z}$, i.e. z is a representative of the class $\tilde{z}$, belonging to Z. If also $z_1 \in \tilde{z}$, then $z_1 = k_0 z$; by virtue of the uniqueness of the canonical decomposition (see lemma of Subsection 2), this is possible only when $z_1 = z$, $k_0 = e$.

In the following we will not distinguish between a non-singular class $\tilde{z}$ and the matrix $z = \begin{Vmatrix} 1 & 0 \\ z & 1 \end{Vmatrix}$ contained in it; therefore it is possible to regard the corresponding parameter z as defining the class. For this purpose it is natural to make the singular class correspond to the point at infinity of the complex z-plane.

The transformation $\tilde{z} \to \tilde{z}\bar{a}$ can then be regarded as a transformation $z \to z\bar{a}$ of the parameter z.

II. *The transformation* $z' = z\bar{a}$ *is given by the formula*

$$z' = \frac{a_{11}z + a_{21}}{a_{12}z + a_{22}}. \tag{1}$$

Proof. We put $a' = za$. The equation $z' = z\bar{a}$ means that the matrix z' is contained in the class $\tilde{z}\bar{a}$. On the other hand, the matrix $a' = za$ is contained in this class; hence $a' = kz'$. Applying formulae (4) Subsection 2 to this equation, we conclude that

$$z' = \frac{a'_{21}}{a'_{22}}. \tag{2}$$

Calculating the product za:

$$a' = za = \begin{Vmatrix} 1 & 0 \\ z & 1 \end{Vmatrix} \begin{Vmatrix} a_{11} & a_{12} \\ a_{21} & a_{22} \end{Vmatrix} = \begin{Vmatrix} a_{11} & a_{12} \\ a_{11}z + a_{21} & a_{12}z + a_{22} \end{Vmatrix},$$

we find:

$$a'_{21} = a_{11}z + a_{21}, \quad a'_{22} = a_{12}z + a_{22}. \tag{3}$$

Substituting these expressions in (2), we obtain (1).

5. Invariant integral on the group Z

We introduce a measure dz (or, what is the same thing, an invariant integral) in the group Z, by writing

$$dz = dx\,dy \quad \text{where} \quad z = x + iy. \tag{1}$$

The measure dz *is invariant under any group displacement* $z \to zz_0$, i.e.

$$\int f(zz_0)dz = \int f(z)dz. \tag{2}$$

In fact, it is possible to regard the function $f(z)$ as a function of x, y, letting $f(z) = f(x, y)$ where $z = x + iy$. In this case, we have by definition (1) of the measure dz:

$$\int f(z)dz = \int_{-\infty}^{\infty}\int_{-\infty}^{\infty} f(x, y)dx\,dy. \tag{3}$$

On the other hand, formula (4) of Subsection 1 shows that the displacement $z \to zz_0$ carries the parameters x and y into $x + x_0$,

$y+y_0$; hence,

$$\int f(zz_0)\mathrm{d}z = \int_{-\infty}^{\infty}\int_{-\infty}^{\infty} f(x+x_0, y+y_0)\mathrm{d}x\,\mathrm{d}y$$

$$= \int_{-\infty}^{\infty}\int_{-\infty}^{\infty} f(x, y)\mathrm{d}x\,\mathrm{d}y = \int f(z)\mathrm{d}z.$$

I. *In the transformation* $z' \to z\bar{a}$ *the measure* $\mathrm{d}z$ *is transformed according to the formula*

$$\mathrm{d}z' = |a_{12}z+a_{22}|^{-4}\mathrm{d}z. \tag{4}$$

Proof. The transformation $z' \to z\bar{a}$ corresponds to a certain transformation of the variables x, y, the Jacobian of which is equal to the square of the modulus† of the derivative $\mathrm{d}z'/\mathrm{d}z$. But from (1) Subsection 4 it follows that $\mathrm{d}z'/\mathrm{d}z = (a_{12}z+a_{22})^{-2}$, so that this Jacobian is equal to $|a_{12}z+a_{22}|^{-4}$. Hence (4) follows.

It is possible to give a group theoretical meaning to formula (4) in the following way. Let us introduce into the group $\mathfrak{A}$ the function $\beta(a)$, by

$$\beta(a) = |a_{22}|^4. \tag{5}$$

II. *The function* $\beta(a)$ *satisfies the relation*

$$\beta(ka) = \beta(k)\beta(a). \tag{6}$$

In fact, in multiplying on the left by $k = \begin{Vmatrix} \lambda^{-1} & \mu \\ 0 & \lambda \end{Vmatrix}$ the element a_{22} goes into λa_{22}, and therefore $\beta(ka) = |\lambda a_{22}|^4 = |\lambda|^4 |a_{22}|^4 = \beta(k)\,\beta(a)$.

In addition, it is evident that

$$\beta(z) = 1. \tag{7}$$

Now letting $a' = za$ and applying formulae (3) of Subsection 4, we see that $\beta(za) = |a_{12}z+a_{22}|^4$. Therefore, one can write formula (4) in the form

$$\mathrm{d}z' = \beta^{-1}(za)\mathrm{d}z. \tag{8}$$

† See Appendix I.

6. The definition of the representations of the principal series

We denote by $L_2(Z)$ the Hilbert space of all measurable functions $f(z)$ on the group Z, satisfying the condition

$$\int |f(z)|^2 dz < \infty; \tag{1}$$

in this case the scalar product in $L_2(Z)$ is given by the formula

$$(f_1, f_2) = \int f_1(z)\overline{f_2(z)} dz. \tag{2}$$

The operators of the representations of the principal series are defined in the space $L_2(Z)$. These operators are constructed in the following way.

Formula (2) § 9, Subsection 3 for the operators of a spinor representation can be written concisely in the form $T_a f(z) = \alpha(z, a) f(z\bar{a})$, where in the case of a spinor representation $f(z) = p(z, \bar{z}) \in R_{m,n}$, and $\alpha(z, a) = (\beta z + \delta)^m \overline{(\beta z + \delta)}^n$. We will investigate the operators of a representation $a \to V_a$ in the space $L_2(Z)$ also of the form

$$V_a f(z) = \alpha(z, a) f(z\bar{a}), \tag{3}$$

where now $f(z) \in L_2(Z)$, $\alpha(z, a)$ is some unknown function of z and a. For the correspondence $a \to V_a$ to be a representation, the condition $V_{a_1 a_2} f = V_{a_1}(V_{a_2} f)$ must be satisfied, i.e., by virtue of (3),

$$\alpha(z, a_1 a_2) f(z\bar{a}_1\bar{a}_2) = V_{a_1}(\alpha(z, a_2) f(z\bar{a}_2))$$
$$= \alpha(z, a_1)\alpha(z\bar{a}_1, a_2) f((z\bar{a}_1)\bar{a}_2) = \alpha(z, a_1)\alpha(z\bar{a}_1, a_2) f(z\bar{a}_1\bar{a}_2).$$

Hence

$$\alpha(z, a_1 a_2) = \alpha(z, a_1)\alpha(z\bar{a}_1, a_2). \tag{4}$$

We introduce the notation $\alpha(a) = \alpha(e, a)$, where e is the unit matrix. From (4) where $z = e$ and $a_2 = a$ we deduce that

$$\alpha(e\bar{a}_1, a) = \frac{\alpha(e, a_1 a)}{\alpha(e, a_1)} = \frac{\alpha(a_1 a)}{\alpha(a_1)}.$$

Now let us suppose $a_1 = k \in K$; because $e\bar{k} = e$, we obtain:

$$\alpha(a) = \frac{\alpha(ka)}{\alpha(k)},$$

whence

$$\alpha(ka) = \alpha(k)\alpha(a). \tag{5}$$

On the other hand, taking $a_1 = z$ and remembering that $e\bar{z} = z$, we find

$$\alpha(z, a) = \frac{\alpha(za)}{\alpha(z)}, \tag{6}$$

and formula (3) takes the form

$$V_a f(z) = \frac{\alpha(za)}{\alpha(z)} f(z\bar{a}). \tag{7}$$

Relation (5) with $k = a = e$ gives

$$\alpha(e) = \alpha(e)\alpha(e),$$

hence $\alpha(e) = 0$, or $\alpha(e) = 1$. However, as we see below, the case $\alpha(e) = 0$ is impossible. Therefore it must be that $\alpha(e) = 1$.

Now let us make use of the condition

$$(V_a f_1, V_a f_2) = (f_1, f_2) \tag{8}$$

of isometry of the operator V_a. Putting $f_1 = f_2 = f$ in this and making use of formulae (2) and (3), we obtain:

$$\int |\alpha(z, a)|^2 |f(z\bar{a})|^2 dz = \int |f(z')|^2 dz'. \tag{9}$$

In the integral on the right hand side of (9) we make the substitution $z' = z\bar{a}$; by virtue of (8) Subsection 5, we obtain:

$$\int |\alpha(z, a)|^2 |f(z\bar{a})|^2 dz = \int \beta^{-1}(za)|f(z\bar{a})|^2 dz.$$

Hence, in view of the arbitrary nature of the function $f(z) \in L^2(Z)$,

$$|\alpha(z, a)| = \beta^{-\frac{1}{2}}(za). \tag{10}$$

In particular, $|\alpha(e)| = |\alpha(e, e)| = \beta^{-\frac{1}{2}}(e) = 1$, and so $\alpha(e) \neq 0$. Conversely, if condition (10) is fulfilled, then it is easy to verify that condition (8) is also satisfied and the operator V_a is isometric. Letting $a = z^{-1}$ in (10) and making use of (6), we deduce that $|\alpha(z)| = 1$. Now we prove that it is sufficient to consider $\alpha(z) \equiv 1$. For otherwise we make the transformation

$$\tilde{f}(z) = \alpha(z) f(z). \tag{11}$$

By virtue of the condition $|\alpha(z)| = 1$, we have also $\tilde{f}(z) \in L^2(Z)$. The operator $\tilde{V}_a$, operating on the corresponding function $\tilde{f}(z)$will correspond in this case to the operator V_a, operating on $f(z)$; we find $\tilde{V}_a$. By definition

$$\tilde{V}_a\tilde{f}(z) = \alpha(z)V_a f(z) = (\alpha z)V_a\left(\frac{\tilde{f}(z)}{\alpha(z)}\right) = \alpha(z)\frac{\alpha(za)}{\alpha(z)}\frac{\tilde{f}(z\bar{a})}{\alpha(z\bar{a})},$$

i.e.

$$\tilde{V}_a\tilde{f}(z) = \frac{\alpha(za)}{\alpha(z\bar{a})}\tilde{f}(z\bar{a}). \tag{12}$$

Let us write

$$\tilde{\alpha}(a) = \frac{\alpha(a)}{\alpha(e\bar{a})};$$

then

$$\tilde{\alpha}(za) = \frac{\alpha(za)}{\alpha(e\overline{z\bar{a}})} = \frac{\alpha(za)}{\alpha(z\bar{a})},$$

and formula (12) takes the form

$$\tilde{V}_a\tilde{f}(z) = \tilde{\alpha}(za)\tilde{f}(z\bar{a}).$$

In this case

$$\tilde{\alpha}(z) = \frac{\alpha(z)}{\alpha(e\bar{z})} = \frac{\alpha(z)}{\alpha(z)} = 1$$

and†

$$\tilde{\alpha}(ka) = \frac{\alpha(ka)}{\alpha(e\overline{ka})} = \frac{\alpha(k)\alpha(a)}{\alpha(e\bar{k})\alpha(e\bar{a})} = \tilde{\alpha}(k)\tilde{\alpha}(a).$$

Consequently, assuming that this transition from f to $\tilde{f}$ was made at the very beginning, it is possible to suppose that

$$\alpha(z) \equiv 1, \tag{13}$$

and formulae (7) and (10) take the form

$$V_a f(z) = \alpha(za)f(z\bar{a}), \tag{14}$$

$$|\alpha(za)| = \beta^{-1/2}(za).$$

---

† We recall that $e\bar{k} = e$ and $\alpha(e\bar{k}) = \alpha(e) = 1$.

From the last formula with $z = e$ we see that

$$|\alpha(a)| = \beta^{-\frac{1}{2}}(a). \tag{15}$$

We now find the general form of the function $\alpha(a)$. Since whenever $a = kz$

$$\alpha(a) = \alpha(kz) = \alpha(k)\alpha(z) = \alpha(k), \tag{16}$$

then it is sufficient to find the general form of $\alpha(k)$.

By virtue of (5), we have

$$\alpha(k_1 k_2) = \alpha(k_1)\alpha(k_2); \tag{17}$$

consequently,

$$\alpha(k_1^{-1} k k_1) = \alpha(k). \tag{18}$$

The matrix

$$k = \begin{Vmatrix} \lambda^{-1} & \mu \\ 0 & \lambda \end{Vmatrix}$$

is given by means of two parameters λ, μ, so that $\alpha(k)$ is in fact a function of two numerical parameters, and we may write

$$\alpha(k) = \hat{\alpha}(\lambda, \mu).$$

We shall prove that in reality $\hat{\alpha}(\lambda, \mu)$ does not depend on μ. For this let us suppose in (18) that $k_1 = \begin{Vmatrix} \lambda_1^{-1} & 0 \\ 0 & \lambda_1 \end{Vmatrix}$; then

$$k_1^{-1} k k_1 = \begin{Vmatrix} \lambda_1 & 0 \\ 0 & \lambda_1^{-1} \end{Vmatrix} \begin{Vmatrix} \lambda^{-1} & \mu \\ 0 & \lambda \end{Vmatrix} \begin{Vmatrix} \lambda_1^{-1} & 0 \\ 0 & \lambda_1 \end{Vmatrix} = \begin{Vmatrix} \lambda^{-1} & \lambda_1^2 \mu \\ 0 & \lambda \end{Vmatrix},$$

so that (18) takes the form

$$\hat{\alpha}(\lambda, \lambda_1^2 \mu) = \hat{\alpha}(\lambda, \mu).$$

In view of the arbitrary nature of the number λ_1 our assertion follows from this. We may therefore write

$$\alpha(k) = \hat{\alpha}(\lambda) \quad \text{where} \quad k = \begin{Vmatrix} \lambda^{-1} & \mu \\ 0 & \lambda \end{Vmatrix}. \tag{19}$$

From (2) of Subsection 1 and (17) it follows then that

$$\hat{\alpha}(\lambda_1 \lambda_2) = \hat{\alpha}(\lambda_1)\hat{\alpha}(\lambda_2).$$

Thus by (5), Subsection 5, and (15), we have

$$|\hat{\alpha}(\lambda)| = |\lambda|^{-2}.$$

Writing,

$$\chi(\lambda) = \hat{\alpha}(\lambda)|\lambda|^2; \tag{20}$$

then

$$\chi(\lambda_1\lambda_2) = \chi(\lambda_1)\chi(\lambda_2) \tag{21}$$

and

$$|\chi(\lambda)| = 1. \tag{22}$$

In particular, when $\lambda = e^t e^{i\phi}$, $-\infty < t < \infty, 0 \leqslant \phi \leqslant 2\pi$, and $\lambda_1 = e^t$, $\lambda_2 = e^{i\phi}$ we obtain

$$\chi(\lambda) = \chi(e^t)\chi(e^{i\phi}), \tag{23}$$

so that it is sufficient to find $\chi(e^t)$ and $\chi(e^{i\phi})$. We define

$$\chi(e^t) = \chi_1(t), \quad \chi(e^{i\phi}) = \chi_2(\phi); \tag{24}$$

from (21) and (22) it follows that

$$\chi_1(t_1+t_2) = \chi_1(t_1)\chi_1(t_2), \quad \chi_2(\phi_1+\phi_2) = \chi_2(\phi_1)\chi_2(\phi_2), \tag{25}$$

$$|\chi_1(t)| = 1, \quad |\chi_2(\phi)| = 1, \tag{26}$$

where, in virtue of the single-valued nature of the function $\chi(\lambda)$:

$$\chi_2(\phi+2\pi) = \chi_2(\phi). \tag{27}$$

However, the unique continuous† solutions of the equations (25), satisfying condition (26) are

$$\chi_1(t) = e^{i\rho t}, \quad \chi_2(\phi) = e^{im\phi},$$

moreover, in virtue of condition (27), m must be an integer. Substituting these expressions in (24), and then in (23), we obtain:

$$\chi(\lambda) = e^{i\rho t}e^{im\phi} = |\lambda|^{i\rho}\left(\frac{\lambda}{|\lambda|}\right)^m = |\lambda|^{i\rho-m}\lambda^m;$$

† As we see below, the continuity of the function $\chi(\lambda)$ for $\lambda \neq 0$ insures the continuity of the representation $a \to V_a$.

hence, by (20) and (19):

$$\alpha(k) = \hat{\alpha}(\lambda) = |\lambda|^{i\rho - m - 2}\lambda^m,$$

and consequently, by virtue of (3) Subsection 2 and (16):

$$\alpha(a) = |a_{22}|^{i\rho - m - 2} a_{22}^m. \tag{28}$$

Conversely, the reasoning on pages 145–146 shows that with arbitrary real ρ and arbitrary integral m formulae (14) and (28) determine an isometric operator V_a in $L^2(Z)$.

The correspondence $a \to V_a$ defined thereby is a representation of the group $\mathfrak{A}$. In fact, by virtue of (13) and (14), $V_e f(z) = \alpha(z) f(z) = f(z)$, so that $V_e = 1$. We shall prove that $V_{a_1} V_{a_2} = V_{a_1 a_2}$; we have:

$$V_{a_1}[V_{a_2} f(z)] = V_{a_1}\{\alpha(z a_2) f(z \bar{a}_2)\} = \alpha(z a_1)\alpha((z\bar{a}_1)a_2) f((z\bar{a}_1)\bar{a}_2),$$

$$V_{a_1 a_2} f(z) = \alpha(z a_1 a_2) f(z \overline{a_1 a_2}).$$

It is evident that $(z\bar{a}_1)\bar{a}_2 = z\overline{a_1 a_2}$; therefore it is sufficient to prove that $\alpha(z a_1)\alpha((z\bar{a}_1)a_2) = \alpha(z a_1 a_2)$. Let us suppose for this purpose that $z a_1 = k_1 z_1$; then $z_1 = z\bar{a}_1$; therefore, making use of (16) and (13), we have:

$$\alpha(z a_1) = \alpha(k_1 z_1) = \alpha(k_1)\alpha(z_1) = \alpha(k_1);$$

$$\alpha(z a_1 a_2) = \alpha(k_1 z_1 a_2) = \alpha(k_1)\alpha(z_1 a_2) = \alpha(z a_1)\alpha((z\bar{a}_1)a_2).$$

It follows that $V_{a_1} V_{a_2} = V_{a_1 a_2}$. It remains to show that for any fixed functions $f_1(z), f_2(z) \in L^2(Z)$ the expression $(V_a f_1, f_2)$ is a continuous function on the group $\mathfrak{A}$.

This, however, follows immediately from the formula (14) for V_a.

From the relations $V_a V_{a^{-1}} = V_{a^{-1}} V_a = V_e = 1$ it follows that the operator V_a has as inverse $V_{a^{-1}}$, also defined and isometric in the whole space $L^2(Z)$; hence the operator V_a is unitary. We thus arrive at the following theorem:

THEOREM 5. *To every pair of numbers m, ρ, where m is an integer and ρ is a real number, there corresponds a unitary representation $a \to V_a$ in the space $L^2(Z)$, defined by the formula*

$$V_a f(z) = \alpha(za) f(z\bar{a}),$$

where $\alpha(a) = |a_{22}|^{-m+i\rho-2} a_{22}^m$.

The set of all representations $a \to V_a$, corresponding to all possible pairs m, ρ, is called the *principal series* of representations of the group $\mathfrak{A}$.

The representation of the principal series corresponding to the parameters m, ρ, is denoted by $\mathfrak{S}_{m,\rho}$.

The space $L^2(Z)$ can clearly be regarded as the set of all measurable functions $f(z)$ of the parameter $z = x+iy$ satisfying the condition

$$\int_{-\infty}^{\infty}\int_{-\infty}^{\infty} |f(z)|^2 dx\,dy < \infty.$$

Here one can write down formula (14) in detail, if one makes use of formulae (28) of the present section and (1), (3) of Subsection 4. From these formulae it follows that

$$\alpha(za) = \alpha(a') = |a'_{22}|^{-m+i\rho-2} a'^m_{22} = |a_{12}z+a_{22}|^{-m+i\rho-2}(a_{12}z + a_{22})^m,$$

and therefore

$$V_a f(z) = |a_{12}z+a_{22}|^{-m+i\rho-2}(a_{12}z+a_{22})^m f\left(\frac{a_{11}z+a_{21}}{a_{12}z+a_{22}}\right). \quad (29)$$

Remark. We may rewrite formula (29) in the form:

$$V_a f(z) = (a_{12}z+a_{22})^{\frac{m}{2}+\frac{i\rho}{2}-1}\overline{(a_{12}z+a_{22})}^{-\frac{m}{2}+\frac{i\rho}{2}-1} f\left(\frac{a_{11}z+a_{21}}{a_{12}z+a_{22}}\right);$$

comparison with formula (2) § 9, Subsection 3 for a spinor representation, shows that the structure of both formulae is the same; only the exponents of the factors $(a_{12}z+a_{22})$, $\overline{(a_{12}z+a_{22})}$ are altered and the function $f(z)$ is used. In the case of a spinor representation $f(z)$ are polynomials $p(z, \bar{z})$ of degree not exceeding a fixed number; in the case of a representation of the principal series they are functions from $L^2(Z)$.

7. Irreducibility of the representations of the principal series

LEMMA. *If every bounded operator which commutes with all the operators of a unitary representation is a multiple of the identity operator, then the representation is irreducible.*

Proof. Let $\mathfrak{M}$ be a closed subspace, invariant with respect to all the operators of a unitary representation $a \to T_a$; it is required to prove that $\mathfrak{M} = (0)$ or $\mathfrak{M}$ is the whole space of the representation R. Let P be the operator projecting R onto $\mathfrak{M}$; we prove that P commutes with all the operators T_a. Since $Pf \in \mathfrak{M}$ for any vector $f \in R$, then, by virtue of the invariance of $\mathfrak{M}$, $T_a Pf \in \mathfrak{M}$ also, and this means that $PT_a Pf = T_a Pf$. Hence, in view of the arbitrary nature of f,

$$PT_a P = T_a P. \tag{1}$$

Replacing a by a^{-1} and using the relation $T_{a^{-1}} = T_a^{-1} = T_a^*$, we have $PT_a^* P = T_a^* P$; hence also $(PT_a^* P)^* = (T_a^* P)^*$, i.e. $PT_a P = PT_a$. Comparison with (1) shows that $T_a P = PT_a$, i.e. P in fact commutes with all the operators T_a. But then, by the hypothesis of the lemma, $P = \lambda 1$, which is only possible when $\lambda = 0$ or 1. In the first case $\mathfrak{M} = (0)$, and in the other $\mathfrak{M} = R$.

From this proof and the spectral theory it follows that the converse proposition is also true.

THEOREM 6. *Every representation of the principal series is irreducible.*

Proof. Let $a \to V_a$ be a fixed representation of the principal series; according to the preceding lemma, it is sufficient to show that every bounded operator A, which commutes with all the operators V_a, is a multiple of the identity operator, i.e. $A = c1$, where c is a number.

Thus let A be a bounded operator which commutes with all the operators V_a; in particular, it commutes with all operators V_{z_0}, $z_0 \in Z$, and V_{a_0}, where $a_0 = \begin{Vmatrix} \lambda^{-1} & 0 \\ 0 & \lambda \end{Vmatrix}$. Moreover, from the general formula (29) Subsection 6, it follows that

$$V_{z_0} f(z) = f(z + z_0), \qquad V_{a_0} f(z) = |\lambda|^{-m+i\rho-2} \lambda^m f(\lambda^{-2} z). \tag{2}$$

We pass from the functions $f(z)$ to their Fourier transforms $\phi(w)$, letting†

$$\phi(w) = \frac{1}{2\pi} \int_{-\infty}^{\infty} \int_{-\infty}^{\infty} f(z) e^{i \operatorname{Re}(z\bar{w})} dx\, dy. \tag{3}$$

We denote by $L^2(W)$ the set of all measurable functions $\phi(w)$, satisfying the condition

$$\int_{-\infty}^{\infty} \int_{-\infty}^{\infty} |\phi(w)|^2 du\, dv < \infty, \qquad w = u + iv; \tag{4}$$

we define a scalar product in $L^2(W)$ by

$$(\phi_1, \phi_2) = \int_{-\infty}^{\infty} \int_{-\infty}^{\infty} \phi_1(w) \overline{\phi_2(w)} du\, dv, \tag{5}$$

and define all remaining operations in the usual way; then $L^2(W)$ becomes a Hilbert space. By virtue of the known properties of the Fourier integral, for any function $f(z) \in L^2(Z)$ the integral in (3) converges in the mean, i.e. in the sense of the norm in $L^2(W)$ and represents a function from $L^2(W)$. Thus formula (3) represents an isometric mapping of the space $L^2(Z)$ on the space $L^2(W)$. This mapping carries the operators V_{z_0}, V_{a_0} and A into some operators in the space $L^2(W)$, which we denote by $\hat{V}_{z_0}$, $\hat{V}_{a_0}$ and $\hat{A}$ respectively; it is evident that, as before, the operator $\hat{A}$ will commute with $\hat{V}_{z_0}$ and $\hat{V}_{a_0}$, and it is sufficient to prove that the operator $\hat{A}$ is a multiple of the identity operator. For this purpose we will find the operators $\hat{V}_{z_0}$ and $\hat{V}_{a_0}$. In virtue of (2) and (3),

---

† Formula (3) represents the expression in complex form of the Fourier transform of a function of two variables $f(x, y) = f(x+iy)$. In order to convince oneself of this it is sufficient to set $w = u+iv$ and $\phi(w) = \phi(u, v)$. Then (3) takes the form

$$\phi(u, v) = \frac{1}{2\pi} \int_{-\infty}^{\infty} \int_{-\infty}^{\infty} f(x, y)\, e^{i(ux+vy)}\, dx dy.$$

we have

$$\hat{V}_{z_0}\phi(w) = \frac{1}{2\pi}\int_{-\infty}^{\infty}\int_{-\infty}^{\infty} f(z+z_0)e^{i\mathrm{Re}(z\bar{w})}\mathrm{d}x\,\mathrm{d}y$$

$$= \frac{1}{2\pi}\int_{-\infty}^{\infty}\int_{-\infty}^{\infty} f(z)\,e^{i\mathrm{Re}((z-z_0)\bar{w})}\mathrm{d}x\,\mathrm{d}y$$

$$= e^{-i\mathrm{Re}(z_0\bar{w})}\frac{1}{2\pi}\int_{-\infty}^{\infty}\int_{-\infty}^{\infty} f(z)e^{i\mathrm{Re}(z\bar{w})}\mathrm{d}x\,\mathrm{d}y,$$

i.e.

$$\hat{V}_{z_0}\phi(w) = e^{-i\mathrm{Re}(z_0\bar{w})}\,\phi(w). \tag{6}$$

Analogously

$$\hat{V}_{a_0}\phi(w) = \frac{1}{2\pi}\int_{-\infty}^{\infty}\int_{-\infty}^{\infty} |\lambda|^{-m+i\rho-2}\lambda^m f(\lambda^{-2}z)e^{i\mathrm{Re}(z\bar{w})}\mathrm{d}x\,\mathrm{d}y;$$

letting $z_1 = \lambda^{-2}z$, we obtain:

$$\hat{V}_{a_0}\phi(w) = \frac{1}{2\pi}\int_{-\infty}^{\infty}\int_{-\infty}^{\infty} |\lambda|^{-m+i\rho-2}\lambda^m f(z_1)e^{i\mathrm{Re}(z_1\overline{\bar{\lambda}^2 w})}|\lambda|^4\mathrm{d}x_1\,\mathrm{d}y_1$$

$$= |\lambda|^{-m+i\rho+2}\lambda^m\frac{1}{2\pi}\int_{-\infty}^{\infty}\int_{-\infty}^{\infty} f(z_1)e^{i\mathrm{Re}(z_1\overline{\bar{\lambda}^2 w})}\mathrm{d}x_1\,\mathrm{d}y_1,$$

i.e.

$$\hat{V}_{a_0}\phi(w) = |\lambda|^{-m+i\rho+2}\lambda^m\phi(\bar{\lambda}^2 w). \tag{7}$$

Formula (6) shows that $\hat{V}_{z_0}$ is an operator of multiplication by $e^{-i\mathrm{Re}(z_0\bar{w})}$. The operator $\hat{A}$ must commute with all such operators of multiplication, and therefore also with their linear combinations, and with the limits of such linear combinations, i.e. with all operators of multiplication by an essentially bounded† measurable

† A measurable function is called *essentially bounded* if it is bounded on a set whose complement has measure equal to zero.

function. But in this case the operator $\hat{A}$ itself must be an operator of multiplication by an essentially bounded measurable function (see Appendix II); thus

$$\hat{A}\phi(w) = c(w)\phi(w), \tag{8}$$

where $c(w)$ is an essentially bounded measurable function. Now we make use of the commutativity of the operator A with the operator V_{a_0}, i.e. the equation

$$\hat{A}\hat{V}_{a_0}\phi(w) = \hat{V}_{a_0}\hat{A}\phi(w). \tag{9}$$

By virtue of (7) and (8) this equation means that

$$c(w)|\lambda|^{-m+i\rho+2}\lambda^m\phi(\bar{\lambda}^2 w) = |\lambda|^{-m+i\rho+2}\lambda^m c(\bar{\lambda}^2 w)\phi(\bar{\lambda}^2 w);$$

in view of the arbitrary nature of the function $\phi(w) \in L^2(W)$ it follows from this that for any λ

$$c(w) = c(\bar{\lambda}^2 w) \tag{10}$$

for almost all w. This is possible only when $c(w)$ is a constant:

$$c(w) = c,$$

for almost all w. But then from (8) it follows that $\hat{A}$ is an operator of multiplication by c, i.e. $\hat{A} = c1$, and the theorem is proved.

§ 11. Description of the Representations of the Principal Series and of Spinor Representations by means of the Unitary Group

1. A description of the space $\tilde{Z}$ in terms of the unitary subgroup

I. *Every matrix $a \in \mathfrak{A}$ can be represented in the form*

$$a = ku, \quad k \in K, \quad u \in \mathfrak{U}. \tag{1}$$

Proof. When written out in full equation (1) takes the form

$$\begin{Vmatrix} a_{11} & a_{12} \\ a_{21} & a_{22} \end{Vmatrix} = \begin{Vmatrix} \lambda^{-1} & \mu \\ 0 & \lambda \end{Vmatrix} \cdot \begin{Vmatrix} \alpha & \beta \\ -\bar{\beta} & \bar{\alpha} \end{Vmatrix}$$

and hence for it to be fulfilled it is necessary and sufficient that

$$a_{21} = -\lambda\bar{\beta}, \quad a_{22} = \lambda\bar{\alpha}, \quad a_{12} = \lambda^{-1}\beta+\mu\bar{\alpha}, \quad a_{11} = \lambda^{-1}\alpha-\mu\bar{\beta}. \tag{2}$$

Hence, making use of the condition

$$|\alpha|^2+|\beta|^2 = 1, \tag{3}$$

we obtain:

$$|\lambda|^2 = |a_{21}|^2+|a_{22}|^2, \quad \alpha = \frac{\bar{a}_{22}}{\bar{\lambda}}, \quad \beta = -\frac{\bar{a}_{21}}{\bar{\lambda}}, \tag{4}$$

$$\mu = \begin{cases} \dfrac{a_{12}-\lambda^{-1}\beta}{\bar{\alpha}} & \text{when} \quad \alpha \neq 0, \\ -\dfrac{a_{11}}{\bar{\beta}} & \text{when} \quad \alpha = 0. \end{cases} \tag{5}$$

By virtue of the relation det $a = 1$, equations (2) will be satisfied. Thus, choosing λ, α, β, μ according to formulae (3–5), we satisfy relation (1).

Formulae (3–5) determine only $|\lambda|$ and hence determine λ, α, β, μ only to within an arbitrary factor $e^{i\omega}$, with modulus equal to unity. This circumstance can also be described in the following way.

We consider the subgroup Γ of all diagonal matrices

$$\gamma = \begin{Vmatrix} e^{-i\omega} & 0 \\ 0 & e^{i\omega} \end{Vmatrix} \tag{6}$$

(see § 5, Subsection 5).

The transition from λ, α, β to $e^{i\omega}\lambda$, $e^{i\omega}\alpha$, $e^{i\omega}\beta$ is equivalent to a transition from k and u to $k\gamma$ and $\gamma^{-1}u$; hence:

II. *The arbitrary nature of* k *and* u *in equation* (1) *is determined by the formulae*:

$$k_1 = k\gamma, \quad u_1 = \gamma^{-1}u. \tag{7}$$

III. *Every class* $\tilde{z}$ *contains unitary matrices, and unitary matrices from the same class differ by a left factor* $\gamma \in \Gamma$.

Proof. If $a \in \tilde{z}$, then from (1) it follows that also $u \in \tilde{z}$; if also $u_1 \in \tilde{z}$, then $u_1 = k'u$. Hence $a = ku = kk'^{-1}u_1$ and, by virtue of (7), $u_1 = \gamma^{-1}u$.

IV. *If z and u belong to the same class $\tilde{z}$, then*

$$|\lambda|^2 = 1+|z|^2, \quad \alpha = \frac{1}{\bar{\lambda}}, \quad \beta = -\frac{\bar{z}}{\bar{\lambda}}. \tag{8}$$

Proof. If $z \in \tilde{z}$ and $u \in \tilde{z}$, then for some k,

$$z = ku,$$

and it only remains to apply formulae (3–5) to the matrix

$$z = \begin{Vmatrix} 1 & 0 \\ z & 1 \end{Vmatrix}.$$

Proposition III means that the set of all matrices $\bar{u} \in \tilde{z}$ forms a residue class Γu of the group $\mathfrak{U}$ with respect to its subgroup Γ. We denote this class by $\tilde{u}$ and place every class $\tilde{z}$ in correspondence with the class $\tilde{u}$—the class containing the matrix u. The transformation $\tilde{z} \to \tilde{z}\bar{a}$ can then be considered as a transformation $\tilde{u} \to \tilde{u}\bar{a}$ of the corresponding classes $\tilde{u}$.

2. The space $L_2^m(\mathfrak{U})$

We denote by $L_2^m(\mathfrak{U})$ the set of all functions $\phi(u)$ on the group $\mathfrak{U}$, which are measurable with respect to the parameters t, θ, θ' and satisfy the condition

$$\phi(\gamma u) = \mathrm{e}^{im\omega}\phi(u) \quad \text{whenever} \quad \gamma = \begin{Vmatrix} \mathrm{e}^{-i\omega} & 0 \\ 0 & \mathrm{e}^{i\omega} \end{Vmatrix} \tag{1}$$

and

$$\int |\phi(u)|^2 \mathrm{d}u < \infty. \tag{2}$$

We introduce into $L_2^m(\mathfrak{U})$ a scalar product, letting

$$(\phi_1, \phi_2) = \int \phi_1(u)\overline{\phi_2(u)}\mathrm{d}u; \tag{3}$$

then $L_2^m(\mathfrak{U})$ becomes a Hilbert space.† From formula (28) § 10, Subsection 6 it follows that

$$\alpha(\gamma) = \mathrm{e}^{im\omega}; \tag{4}$$

† In fact, $L_2^m(\mathfrak{U})$ is a closed subspace of the Hilbert space $L^2(\mathfrak{U})$ (see § 6, Subsection 7), and so is complete.

therefore condition (1) can also be written in the form

$$\phi(\gamma u) = \alpha(\gamma)\phi(u). \tag{5}$$

3. The realization of the representations of the principal series in the space $L_2^m(\mathfrak{U})$

Now let $\mathfrak{S}_{m,\rho}$ be a given arbitrary representation of the principal series in the space $L^2(Z)$. To every function $f(z) \in L^2(Z)$ we assign a function

$$\phi(u) = \sqrt{(\pi)}\alpha(u)f(z) \quad \text{where} \quad u, z \in \tilde{z}. \tag{1}$$

This correspondence is an isometric mapping of $L^2(Z)$ on $L_2^m(\mathfrak{U})$. In fact, since u and γu belong to the same class $\tilde{z}$, then

$$\phi(\gamma u) = \sqrt{(\pi)}\alpha(\gamma u)f(z) = \sqrt{(\pi)}\alpha(\gamma)\alpha(u)f(z) = \alpha(\gamma)\phi(u), \tag{2}$$

so that condition (5) Subsection 2 is satisfied. Further, by virtue of (9) Subsection 7 Section 1,

$$\int |\phi(u)|^2 \mathrm{d}u = \frac{1}{4\pi^2}\int |\phi(u)|^2 \mathrm{d}t\,\mathrm{d}\theta\,\mathrm{d}\theta' = \frac{1}{4\pi}\int |f(z)|^2\,|\alpha(u)|^2 \mathrm{d}t\,\mathrm{d}\theta\,\mathrm{d}\theta'; \tag{3}$$

on the other hand, letting

$$z = re^{i\varkappa}, \quad \arg\lambda = \omega, \quad u = \begin{Vmatrix} u_{11} & u_{12} \\ u_{21} & u_{22} \end{Vmatrix}, \tag{4}$$

and making use of formulae (8) subsection 1, we have:

$$t = |u_{22}|^2 = \frac{1}{1+|z|^2} = \frac{1}{1+r^2}, \quad \theta = \arg u_{11} = -\omega, \; \theta' = \arg u_{12} = \pi+\omega-\kappa.$$

Hence after a simple calculation we obtain:

$$\frac{\partial(t, \theta, \theta')}{\partial(r, \omega, \kappa)} = \frac{2r}{(1+r^2)^2} = |u_{22}|^4 2r = |\alpha(u)|^{-2}\,2r,$$

and

$$|\alpha(u)|^2 \mathrm{d}t\,\mathrm{d}\theta\,\mathrm{d}\theta' = 2r\,\mathrm{d}r\,\mathrm{d}\kappa\,\mathrm{d}\omega = 2\mathrm{d}\omega\,\mathrm{d}z,$$

or, by virtue of (15) §, 10 Subsection 6:

$$|\beta(u)|^{-1}\mathrm{d}t\,\mathrm{d}\theta\,\mathrm{d}\theta' = 2\mathrm{d}\omega\,\mathrm{d}z. \tag{5}$$

Therefore (3) gives

$$\int |\phi(u)|^2 du = \frac{1}{4\pi} 2 \int_0^{2\pi} d\omega \int |f(z)|^2 dz = \int |f(z)|^2 dz, \tag{6}$$

so that $\phi \in L_2^m(\mathfrak{U})$, and in the transition from f to ϕ the norm is preserved. Finally, if $\phi(u)$ is an arbitrary function from $L_2^m(\mathfrak{U})$, then, letting

$$f(z) = \frac{1}{\sqrt{(\pi)}} \alpha^{-1}(u)\phi(u),\ u,\ z \in \tilde{z}, \tag{7}$$

we obtain the function $f(z) \in L^2(Z)$, which goes into $\phi(u)$ by our mapping; here, by virtue of condition (5) Subsection 2, the arbitrary choice of the matrix $u \in \tilde{z}$ plays no part. Hence, the isometric mapping $f \to \phi$ is a mapping on the whole space $L_2^m(\mathfrak{U})$.

In this mapping an operator V_a of a representation of the principal series goes into an operator in $L_2^m(\mathfrak{U})$, which we again denote by V_a. We will find an expression for V_a in $L_2^m(\mathfrak{U})$; by the definition of this operator, we have

$$V_a\phi(u) = \sqrt{(\pi)}\alpha(u)V_a f(z) = \sqrt{(\pi)}\alpha(u)\alpha(za)f(z\bar{a}) = \alpha(u)\frac{\alpha(za)}{\alpha(u\bar{a})}\phi(u\bar{a}), \tag{8}$$

where $u\bar{a}$ is an arbitrary element of the class $\widetilde{u\bar{a}}$ (it is easy to see that the arbitrary nature of this choice is immaterial).

On the other hand, z, $u \in \tilde{z}$; $z\bar{a}$, $u\bar{a} \in \widetilde{z\bar{a}}$; therefore one can set $z = k_0 u$, $ua = k \cdot u\bar{a}$. Hence

$$\alpha(za) = \alpha(k_0 ua) = \alpha(k_0)\alpha(ua) = \frac{\alpha(ua)}{\alpha(u)},$$

and therefore

$$\frac{\alpha(u)\alpha(za)}{\alpha(u\bar{a})} = \frac{\alpha(ua)}{\alpha(u\bar{a})}.$$

Substituting this expression in formula (8), we arrive at the following result:

THEOREM 7. *The representation $\mathfrak{S}_{m,\rho}$ of the principal series in the space $L_2^m(\mathfrak{U})$ is determined by the formula*

$$V_a\phi(u) = \frac{\alpha(ua)}{\alpha(u\bar{a})}\phi(u\bar{a}), \tag{9}$$

where $u\bar{a}$ is an arbitrary matrix from the class $\tilde{u\bar{a}}$.

Remark. From the unitary nature of a representation of the principal series it follows that

$$du' = \frac{\beta(u\bar{a})}{\beta(ua)}du \quad \text{if} \quad u' = u\bar{a}. \tag{10}$$

In fact we have

$$\int\left|\frac{\alpha(ua)}{\alpha(u\bar{a})}\right|^2 |f(u\bar{a})|^2 du = \int |f(u')|^2 du';$$

making the substitution $u' = u\bar{a}$ in the last integral and taking into account the arbitrary nature of the function $f(u)$ and formula (6) § 10, Subsection 6, we conclude that

$$du' = \left|\frac{\alpha(ua)}{\alpha(u\bar{a})}\right|^2 du = \frac{\beta(u\bar{a})}{\beta(ua)}du \quad \text{if} \quad u' = u\bar{a}.$$

4. The representations S_k, contained in $\mathfrak{S}_{m,\rho}$

We consider the irreducible representation S_k of weight k of the group $\mathfrak{U}$; let $c^k(u) = \|c^k_{pq}(u)\|, p, q = -k, -k+1, \ldots, k$, be the matrix operators of this representation in canonical form. Then (see (6) § 5, Subsection 5)

$$c^k_{pq}(\gamma u) = e^{ipt}c^k_{pq}(u), \tag{1}$$

$$c^k_{pq}(u\gamma) = c^k_{pq}(u)e^{iqt} \tag{2}$$

where

$$\gamma = \left\|\begin{matrix} e^{-\frac{it}{2}} & 0 \\ 0 & e^{\frac{it}{2}} \end{matrix}\right\|.$$

If now we set

$$\gamma = \left\|\begin{matrix} e^{-i\omega} & 0 \\ 0 & e^{i\omega} \end{matrix}\right\|,$$

i.e. $t = 2\omega$, then these relations take the form

$$c^k_{pq}(\gamma u) = e^{2ip\omega} c^k_{pq}(u), \tag{3}$$

$$c^k_{pq}(u\gamma) = e^{2iq\omega} c^k_{pq}(u). \tag{4}$$

THEOREM 8. *The representation S_k is contained at most once in $\mathfrak{S}_{m,\rho}$; in this case S_k is contained in $\mathfrak{S}_{m,\rho}$ if and only if $m/2$ is one of the numbers $-k, -k+1, \ldots, k$.*

Proof. Let S_k be contained in $\mathfrak{S}_{m,\rho}$; this means that in $L^m_2(\mathfrak{U})$ there is a subspace $\mathfrak{R}$, in which the representation $u \to V_u$ coincides with S_k.

Let $\phi_p(u)$, $p = -k, -k+1, \ldots, k$, be a canonical basis in $\mathfrak{R}$; then

$$V_{u_0}\phi_\nu(u) = \sum_{j=-k}^{k} c^k_{j\nu}(u_0)\phi_j(u). \tag{5}$$

We prove that $\phi_p(u) = \sigma_{\nu_0} c^k_{\nu_0 p}(u)$, where $\nu_0 = m/2$ and σ_{ν_0} is a constant.

Applying formula (9) Subsection 3, we have:

$$V_{u_0}\phi(u) = \phi(uu_0),$$

because one can set $\overline{uu_0} = uu_0$. Therefore (5) takes the form

$$\phi_\nu(uu_0) = \sum_{j=-k}^{k} c^k_{j\nu}(u_0)\phi_j(u). \tag{6}$$

Multiplying both sides of (6) by $\overline{c^k_{p\nu}(u_0)}$, integrating with respect to du_0 and taking into account the relations of orthogonality (see II § 5, Subsection 5). We obtain:

$$\int \phi_\nu(uu_0)\overline{c^k_{p\nu}(u_0)}\,du_0 = \sigma\phi_p(u),$$

where

$$\sigma = \int |c^k_{p\nu}(u_0)|^2 du_0 = 2k+1.$$

Hence

$$\phi_p(u) = \frac{1}{\sigma}\int \phi_\nu(uu_0)\overline{c^k_{p\nu}(u_0)}\,du_0 = \frac{1}{\sigma}\int \phi_\nu(u_0)\overline{c^k_{p\nu}(u^{-1}u_0)}\,du_0$$

$$= \frac{1}{\sigma}\int \phi_\nu(u_0)\sum_{j=-k}^{k}\overline{c^k_{pj}(u^{-1})c^k_{j\nu}(u_0)}\,du_0 = \sum_{j=-k}^{k}\sigma_j \cdot c^k_{jp}(u), \tag{7}$$

where

$$\sigma_j = \frac{1}{\sigma}\int \phi_\nu(u_0)\overline{c^k_{j\nu}(u_0)}\,\mathrm{d}u_0 .$$

However, $\phi_p(u) \in L_2^m(\mathfrak{U})$, so that $\phi_p(\gamma u) = \mathrm{e}^{im\omega}\phi_p(u)$; therefore, replacing u by γu in (7) and making use of relation (3), we obtain:

$$\mathrm{e}^{im\omega}\phi_p(u) = \sum_{\nu=-k}^{k} \sigma_\nu \mathrm{e}^{2i\nu\omega} c^k_{\nu p}(u).$$

This equation is only possible when $m/2$ coincides with one of the numbers $\nu = -k, -k+1, \ldots, k$, and if $m/2 = \nu_0$, then $\sigma_\nu = 0$ where $\nu \neq \nu_0$. Therefore it follows from (7) that†

$$\phi_p(u) = \sigma_{\nu_0} c^k_{\nu_0 p}(u), \tag{8}$$

so that $\mathfrak{N}$ is determined uniquely as the subspace spanned by the functions $c^k_{\nu_0 p}(u)$, $p = -k, -k+1, \ldots, k$. This means that S_k occurs only once in $\mathfrak{S}_{m,\rho}$, where $m/2$ is one of the numbers $\nu = -k, -k+1, \ldots, k$. Conversely, if $\nu_0 = m/2$ is one of the numbers $-k, -k+1, \ldots, k$, then in the subspace $\mathfrak{N}$ spanned by the functions $\phi_p(u) = c^k_{\nu_0 p}(u)$, $p = -k, -k+1, \ldots, k$, the representation $u \to V_u$ coincides with S_k, so that S_k is contained in $\mathfrak{S}_{m,\rho}$. In fact,

$$V_{u_0}\phi_p(u) = \phi_p(uu_0) = c^k_{\nu_0 p}(uu_0) = \sum_{j=-k}^{k} c^k_{\nu_0 j}(u)c^k_{jp}(u_0)$$
$$= \sum_{j=-k}^{k} c^k_{jp}(u_0)\phi_j(u).$$

This completes the proof of the theorem.

Remark. By the theorem of completeness proved in § 6, Subsection 2, the functions $c^k_{\nu_0 p}(u)$ where $\nu_0 = m/2$ generate an orthogonal basis in the space $L_2^m(\mathfrak{U})$. Formula (8) shows that the elements $c^k_{\nu_0 p}(u)$ differ only by a factor from the vectors of the canonical basis:

$$\phi^k_{\nu_0 p}(u) = \sqrt{[2k+1]}\,\kappa^k_{\nu_0 p} c^k_{\nu_0 p}(u), \tag{9}$$

where

$$|\kappa^k_{\nu_0 p}| = 1.$$

† From the relation of orthogonality (see II, § 5, Subsection 5), it follows that $\sigma_{\nu_0} = \sqrt{[2k+1]}\,\kappa^k_{\nu_0 p}$, $|\kappa^k_{\nu_0 p}| = 1$.

We will find an explicit expression for the factor $\kappa_{\nu_0 \rho}^k$. For this purpose we set, as in formula (7) Subsection 3,

$$f_{\nu_0 p}^k(z) = \frac{1}{\sqrt{(\pi)}} \alpha^{-1}(u) \phi_{\nu_0 p}^k(u), \quad u, z \in \tilde{z}; \tag{10}$$

then the functions $f_{\nu_0 p}^k(z)$ generate a canonical basis of the representation $\mathfrak{S}_{m,\rho}$, realized in $L^2(Z)$.

From the formulae for the infinitesimal operators of the representation $\mathfrak{S}_{m,\rho}$ it follows that

$$F_+ f_{\nu_0 k}^k(z) = \sqrt{[(2k+1)(2k+2)]}\, C_{k+1} f_{\nu_0, k+1}^{k+1}(\bar{z}), \tag{11}$$

where

$$C_{k+1} = \frac{i}{k+1} \sqrt{\left[\frac{[(k+1)^2 - k_0^2][(k+1)^2 - c^2]}{4(k+1)^2 - 1}\right]}, \tag{12}$$

$$k_0 = \left|\frac{m}{2}\right| = |\nu_0|, \quad c^2 = -\frac{\rho^2}{4}. \tag{13}$$

(The relations (13) are derived below—see I, Subsection 6.)

On the other hand, we make use of the expressions (7) § 5, Subsection 4 for the functions $c_{\mu\nu}^k(u)$ with $p = k$; it follows that

$$c_{\nu_0 k}^k(u) = (-1)^{k-\nu_0} \sqrt{(C_{2k}^{k-\nu_0})}\, u_{12}^{k-\nu_0} u_{22}^{k+\nu_0}. \tag{14}$$

Taking into account formulae (8) Subsection 1, connecting the parameters of the matrices z and u where $z, u \in \tilde{z}$, we obtain:

$$\alpha^{-1}(u) = |u_{22}|^{m - i\rho + 2} u_{22}^{m} = (1 + |z|^2)^{i\frac{\rho}{2} - 1} e^{-im\omega},$$

where $\omega = \arg u_{22}$; further,

$$f_{\nu_0 k}^k(z) = \frac{1}{\sqrt{(\pi)}} \sqrt{[C_{2k}^{k-\nu_0}(2k+1)]}\, \kappa_{\nu_0 \rho}^k \bar{z}^{k-\nu_0} (1 + |z|^2)^{-k + i\frac{\rho}{2} - 1}. \tag{15}$$

As was done in § 9, Subsection 4 for spinor representations, one can express the infinitesimal operators in the form of differential operators† in the space $L^2(Z)$; in particular,

$$F_+ f(z) = i\frac{\partial f}{\partial z} - i\bar{z}^2 \frac{\partial f}{\partial \bar{z}} + i\left(-\frac{m}{2} + i\frac{\rho}{2} - 1\right)\bar{z} f. \tag{16}$$

† Differential, and hence infinitesimal operators are defined on a set dense in $L^2(Z)$.

Applying F_+ to the functions $f^k_{\nu_0 k}$ from (15), we find:

$$F_+ f^k_{\nu_0 k}(z)$$
$$= \frac{i}{\sqrt{(\pi)}} \sqrt{[C^{k-\nu_0}_{2k}(2k+1)]}\, \kappa^k_{\nu_0\rho}(i\rho-2k-2)\, \bar{z}^{k-\nu_0+1}(1+|z|^2)^{-k+i\frac{\rho}{2}-2}. \tag{17}$$

By virtue of (11) and (12), this expression must be equal to

$$\frac{i\sqrt{[(2k+1)(2k+2)]}}{\sqrt{(\pi)}(k+1)} \cdot \sqrt{\left[\frac{[(k+1)^2-\nu_0^2]\left[(k+1)^2+\frac{\rho^2}{4}\right]}{4(k+1)^2-1}\right]} \times$$
$$\times \sqrt{[C^{k-\nu_0+1}_{2k+2}(2k+3)]}\kappa^{k+1}_{\nu_0\rho}\bar{z}^{k-\nu_0+1}(1+|z|^2)^{-k+i\frac{\rho}{2}-2};$$

hence we find that

$$\frac{\kappa^{k+1}_{\nu_0\rho}}{\kappa^k_{\nu_0\rho}} = \frac{-2k-2+i\rho}{\sqrt{[4(k+1)^2+\rho^2]}}. \tag{18}$$

Because the value of $\kappa^k_{\nu_0\rho}$ where $k = k_0$ is inessential, one can set $\kappa^{k_0}_{\nu_0\rho} = \dfrac{-2k_0+i\rho}{\sqrt{[4k_0^2+\rho^2]}}$ then from (18) it follows that

$$\kappa^k_{\nu_0\rho} = \prod_{\nu=k_0}^{k} \frac{-2\nu+i\rho}{\sqrt{[4\nu^2+\rho^2]}}. \tag{19}$$

We observe that

$$\kappa^k_{-\nu_0,-\rho} = \overline{\kappa^k_{\nu_0\rho}}. \tag{20}$$

5. Elementary spherical functions

Now we consider the representations $\mathfrak{S}_{m,\rho}$ of the principal series which contain the representation S_0 of the unitary subgroup. In this case $k = 0$ and the set of numbers $-k, -k+1, \ldots, k$ consists of zero alone; in view of Theorem 8 we must have $m/2 = 0$, $m = 0$. Hence, the $\mathfrak{S}_{0,\rho}$ are the representations of the principal series containing S_0, where S_0 is contained in $\mathfrak{S}_{0,\rho}$ exactly once.

This means that, except for a numerical factor, only one function ϕ_0 in $L_2^0(\mathfrak{U})$ satisfies

$$V_{u_0}\phi_0(u) = \phi_0(u), \tag{1}$$

i.e. $\phi_0(uu_0) = \phi_0(u)$ for all $u_0 \in \mathfrak{U}$.

It is evident that this function will be constant; letting $\phi_0(u) \equiv 1$, we obtain a normalized function ϕ_0.

The function

$$\psi(a) = (V_a\phi_0, \phi_0) \tag{2}$$

is called the elementary spherical function† *of the representation* $\mathfrak{S}_{0,\rho}$.

I. *The function* $\psi(a)$ *satisfies the condition*

$$\psi(au) = \psi(ua) = \psi(a). \tag{3}$$

In fact, by virtue of (1):

$$\psi(au) = (V_{au}\phi_0, \phi_0) = (V_a V_u\phi_0, \phi_0) = (V_a\phi_0, \phi_0) = \psi(a),$$

and similarly

$$\psi(ua) = \psi(a).$$

We will find an explicit expression for $\psi(a)$. We agree to denote by ε matrices of the form

$$\varepsilon = \begin{Vmatrix} \varepsilon_1 & 0 \\ 0 & \varepsilon_2 \end{Vmatrix}, \quad \varepsilon_1\varepsilon_2 = 1. \tag{4}$$

It is evident that these matrices generate a commutative subgroup of the group $\mathfrak{A}$; we denote this subgroup by E.

II. *Every matrix* $a \in \mathfrak{A}$ *can be represented in the form*

$$a = u_1\varepsilon u_2. \tag{5}$$

Proof. We denote by a^* transpose conjugate of a, and we set $b = a^*a$. Then b is a Hermitian matrix with positive eigenvalues which we denote by $\varepsilon_1^2, \varepsilon_2^2$; hence it is possible to reduce it by unitary transformations to diagonal form. This means that

$$b = v^*\varepsilon^2 v,$$

† The concept of a spherical function permits a generalization to the representations of other classes of groups; see in this connection: Refs: [6], [9], [10d], [12d] and [16].

where ε is the matrix (4), and v is a unitary matrix. Letting $u = av^* \varepsilon^{-1} v$, we have:

$$a = uv^* \varepsilon v \tag{6}$$

and

$$uu^* = av^* \varepsilon^{-1} vv^* \varepsilon^{-1} va^* = ab^{-1} a^* = aa^{-1} a^{*-1} a^* = e.$$

Hence u is a unitary matrix. Letting $u_1 = uv^*$, $u_2 = v$, in (6), we obtain (5). By virtue of (5) and (3) we have

$$\psi(a) = \psi(u_1 \varepsilon u_2) = \psi(\varepsilon);$$

therefore it is sufficient to determine $\psi(\varepsilon)$. On the other hand, according to (9) Subsection 3,

$$V_a \phi_0(u) = \frac{\alpha(ua)}{\alpha(u\bar{a})} \cdot 1 = \frac{\alpha(ua)}{\alpha(u\bar{a})}.$$

Thus

$$\psi(a) = \left(\frac{\alpha(ua)}{\alpha(u\bar{a})}, \quad 1 \right) = \int \frac{\alpha(ua)}{\alpha(u\bar{a})} du; \tag{7}$$

in particular,

$$\psi(\varepsilon) = \int \frac{\alpha(u\varepsilon)}{\alpha(u\bar{\varepsilon})} du. \tag{8}$$

We set $u\varepsilon = ku'$; then it is possible to take $u' = u\varepsilon$, because, by virtue of the condition $m = 0$, the choice of the factor γ plays no part. Therefore $\alpha(u\varepsilon) = \alpha(k)\alpha(u') = \alpha(k)\alpha(u\bar{\varepsilon})$ and

$$\frac{\alpha(u\varepsilon)}{\alpha(u\bar{\varepsilon})} = \alpha(k). \tag{9}$$

We set

$$k = \begin{Vmatrix} \lambda^{-1} & \mu \\ 0 & \lambda \end{Vmatrix}, \quad u = \begin{Vmatrix} u_{11} & u_{12} \\ u_{21} & u_{22} \end{Vmatrix}.$$

Applying formula (4), Subsection 1 with $a = u\varepsilon$, we obtain:

$$|\lambda|^2 = \varepsilon_1^2 |u_{21}|^2 + \varepsilon_2^2 |u_{22}|^2 = \varepsilon_1^2 (1-t) + \varepsilon_2^2 t, \quad t = |u_{22}|^2.$$

Hence by definition (28), § 10, Subsection 6, of the function $\alpha(a)$,

$$\alpha(k) = [\varepsilon_1^2(1-t) + \varepsilon_2^2 t]^{-1+i\frac{\rho}{2}},$$

and so formulae (8) and (9) give

$$\psi(\varepsilon) = \int [\varepsilon_1^2(1-t)+\varepsilon_2^2 t]^{-1+i\frac{\rho}{2}} du$$

$$= \frac{1}{4\pi^2}\int_0^{2\pi} d\theta \int_0^{2\pi} d\theta \int_0^1 [\varepsilon_1^2(1-t)+\varepsilon_2^2 t]^{-1+i\frac{\rho}{2}} dt.$$

Performing the calculations, we obtain:

$$\psi(\varepsilon) = 2\,\frac{\varepsilon_2^{i\rho}-\varepsilon_1^{i\rho}}{i\rho(\varepsilon_2^2-\varepsilon_1^2)}. \tag{10}$$

Formula (10) can be given in another more convenient form, if we set

$$\varepsilon_2 = e^{\tau}, \quad \varepsilon_1 = e^{-\tau}.$$

Substituting in (10), we arrive at the following result:

The spherical function of the representation $\mathfrak{S}_{0,\rho}$ *is given by the formula*

$$\psi(\varepsilon) = \frac{2}{\rho}\,\frac{\sin\rho\tau}{\sinh 2\tau} \quad \text{where} \quad \varepsilon = \begin{Vmatrix} e^{-\tau} & 0 \\ 0 & e^{\tau} \end{Vmatrix}. \tag{11}$$

6. Infinitesimal operators of the representation $\mathfrak{S}_{m,\rho}$ in a canonica basis

Theorem 8, proved in Subsection 4, states that the representation $\mathfrak{S}_{m,\rho}$ satisfies condition **B** of § 7, Subsection 3. It is evident that conditions **A** and **C** will also be satisfied; if one considers $\mathfrak{S}_{m,\rho}$ as a representation in the space $L^2(Z)$, then one can take $\mathfrak{D}$ to be the set of all regular analytic functions $f(z) = f(x, y)$ of the real variables x, y, which decrease sufficiently rapidly at infinity. Therefore all the results of § 8, Subsection 3 are applicable to the representation $\mathfrak{S}_{m,\rho}$, and for the infinitesimal operators of this representation formulae (51–55) § 8, Subsection 3 hold. We will find the connection between the parameters k_0, c in these formulae and the parameters m, ρ of the representation $\mathfrak{S}_{m,\rho}$. The number k_0 is the least number k such that the representation S_k is contained in $\mathfrak{S}_{m,\rho}$. Then it follows from Theorem 8 Subsection 4 that $k \geqslant |\frac{1}{2}m|$ and $k_0 = |\frac{1}{2}m|$. We consider the operators

$$\Delta = F_+F_- + F_-F_+ + 2F_3^2 - (H_+H_- + H_-H_+ + 2H_3^2), \quad (1)$$

$$\Delta' = H_+F_- + H_-F_+ + F_+H_- + F_-H_+ + 4H_3F_3. \quad (2)$$

Applying formulae (51–55) § 8, Subsection 3 we find after a simple calculation that†

$$\Delta f_\nu^k = -2(k_0^2 + c^2 - 1)f_\nu^k; \quad (3)$$

$$\Delta' f_\nu^k = -4ik_0 c f_\nu^k. \quad (4)$$

On the other hand, we consider the representation $\mathfrak{S}_{m,\rho}$ in the space $L^2(Z)$. Calculating its infinitesimal operators,‡ we obtain formulae (3–8) § 9, Subsection 4, in which it is necessary to replace m and n by $\frac{1}{2}m + \frac{1}{2}i\rho - 1$ and $-\frac{1}{2}m + \frac{1}{2}i\rho - 1$ respectively (see the remark on page 150). Substituting these expressions for the infinitesimal operators in (1) and (2), we find after some calculation that

$$\Delta f(z) = -2\left[\left(\frac{m}{2}\right)^2 - \left(\frac{\rho}{2}\right)^2 - 1\right] f(z), \quad (5)$$

$$\Delta' f(z) = -m\rho f(z). \quad (6)$$

Comparison of these formulae with (3) and (4) shows that

$$\left(\frac{m}{2}\right)^2 - \left(\frac{\rho}{2}\right)^2 = k_0^2 + c^2, \quad (7)$$

$$m\rho = 4ik_0 c. \quad (8)$$

---

† Formulae (3), (4) mean that the operators Δ, Δ' reduce to multiplications by constants (namely by $-2(k_0^2 + c^2 - 1)$, $-4ik_0 c$).

By virtue of the irreducibility of the representation this also follows from the fact that Δ, Δ' commute with each of the operators $H_+, H_-, H_3, F_+, F_-, F_3$; this fact is easily verified by appling relations (4–9) § 8, Subsection 1. For a general rule for forming polynomials of infinitesimal operators which commute with each of them, see [10c].

‡ See footnote on page 162.

First let $k_0 \neq 0$; since $k_0 = |m/2|$, then it follows from (8) that

$$c = -i(\operatorname{sign} m)\frac{\rho}{2}.$$

If however $k_0 = 0$, then $m = 0$, and (7) gives

$$c = \pm i\frac{\rho}{2}.$$

Thus we have

I. *For the representation* $\mathfrak{S}_{m,\rho}$ *of the principal series the parameters* k_0, c *and* m, ρ *are connected by the following relations*:

$$k_0 = \left|\frac{m}{2}\right|, \quad c = -i(\operatorname{sign} m)\frac{\rho}{2} \quad \text{when} \quad m \neq 0, \tag{9}$$

$$k_0 = 0, \quad c = \pm i\frac{\rho}{2} \quad \text{when} \quad m = 0. \tag{10}$$

Since for the representation $\mathfrak{S}_{m,\rho}$, m can be an arbitrary integer, and ρ is an arbitrary real number, we arrive at the following result:

II. *For any integral or half-integral non-negative number* k_0 *and any pure imaginary number* c *the formulae* (51–55) *of* § 8, *Subsection* 3 *realize an irreducible unitary representation of the group* $\mathfrak{A}$, *in fact a representation of the principal series.* Two unitary representations $a \to T_a$, $a \to T'_a$ in the spaces R and R' will be called *unitarily equivalent* if there exists an isometric mapping of R on R', by which T_a goes into T'_a. Obviously, unitary equivalence means that a suitable choice of orthonormal bases in R and R' will ensure that the operators T_a and T'_a are given by the same matrix.

III. *The representations* $\mathfrak{S}_{m,\rho}$ *and* $\mathfrak{S}_{-m,-\rho}$ *are unitarily equivalent.*

Proof. First let $m \neq 0$; from formulae (9) it follows that $\mathfrak{S}_{m,\rho}$ and $\mathfrak{S}_{-m,-\rho}$ have the same numbers k_0 and c. Therefore in the corresponding canonical bases, the same formulae (51–55) of § 8, Subsection 3 will define both representations. Hence the assertion follows, because a representation is defined completely by its infinitesimal operators (see I § 7, Subsection 3 and remark 4 in § 13, Subsection 5).

Now let $m = 0$; by virtue of (10) we have $k_0 = 0$ for both representations and Im c is determined to within sign. However, it is easy to see from formulae (51–55) § 8, Subsection 3 that a change of sign for Im c does not affect these formulae; in fact, c occurs to the first power only in the coefficient A_k, which is equal to zero in the case under consideration. Hence the assertion is also proved in this case.

If $(m,\rho) \neq (m',\rho')$ and $(m,\rho) \neq (-m',-\rho')$, then representations $\mathfrak{S}_{m,\rho}$ and $\mathfrak{S}_{m',\rho'}$ are not equivalent (see below, IV § 13, Subsection 7, and also Theorem 15 of § 15, Subsection 9).

Using formulae (9), (19) Subsection 4, it is possible to obtain an explicit expression for an isometric operator U, transforming $\mathfrak{S}_{-m,-\rho}$ into $\mathfrak{S}_{m,\rho}$. In fact, the operator U must transform a canonical basis $\phi^k_{-\nu_0 \rho}$ of the representation $\mathfrak{S}_{-m,-\rho}$ to a canonical basis $\phi^k_{-\nu_0 \rho}$ of the representation $\mathfrak{S}_{m,\rho}$; hence in a basis consisting of the functions $c^k_{\nu_0 \rho}(u)$, the operator U is given by the formula

$$U[\kappa^k_{\nu_0 \rho}\sqrt{(2k+1)}\, c^k_{-\nu_0 \rho}(u)] = \kappa^{-k}_{\nu_0 \rho}\sqrt{(2k+1)}\, c^k_{\nu_0 \rho}(u), \tag{11}$$

where ($k_0 = |\nu_0|$):

$$\kappa^k_{\nu_0 \rho} = \prod_{\nu=k_0}^{k} \frac{-2\nu+i\rho}{\sqrt{(4\nu^2+\rho^2)}} .$$

7. The case of spinor representations

Now we consider a spinor representation $S_{m,n}$ of the group $\mathfrak{A}$. We recall that the space $R_{m,n}$ of this representation consists of polynomials

$$p(z,\bar{z}) = \sum_{p=0}^{m} \sum_{q=0}^{n} c_{pq} z^p \bar{z}^q \tag{1}$$

of complex variables z and $\bar{z}$ having degree $\leqslant m$ in z and degree $\leqslant n$ in $\bar{z}$, and where

$$T_a p(z,\bar{z}) = (\beta z+\delta)^m \overline{(\beta z+\delta)}^n p\left(\frac{\alpha z+\gamma}{\beta z+\delta}, \frac{\overline{\alpha z}+\bar{\gamma}}{\overline{\beta z}+\bar{\delta}}\right). \tag{2}$$

Letting $p(z,\bar{z}) = f(z)$ and

$$\alpha(g) = g_{22}^m \bar{g}_{22}^n, \tag{3}$$

we can rewrite formula (2) in the form

$$T_a f(z) = \alpha(za) f(z\bar{a}) \tag{4}$$

(see in this connection § 10, Subsection 6). Let us write, as in Subsection 3,

$$\phi(u) = \sqrt{(\pi)}\,\alpha(u) f(z) \quad \text{where} \quad u, z \in \tilde{z}; \tag{5}$$

$$z = \frac{u_{21}}{u_{22}} \quad \text{where} \quad u, z \in \tilde{z}$$

(see (4) § 10, Subsection 2), then it follows from (1) and (3) that

$$\phi(u) = \sqrt{(\pi)} \sum_{p=0}^{m} \sum_{q=0}^{n} c_{pq} u_{21}^{p} u_{22}^{m-p} \bar{u}_{21}^{q} \bar{u}_{22}^{n-q}, \tag{6}$$

so that $\phi(u)$ runs through all polynomials which are homogeneous, in u_{21}, u_{22} of degree m and in $\bar{u}_{21}, \bar{u}_{22}$ of degree n. Let $\tilde{R}_{m,n}$ denote the set of all such polynomials. It is easy to see that $\tilde{R}_{m,n}$ is the set of all polynomials homogeneous of degree $m+n$ in u_{21}, u_{22}s $\bar{u}_{21}, \bar{u}_{22}$, satisfying the condition

$$\phi(\gamma u) = \alpha(\gamma)\phi(u) = e^{i(m-n)\omega}\phi(u) \tag{7}$$

where $\gamma_{22} = e^{i\omega}$.

Repeating the argument in Subsection 3, we conclude that the operators of the representation in the space $\tilde{R}_{m,n}$ are given by the formula

$$T_a \phi(u) = \frac{\alpha(ua)}{\alpha(u\bar{a})} \phi(u\bar{a}) \quad \text{where} \quad \phi(u) \in \tilde{R}_{m,n}. \tag{8}$$

§ 12. Complementary Series of Representations of the Group $\mathfrak{A}$

1. Statement of the problem of complementary series

In § 10, Subsection 6 it was proved that for any real ρ the formula

$$V_a f(z) = \alpha(za) f(z\bar{a}), \quad \alpha(g) = |g_{22}|^{-m+i\rho-2} a_{22}^{m} \tag{1}$$

defines a unitary representation (a representation of the principal series) in the space $L^2(Z)$; we recall that the scalar product in $L^2(Z)$ is given by the formula

$$(f_1, f_2) = \int f_1(z)\overline{f_2(z)}\,dz. \tag{2}$$

In point of fact it follows from this proof that formula (1) defines a unitary representation in $L^2(Z)$ *only for real* ρ. The question arises whether it is possible to construct such a Hilbert space, i.e. to define a scalar product in such a way, that formula (1) defines a unitary representation in this space for other values of ρ. Below we shall see that such a definition is in fact possible; as a result yet another series of unitary representations is obtained, the so-called *complementary series.*

In a finite dimensional space the general form of the scalar product is a positive-definite Hermitian quadratic form

$$(x, y) = \sum_{p,q} a_{pq} x_p \bar{y}_q, \tag{3}$$

a special case of which is

$$(x, y) = \sum_{p} x_p \bar{y}_p. \tag{4}$$

It is evident that the scalar product (2) can be regarded as the analogue of expression (4); the analogue of expression (3) will then be

$$(f_1, f_2) = \iint K(z_1, z_2) f_1(z_1) \overline{f_2(z_2)} \mathrm{d}z_1 \mathrm{d}z_2, \tag{5}$$

where $K(z_1, z_2)$ is some function of z_1, z_2.

We suppose that a linear space $\mathfrak{H}'$ of functions $f(z)$ exists which satisfies the following conditions:

(1) $\mathfrak{H}'$ contains all bounded measurable functions $f(z)$ which vanish in the exterior of some bounded set in the z-plane;

(2) the integral (5) converges absolutely for all $f_1(z), f_2(z) \in \mathfrak{H}'$;

(3) $\mathfrak{H}'$ is invariant with respect to all V_a.

Such a space will be constructed at the end of this subsection. Because the expression (f_1, f_2) in (5) must be a scalar product, the function $K(z_1, z_2)$ must satisfy the condition $(f, f) \geqslant 0$ for all $f \in \mathfrak{H}'$. For the representation to be unitary it is necessary that the scalar product (5) remain invariant under an application of the operator V_a, i.e. that

$$(V_a f_1, V_a f_2) = (f_1, f_2).$$

When written out in detail this condition takes the form

$$\iint K(z_1, z_2) \alpha(z_1 a) f_1(z_1 \bar{a}) \overline{\alpha(z_2 a) f_2(z_2 \bar{a})} \mathrm{d}z_1 \mathrm{d}z_2 = \\ = \iint K(z_1', z_2') f_1(z_1') \overline{f_2(z_2')} \mathrm{d}z_1' \mathrm{d}z_2'. \tag{6}$$

In the right side of (6) we make the substitution

$$z_1' = z_1\bar{a}, \quad z_2' = z_2\bar{a};$$

taking into account the formula

$$d(z\bar{a}) = \beta^{-1}(za)dz \tag{7}$$

(see (8) § 10, Subsection 5), we obtain:

$$\iint K(z_1, z_2)\alpha(z_1 a)f_1(z_1\bar{a})\overline{\alpha(z_2 a)f_2(z_2\bar{a})}dz_1 dz_2$$
$$= \iint K(z_1\bar{a}, z_2\bar{a})f_1(z_1\bar{a})\overline{f_2(z_2\bar{a})}\beta^{-1}(z_1 a)\beta^{-1}(z_2 a)dz_1 dz_2;$$

hence in view of condition (1)

$$K(z_1, z_2)\alpha(z_1 a)\overline{\alpha(z_2 a)} = K(z_1\bar{a}, z_2\bar{a})\beta^{-1}(z_1 a)\beta^{-1}(z_2 a),$$

or when written out in full,

$$K(z_1, z_2)|a_{12}z_1+a_{22}|^{-m+i\rho-2}(a_{12}z_1+a_{22})^m|a_{12}z_2+a_{22}|^{-m-i\bar{\rho}-2} \times$$
$$\times \overline{(a_{12}z_2+a_{22})}^m$$
$$= K\left(\frac{a_{11}z_1+a_{21}}{a_{12}z_1+a_{22}}, \frac{a_{11}z_2+a_{21}}{a_{12}z_2+a_{22}}\right)|a_{12}z_1+a_{22}|^{-4}|a_{12}z_2+a_{22}|^{-4}.$$

Hence,

$$K\left(\frac{a_{11}z_1+a_{21}}{a_{12}z_1+a_{22}}, \frac{a_{11}z_2+a_{21}}{a_{12}z_2+a_{22}}\right)$$
$$= K(z_1, z_2)|a_{12}z_1+a_{22}|^{-m+i\rho+2}$$
$$(a_{12}z_1+a_{22})^m|a_{12}z_2+a_{22}|^{-m-i\bar{\rho}+2}\overline{(a_{12}z_2+a_{22})}^m. \tag{8}$$

In particular, taking $a = z_0$, in (8), we obtain:

$$K(z_1+z_0, z_2+z_0) = K(z_1, z_2);$$

hence when $z_0 = -z_2$

$$K(z_1, z_2) = K(z_1-z_2, 0) = K_1(z_1-z_2), \tag{9}$$

where the notation is $K_1(z) = K(z, 0)$. Substituting this expression in (8), we get the condition

$$K_1\left(\frac{z_1-z_2}{(a_{12}z_1+a_{22})(a_{12}z_2+a_{22})}\right)$$
$$= K_1(z_1-z_2)|a_{12}z_1+a_{22}|^{-m+i\rho+2} \times$$
$$\times (a_{12}z_1+a_{22})^m|a_{12}z_2+a_{22}|^{-m-i\bar{\rho}+2}\overline{(a_{12}z_2+a_{22})}^m. \tag{10}$$

Letting $z_2 = 0$ here and choosing a_{12} so that $a_{12}z_1 + a_{22} = 1$, we obtain:

$$K_1\left(\frac{z_1}{a_{22}}\right) = K_1(z_1)|a_{22}|^{-m-i\bar{\rho}+2}\bar{a}_{22}^m. \tag{11}$$

On the other hand, letting $z_1 = 0$ in (10) and choosing a_{12} so that $a_{12}z_2 + a_{22} = 1$, we get

$$K_1\left(-\frac{z_2}{a_{22}}\right) = K_1(-z_2)|a_{22}|^{-m+i\rho+2}a_{22}^m. \tag{12}$$

Comparing (11) and (12) and taking into account the arbitrary nature of z_1, z_2, we conclude that

$$|a_{22}|^{-i\bar{\rho}}\bar{a}_{22}^m = |a_{22}|^{i\rho}a_{22}^m. \tag{13}$$

Let us put $a_{22} = e^{i\theta}$ in (13), where θ is a real number; we obtain $e^{-im\theta} = e^{im\theta}$ which is possible only when $m = 0$. However it then follows from (13) that $\bar{\rho} = -\rho$, i.e. ρ is a pure imaginary number. Let us put $\rho = i\sigma$; then from (11) when $a_{22} = z_1 = z$ it follows that

$$K_1(z) = C|z|^{-2+\sigma}$$

and hence

$$K(z_1, z_2) = C|z_1 - z_2|^{-2+\sigma}, \tag{14}$$

where $C = K_1(1)$ is an arbitrary constant; expression (5) for the scalar product takes the form

$$(f_1, f_2) = C\iint |z_1 - z_2|^{-2+\sigma} f_1(z_1)\overline{f_2(z_2)}\,dz_1\,dz_2. \tag{15}$$

In this case formula (1) for the operator of a representation will be written in the form

$$V_a f(z) = |a_{12}z + a_{22}|^{-2-\sigma} f\left(\frac{a_{11}z + a_{21}}{a_{12}z + a_{22}}\right). \tag{16}$$

We note that for the convergence of the integral in (15) it is necessary to satisfy the condition

$$\sigma > 0. \tag{17}$$

Finally we show how to construct the space $\mathfrak{H}'$; we take the set of all measurable functions $f(z)$ satisfying an inequality

$$|f(z)| \leqslant C(1 + |z|^2)^{-1-2\frac{\sigma}{2}}, \tag{18}$$

for almost all complex z, where C is a constant depending on f. It is not hard to show that this set satisfies conditions (1)–(3).

2. The condition for positive definiteness

Formula (15) Subsection 1 defines a scalar product only if $(f, f) \geqslant 0$, i.e. if

$$C \iint |z_1 - z_2|^{-2+\sigma} f(z_1)\overline{f(z_2)}\,dz_1 dz_2 \geqslant 0. \tag{1}$$

We discuss the restriction on the number σ which this condition imposes.

We denote by $\mathfrak{H}''$ the set of all functions $f(z)$ which vanish outside some circle (depending on the function) and are differentiable with respect to x, y $(z = x+iy)$ as many times as desired, so that the Fourier transforms

$$\phi(w) = \frac{1}{2\pi} \int f(z) e^{-i\,\mathrm{Re}(\bar{z}w)} dz \tag{2}$$

will be summable functions

$$\int |\phi(w)|\,dw < \infty \tag{3}$$

$(dw = du\,dv,\ w = u+iv)$; clearly $\mathfrak{H}'' \subset \mathfrak{H}'$. We denote the set of all such Fourier transforms by H''. We consider first the case $0 < \sigma < \frac{1}{2}$. Then

$$\int |z_1 - z_2|^{-2+\sigma} f(z_1)\,dz_1 = \int |z|^{-2+\sigma} f(z+z_2)\,dz$$

$$= \frac{1}{2\pi} \int |z|^{-2+\sigma} \left[\int \phi(w) e^{i\,\mathrm{Re}((z+z_2)\bar{w})} dw \right] dz.$$

In the integral with respect to z we go over to polar coordinates, letting $z = re^{i\theta}$; in addition we set $w = r_1 e^{i\theta_1}$. We obtain:

$$\int |z_1 - z_2|^{-2+\sigma} f(z_1)\,dz_1$$

$$= \frac{1}{2\pi} \int_0^\infty r^{-1+\sigma} dr \int_0^{2\pi} \left[\int \phi(w) e^{i\,\mathrm{Re}(rr_1} e^{i\mathrm{Re}(rr_1 e^{i(\theta-\theta_1)})} e^{i\,\mathrm{Re}(z_2\bar{w})}\, dw \right] d\theta.$$

However the inner integral converges uniformly with respect to θ, because its modulus never exceeds $\int |\phi(w)|\,dw$; therefore one can integrate with respect to θ under the integral sign. Performing this integration we obtain:

$$\int |z_1-z_2|^{-2+\sigma} f(z_1)\,dz_1 = \int_0^\infty r^{-1+\sigma}\left[\int \phi(w) e^{i \operatorname{Re}(z_2\bar{w})} I_0(rr_1)\,dw\right] dr, \quad (4)$$

where I_0 is a Bessel function of zero order. For $0 < \sigma < \frac{1}{2}$ this integral converges absolutely with respect to r and w, and therefore one can change the order of the integration in it. Hence,

$$\int |z_1-z_2|^{-2+\sigma} f(z_1)\,dz_1 = \int \phi(w) e^{i \operatorname{Re}(z_2\bar{w})}\,dw \int_0^\infty r^{-1+\sigma} I_0(rr_1)\,dr$$

$$= 2^{-1+\sigma} \frac{\Gamma\left(\frac{\sigma}{2}\right)}{\Gamma\left(1-\frac{\sigma}{2}\right)} \int \phi(w) e^{i \operatorname{Re}(z_2\bar{w})} r_1^{-\sigma}\,dw$$

$$= 2^{-1+\sigma} \frac{\Gamma\left(\frac{\sigma}{2}\right)}{\Gamma\left(1-\frac{\sigma}{2}\right)} \int \phi(w) e^{i \operatorname{Re}(z_2\bar{w})} |w|^{-\sigma}\,dw$$

(see Ref. [34], page 259). Multiplying both sides of this equation by $\overline{f(z_2)}$ and integrating with respect to z_2, we obtain:

$$\iint |z_1-z_2|^{-2+\sigma} f(z_1)\overline{f(z_2)}\,dz_1\,dz_2$$

$$= 2^\sigma \pi \frac{\Gamma\left(\frac{\sigma}{2}\right)}{\Gamma\left(1-\frac{\sigma}{2}\right)} \int |\phi(w)|^2 |w|^{-\sigma}\,dw. \quad (5)$$

Formula (5) was derived under the condition $0 < \sigma < \frac{1}{2}$, but the left and right sides of this are analytic functions when $0 < \operatorname{Re}\sigma < 2$; hence, formula (5) is valid for $0 < \operatorname{Re}\sigma < 2$. In particular, formula (5) is valid for $0 < \sigma < 2$. Obviously, the right hand side is positive for $0 < \sigma < 2$; hence;

Condition (1) *of positive definiteness is satisfied for* $0 < \sigma < 2$; *one can set* $C = 1$.

When $\sigma = 2$ and $C = 1$ formula (15), Subsection 1 becomes

$$(f_1, f_2) = \int\int f_1(z_1)\overline{f_2(z_2)}\mathrm{d}z_1\mathrm{d}z_2 = \int f_1(z_1)\mathrm{d}z_1 \overline{\int f_2(z_2)\mathrm{d}z_2}; \qquad (6)$$

in particular,

$$(f, f) = \left|\int f(z)\mathrm{d}z\right|^2 \geqslant 0 \qquad (7)$$

and $(f,f) = 0$, only if $\int f(z)\mathrm{d}z = 0$. Now we will consider the functions $f(z)$ as elements of a Hilbert space R, in which the scalar product is defined by formula (6); we may say that $f(z)$ is equal to zero as an element of the Hilbert space if $\int f(z)\mathrm{d}z = 0$, because in this case $(f,f) = 0$. This Hilbert space R is one-dimensional. In fact, if $\int f_2(z)\mathrm{d}z \neq 0$, then, letting

$$c = \frac{\int f_1(z)\mathrm{d}z}{\int f_2(z)\mathrm{d}z}, \qquad f = f_1 - cf_2,$$

we have $\int f(z)\mathrm{d}z = 0$, i.e. $f = f_1 - cf_2 = 0$, $f_1 = cf_2$. This means that any two elements $f_1, f_2 \in R$ are linearly dependent, i.e. R is one-dimensional. We prove that in this case $V_a = 1$. In fact, when $\sigma = 2$ formula (16) Subsection 1 takes the form

$$V_a f(z) = |a_{12}z + a_{22}|^{-4} f\left(\frac{a_{11}z + a_{21}}{a_{12}z + a_{22}}\right),$$

and it is easy to verify that $\int V_a f(z)\mathrm{d}z = \int f(z)\mathrm{d}z$; by the definition of equality in R this means that

$$V_a f = f, \quad \text{i.e.} \quad V_a = 1. \qquad (8)$$

The one-dimensional representation $a \to 1$ obtained is therefore the unit representation (see § 9, Subsection 6). Thus, *one can consider the unit representation as the limit of the representations of the complementary series at* $\sigma = 2$.

On the other hand, we could change the definition of the scalar product (f_1, f_2) in an inessential way, for $0 < \sigma < 2$ letting

$$(f_1, f_2) = \Gamma\left(1 - \frac{\sigma}{2}\right)\int\int |z_1 - z_2|^{-2+\sigma} f_1(z_1)\overline{f_2(z_2)}\mathrm{d}z_1\mathrm{d}z_2.$$

Formula (5) shows then that

$$(f,f) = 2^{\sigma}\pi\Gamma\left(\frac{\sigma}{2}\right)\int |\phi(w)|^2|w|^{-\sigma}\mathrm{d}w. \qquad (9)$$

Let $f \in \mathfrak{H}''$ and suppose that

$$\phi(0) = \frac{1}{2\pi}\int f(z)\mathrm{d}z = 0. \qquad (10)$$

Then the limit as $\sigma \to 2{-}0$ of the right hand side of (9) exists; hence taking limits we find that

$$(f,f) = 4\pi \int |\phi(w)|^2|w|^{-2}\mathrm{d}w. \qquad (11)$$

We let

$$\tilde{f}(z) = 2\sqrt{(\pi)}\frac{1}{2\pi}\int \frac{\phi(w)}{w}\mathrm{e}^{iRe(z\bar{w})}\mathrm{d}w, \qquad (12)$$

so that $\tilde{f}$ is the product by $2\sqrt{(\pi)}$ of the Fourier transform of the function $\frac{\phi(w)}{w}$. Therefore

$$\int |\tilde{f}(z)|^2\mathrm{d}z = 4\pi \int |\phi(w)|^2|w|^{-2}\mathrm{d}w$$

and from (11) it follows that

$$(f,f) = \int |\tilde{f}(z)|^2\mathrm{d}z, \qquad (13a)$$

hence,

$$(f_1,f_2) = \int \tilde{f}_1(z)\bar{\tilde{f}}_2(z)\mathrm{d}z. \qquad (13b)$$

Since $\mathrm{Re}(z\bar{w}) = \frac{1}{2}(\bar{z}w+z\bar{w})$, then, differentiating both sides of (12) with respect to $\bar{z}$, we conclude that

$$\frac{\partial\tilde{f}}{\partial\bar{z}} = 2\sqrt{(\pi)}\frac{i}{2}\frac{1}{2\pi}\int \phi(w)\mathrm{e}^{iRe(z\bar{w})}\mathrm{d}w = i\sqrt{(\pi)}f(z). \qquad (14)$$

Relation (13a) shows that $\tilde{f} \in L^2(Z)$, therefore one can apply the operators of the principal series to $\tilde{f}$.

We consider in particular the representation $\mathfrak{S}_{-2,0}$ of the principal series; we denote its operators by W_a. Then

$$W_a\tilde{f}(z) = (a_{12}z+a_{22})^{-2}\tilde{f}\left(\frac{a_{11}z+a_{21}}{a_{12}z+a_{22}}\right);$$

hence

$$\frac{1}{i\sqrt{(\pi)}}\frac{\partial}{\partial \bar{z}}(W_a\tilde{f}(z))$$

$$= (a_{12}z+a_{22})^{-2}\overline{(a_{12}z+a_{22})}^{-2}\frac{1}{i\sqrt{(\pi)}}\tilde{f}'\left(\frac{a_{11}z+a_{21}}{a_{12}z+a_{22}}\right)$$

$$= |a_{12}z+a_{22}|^{-4}f\left(\frac{a_{11}z+a_{21}}{a_{12}z+a_{22}}\right) = V_af(z).$$

This means that in the transition from $\tilde{f}$ to f by formula (14) the operator W_a goes into V_a.

Thus, taking into account formulae (8), it is natural to consider that *in proceeding to the limit at* $\sigma = 2$ *the representation of the complementary series tends to the identity representation and the representation* $\mathfrak{S}_{-2,0}$ *of the principal series.* This shows that the space of all irreducible representations of $\mathfrak{U}$ with a natural topology is not Hausdorff. For further information on this subject we refer the reader to J. M. G. Fell, the dual space of C*—algebras, Trans. Ame-. Math. Soc. 1960, 365–403.

For $\sigma > 2$ formulae (15) and (16) Subsection 1 *do not determine a unitary representation.* Suppose for instance that $2 < \sigma < 4$. From the preceding reasoning it follows that formula (5) remains true as before for the functions $f(z) \in \mathfrak{H}''$ such that

$$\phi(0) = \frac{1}{2\pi}\int f(z)dz = 0. \tag{15}$$

The set $\mathfrak{H}'''$ of all such functions $f(z)$ forms a subspace in $\mathfrak{H}'$; for a positive definite expression (f_1, f_2) on $\mathfrak{H}'''$ it is necessary to take $C < 0$, because for $2 < \sigma < 4$ the factor in front of the integral on the right side of (5) is negative. On the other hand, for $C < 0$ and $f(z) > 0$ the left side of (5), will be negative, hence the form (f_1, f_2) will not be positive definite in $\mathfrak{H}'$. In addition, $\mathfrak{H}'$ has no subspace invariant with respect to all operators V_a, on which the form (f_1, f_2) is positive definite; it follows from this that for $2 < \sigma < 4$ condition (10) is not invariant with respect to the transformation V_a (see (16) Subsection 1).

3. The spaces $\mathfrak{H}_\sigma$ and H_σ

Let $0 < \sigma < 2$. We will introduce into $\mathfrak{H}''$ a scalar product

$$(f_1, f_2) = \iint |z_1 - z_2|^{-2+\sigma} f_1(z_1)\overline{f_2(z_2)}\,dz_1\,dz_2, \tag{1}$$

and into H'' a scalar product

$$(\phi_1, \phi_2) = 2^\sigma \pi \frac{\Gamma\left(\frac{\sigma}{2}\right)}{\Gamma\left(1-\frac{\sigma}{2}\right)} \int \phi_1(w)\overline{\phi_2(w)}|w|^{-\sigma}\,dw. \tag{2}$$

Then $\mathfrak{H}''$ and H'' become Euclidean spaces; we denote their completions† by $\mathfrak{H}_\sigma$ and H_σ respectively. Formula (5) Subsection 2 means that the Fourier transform

$$\phi(w) = \frac{1}{2\pi} \int f(z) e^{-iRe(w\bar{z})}\,dz \tag{3}$$

† If R is an incomplete normed (in particular, Euclidean) space, then one can complete it, i.e. include it in a complete normed (respectively Hilbert) space $\tilde{R}$. The construction of the space $\tilde{R}$ is analogous to the Cantor construction of the set of all real numbers (see, for example, Ref. [29] Chapter II) and consists of the following. The elements of the space $\tilde{R}$ are all possible fundamental sequences $x = \{x_n\}$ in R, where two such sequences $x = \{x_n\}$, $y = \{y_n\}$ are not considered distinct if $|x_n - y_n| \to 0$, and an element $x \in R$ is identified with the sequence $\{x, x, x, \ldots\}$. The operations with these sequences and the norm are defined by the formulae:

$$\alpha x = \{\alpha x_n\}, x+y = \{x_n+y_n\}, |x| = \lim_{n\to\infty} |x_n|$$

and (if R is a Euclidean space)

$$\{x, y\} = \lim_{n\to\infty} (x_n, y_n)$$

for $x = \{x_n\}$, $y = \{y_n\}$. It is easy to verify that $\tilde{R}$ is then a complete normed (respectively Hilbert) space (for a detailed proof of this see, for example, Ref. [26], (§ 5). It is called *the completion of the space R*. If now A is a bounded operator in R, and $x = \{x_n\}$ is a fundamental sequence in R, then $\{Ax_n\}$ is also a fundamental sequence in R, and we let $Ax = \{Ax_n\}$. It is easy to see that A will be a bounded operator in $\tilde{R}$; we call it *the continuation by continuity* of the original operator A. In an analogous way the continuation by continuity of an isometric operator is defined; clearly it will also be an isometric operator.

is an isometric mapping of $\mathfrak{H}''$ on H''; by continuity this mapping is extended, in a unique way, to an isometric mapping of $\mathfrak{H}_\sigma$ on H_σ.

The space H_σ is the set of all measurable functions $\phi(w)$, satisfying the condition

$$\int |\phi(w)|^2 |w|^{-\sigma} dw < \infty . \tag{4}$$

In fact, if we temporarily denote this set by $\tilde{H}_\sigma$ then it is easy to convince oneself that H'', and hence also H_σ, is dense in $\tilde{H}_\sigma$. Because H_σ and $\tilde{H}_\sigma$ are both complete, $\tilde{H}_\sigma = H_\sigma$. It is easy to prove that $\mathfrak{H}' \subset \mathfrak{H}_\sigma$; hence $\mathfrak{H}_\sigma$ is also the completion of $\mathfrak{H}'$

4. A description of the representations of the complementary series in the space $\mathfrak{H}_\sigma$.

From the reasoning in Subsection 1 it follows that formula (16) Subsection 1 defines an isometric operator V_a in $\mathfrak{H}'$; hence it can be uniquely extended by continuity to an isometric operator V_a in the completion $\mathfrak{H}_\sigma$ of the space $\mathfrak{H}'$. Repeating the reasoning of § 10, Subsection 6, it is easy to convince oneself that $V_e f = f$ and $V_{a_1} V_{a_2} f = V_{a_1, a_2} f$ for $f \in \mathfrak{H}''$. Hence by continuity it follows that $V_e f = f$, $V_{a_1} V_{a_2} f = V_{a_1 a_2} f$ for all $f \in \mathfrak{H}_\sigma$, so that $V_e = 1$ and $V_{a_1} V_{a_2} = V_{a_1 a_2}$. This means that the correspondence $a \to V_a$ is a representation, in fact a unitary representation, of the group $\mathfrak{A}$. We arrive at the following result:

I. *For* $0 < \sigma < 2$ *the formula*

$$V_a f(z) = |a_{12} z + a_{22}|^{-2-\sigma} f\left(\frac{a_{11} z + a_{21}}{a_{12} z + a_{22}}\right)$$

defines a unitary representation $a \to V_a$ *of the group* $\mathfrak{A}$ *in the space* $\mathfrak{H}_\sigma$.

This representation is denoted by $\mathfrak{D}_\sigma$, and the set of all representations $\mathfrak{D}_\sigma$, $0 < \sigma < 2$, will be called the *complementary series* of representations of the group $\mathfrak{A}$.

II. *The representations of the complementary series are irreducible.*

Proof. Let A be a bounded linear operator in $\mathfrak{H}_\sigma$, which commutes with all the operators V_a of a representation of the complementary series. We must prove that A is a multiple of the identity operator. As in the proof for the principal series (see § 10,

Subsection 7), we consider the operators V_z, $z \in Z$, and V_{a_0}, where $a_0 = \begin{Vmatrix} \lambda^{-1} & 0 \\ 0 & \lambda \end{Vmatrix}$, so that for $f \in \mathfrak{H}''$

$$V_{z_0} f(z) = f(z+z_0), \quad V_{a_0} f(z) = |\lambda|^{-2-\sigma} f(\lambda^{-2} z). \tag{1}$$

We pass from the functions $f \in \mathfrak{H}''$ to their Fourier transforms

$$\phi(w) = \frac{1}{2\pi} \int f(z) e^{-iRe(\bar{z}w)} dz. \tag{2}$$

The transition from f to ϕ by means of this formula is an isometric mapping of $\mathfrak{H}''$ on H'', continued in a unique way to an isometric mapping of $\mathfrak{H}_\sigma$ on H_σ, where in H_σ

$$(\phi_1, \phi_2) = \int \phi_1(w) \overline{\phi_2(w)} |w|^{-\sigma} dw \tag{3}$$

(see Subsection 3).

We denote by $\hat{A}$, $\hat{V}_{z_0}$, $\hat{V}_{a_0}$ the operators in H_σ, into which A, V_{z_0}, V_{a_0} pass in this mapping; as before $\hat{A}$ commutes with $\hat{V}_{z_0}$ and $\hat{V}_{a_0}$.

From formulae (1) and (2) it follows that for $\phi \in H''$

$$\hat{V}_{z_0} \phi(w) = e^{iRe(\bar{z}_0 w)} \phi(w), \quad \hat{V}_{a_0} \phi(w) = |\lambda|^{2-\sigma} \phi(\bar{\lambda}^2 w). \tag{4}$$

But the left and right sides in (4) define bounded linear operators in the whole of H_σ, and since H'' is dense in H_σ, formulae (4) are valid for all $\phi \in H_\sigma$. Now we set

$$\psi(w) = \phi(w) |w|^{-\frac{\sigma}{2}}; \tag{5}$$

then by virtue of (3) we have

$$(\phi_1, \phi_2) = \int \psi_1(w) \overline{\psi_2(w)} dw,$$

hence the transition from ϕ to ψ by means of formula (5) is an isometric mapping of the space H_σ on the Hilbert space $L^2(W)$ of all measurable functions $\psi(w)$, satisfying the condition $\int |\psi(w)|^2 dw < \infty$ with the scalar product $(\psi_1, \psi_2) = \int \psi_1(w) \overline{\psi_2(w)} dw$. Let A', V'_{z_0}, V'_{a_0} be the operators in $L^2(W)$, into which $\hat{A}$, $\hat{V}_{z_0}$, $\hat{V}_{a_0}$ pass in this mapping; then A' commutes with V'_{z_0}

and V'_{a_0}, and we must prove that A' is a multiple of the identity operator. For this purpose we will find V'_{z_0} and V'_{a_0}. By virtue of (4) and (5):

$$V'_{z_0}\psi(w) = |w|^{-\frac{\sigma}{2}}\hat{V}_{z_0}[\psi(w)|w|^{\frac{\sigma}{2}}] = |w|^{-\frac{\sigma}{2}}e^{iRe(\bar{z}_0 w)}\psi(w)|w|^{\frac{\sigma}{2}}$$
$$= e^{iRe(\bar{z}_0 w)}\psi(w),$$

$$V'_{a_0}\psi(w) = |w|^{-\frac{\sigma}{2}}\hat{V}_{a_0}[\psi(w)|w|^{\frac{\sigma}{2}}] = |w|^{-\frac{\sigma}{2}}[|\lambda|^{2-\sigma}\psi(\bar{\lambda}^2 w)|\bar{\lambda}^2 w|^{\frac{\sigma}{2}}]$$
$$= |\lambda|^2\psi(\bar{\lambda}^2 w). \tag{6}$$

The operator A' in $L^2(W)$ commutes with all operators V'_{z_0}, which are operators of multiplication by $e^{i\,\mathrm{Re}(\bar{z}_0,\,w)}$; hence, as in the proof of Theorem 6 § 10, Subsection 7, we conclude that

$$A'\psi(w) = c(w)\psi(w),$$

where $c(w)$ is an essentially bounded measurable function. But then, by virtue of (6), the condition of the commutability of A' with V'_{a_0} gives $c(w) = c(\bar{\lambda}^2 w)$ for almost all w. Hence $c(w)$ is a constant, $c(w) = c$ for almost all w, i.e. $A' = c1$, and the theorem is proved.

5. A description of the representations of the complementary series with the aid of the unitary subgroup

The representation $\mathfrak{D}_\sigma$ can be described by means of operators in a space of functions $f(u)$, $u \in \mathfrak{U}$, in a manner similar to what was done in § 11 for the representations $\mathfrak{S}_{m,\rho}$, of the principal series. We set for $f(z) \in \mathfrak{H}'$

$$\phi(u) = \sqrt{(\pi)}\alpha(u)f(z) \quad \text{for} \quad u, z \in \tilde{z}, \tag{1}$$

where now

$$\alpha(a) = |a_{22}|^{-2-\sigma}. \tag{2}$$

Since

$$\alpha(\gamma u) = \alpha(u), \tag{3}$$

the function $\phi(u)$ will satisfy the condition

$$\phi(\gamma u) = \phi(u). \tag{4}$$

We will find an expression for the scalar product of functions $\phi(u)$. From (1) it follows that

$$(f_1, f_2) = \iint |z'-z''|^{-2+\sigma} f_1(z')\overline{f_2(z'')}\,dz'\,dz''$$

$$= \frac{1}{\pi}\iint |z'-z''|^{-2+\sigma}\alpha^{-1}(u')\phi_1(u')\alpha^{-1}(u'')\overline{\phi_2(u'')}\,dz'\,dz''. \qquad (5)$$

Here we pass from integration with respect to z', z'' to integration with respect to u', u''. Because z' and u' belong to the same class $\tilde{z}$ (analogously z'' and u''), we have

$$u' = k'z', \quad u'' = k''z''. \qquad (6)$$

Then by virtue of (5) § 11, Subsection 3:

$$\beta^{-1}(u')\,du' = \frac{1}{2\pi^2}\,d\omega'\,dz', \quad \beta^{-1}(u'')\,du'' = \frac{1}{2\pi^2}\,d\omega''\,dz'', \qquad (7)$$

where

$$\omega' = \arg k'_{22}, \quad \omega'' = \arg k''_{22}. \qquad (8)$$

But, by virtue of (3) and (4), the inner integral function on the right side of (5) does not depend on ω' and ω''; therefore

$$(f_1, f_2) = \frac{2}{(2\pi)^3}\int_0^{2\pi} d\omega' \int_0^{2\pi} d\omega'' \iint |z'-z''|^{-2+\sigma}\alpha^{-1}(u')\phi_1(u')\times$$

$$\times\alpha^{-1}(u'')\overline{\phi_2(u'')}\,dz'\,dz'' = \frac{2}{(2\pi)^3}(2\pi^2)^2\iint |z'-z''|^{-2+\sigma}\alpha^{-1}(u')\times$$

$$\times\beta^{-1}(u')\phi_1(u')\alpha^{-1}(u'')\beta^{-1}(u'')\overline{\phi_2(u'')}\,du'\,du'',$$

or, taking into account formula (2) for $\alpha(a)$ and the formula $\beta(a) = |a_{22}|^4$ for $\beta(a)$ (see (5) § 10, Subsection 5).

$$(f_1, f_2) = \pi \iint |z'-z''|^{-2+\sigma}|u'_{22}|^{-2+\sigma}|u''_{22}|^{-2+\sigma}\times$$

$$\times\phi_1(u')\overline{\phi_2(u'')}\,du'\,du''. \qquad (9)$$

We will express z' and z'' in terms of u' and u''. Applying formula (4) § 10, Subsection 2 to (6), we have:

$$z' = \frac{u'_{21}}{u'_{22}}, \qquad z'' = \frac{u''_{21}}{u''_{22}};$$

hence

$$|z'-z''|^{-2+\sigma} = |u'_{21}u''_{22}-u'_{22}u''_{21}|^{-2+\sigma}|u'_{22}|^{2-\sigma}|u''_{22}|^{2-\sigma}.$$

Substituting these expressions in (9), we obtain:

$$(f_1, f_2) = \pi \iint |u'_{21}u''_{22}-u'_{22}u''_{21}|^{-2+\sigma}\phi_1(u')\overline{\phi_2(u'')}du'du''. \quad (10)$$

Formula (10) can be given a still more simple form, if one introduces the function

$$\Phi(u) = |u_{21}|^{-2+\sigma}; \quad (11)$$

then it is easy to verify that

$$\Phi(u'u''^{-1}) = |u'_{21}u''_{22}-u'_{22}u''_{21}|^{-2+\sigma}, \quad (12)$$

and so

$$(f_1, f_2) = \pi \iint \Phi(u'u''^{-1})\phi_1(u')\overline{\phi_2(u'')}du'du''. \quad (13)$$

We denote by H' the set of all bounded measurable functions $\phi(u)$, satisfying the condition

$$\phi(\gamma u) = \phi(u). \quad (14)$$

For ϕ_1, $\phi_2 \in H'$ the integral on the right side of (13) converges absolutely. We introduce into H' the scalar product

$$(\phi_1, \phi_2) = \pi \iint \Phi(u'u''^{-1})\phi_1(u')\overline{\phi_2(u'')}du'du''. \quad (15)$$

Then H' becomes a Euclidean space; we denote its completion by H_σ. By virtue of (13), formula (1) establishes an isometric mapping of $\mathfrak{H}'$ on H', which is extended in a unique way by continuity to an isometric mapping of $\mathfrak{H}_\sigma$ on H_σ. The operators V_a of a representation of the complementary series in the space $\mathfrak{H}_\sigma$ pass into operators in the space H_σ, which we again denote by V_a. For a derivation of the form of these last operators it is sufficient to repeat the reasoning of § 11, Subsection 3. We arrive at the following result.

The operators V_a of a representation of the complementary series in the space H_σ are defined by the formula

$$V_a\phi(u) = \frac{\alpha(ua)}{\alpha(u\bar{a})}\phi(u\bar{a}) \text{ for } \phi \in H', \tag{16}$$

where

$$\alpha(a) = |a_{22}|^{-2-\sigma}. \tag{17}$$

6. The representations S_k contained in $\mathfrak{D}_\sigma$

A representation S_k of the group $\mathfrak{U}$ is contained in the representation $\mathfrak{D}_\sigma$ of the complementary series if and only if k is an integer. In this case S_k is contained in $\mathfrak{D}_\sigma$ exactly once.

The proof is similar to the proof of Theorem 8 § 11, Subsection 4. In our case the number $\frac{1}{2}m = 0$ must be one of the numbers $-k$, $-k+1, \ldots, k$, which is the case if and only if k is an integer.

7. The elementary spherical functions of the representations of the complementary series

From the result of Subsection 6 it follows that H_σ has (to within a numerical factor) only one vector $\phi_0(u)$ which is invariant with respect to all operators V_u; this vector is $\phi_0(u) = c$. We choose c so that $(\phi_0, \phi_0) = 1$, i.e. so that

$$\pi \int\int \Phi(u'u''^{-1})|c|^2 du' du'' = 1;$$

hence

$$\pi|c|^2 \int du'' \int \Phi(u) du = \pi|c|^2 \int \Phi(u) du = 1,$$

i.e., by virtue of (11) Subsection 5, and (9) § 1, Subsection 7:

$$\pi|c|^2 \frac{1}{4\pi^2} \int_0^{2\pi} d\theta \int_0^{2\pi} d\theta' \int_0^1 t^{-1+\frac{\sigma}{2}} dt = 1,$$

or

$$2\pi|c|^2\sigma^{-1} = 1.$$

Hence, letting

$$\phi_0(u) = \frac{\sqrt{(\sigma)}}{\sqrt{(2\pi)}}, \tag{1}$$

we obtain a normalized vector $\phi_0(u)$.

As for the representations of the principal series, the spherical function $\psi(a)$ is defined by the formula

$$\psi(a) = (V_a\phi_0, \phi_0). \tag{2}$$

Since

$$V_a\phi_0 = \frac{\alpha(ua)}{\alpha(u\bar{a})} c,$$

we have

$$\psi(a) = \pi \iint \Phi(u'u''^{-1}) \frac{\alpha(u'a)}{\alpha(u'\bar{a})} |c|^2 du' du''$$

$$= \pi |c|^2 \int \frac{\alpha(u'a)}{\alpha(u'\bar{a})} du' \int \Phi(u'u''^{-1}) du''$$

$$= \pi |c|^2 \int \frac{\alpha(u'a)}{\alpha(u'\bar{a})} du' \int \Phi(u) du = \int \frac{\alpha(u'a)}{\alpha(u'\bar{a})} du'.$$

Repeating essentially the same calculations as in § 11, Subsection 5, we find that

$$\psi(\varepsilon) = \frac{2 \sinh \rho\tau}{\rho \sinh 2\tau} \quad \text{for} \quad \varepsilon = \begin{Vmatrix} e^{-\tau} & 0 \\ 0 & e^{\tau} \end{Vmatrix}. \tag{3}$$

8. The infinitesimal operators of the representations $\mathfrak{D}_\sigma$ in a canonical basis

From the formula of Subsection 4 for the operator V_a and from the result of Subsection 6 it follows that the representations $\mathfrak{D}_\sigma$ of the complementary series satisfy the conditions **A, B, C** of § 7, Subsection 3. Hence, for the infinitesimal operators of these representations formulae (51–55) § 8, Subsection 3 must hold.

The least number k for which the representations S_k is contained in a $\mathfrak{D}_\sigma$, is equal to zero, i.e. $k_0 = 0$. To find the parameter c we consider again the operator Δ (see § 11, Subsection 6). Calculating this operator with the aid of formulae (51–55) § 8, Subsection 3 and of formulae (3–8) § 9, Subsection 4 (in which m and n must be replaced by $-\frac{1}{2}\sigma - 1$ and $-\frac{1}{2}\sigma - 1$),

$$\Delta f_\nu^k = -2(c^2-1) f_\nu^k, \quad \Delta f(z) = -2\left[\left(\frac{\sigma}{2}\right)^2 - 1\right] f(z).$$

Hence $c^2 = (\sigma/2)^2$ and $c = \pm\sigma/2$; here the choice of the sign $\pm$ plays no part. Thus, for the representations of the complementary series

$$k_0 = 0, \quad c = \pm\frac{\sigma}{2}.$$

Combining this result with proposition II § 11, Subsection 6 and Theorem 3 § 8, Subsection 4, we conclude that:

I. *For any pair of numbers* (k_0, c) *satisfying one of the conditions:*

(1) *c is a pure imaginary number, k_0 is an arbitrary non-negative integral or semi-integral number;*

(2) *c is a real number from the interval* $0 < c \leqslant 1$, $k_0 = 0$, *— there exists an irreducible unitary representation $a \to T_a$ of the group $\mathfrak{A}$, the infinitesimal operators of which are given by formulae* (51–55) § 8, *Subsection* 3 *with these values of k_0 and c. In case* (1) *this representation $a \to T_a$ is a representation of the principal series, and in case* (2) *a representation of the complementary series,* or (for $c = 1$) the identity representation. Hence:

II. *The representations of the principal and complementary series and the identity representation realize all the irreducible unitary representations described by formulae* (51–55) § 8, Subsection 3.

This last result admits the following strengthening.

III. *The representations of the principal and complementary series realize all irreducible unitary representations of the group $\mathfrak{A}$ (to within unitary equivalence) i.e. every irreducible unitary representation of the group $\mathfrak{A}$ is unitarily equivalent to a representation of the principal or complementary series.*

Proposition III is in complete agreement with the results of § 8, Subsection 4, which may be considered as a proof of this proposition if one assumes that conditions **A**, **B**, **C** § 7, Subsection 3 are satisfied. A complete proof of proposition III, not making use of conditions **A**, **B**, **C** § 7, Subsection 3, was first given in the article [12b] by I. M. GELFAND and the author.

Another, and indeed a more simple, proof of proposition III is derived from a general result of the author, presented below in § 15.

§ 13. The Trace of a Representation of the Principal or Complementary Series

By the *trace* of an operator in a finite dimensional space we understand the sum of all its eigenvalues. Analogously one can define the trace of an operator with pure discrete spectrum in an infinite-dimensional Hilbert space, requiring in addition that the sum of the eigenvalues of this operator be an absolutely convergent series. An example of such an operator is the integral operator in $L^2(a, b)$ with continuous positive definite kernel $K(x, y)$, $a \leqslant x, y \leqslant b$; from the theory of integral equations it is known that the trace of this operator is $\int_a^b K(x, x)dx$. On the other hand, the unitary operators in infinite-dimensional Hilbert space do not have traces in the sense of this definition, because their spectrum consists of numbers of unit modulus, and moreover, can contain a continuous part. In particular, the operators V_a of the representations of the principal and complementary series do not have trace in the sense of this definition. We prove, however, that by means of an integral of the operators V_a one can obtain operators having trace, and that by the same token one can carry over to the representations of the principal and complementary series the theory of characters of finite and compact groups. Here the concept of an invariant integral on the group $\mathfrak{A}$ and some of the relations for this integral will play an essential part.

1. An invariant integral on the group $\mathfrak{A}$

By definition of the group $\mathfrak{A}$, the elements $\alpha, \beta, \gamma, \delta$ of the matrix $a \in \mathfrak{A}$ are connected by the relation

$$\alpha\delta - \beta\gamma = 1, \tag{1}$$

so that one of these parameters, α for example, can be expressed in terms of the remaining parameters β, γ, δ, provided $\delta \neq 0$.

Hence one can consider a function $f(a)$ on the group $\mathfrak{A}$ as a function $f(\beta, \gamma, \delta)$ of three complex parameters, defined when $\delta \neq 0$.

We introduce the following notations:

$$\alpha = \alpha_1 + i\alpha_2, \quad \beta = \beta_1 + i\beta_2, \quad \gamma = \gamma_1 + i\gamma_2, \quad \delta = \delta_1 + i\delta_2, \tag{2}$$

and consider the integral

$$I(f) = \int f(a)\omega(a)\mathrm{d}\beta_1\mathrm{d}\beta_2\mathrm{d}\gamma_1\mathrm{d}\gamma_2\mathrm{d}\delta_1\mathrm{d}\delta_2, \tag{3}$$

where $\omega(a)$ is a fixed continuous non-negative function on the group $\mathfrak{A}$. We will consider this integral for measurable functions $f(a) = f(\beta, \gamma, \delta)$ of the variables β, γ, δ, satisfying the condition

$$\int |f(a)|\omega(a)\mathrm{d}\beta_1\mathrm{d}\beta_2\mathrm{d}\gamma_1\mathrm{d}\gamma_2\mathrm{d}\delta_1\mathrm{d}\delta_2 < \infty; \tag{4}$$

for brevity we denote the set of all such functions $f(a)$ by F. The integral I(f) is called *invariant* if

$$\int f(a_0 a)\omega(a)\mathrm{d}\beta_1\mathrm{d}\beta_2\mathrm{d}\gamma_1\mathrm{d}\gamma_2\mathrm{d}\delta_1\mathrm{d}\delta_2 = \int f(a)\omega(a)\mathrm{d}\beta_1\mathrm{d}\beta_2\mathrm{d}\gamma_1\mathrm{d}\gamma_2\mathrm{d}\delta_1\mathrm{d}\delta_2, \tag{5}$$

and

$$\int f(a a_0)\omega(a)\mathrm{d}\beta_1\mathrm{d}\beta_2\mathrm{d}\gamma_1\mathrm{d}\gamma_2\mathrm{d}\delta_1\mathrm{d}\delta_2 = \int f(a)\omega(a)\mathrm{d}\beta_1\mathrm{d}\beta_2\mathrm{d}\gamma_1\mathrm{d}\gamma_2\mathrm{d}\delta_1\mathrm{d}\delta_2 \tag{6}$$

for an arbitrary function $f \in F$ and arbitrary $a_0 \in \mathfrak{A}$.

We will show that *there exists a function* $\omega(a)$, *unique to within a constant factor, for which the integral* I(f) *is invariant.*

Moreover, we immediately find this function $\omega(a)$.

For this purpose we write down condition (5) in more detail. Letting

$$a_0 = \begin{Vmatrix} \alpha_0 & \beta_0 \\ \gamma_0 & \delta_0 \end{Vmatrix}, \quad a = \begin{Vmatrix} \alpha & \beta \\ \gamma & \delta \end{Vmatrix}, \quad a' = a_0 a = \begin{Vmatrix} \alpha' & \beta' \\ \gamma' & \delta' \end{Vmatrix}, \tag{7}$$

$$\beta' = \beta'_1 + i\beta'_2, \quad \gamma' = \gamma'_1 + i\gamma'_2, \quad \delta' = \delta'_1 + i\delta'_2, \tag{8}$$

we have:

$$\beta' = \alpha_0\beta + \beta_0\delta, \quad \gamma' = \gamma_0\alpha + \delta_0\gamma, \quad \delta' = \gamma_0\beta + \delta_0\delta, \tag{9}$$

and condition (5) takes the form

$$\int f(\beta', \gamma', \delta')\omega(a)\mathrm{d}\beta_1\mathrm{d}\beta_2\mathrm{d}\gamma_1\mathrm{d}\gamma_2\mathrm{d}\delta_1\mathrm{d}\delta_2 = \int f(\beta', \gamma', \delta')\omega(a')\mathrm{d}\beta'_1\mathrm{d}\beta'_2\mathrm{d}\gamma'_1\mathrm{d}\gamma'_2\mathrm{d}\delta'_1\mathrm{d}\delta'_2; \tag{10}$$

here we denoted the variables of integration on the right side by $\beta'_1, \beta'_2, \gamma'_1, \gamma'_2, \delta'_1, \delta'_2$.

Now we pass on the right hand side from the variables of integration $\beta_1', \beta_2', \gamma_1', \gamma_2', \delta_1', \delta_2'$ to the variables $\beta_1, \beta_2, \gamma_1, \gamma_2, \delta_1, \delta_2$ by means of formulae (8), (9).

The Jacobian of this transformation is equal to the square of the modulus of the complex Jacobian† of the transformation (9):

$$\frac{\partial(\beta', \gamma', \delta')}{\partial(\beta, \gamma, \delta)} = \begin{vmatrix} \alpha_0 & 0 & \beta_0 \\ \gamma_0 \dfrac{\partial\alpha}{\partial\beta} & \gamma_0 \dfrac{\partial\alpha}{\partial\gamma} + \delta_0 & \gamma_0 \dfrac{\partial\alpha}{\partial\delta} \\ \gamma_0 & 0 & \delta_0 \end{vmatrix}$$

$$= \left(\gamma_0 \frac{\partial\alpha}{\partial\gamma} + \delta_0\right) \begin{vmatrix} \alpha_0 & \beta_0 \\ \gamma_0 & \delta_0 \end{vmatrix} = \gamma_0 \frac{\partial\alpha}{\partial\gamma} + \delta_0. \quad (11)$$

On the other hand, by virtue of (1):

$$\alpha = \frac{1+\beta\gamma}{\delta},$$

and so

$$\frac{\partial\alpha}{\partial\gamma} = \frac{\beta}{\delta}.$$

Substituting this expression in (11), we obtain:

$$\frac{\partial(\beta', \gamma', \delta')}{\partial(\beta, \gamma, \delta)} = \gamma_0 \frac{\beta}{\delta} + \delta_0 = \frac{\gamma_0 \beta + \delta_0 \delta}{\delta} = \frac{\delta'}{\delta};$$

hence the Jacobian of the transformation of the variables of integration indicated above is equal to $\left|\dfrac{\delta'}{\delta}\right|^2$, and after this transformation of the variables condition (10) takes the form:

$$\int f(\beta', \gamma', \delta')\omega(a)\, d\beta_1\, d\beta_2\, d\gamma_1\, d\gamma_2\, d\delta_1\, d\delta_2$$

$$= \int f(\beta', \gamma', \delta')\omega(a') \left|\frac{\delta'}{\delta}\right|^2 d\beta_1\, d\beta_2\, d\gamma_1\, d\gamma_2\, d\delta_1\, d\delta_2.$$

† See Appendix I.

In view of the arbitrary nature of the function $f(a) = f(\beta, \gamma, \delta)$ it follows from this that

$$\omega(a) = \omega(a')\left|\frac{\delta'}{\delta}\right|^2,$$

i.e.

$$\omega(a)|\delta|^2 = \omega(a')|\delta'|^2.$$

Thus the function $\omega(a)|\delta|^2$ must be constant: $\omega(a)|\delta|^2 = c$. Hence

$$\omega(a) = \frac{c}{|\delta|^2}. \tag{12}$$

In this way it is proved that $\omega(a)$ *is determined by condition* (5) *uniquely to within a constant factor* c; following the above reasoning in the reverse order, it is easy to convince oneself that the function $\omega(a) = c/|\delta|^2$ defines an integral $\mathrm{I}(f)$, satisfying condition (5). Also it is seen that condition (6) is satisfied; the argument is similar and we leave the details to the reader. Hence the function $\omega(a) = c/|\delta|^2$ defines an invariant integral.

In what follows we will take the immaterial constant factor c to be equal to one; then the invariant integral can be written in the form

$$\int f(a)\frac{1}{|\delta|^2}\mathrm{d}\beta_1\,\mathrm{d}\beta_2\,\mathrm{d}\gamma_1\mathrm{d}\gamma_2\,\mathrm{d}\delta_1\,\mathrm{d}\delta_2. \tag{13}$$

The expression

$$\frac{1}{|\delta|^2}\mathrm{d}\beta_1\,\mathrm{d}\beta_2\,\mathrm{d}\gamma_1\,\mathrm{d}\gamma_2\,\mathrm{d}\delta_1\,\mathrm{d}\delta_2 \tag{14}$$

is called *a differential of invariant volume on the group* $\mathfrak{A}$ and is denoted by $\mathrm{d}a$. Using this notation, we can rewrite the expression for the invariant integral on $\mathfrak{A}$ in the following simplified form:

$$\int f(a)\,\mathrm{d}a. \tag{15}$$

Here, with the same definition of invariant integral:

$$\int f(a_0 a)\,\mathrm{d}a = \int f(a a_0)\,\mathrm{d}a = \int f(a)\,\mathrm{d}a \tag{16}$$

for any function $f \in F$ and any element $a \in \mathfrak{A}$.

Moreover, by an immediate calculation one can verify that

$$\int f(a^{-1})\mathrm{d}a = \int f(a)\mathrm{d}a \tag{17}$$

for any function $f \in F$.

Remark. If the function $f(a)$ differs from zero only in a sufficiently small neighbourhood of the point $a^0 = \begin{Vmatrix} \alpha^0 & \beta^0 \\ \gamma^0 & 0 \end{Vmatrix}$, then it is convenient to take $\alpha_1, \alpha_2, \beta_1, \beta_2, \delta_1, \delta_2$ as parameters. Repeating the preceding argument, it is easy to convince oneself that in this case

$$\mathrm{d}a = \frac{1}{|\gamma|^2}\mathrm{d}\alpha_1\,\mathrm{d}\alpha_2\,\mathrm{d}\beta_1\,\mathrm{d}\beta_2\,\mathrm{d}\gamma_1\,\mathrm{d}\gamma_2.$$

2. Invariant integrals on the group K

The group K is the group of matrices

$$k = \begin{Vmatrix} \lambda^{-1} & \mu \\ 0 & \lambda \end{Vmatrix}, \quad \lambda \neq 0 \tag{1}$$

(see § 10, Subsection 1), and so every function $f(k)$ on K is a function $f(\lambda, \mu)$ of the variables λ, μ, defined for $\lambda \neq 0$.

A left-invariant integral on the group K is an integral

$$I_l(f) = \int f(k)\omega_l(k)\mathrm{d}\lambda_1\,\mathrm{d}\lambda_2\,\mathrm{d}\mu_1\,\mathrm{d}\mu_2, \quad \lambda = \lambda_1 + i\lambda_2, \quad \mu = \mu_1 + i\mu_2 \tag{2}$$

in the domain $-\infty < \lambda_j < \infty$, $-\infty < \mu_j < \infty$, $j = 1, 2$, satisfying the condition

$$\int f(k_0 k)\omega_l(k)\mathrm{d}\lambda_1\,\mathrm{d}\lambda_2\,\mathrm{d}\mu_1\,\mathrm{d}\mu_2 = \int f(k)\omega_l(k)\mathrm{d}\lambda_1\,\mathrm{d}\lambda_2\,\mathrm{d}\mu_1\,\mathrm{d}\mu_2. \tag{3}$$

Analogously, *a right-invariant integral* on the group K is an integral

$$I_r(f) = \int f(k)\omega_r(k)\mathrm{d}\lambda_1\,\mathrm{d}\lambda_2\,\mathrm{d}\mu_1\,\mathrm{d}\mu_2 \tag{4}$$

in the domain $-\infty < \lambda_j < \infty$, $-\infty < \mu_j < \infty$, $j = 1, 2$, satisfying the condition

$$\int f(kk_0)\omega_r(k)\mathrm{d}\lambda_1\,\mathrm{d}\lambda_2\,\mathrm{d}\mu_1\,\mathrm{d}\mu_2 = \int f(k)\omega_r(k)\mathrm{d}\lambda_1\,\mathrm{d}\lambda_2\,\mathrm{d}\mu_1\,\mathrm{d}\mu_2. \tag{5}$$

Repeating the reasoning in Subsection 1, we convince ourselves of the fact that *conditions* (3) *and* (5) *define functions* $\omega_l(k)$ *and* $\omega_r(k)$ *uniquely to within a constant factor, namely*:

$$\omega_l(k) = c_1, \quad \omega_r(k) = c_2|\lambda|^{-4}. \tag{6}$$

Letting $c_1 = c_2 = 1$ and

$$\mathrm{d}_l k = \mathrm{d}\lambda_1 \mathrm{d}\lambda_2 \mathrm{d}\mu_1 \mathrm{d}\mu_2, \quad \mathrm{d}_r k = |\lambda|^{-4} \mathrm{d}\lambda_1 \mathrm{d}\lambda_2 \mathrm{d}\mu_1 \mathrm{d}\mu_2, \tag{7}$$

we obtain for the integrals $I_l(f)$, $I_r(f)$ the expressions:

$$I_l(f) = \int f(k)\mathrm{d}_l k, \quad I_r(f) = \int f(k)\mathrm{d}_r k. \tag{8}$$

Conditions (3) and (5) then take the form

$$\int f(k_0 k)\mathrm{d}_l k = \int f(k)\mathrm{d}_l k, \tag{9}$$

$$\int f(k k_0)\mathrm{d}_r k = \int f(k)\mathrm{d}_r k. \tag{10}$$

From (7) it follows that†

$$\mathrm{d}_l k = \beta(k)\mathrm{d}_r k. \tag{11}$$

3. Some integral relations

We will now show that an invariant integral with respect to $\mathfrak{A}$ can be replaced by successive invariant integrals with respect to k and z.

I. *In the relations*

$$\int f(a)\mathrm{d}a = \iint f(kz)\mathrm{d}_l k \mathrm{d}z, \tag{1}$$

$$\int f(a)\mathrm{d}a = \pi \iint f(ku)\mathrm{d}_l k \mathrm{d}u, \tag{2}$$

the absolute convergence of each side implies the absolute convergence of the other, and then the two sides are equal.

Proof. The equation $a = kz$ is equivalent to the equations

$$\lambda = \delta, \quad z = \frac{\gamma}{\delta}, \quad \mu = \beta \tag{3}$$

(see (4) § 10, Subsection 2). The Jacobian of the transformation from λ, μ, z to β, γ, δ is equal to the square of the modulus of the corresponding complex Jacobian, i.e. equal to

$$\left|\frac{\partial(\lambda, \mu, z)}{\partial(\delta, \beta, \gamma)}\right|^2 = \frac{1}{|\delta|^2}. \tag{4}$$

† We recall that $\beta(a) = |a_{22}|^4$ (see § 10, Subsection 5).

Hence, taking into account the formulae

$$da = \frac{d\beta_1 d\beta_2 d\gamma_1 d\gamma_2 d\delta_1 d\delta_2}{|\delta|^2},$$

$$d_l k = d\lambda_1 d\lambda_2 d\mu_1 d\mu_2, \quad dz = dx dy \tag{5}$$

(see (14) Subsection 1; (1) § 10, Subsection 5 and (7) Subsection 2), we conclude that when $a = kz$,

$$da = d_l k dz.$$

Substituting this expression in $\int f(a) da$ and applying Fubini's theorem, we obtain (1).

For the derivation of formulae (2) we set

$$F(z) = \int f(kz) d_l k, \quad \Phi(u) = \pi \int f(ku) d_l k; \tag{6}$$

if $z = k_0 u$ then

$$\begin{aligned} F(z) &= \int f(kk_0 u) d_l k = \int f(kk_0 u) \beta(k) d_r k \\ &= \int f(ku) \beta(kk_0^{-1}) d_r k = \beta^{-1}(k_0) \int f(ku) \beta(k) d_r k \\ &= \beta^{-1}(k_0) \int f(ku) d_l k = \frac{1}{\pi} \beta^{-1}(k_0) \Phi(u). \end{aligned} \tag{7}$$

On the other hand, $\beta(k_0)\beta(u) = \beta(z) = 1$, and so from (7) it follows that

$$\Phi(u) = \pi \beta^{-1}(u) F(z) \quad \text{when} \quad z = k_0 u. \tag{8}$$

Applying to (8) the reasoning of § 11, Subsection 3 (see pages 157-158), we conclude that

$$\int \Phi(u) du = \int F(z) dz;$$

substituting here expression (6) and taking (1) into account, we obtain:

$$\pi \iint f(ku) d_l k du = \iint f(kz) d_l k dz = \int f(a) da.$$

II. *Every matrix $a \in \mathfrak{A}$ can be represented in the form*

$$a = u^{-1} k u, \tag{9}$$

and when $a_{12} \neq 0$ also in the form

$$a = z^{-1} k z; \tag{10}$$

here $\lambda^{-1} = k_{11}$ *and* $\lambda = k_{22}$ *are the eigenvalues of the matrix* a, *taken in any order.*

If these eigenvalues are distinct, then for a given ordering of them, the matrices k, z *in* (10) *are determined uniquely by the matrix* a.

Proof. Formula (9) is simply a well known result concerning the possibility of transforming a given matrix to triangular form by a unitary matrix† since a and k are unitarily equivalent, their eigenvalues coincide, i.e. $\lambda^{-1} = k_{11}$, $\lambda = k_{22}$ are the eigenvalues of the matrix a.

If $u_{22} = 0$, then $u_{11} = 0$ also, and from (9) it then follows that $a_{12} = 0$. Hence when $a_{12} \neq 0$ then also $u_{22} \neq 0$, and so u can be represented in the form $u = k_0 z$ (see § 10, Subsection 2). Substituting in (9), we obtain $a = z^{-1}k_0^{-1}kk_0z$, i.e. formula (10) is valid.

It remains to prove the final assertion. For this we note that if

$$k = \begin{Vmatrix} \lambda^{-1} & \mu \\ 0 & \lambda \end{Vmatrix}$$

equation (10) is equivalent to the equations:

$$a_{12} = \mu, \quad a_{21} = -\mu z^2 + (\lambda - \lambda^{-1})z, \quad a_{22} = -\mu z + \lambda. \tag{11}$$

From (11) it follows that with a given choice of λ and with $a_{12} \neq 0$ the parameters μ and z are uniquely defined by the matrix a.

We note that with $a_{12} \neq 0$ and $\lambda \neq \lambda^{-1}$ there are exactly two representations of the matrix a by means of formula (10) (and this means also (9)), corresponding to two distinct possibilities in formula (10), namely:

$$k_{11} = \lambda^{-1}, \quad k_{22} = \lambda \quad \text{and} \quad k_{11} = \lambda, \quad k_{22} = \lambda^{-1}.$$

III. *Let* λ_a, λ_a^{-1} *be the eingenvalues of the matrix* a; *then*

$$\iint f(z^{-1}kz)\phi(k)d_l k dz = \int f(a)\frac{\sum \phi(k_a)\beta^{\frac{1}{2}}(k_a)}{|\lambda_a - \lambda_a^{-1}|^2} da, \tag{12}$$

and, if $\phi(k_1k_2) = \phi(k_1)\phi(k_2)$,

$$\pi \iint f(u^{-1}ku)\phi(k)d_l k dz = \int f(a)\frac{\sum \phi(k_a)\beta^{\frac{1}{2}}(k_a)}{|\lambda_a - \lambda_a^{-1}|^2} da, \tag{13}$$

† See, for example, Ref. [10b].

where k_a is defined by the formulae $a = z^{-1}k_a z$, and $a = u^{-1}k_a u$, respectively and the sum on the right sides of these equations consists of two summands, corresponding to the two possibilities in the choice of k_a. Here, from the absolute convergence of the one side of equations (12) and (13) follows the absolute convergence of the other side.

Proof. We eliminate from K those elements k for which $|\lambda| = 1$. Then we separate K into two domains K_1 and K_2, in each of which no two matrices differ only in the order of their diagonal elements. In correspondence with this partition the integral on the left side of (12) is represented in the form of a sum of two integrals

$$\int\int f(z^{-1}kz)\phi(k)\mathrm{d}_l k\,\mathrm{d}z$$
$$= \int \mathrm{d}z \int_{K_1} f(z^{-1}kz)\phi(k)\mathrm{d}_l k + \int \mathrm{d}z \int_{K_2} f(z^{-1}kz)\phi(k)\mathrm{d}_l k. \quad (14)$$

When z runs through Z, and k through one of the domains K_1 or K_2, then, by virtue of II, the matrix $a = z^{-1}kz$ runs once through all the matrices of the group $\mathfrak{A}$, except for a subset of lower dimension.

In each summand on the right-hand side of (14) we change the variables k, z to the variable of integration a, thus reducing each of these integrals to an integral on the whole group $\mathfrak{A}$. But this transformation of the variables is equivalent to the transition (11) from λ, μ, z to a_{12}, a_{21}, a_{22}. The Jacobian of this transition is equal to

$$\left|\frac{\partial(a_{12}, a_{21}, a_{22})}{\partial(\mu, z, \lambda)}\right|^{-2} = \left|\frac{1}{\lambda}\left(\lambda - \frac{1}{\lambda}\right)a_{22}\right|^{-2}.$$

Therefore, taking formulae (5) into account, we obtain:

$$\int \mathrm{d}z \int_{K_1} f(z^{-1}kz)\phi(k)\mathrm{d}_l k = \int f(a)\frac{\phi(k_a)\beta^{\frac{1}{2}}(k_a)}{|\lambda_a - \lambda_a^{-1}|^2}\mathrm{d}a, \qquad k_a \in K_1,$$

$$\int \mathrm{d}z \int_{K_2} f(z^{-1}kz)\phi(k)\mathrm{d}_l k = \int f(a)\frac{\phi(k_a)\beta^{\frac{1}{2}}(k_a)}{|\lambda_a - \lambda_a^{-1}|^2}\mathrm{d}a, \qquad k_a \in K_2.$$

Adding these two equations term by term, we obtain (12).

With the condition $\phi(k_1k_2) = \phi(k_1)\phi(k_2)$ formula (13) follows from (12) in the same way that (2) follows from (1). Letting

$$F(z) = \int f(z^{-1}kz)\phi(k)\mathrm{d}_l k, \quad \Phi(u) = \pi \int f(u^{-1}ku)\phi(k)\mathrm{d}_l k, \qquad (15)$$

it is easy to see that $\Phi(u) = \pi\beta^{-1}(u)F(z)$ when $z = ku$. Hence it follows that

$$\int F(z)\mathrm{d}z = \int \Phi(u)\mathrm{d}u.$$

Substituting in this the expressions (15) and using (12), we obtain (13).

4. The group ring of the group $\mathfrak{A}$

A set X of elements $x, y, z, \ldots$ is called a *ring*, if:

1. X is a linear space with multiplication by complex numbers;

2. there is defined in X an operation of multiplication of the elements (in general, non-commutative), which commutes with the operation of multiplication by complex numbers and satisfies the usual algebraic conditions.

Here the nature of the elements of the set X, and also the method of defining the operations in it, can be completely arbitrary.

We will show that one can associate with the group $\mathfrak{A}$ a ring X, whose elements are functions on the group $\mathfrak{A}$ and which is called the *group ring* of this group. This ring is defined in the following way:

A set of matrices $a \in \mathfrak{A}$ will be called *bounded*, if every matrix a of this set satisfies an inequality of the form

$$|a_{11}|^2 + |a_{12}|^2 + |a_{21}|^2 + |a_{22}|^2 \leqslant c, \qquad (1)$$

where c is some constant; let us denote by $\mathfrak{A}_c$ the set of all matrices for which (1) is satisfied.

An example of a bounded set is the unitary subgroup $\mathfrak{U}$, because

$$|u_{11}|^2 + |u_{12}|^2 + |u_{21}|^2 + |u_{22}|^2 = 2.$$

The intersection of a bounded set with one of the subgroups Z, K forms a bounded set in Z, K respectively. Now we denote by X the set of all infinitely differentiable functions† $x(a)$ on the group

† It is convenient here to change the notation and write $x(a)$ instead of $f(a)$.

$\mathfrak{A}$, which are equal to zero outside some bounded set (generally depending on the function $x(a)$). The set X forms a linear space if one defines addition and multiplication by a number as addition of functions and their multiplication by a number. These operations do not depend on the bounds of the sets: in fact, if $x_1(a)$, $x_2(a)$ are infinitely differentiable and vanish outside the bounded sets $\mathfrak{A}_{c_1}$, $\mathfrak{A}_{c_2}$, then $\lambda_1 x_1(a)+\lambda_2 x_2(a)$ is an infinitely differentiable function equal to zero outside the set $\mathfrak{A}_c$, $c = \max\{c_1, c_2\}$.

In order to define multiplication in X, we proceed in the following manner. Let there be given a representation $a \to T_a$ of the group $\mathfrak{A}$; we set

$$T_x = \int x(a)\, T_a da, \tag{2}$$

where $x(a) \in X$. This integral exists because the integration is carried out over a closed bounded set $\mathfrak{A}_c$ and is a bounded operator. An estimate of its norm is given by

$$|T_x| \leqslant \sup_{a\in\mathfrak{A}_c} |T_a| \int |x(a)|\, da \tag{3}$$

(see § 6, Subsection 5). Now consider two such operators:

$$T_{x_1} = \int x_1(a)\, T_a da, \quad T_{x_2} = \int x_2(a)\, T_a da, \tag{4}$$

where x_1, $x_2 \in X$; we shall prove that their product $T_{x_1}\, T_{x_2}$ can also be written in the form (2). Multiplying the expressions (4), we have:

$$\begin{aligned} T_{x_1} T_{x_2} &= \int x_1(a_1)\, T_{a_1} da_1 \int x_2(a_2)\, T_{a_2} da_2 \\ &= \int x_1(a_1) da_1 \int x_2(a_2)\, T_{a_1 a_2} da_2 = \int x_1(a_1) da_1 \int x_2(a_1^{-1}a)\, T_a da \\ &= \int [\int x_1(a_1) x_2(a_1^{-1}a) da_1]\, T_a da = \int x(a)\, T_a da = T_x, \end{aligned}$$

where

$$x(a) = \int x_1(a_1) x_2(a_1^{-1}a) da_1. \tag{5}$$

The function $x(a)$ defined by formula (5), will be called the *product* of the functions x_1, x_2 and denoted by $x_1\, x_2(a)$. We note that $x_1\, x_2 \in X$. In fact, let x_1, x_2 vanish outside the sets $\mathfrak{A}_{c_1}$, $\mathfrak{A}_{c_2}$ respectively; then $x(a)$ is infinitely differentiable because integration is in fact carried out over the set $\mathfrak{A}_{c_1}$; moreover, $x_1(a_1)x_2(a_1^{-1}a)$

can be distinct from zero only when $a_1 \in \mathfrak{A}_{c_1}$, $a_1^{-1}a \in \mathfrak{A}_{c_2}$, i.e. when† $a \in \mathfrak{A}_{c_1} \cdot \mathfrak{A}_{c_2}$. But it is easy to see that $\mathfrak{A}_{c_1} \cdot \mathfrak{A}_{c_2}$ is a set of the form $\mathfrak{A}_{c_1 c_2}$; the function $x(a)$ vanishes outside this set and so $\in X$. Hence, *if multiplication is defined by means of formula* (5), *the set X forms a ring.*

This ring is called the *group ring* of the group $\mathfrak{A}$.

5. The relation between the representations of the group $\mathfrak{A}$ and its group ring

Suppose there is put into correspondence with every element x of the ring X a bounded operator T_x in some Banach space R; this correspondence $x \to T_x$ is called *a representation of the ring X, if*

$$T_{\lambda_1 x_1 + \lambda_2 x_2} = \lambda_1 T_{x_1} + \lambda_2 T_{x_2} \tag{1}$$

and

$$T_{x_1 x_2} = T_{x_1} T_{x_2}. \tag{2}$$

I. *If* $a \to T_a$ *is a representation of the group* $\mathfrak{A}$, *then the formula* $T_x = \int x(a) T_a \, da$ *defines a representation of its group ring.* In fact, relation (1) in this case is obvious, and relation (2) coincides with (5) Subsection 4.

II. *If the representation* $a \to T_a$ *of the group* $\mathfrak{A}$ *is irreducible, then the corresponding representation* $x \to T_x$ *of its group ring X is also irreducible.*

Proof. Suppose the contrary: let the representation $x \to T_x$ be reducible and let $\mathfrak{M}$ be a closed subspace in R, distinct from (0) and R and invariant with respect to all the operators T_x. We denote by $\mathfrak{M}_1$ the subspace consisting of all finite linear combinations of the vectors $T_x f$, $x \in X, f \in \mathfrak{M}$, and their limits; clearly $\mathfrak{M}_1 \neq (0)$‡ and $\mathfrak{M}_1 \subset \mathfrak{M}$, so that $\mathfrak{M}_1 \neq R$. We shall prove that $\mathfrak{M}_1$ is invariant with respect to all the operators T_a; this will contradict the presupposed irreducibility of the representation $a \to T_a$, and proposition II will thus be proved.

† If $\mathfrak{A}'$, $\mathfrak{A}''$ are two sets in $\mathfrak{A}$, then $\mathfrak{A}'\mathfrak{A}''$ denotes the set of all products $a'a''$, where $a' \in \mathfrak{A}'$, $a'' \in \mathfrak{A}''$.

‡ In fact, if $T_x f = \int x(a) \, T_a f \, da = 0$ for all $x \in X$, then $0 = F(T_x f) = \int x(a) \, F(T_a) \, da$ for all functionals $F \in R'$ and all $x \in X$. This implies that $F(T_a f) = 0$ for all $F \in R'$, hence $T_a f = 0$ and in particular $f = T_e f = 0$.

If $f \in \mathfrak{M}$, $x \in X$ then

$$T_{a_0} T_x f = T_{a_0} \int x(a) T_a f da = \int x(a) T_{a_0 a} f da = \int x(a_0^{-1} a) T_a f da$$
$$= \int x_1(a) T_a f da, \tag{3}$$

where $x_1(a) = x(a_0^{-1} a)$ also belongs to the ring X. Therefore $T_{a_0} T_x f \in \mathfrak{M}_1$, i.e. T_{a_0} carries into $\mathfrak{M}_1$ every function of the form $T_x f$, $x \in X$, $f \in \mathfrak{M}$; hence, it also carries into $\mathfrak{M}_1$ the linear combinations of these vectors and their limits, i.e. it carries $\mathfrak{M}_1$ into $\mathfrak{M}_1$.

Propositions I and II reduce the problem of finding all irreducible representations of the group $\mathfrak{A}$ to the analogous problem for its group ring X. In fact, by giving all irreducible representations of the ring X, we can be sure that we have not omitted a single irreducible representation of the group $\mathfrak{A}$.

Remark 1. From the above reasoning it also follows that *any representation* $a \to T_a$ *of the group* $\mathfrak{A}$ *satisfies condition* **A** § 7, *Subsection* 3.

In fact, let $\mathfrak{D}$ be the set of all finite linear combinations of the vectors $\eta = T_x f$, $x \in X$, $f \in R$. Then $\mathfrak{D}$ is dense in R; otherwise there exists a functional $F \in R'$, $F \neq 0$ such that

$$F(T_x f) = \int x(a) F(T_a f) da = 0$$

for all $x \in X$, $f \in R$. Hence $F(T_a f) = 0$ for all $a \in \mathfrak{A}$, $f \in R$. Letting $a = e$, we find that $F(f) = 0$ for all $f \in R$, and this contradicts the condition $F \neq 0$.

From formula (3) and the properties of the function $x(a)$ it follows that $\mathfrak{D}$ is invariant with respect to all the operators T_a and that $T_{a_0} \eta = T_{a_0} T_x f$ is an infinitely differentiable function on the group $\mathfrak{A}$. Hence, $T_{a_0} \eta$ possesses these same properties for those vectors η which are finite linear combinations of the vectors $T_x f$, i.e. for all $\eta \in \mathfrak{D}$. Thus the constructed set $\mathfrak{D}$ satisfies condition **A**(2) § 7, Subsection 3.

From this we conclude that conditions **A**, (1), (3′) is also satisfied. In fact, let $A_j(t) = T_{aj(t)}$, $j = 1, \ldots, n$ be the one-parameter groups defined in **A** (3), and let $\eta \in \mathbf{D}$. Then **A** (2) implies that $\mathrm{A}_1(\mathrm{t}_1) \cdots \mathrm{A}_n(\mathrm{t}_n)\eta = T_{a_1(t_1) \ldots a_n(t_n)}\eta$ is an infinitely differentiable function of $\mathrm{t}_1, \ldots, \mathrm{t}_n$.

Taking some or all $t_j = 0$ in its derivatives we deduce that conditions **A** (1) and **A** (3′) are satisfied.

Now differentiating both sides of the relation

$$A(t+t_1)\eta = A(t)A(t_1)\eta = A(t_1)A(t)\eta$$

with respect to t_1 and putting $t_1 = 0$ we see that equation (7) § 7, Subsection 3 holds. Finally, relation (8a) § 7, Subsection 3 is Taylors formula and therefore it follows easily from condition **A**, (2), by integration by parts.

Replacing X by the set $\tilde{X}$ of analytical functions of Re a_{jk} and Im a_{jk} which decrease sufficiently quickly at infinity (see below, remark 2), one can also satisfy condition (8b) § 7, Subsection 3. However, in the theory set out in §§ 15 and 16 this condition is necessary only for representations of the principal series and, moreover, only for the elements ξ_p^k (for the proof of proposition III § 11, Subsection 6 used in §§ 15 and 16), and this is verified in Appendix IX.

We note that $\mathfrak{D}$ is invariant with respect to the operators E_{jl}^k (see § 6, Subsection 6), because

$$E_{jl}^k \eta = (2k+1)\int \overline{c_{jl}^k(u)}\, T_u \eta\, du = (2k+1)\int\int \overline{c_{jl}^k(u)}\, x(a)\, T_u T_a \xi\, du\, da$$

$$= (2k+1)\int\int \overline{c_{jl}^k(u)}\, x(u^{-1}a)\, T_a \xi\, du\, da = \int x_1(a)\, T_a \xi\, da,$$

where $x_1(a) = (2k+1)\int \overline{c_{jl}^k(u)}\, x(u^{-1}a) du \in X$, if $x \in X$.

Remark 2. The operators T_x can be constructed for a class of functions wider than X. This construction is based on the following proposition:

III. *For any representation $a \to T_a$ the inequality*

$$|T_a| \leqslant b|a|^c, \tag{4}$$

is satisfied, where $|a|$ is the norm† *of the matrix a: and b, c are some positive constants.*

---

† i.e. the norm of the linear operator with matrix a in two-dimensional Euclidean space.

Proof. We set $a = u_1 \varepsilon u_2$, where $u_1, u_2 \in \mathfrak{U}$ and

$$\varepsilon = \begin{Vmatrix} e^{-t} & 0 \\ 0 & e^{t} \end{Vmatrix}, \qquad -\infty < t < \infty; \tag{5}$$

then $T_a = T_{u_1} T_\varepsilon T_{u_2}$. On the other hand, since $\mathfrak{U}$ is bounded, $|T_u| \leqslant C$ for all $u \in \mathfrak{U}$, where C is some constant (see V § 6, Subsection 4); hence

$$|T_a| \leqslant C^2 |T_\varepsilon| \quad \text{whenever} \quad a = u_1 \varepsilon u_2. \tag{6}$$

We introduce the notation

$$\alpha(t) = \log |T_\varepsilon| \quad \text{where} \quad \varepsilon = \begin{Vmatrix} e^{-t} & 0 \\ 0 & e^{t} \end{Vmatrix}, \qquad -\infty < t < \infty. \tag{7}$$

Then

$$\alpha(t_1 + t_2) = \log |T_{\varepsilon_1 \varepsilon_2}| = \log |T_{\varepsilon_1} T_{\varepsilon_2}| \leqslant \log(|T_{\varepsilon_1}| |T_{\varepsilon_2}|)$$
$$= \log |T_{\varepsilon_1}| + \log |T_{\varepsilon_2}| = \alpha(t_1) + \alpha(t_2)$$

where

$$\varepsilon_1 = \begin{Vmatrix} e^{-t_1} & 0 \\ 0 & e^{t_1} \end{Vmatrix}, \qquad \varepsilon_2 = \begin{Vmatrix} e^{-t_2} & 0 \\ 0 & e^{t_2} \end{Vmatrix}.$$

Thus

$$\alpha(t_1 + t_2) \leqslant \alpha(t_1) + \alpha(t_2). \tag{8}$$

Moreover, the function $|T_\varepsilon|$, and that means also the function $\alpha(t)$, is bounded above in every finite interval; let

$$\alpha(t) \leqslant c \quad \text{when} \quad -1 \leqslant t \leqslant 1; \text{ in particular } \alpha(\pm 1) \leqslant c. \tag{9}$$

Every real number t can be represented in the form $t = n + \tau$, where n is an integer and $0 \leqslant \tau < 1$. Hence, by virtue of (8) and (9),

$$\alpha(t) = \alpha(n + \tau) \leqslant |n| \alpha(\pm 1) + \alpha(\tau) \leqslant c(n+1) \leqslant c(|t| + 2);$$

consequently,

$$|T_\varepsilon| = e^{\alpha(t)} \leqslant e^{c(|t|+2)} = b_1 (e^{|t|})^c,$$

where $b_1 = e^{2c}$. But $e^{|t|}$ is the greater of the two numbers $\varepsilon_{22} = e^t$, $\varepsilon_{22}^{-1} = e^{-t}$, i.e. is the norm of the matrix ε. Thus

$$|T_\varepsilon| \leqslant b_1 |\varepsilon|^c.$$

Hence by virtue of (6)

$$|T_a| \leqslant c^2 b_1 |\varepsilon|^c \quad \text{where} \quad a = u_1 \varepsilon u_2. \tag{10}$$

On the other hand,

$$|a|^2 = |a^* a| = |u_2 \varepsilon^2 u_2^*| = |\varepsilon^2| = |\varepsilon|^2; \tag{11}$$

hence, the inequality (10) can be rewritten in the form $|T_a| \leqslant c^2 b_1 |a|^c$. Letting $b = c^2 b_1$, we obtain the inequality (4).

Inequality (4) can be replaced by a coarser, but on the other hand simpler, estimate, if one notices that the norm $|a^*a|$ of the matrix a^*a does not exceed its trace i.e. the sum of all its eigenvalues:

$$|a|^2 = |a^*a| \leqslant \sum_{j,k=1}^{2} |a_{jk}|^2. \tag{12}$$

From the condition $\det(a^*a) = 1$ it follows that $|a^*a| \geqslant 1$, because $|a^*a|$ is the greater of the two eigenvalues of the matrix a^*a.

Hence, combining inequalities (4) and (12), we conclude that

$$|T_a| \leqslant \omega(a), \tag{13}$$

where

$$\omega(a) = b\Big(\sum_{j,k=1}^{2} |a_{jk}|^2\Big)^{\frac{1}{2}c}. \tag{14}$$

Now let $\hat{X}$ denote the set of all measurable functions $x(a)$, satisfying the condition†

$$\int |x(a)|\,\omega(a)\,da < \infty. \tag{15}$$

We set, for $x \in \hat{X}$,

$$T_x = \int x(a)\, T_a\, da; \tag{16}$$

from the estimate (13) it follows that the integral on the right side of (16) converges, and moreover in the sense of the norm of the operator; hence, this definition is justified.

We note that in the case of a unitary representation $a \to T_a$ the factor $\omega(a)$ in condition (15) can be replaced by unity, because then $|T_a| = 1$.

---

† Unlike X, the set $\hat{X}$ depends on the given representation $a \to T_a$, because $\omega(a)$ depends on it.

6. The case of a unitary representation of the group $\mathfrak{A}$

Now we suppose that the representation $a \to T_a$ of the group $\mathfrak{A}$ is unitary. This means that

$$T_{a^{-1}} = T_a^{-1} = T_a^*. \tag{1}$$

From this it follows that

$$\begin{aligned}(T_x)^* = (\int x(a)\, T_a da)^* &= \int \overline{x(a)}\, T_a^* da = \int \overline{x(a)}\, T_{a^{-1}} da \\ &= \int \overline{x(a^{-1})}\, T_a da\end{aligned} \tag{2}$$

(see (17) Subsection 1). We set

$$x^*(a) = \overline{x(a^{-1})}; \tag{3}$$

then (2) can be rewritten in the form

$$(T_x)^* = T_{x^*}. \tag{4}$$

The function $x^*(a)$ is called the *Hermitian adjoint* of the function $x(a)$; if $x(a) \in X$, then, clearly, $x^*(a) \in X$. It is easy to verify that the operation of transition from x to x^* possesses the following properties:

$$x^{**} = x,\ \ (\lambda x)^* = \bar{\lambda} x^*,\ \ (x_1 + x_2)^* = x_1^* + x_2^*,\ \ (x_1 x_2)^* = x_2^* x_1^*. \tag{5}$$

Every ring in which there is defined an operation $x \to x^*$, satisfying conditions (5), is called a *ring with involution*; the operation $x \to x^*$ is itself called an *involution.*

Thus, *the group ring X of the group $\mathfrak{A}$ is a ring with involution.* A representation $x \to T_x$ of a ring with involution is called *symmetric* if $(T_x)^* = T_{x^*}$. The preceding reasoning shows that a *unitary representation $a \to T_a$* of the group $\mathfrak{A}$ *corresponds to a symmetric representation $x \to T_x$ of its group ring.*†

Remark. It is easy to verify that the converse assertion is also true: *if the representation $x \to T_x$ of the group ring X is symmetric, then the corresponding representation $a \to T_a$ of the group $\mathfrak{A}$ is unitary.*

---

† For the general theory of rings with involution and their symmetric representations see [12c], and also [28a] and [28e].

7. The trace of a representation of the principal series

Now we apply the preceding results to a representation $a \to V_a$ of the principal series. We recall that the operators of such a representation in the space $L_2^m(\mathfrak{U})$ are given by the formula

$$V_a \phi(u) = \frac{\alpha(ua)}{\alpha(u\bar{a})} \phi(u\bar{a}), \tag{1}$$

where

$$\alpha(a) = |a_{22}|^{-m+i\rho-2} a_{22}^m. \tag{2}$$

We determine the corresponding operator T_x. By the definition of this operator, we have

$$T_x \phi(u) = \int x(a) V_a \phi(u) \mathrm{d}a = \int x(a) \frac{\alpha(ua)}{\alpha(u\bar{a})} \phi(u\bar{a}) \mathrm{d}a$$

$$= \int x(u^{-1}a) \frac{\alpha(a)}{\alpha(\overline{uu^{-1}a})} \phi(\overline{uu^{-1}a}) \mathrm{d}a = \int x(u^{-1}a) \frac{\alpha(a)}{\alpha(e\bar{a})} \phi(e\bar{a}) \mathrm{d}a. \tag{3}$$

In the last integral we pass from integration with respect to da to integration with respect to $\mathrm{d}_l k$ and du by means of formula (2) Subsection 3; letting $a = ku_1$, in (3) we have $ea = eku_1 = ku_1$, and so one can take $e\bar{a} = u_1$; moreover, $\alpha(a) = \alpha(ku_1) = \alpha(k)\alpha(u_1)$. Substituting these relations in (3), we obtain:

$$T_x \phi(u) = \pi \int x(u^{-1}ku_1)\alpha(k)\phi(u_1)\mathrm{d}_l k \mathrm{d}u_1. \tag{4}$$

We set

$$K(u, u_1) = \pi \int x(u^{-1}ku_1)\alpha(k)\mathrm{d}_l k; \tag{5}$$

then (4) can be rewritten in the form

$$T_x \phi(u) = \int K(u, u_1)\phi(u_1)\mathrm{d}u_1. \tag{6}$$

Formula (6) means that T_x *is an integral operator with kernel* $K(u, u_1)$.

We note that:

I. *For* $x \in X$ *the integral in* (5) *exists and represents a continuous function* $K(u, u_1)$ *of* u *and* u_1. In fact, if $x(a)$ vanishes outside a set $\mathfrak{A}_c$, then the function $x(u^{-1}ku_1)$ can be distinct from zero only for $u^{-1}ku_1 \in \mathfrak{A}_c$, that is only for $k \in \mathfrak{U}\mathfrak{A}_c\mathfrak{U}$. Thus the integral in (5) is an integral on a bounded set $K_c = K \cap (\mathfrak{U}\mathfrak{A}_c \mathfrak{U})$ of a continuous function $x(u^{-1}ku_1)\,\alpha(k)$ of u, $u_1 \in \mathfrak{U}$, $k \in K_c$, and so is a continuous function of u, u_1. But in that case $\int\int |K(u, u_1)|^2 \times du du_1$ exists, i.e.:

II. *T_x is an integral operator with Hilbert–Schmidt kernel.* We also note the following obvious property of the kernel K:

III. *The correspondence $x \to K$ defined by formula* (5), *possesses the following properties*:

(1) *if $x \to K$, then $x^* \to K^*$, where*

$$K^*(u_1, u_2) = \overline{K(u_2, u_1)} \tag{7}$$

is the Hermitian adjoint kernel;

(2) *if $x_1 \to K_1, x_2 \to K_2$, then*

$$\lambda_1 x_1 + \lambda_2 x_2 \to \lambda_1 K_1 + \lambda_2 K_2, \quad x_1 x_2 \to K_1 K_2,$$

where $K = K_1 K_2$ is the composition of the kernels K_1, K_2, *i.e. the kernel defined by the formula*

$$K(u_1, u_2) = \int K_1(u_1, u) K_2(u, u_2) du. \tag{8}$$

In fact the transition from x to x^* corresponds to the transition from T_x to the adjoint operator $(T_x)^*$, whose kernel must be the Hermitian adjoint of the kernel of the operator T_x. Analogously the product $x_1\, x_2$ corresponds to the product of the operators T_{x_1}, T_{x_2}, whose kernel is the composition of the kernels K_1, K_2 of these operators.

We will call a function $x \in X$ *positive definite* if x can be represented in the form $x = x_1^* x_1$, where $x_1 \in X$. From II and III it follows that a positive definite function x corresponds to a positive definite Hilbert–Schmidt kernel $K = K_1^* K_1$. From the theory of integral equations it is known (see, for example,† [31]), that such a kernel has trace $S(K)$, where

$$S(K) = \int K(u, u) du.$$

† The usual theory of integral equations is applicable to functions on the group $\mathfrak{U}$; this follows for instance from the fact that, if

$$u = \begin{Vmatrix} \alpha & \beta \\ -\bar{\beta} & \bar{\alpha} \end{Vmatrix}, \quad \alpha = \alpha_1 + i\alpha_2, \quad \beta = \beta_1 + i\beta_2,$$

we can consider every function $f(u)$ as a function $f(\alpha_1, \alpha_2, \beta_1, \beta_2)$ of four real variables $\alpha_1, \alpha_2, \beta_1, \beta_2$. defined on the surface of the sphere $\alpha_1^2 + \alpha_2^2 + \beta_1^2 + \beta_2^2 = 1$.

Substituting in this the expression (5) for the kernel K, we find

$$S(K) = \pi \int x(u^{-1}ku)\alpha(k)\mathrm{d}_l k\,\mathrm{d}u.$$

Formula (13) Subsection 3 is applied to the last integral giving

$$S(K) = \int x(a) \frac{\sum \alpha(k_a)\beta^{\frac{1}{2}}(k_a)}{|\lambda_a - \lambda_a^{-1}|^2}\, da$$

$$= \int x(a) \frac{|\lambda_a|^{i\rho - m}\lambda_a^m + |\lambda_a|^{-i\rho + m}\lambda_a^{-m}}{|\lambda_a - \lambda_a^{-1}|^2}\, da.$$

We arrive at the following result:†

THEOREM 9. *For any function $x \in X$ the operator T_x corresponding to a representation $\mathfrak{S}_{m,\rho}$ of the principal series, is an integral operator with Hilbert–Schmidt kernel*

$$K(u, u_1) = \pi \int x(u^{-1}ku_1)\alpha(k)\mathrm{d}_l k. \tag{9}$$

If x is a positive definite function of the ring X, then the operator T_x has trace $S(T_x)$, defined by the formulae

$$S(T_x) = \pi \int x(u^{-1}ku)\alpha(k)\mathrm{d}_l k\,\mathrm{d}u, \tag{10}$$

$$S(T_x) = \int x(a) \frac{|\lambda_a|^{i\rho - m}\lambda_a^m + |\lambda_a|^{-i\rho + m}\lambda_a^{-m}}{|\lambda_a - \lambda_a^{-1}|^2}\, da, \tag{11}$$

where λ_a, λ_a^{-1} are the eigenvalues of the matrix a.

From this theorem we deduce:

IV.‡ *If the pairs (m, ρ), (m_1, ρ_1) are such that $(m, \rho) \neq (m_1, \rho_1)$ and $(m, \rho) \neq (-m_1, -\rho_1)$, then the representations $\mathfrak{S}_{m,\rho}$ and $\mathfrak{S}_{m_1,\rho_1}$ of the principal series cannot be unitarily equivalent.*

In fact, formula (11) shows that in this case the traces of the corresponding operators T_x of the representations $\mathfrak{S}_{m,\rho}$, $\mathfrak{S}_{m_1,\rho_1}$ do not coincide. But for equivalent representations the traces must coincide; therefore $\mathfrak{S}_{m,\rho}$ and $\mathfrak{S}_{m_1,\rho_1}$ cannot be unitarily equivalent.

---

† Another method of calculating traces was recently suggested by M. I. GRAEV [17].

‡ Proposition IV is a particular case of a more general result, proved below in § 15 (see Theorem 15 § 15, Subsection 9).

Remark. It is also possible to define the operator T_x in the case of the realization of a representation of the principal series in the space $L^2(Z)$. Repeating the reasoning at the beginning of this section, we conclude that

$$T_x f(z) = \int \hat{K}(z, z_1) f(z_1) \mathrm{d}z_1, \tag{12}$$

where

$$\hat{K}(z, z_1) = \int x(z^{-1} k z_1) \alpha(k) \mathrm{d}_l k. \tag{13}$$

By virtue of (12) and (13) Subsection 3, we have

$$\int \hat{K}(z, z) \mathrm{d}z = \int K(u, u) \mathrm{d}u. \tag{14}$$

8. The trace of a representation of the complementary series

The reasoning of Subsection 7 carries over to a significant extent to the representations of the complementary series. In particular the operator T_x is again an integral operator with kernel

$$K(u, u_1) = \pi \int x(u^{-1} k u_1) \alpha(k) \mathrm{d}_l k, \tag{1}$$

where now

$$\alpha(a) = |a_{22}|^{-2-\sigma}. \tag{2}$$

We have

$$\int K(u, u) \mathrm{d}u = \pi \int x(u^{-1} k u) \alpha(k) \mathrm{d}_l k \, \mathrm{d}u = \int x(a) \frac{|\lambda_a|^{-\sigma} + |\lambda_a|^{\sigma}}{|\lambda_a - \lambda_a^{-1}|^2}. \tag{3}$$

Nevertheless, it is not clear *a priori* whether expression (3) will be the trace of the operator T_x when $x = x_1^* x_1$, because T_x is now an operator in the space H_σ, in which the scalar product is not the integral of the product, but the expression

$$(\phi_1, \phi_2) = \pi \iint \Phi(u' u''^{-1}) \phi_1(u') \overline{\phi_2(u'')} \mathrm{d}u' \mathrm{d}u''$$

(for the notation see Subsection 5 Section 12). Nevertheless, one can show that expression (3) is the trace of the operator T_x. For the proof it is sufficient to go over to the realization of the operator T_x in the space H_σ. A simple calculation shows that T_x is an integral operator in H_σ with kernel $\tilde{K}(w, w_1)$, satisfying the relation

$$\iint \tilde{K}(w, w) \mathrm{d}w' \mathrm{d}w'' = \int K(u, u) \mathrm{d}u, \quad w = w' + iw''. \tag{4}$$

On the other hand, the left-hand side of (4) is the trace of the operator T_x, because the scalar product in H_σ is given by the formula

$$(\phi_1, \phi_2) = c \int\int |w|^{-\sigma} \phi_1(w) \overline{\phi_2(w)} dw' dw''. \tag{5}$$

Thus the following theorem holds.†

THEOREM 10. *For any positive definite function $x \in X$ the operator T_x, corresponding to a representation $\mathfrak{D}_\sigma$ of the complementary series, has trace defined by the formulae*

$$S(T_x) = \pi \int x(u^{-1}ku) \alpha(k) d_l k du, \tag{6}$$

$$S(T_x) = \int x(a) \frac{|\lambda_a|^\sigma + |\lambda_a|^{-\sigma}}{|\lambda_a - \lambda_a^{-1}|^2} da, \tag{7}$$

where λ_a, λ_a^{-1} are the eigenvalues of the operator a.

From this theorem we conclude that *the representations of the complementary series corresponding to different values of σ, are not unitarily equivalent to each other and are not equivalent (unitarily) to any representation of the principal series.* Besides, this proposition follows also from the formulae for the spherical functions of the representations of the principal and complementary series (see (11) § 11, Subsection 5 and (3) § 12, Subsection 7). This proposition is a particular case of a more general result, proved below in § 15 (see Theorem 15 § 15, Subsection 9).

Remark 1. As $\sigma \to 2$, expression (7) for the trace tends to the limit

$$\int x(a) \frac{|\lambda_a|^2 + |\lambda_a|^{-2}}{|\lambda_a - \lambda_a^{-1}|^2} da = \int x(a) da + \int x(a) \frac{|\lambda_a|^2 \lambda_a^{-2} + |\lambda_a|^{-2} \lambda_a^2}{|\lambda_a - \lambda_a^{-1}|^2} da. \tag{8}$$

The right-hand side of (8) is the sum of the traces of the identity representation and the representation $\mathfrak{S}_{-2,0}$ of the principal series. Thus it is natural to conclude that the limit of the representation $\mathfrak{D}_\sigma$ as $\sigma \to 2$ is the semi-direct sum of the identity representation and the representation $\mathfrak{S}_{-2,0}$ of the principal series (in this connection see § 12, Subsection 2).

† For a detailed proof of this theorem see Ref. [12b].

Remark 2. We have defined the operator T_x for functions $x \in X$; in fact, it is easy to see that one can define this operator for any measurable function $x(a)$, satisfying the condition

$$\int |x(a)||T_a| da < \infty.$$

It is easy to see that, for the operations previously defined, the set of all such functions $x(a)$ forms a ring with involution (which we denote by $\tilde{X}$), containing X.

The reasoning of Subsections 7 and 8 shows that all the results of Subsections 7 and 8 in fact remain true for a class of functions $x(a)$ wider than X, for instance for all continuous functions which vanish outside some bounded set.

§ 14. An Analogue of Plancherel's Formula

1. Statement of the problem

Let $f(x)$ be a measurable function with integrable square on the real line $-\infty < x < \infty$; we consider its Fourier transform

$$\phi(\alpha) = \frac{1}{\sqrt{(2\pi)}} \int_{-\infty}^{\infty} f(x) e^{-i\alpha x} dx. \tag{1}$$

The well known theorem of Plancherel states that the integral in (1) converges in the mean and

$$\int_{-\infty}^{\infty} |\phi(\alpha)|^2 d\alpha = \int_{-\infty}^{\infty} |f(x)|^2 dx. \tag{2}$$

Formula (2) is called *Plancherel's formula.*

One can give the following group theoretical interpretation of Plancherel's theorem. The set of all real numbers x can be considered as a group, by defining the group operation to be the addition of numbers; this group is called *the additive group of real numbers.* We denote this group by $\mathfrak{G}_1$. We consider, for fixed real α, the function

$$\chi_\alpha(x) = e^{i\alpha x} . \tag{3}$$

Clearly

$$\chi_\alpha(x_1+x_2) = \chi_\alpha(x_1)\chi_\alpha(x_2), \quad |\chi_\alpha(x)| = 1. \tag{4}$$

Hence, the operator of multiplication by $\chi_\alpha(x)$ in a one-dimensional space realizes a one-dimensional representation of the group $\mathfrak{G}_1$ (we recall that x_1+x_2 denotes the *product* of the elements x_1, x_2 of the group $\mathfrak{G}_1$).

The measurable functions $f(x)$ with integrable square on the real line $-\infty < \alpha < \infty$ form a Hilbert space, denoted by $L^2(-\infty, \infty)$. In the space $L^2(-\infty, \infty)$ one can define a representation of the group $\mathfrak{G}_1$, letting

$$T_{x_0}f(x) = f(x+x_0); \tag{5}$$

the representation is unitary since

$$|T_{x_0}f|^2 = \int_{-\infty}^{\infty} |f(x+x_0)|^2 dx = \int_{-\infty}^{\infty} |f(x)|^2 dx = |f|^2.$$

This representation is called the *regular representation of the group* $\mathfrak{G}_1$. Now we will consider $\phi(\alpha)$ in (1) as a vector-valued function $\phi(\alpha) = \phi_\alpha$ of the argument α, $-\infty < \alpha < \infty$, with values in a *one-dimensional* complex space (namely, the space R_1 of all complex numbers). The set of all such measurable vector-valued functions, satisfying the condition $\int_{-\infty}^{\infty} |\phi(\alpha)|^2 d\alpha < \infty$, can be considered as the continued direct sum† of continuously many images of the space R_1. Plancherel's formula (2) shows that the space $L^2(-\infty, \infty)$ of functions $f(x)$ is isometric to this continued sum, where the isometry is given by formula (1). In this isometric mapping the operator T_x of the regular representation goes into an operator

† The usual (discrete) direct sum of the spaces R_k, $k = 1, 2, \ldots, n$, is the set of all systems $f = \{f_1, f_2, \ldots, f_n\}$, $f_k \in R_k$, where $|f|^2 = \sum_{k=1}^{n} |f_k|^2$. One can also treat it as the set of all vector-valued functions f_k of an integral argument k with values in R_k, in which the norm is defined by the formula $\left(\sum_{k=1}^{n} |f_k|^2\right)^{1/2}$.

which we denote by $\hat{T}_x$. We will find $\hat{T}_x$. For this purpose we note that an application to $f(x)$ of the operator T_{x_0} of the regular representation takes the function $\phi(\alpha)$ into

$$\frac{1}{\sqrt{(2\pi)}}\int_{-\infty}^{\infty} f(x+x_0)e^{-i\alpha x}dx$$

$$= \frac{1}{\sqrt{(2\pi)}}\int_{-\infty}^{\infty} f(x)e^{-i\alpha(x-x_0)}dx = e^{i\alpha x_0}\phi(\alpha),$$

i.e. application of the operator $\hat{T}_{x_0}$ to $\phi(\alpha)$ reduces to a transformation of each separate one-dimensional image of R_1 according to a one-dimensional representation of the group $\mathfrak{G}_1$; namely, a transformation which multiplies the α th image by $\chi_\alpha(x_0) = e^{i\alpha x_0}$.

By analogy with the definition of the usual (discrete) orthogonal direct sum of representations we will say that *the representation* $x \to \hat{T}_x$ *is the continued direct sum of the one-dimensional representations* $x \to \chi_\alpha(x)$. Thus, *the Fourier transform* (1) *realizes an isometric mapping of the regular representation of the additive group* $\mathfrak{G}_1$ *of real numbers into the continued direct sum of its irreducible* (*that is, one-dimensional*) *representations, i.e. it realizes a decomposition of the regular representation of the group* $\mathfrak{G}_1$ *into its irreducible representations.*

In this lies the group-theoretical significance of the Fourier transform and Plancherel's formula.†

As a second example we consider the set $L^2(\mathfrak{U})$ of all measurable functions $f(u)$ on the group $\mathfrak{U}$ with integrable square with respect to the measure du, i.e. such that $\int |f(u)|^2 du < \infty$. This set $L^2(\mathfrak{U})$ is a Hilbert space where the addition of functions and multiplication by a number are defined in the usual way, and where the scalar product is given by the formula

$$(f_1, f_2) = \int f_1(u)\overline{f_2(u)}du.$$

† The results described here are of a general character and carry over to arbitrary locally compact commutative groups (see, for instance, Refs. [8] or [28 e]).

Let $c^k_{jl}(u)$ be the matrix elements of the irreducible representations of the group $\mathfrak{U}$ in their canonical bases; we set

$$\phi^k_{jl}(u) = \sqrt{(2k+1)}\, c^k_{jl}(u). \tag{6}$$

By virtue of the results of § 5, Subsection 5 and § 6, Subsection 2 the functions $\phi^k_{jl}(u)$ form a complete orthogonal system in $L^2(\mathfrak{U})$; hence,

$$\int |f(u)|^2 \mathrm{d}u = (f, f) = \sum_k \sum_{j,l} |\alpha^k_{jl}|^2, \tag{7}$$

where

$$\alpha^k_{jl} = (f, \phi^k_{jl}) = \int f(u)\overline{\phi^k_{jl}(u)}\,\mathrm{d}u, \tag{8}$$

and where the summation is carried out for $k = 0, \frac{1}{2}, 1, \frac{3}{2}, 2, \frac{5}{2}, \ldots$ and $j, l = -k, -k+1, \ldots, k$.

Now we rewrite formulae (7) and (8) in another notation for which we set

$$F^k = \int f(u)(c^k(u))^* \mathrm{d}u, \tag{9}$$

where $c^k(u) = \|c^k_{jl}(u)\|$ is the matrix of the irreducible representation of weight k, so that F^k is also a matrix with elements

$$F^k_{jl} = \int f(u)\overline{c^k_{lj}(u)}\,\mathrm{d}u. \tag{10}$$

Formula (9) can be considered as an analogue of the Fourier transform (1); only in the present case the irreducible representations are not one-dimensional, and so the part of the numerical function $\phi(\alpha)$ of the argument α, labelling the irreducible representations of the group $\mathfrak{G}_1$ (the additive group of real numbers), is played by the matrix function F^k of discrete argument k, labelling the irreducible representations of the group $\mathfrak{U}$.

From (6), (8) and (10) we conclude that

$$\alpha^k_{jl} = \sqrt{(2k+1)} \int f(u)\overline{c^k_{jl}(u)}\,\mathrm{d}u = \sqrt{(2k+1)}\, F^k_{lj},$$

and substitution in formula (7) gives

$$\int |f(u)|^2 \mathrm{d}u = \sum_k (2k+1) \sum_{j,l} |F^k_{lj}|^2. \tag{11}$$

But $\sum_{j,l} |F^k_{lj}|^2$ is the trace $S(F^{k*}F^k)$ of the matrix $F^{k*}F^k$; in fact, the trace of a matrix is equal to the sum of its diagonal elements and, consequently,

$$S(F^{k*}F^k) = \sum_{j=-k}^{k} (F^{k*}F^k)_{jj} = \sum_{j=-k}^{k} \sum_{l=-k}^{k} (F^{k*})_{jl} F^k_{lj}$$
$$= \sum_{j,l} \overline{F}^k_{lj} F^k_{lj} = \sum_{j,l} |F^k_{lj}|^2.$$

Therefore from (11) we conclude that

$$\int |f(u)|^2 du = \sum_k (2k+1) S(F^{k*}F^k). \tag{12}$$

Formula (12) can be considered as Plancherel's formula for the group $\mathfrak{U}$, analogous to formula (2). Now the part of the integral with respect to $d\alpha$ is played by the sum with respect to the discrete index k; this is explained by the fact that the group $\mathfrak{U}$ possesses only a countable set of non-equivalent irreducible representations. Further, the part of $|\phi(\alpha)|^2 = \overline{\phi(\alpha)}\phi(\alpha)$ is now played by $S(F^{k*}F^k)$, which is explained by the fact that the irreducible representations of the group $\mathfrak{U}$ are not one-dimensional.

As for the group $\mathfrak{G}_1$, we define the regular representation $u \to T_u$ of the group $\mathfrak{U}$ in the space $L^2(\mathfrak{U})$, letting

$$T_{u_0} f(u) = f(uu_0) \quad \text{for} \quad f \in L^2(\mathfrak{U}).$$

This is unitary by virtue of the invariant nature of the measure du:

$$\int |f(uu_0)|^2 du = \int |f(u)|^2 du.$$

We determine how the matrix elements F^k_{jl} are transformed in the transition from $f(u)$ to $f(uu_0)$. By (10), F^k_{jl} then becomes

$$F'^k_{jl} = \int f(uu_0)\overline{c^k_{lj}(u)}\, du = \int f(u)\overline{c^k_{lj}(uu_0^{-1})}\, du$$
$$= \sum_{p=-k}^{k} \int f(u)\overline{c^k_{lp}(u)}\,\overline{c^k_{pj}(u_0^{-1})}\, du = \sum_{p=-k}^{k} \overline{c^k_{pj}(u_0^{-1})} F^k_{pl},$$

i.e.

$$F'^k_{jl} = \sum_{p=-k}^{k} c^k_{jp}(u_0) F^k_{pl}. \tag{13}$$

We denote by R^k the finite-dimensional, in fact $(2k+1)$-dimensional, space composed of all possible systems $\xi = \{\xi_{-k}, \xi_{-k+1}, \ldots, \xi_k\}$ of numbers $\xi_{-k}, \xi_{-k+1}, \ldots, \xi_k$; for this we define the operations of addition and multiplication in R^k in the usual way, and a scalar product by means of the formula

$$(\xi, \eta) = (2k+1) \sum_{p=-k}^{k} \xi_p \bar{\eta}_p. \tag{14}$$

For fixed j and k the numbers F^k_{jl}, $l = -k, -k+1, \ldots, k$, are elements $\xi^k_j = (F^k_{j,-k}, F^k_{j,-k+1}, \ldots, F^k_{j,k})$ of the space R^k; therefore the function F^k can be considered as a vector-valued function $\xi = \{\xi^k_j\}$ with values in $R^k_j = R^k$.

From (11) and (14) it follows that

$$|f|^2 = \int |f(u)|^2 du = \sum_{k,j} |\xi^k_j|^2;$$

this means that the transition from f to F^k by means of formula (10) is an isometric mapping of the space $L^2(\mathfrak{U})$ on the direct sum of spaces R^k, in which each R^k occurs $2k+1$ times. Let $\hat{T}_u$ be the operator to which T_u corresponds in this mapping; formula (13) shows that each of the subspaces $R^k_j = R^k$ is invariant with respect to $\hat{T}_u$ and the matrix of the operator $\hat{T}_u$ in this subspace coincides with $\|c^k_{jl}(u)\|$. Hence, the general Fourier transform (9) realizes an isometric mapping of the regular representation $u \to T_u$ onto the direct sum of irreducible representations $u \to c^k(u)$, where each representation $u \to c^k(u)$ is contained in this direct sum $2k+1$ times.†

The purpose of this section is to obtain analogous results for the group $\mathfrak{A}$. We will see below that a regular representation of the group $\mathfrak{A}$ is decomposed into the direct sum of representations $\mathfrak{S}_{m,\rho}$ of the principal series. Because the representations $\mathfrak{S}_{m,\rho}$ are not one-dimensional (being even infinite-dimensional), the corresponding Plancherel formula, and the corresponding formula (12), will contain the trace of the operators of these representations. On the other hand, in view of the dependence of the representa-

† An analogous proposition and a formula similar to formula (12), hold for any compact topological group (see, for instance, Ref. [28 e]).

tions $\mathfrak{S}_{m,\rho}$ on the discrete index m and the continuous index ρ this Plancherel formula will contain a summation with respect to m and an integral with respect to ρ. Its derivation is based on the circumstance that the transition $x \to K$ from the functions $x(a)$ to the kernel $K(u_1, u_2)$ of an operator T_x of a representation of the principal series can be achieved by means of successive applications of Fourier transforms and a point transformation. In this an important part will be played by two subgroups of the group K.

2. Some subgroups of the group K

(a) *The subgroup D.* We denote by D the set of all matrices

$$\delta = \begin{Vmatrix} \lambda^{-1} & 0 \\ 0 & \lambda \end{Vmatrix}; \tag{1}$$

clearly D is a subgroup of the group K. Every function $f(\delta)$ on the group D can be considered as a function $f(\lambda)$ of the parameter λ, defined for $\lambda \neq 0$. Multiplication of the matrices δ corresponds to multiplication of the corresponding parameters λ; hence it is easy to verify that an invariant integral on the group D is defined by the formula

$$I = \int f(\delta) \frac{d\sigma d\tau}{|\lambda|^2}, \quad \lambda = \sigma + i\tau. \tag{2}$$

Letting

$$d\delta = \frac{d\sigma d\tau}{|\lambda|^2}, \quad \lambda = \sigma + i\tau, \tag{3}$$

we can write down an expression for this invariant integral in the form

$$I = \int f(\delta) d\delta. \tag{4}$$

With this definition of invariant integral, we have

$$\int f(\delta_0 \delta) d\delta = \int f(\delta \delta_0) d\delta = \int f(\delta) d\delta; \tag{5}$$

moreover, it is easy to verify that

$$\int f(\delta^{-1}) d\delta = \int f(\delta) d\delta. \tag{6}$$

(b) *The subgroup Z.* We denote by Z the set of all matrices ζ of the form

$$\zeta = \begin{Vmatrix} 1 & \zeta \\ 0 & 1 \end{Vmatrix}, \tag{7}$$

clearly, Z is a subgroup of the group K. Every function $f(\zeta)$ on the group Z can be considered as a function $f(\zeta)$ of the parameter ζ. Multiplication of the matrices ζ corresponds to addition of the corresponding parameters ζ; it follows that an invariant integral over the group Z is defined by the formula

$$I = \int f(\zeta) \mathrm{d}\xi \mathrm{d}\eta, \quad \zeta = \xi + i\eta. \tag{8}$$

Letting

$$\mathrm{d}\zeta = \mathrm{d}\xi \, \mathrm{d}\eta, \quad \zeta = \xi + i\eta; \tag{9}$$

we can write the expression for this invariant integral in the form

$$I = \int f(\zeta) \mathrm{d}\zeta. \tag{10}$$

Here, by definition of invariant integral:

$$\int f(\zeta_0 \zeta) \mathrm{d}\zeta = \int f(\zeta \zeta_0) \mathrm{d}\zeta = \int f(\zeta) \mathrm{d}\zeta; \tag{11}$$

moreover,

$$\int f(\zeta^{-1}) \mathrm{d}\zeta = \int f(\zeta) \mathrm{d}\zeta. \tag{12}$$

3. Canonical decomposition of the elements of the group K

I. *Every matrix $k \in K$ can be represented uniquely in the form*

$$k = \delta \zeta, \tag{1a}$$

and also in the form

$$k = \zeta \delta. \tag{1b}$$

Proof. Written out in detail (1a) takes the form

$$\begin{Vmatrix} k_{11} & k_{12} \\ 0 & k_{22} \end{Vmatrix} = \begin{Vmatrix} \lambda^{-1} & 0 \\ 0 & \lambda \end{Vmatrix} \begin{Vmatrix} 1 & \zeta \\ 0 & 1 \end{Vmatrix}, \quad k_{11} = k_{22}^{-1}. \tag{2}$$

Hence we conclude that

$$k_{11} = \lambda^{-1}, \quad k_{22} = \lambda, \quad k_{12} = \lambda^{-1}\zeta, \quad \zeta = \lambda k_{12} = k_{22} k_{12}; \tag{3}$$

consequently the uniqueness of equation (1a) holds. Conversely, choosing λ and ζ according to formulae (3), we satisfy relation (2), i.e. (1a).

The assertion with regard to (1b) is proved similarly.

We saw above that when $a_{22} \neq 0$ the equation $a = kz$ holds (see § 10, Subsection 2); combining this result with proposition I, we obtain:

II. *Every matrix* $a \in \mathfrak{A}$ *satisfying the condition* $a_{22} \neq 0$, *can be represented uniquely in the form*

$$a = \delta\zeta z, \tag{4a}$$

and also in the form

$$a = \zeta\delta z. \tag{4b}$$

In what follows we will also need the following proposition:

III. *Every matrix* $a \in \mathfrak{A}$ *satisfying the condition* $a_{12} \neq 0$, *can be represented uniquely in the form*

$$a = z_1^{-1} s\delta z, \tag{5}$$

where

$$s = \begin{Vmatrix} 0 & 1 \\ -1 & 0 \end{Vmatrix}. \tag{6}$$

Proof. We apply (4b) to the matrix $s^{-1}a$; this is permissible, because for the matrix $s^{-1}a$ the part of a_{22} is played by $a_{12} \neq 0$. Thus, $s^{-1}a = \zeta\delta z$, whence $a = s\zeta s^{-1} \cdot s\delta z$. But it is easy to see that $s\zeta s^{-1} \in Z$; letting $s\zeta s^{-1} = z_1^{-1}$, we obtain (5).

4. Some integral relations

I. *The relations*

$$\int f(k)\mathrm{d}_l k = \iint f(\delta\zeta)\mathrm{d}\delta\mathrm{d}\zeta, \tag{1a}$$

$$\int f(k)\mathrm{d}_r k = \iint f(\zeta\delta)\mathrm{d}\delta\mathrm{d}\zeta, \tag{1b}$$

hold, where the absolute convergence of the one side implies the absolute convergence of the other.

Proof. The transition from $\mathrm{d}_l k$ to $\mathrm{d}\delta$, $\mathrm{d}\zeta$ where $k = \delta\zeta$ is equivalent to the transition

$$k_{22} = \lambda, \quad k_{12} = \lambda^{-1}\zeta \tag{2}$$

from k_{22}, k_{12} to λ and ζ, the Jacobian of which is equal to

$$\left|\frac{\partial(k_{22}k_{12})}{\partial(\lambda, \zeta)}\right|^2 = |\lambda|^{-2}. \tag{3}$$

Hence, taking into account the formulae for $\mathrm{d}_l k$, $\mathrm{d}\delta$, $\mathrm{d}\zeta$, we see that $\mathrm{d}_l k = \mathrm{d}\delta \mathrm{d}\zeta$ when $k = \delta\zeta$. Substituting these expressions in $\int f(k)\mathrm{d}_l k$ and applying Fubini's theorem, we obtain (1a); (1b) is proved analogously.

II. *The relations*

$$\int f(a)\mathrm{d}a = \iiint f(\delta\zeta z)\mathrm{d}\delta \mathrm{d}\zeta \mathrm{d}z = \iiint f(\zeta\delta z)\beta(\delta)\mathrm{d}\delta \mathrm{d}\zeta \mathrm{d}z, \quad (4)$$

$$\int f(a)\mathrm{d}a = \iiint f(z^{-1}s\delta z_1)\beta(\delta)\mathrm{d}\delta \mathrm{d}z \mathrm{d}z_1, \quad (5)$$

hold, where the absolute convergence of one of these expressions implies the absolute convergence of the remaining ones.

Proof. On the basis of I § 13, Subsection 3 we have

$$\int f(a)\mathrm{d}a = \int f(kz)\mathrm{d}_l k \mathrm{d}z; \quad (6)$$

applying formulae (1a) and (1b) to the function $f_1(k) = \int f(kz)\mathrm{d}z$, we obtain:

$$\int f(a)\mathrm{d}a = \int f_1(k)\mathrm{d}_l k = \iint f_1(\delta\zeta)\mathrm{d}\delta \mathrm{d}\zeta = \iiint f(\delta\zeta z)\mathrm{d}\delta \mathrm{d}\zeta \mathrm{d}z,$$

$$\int f(a)\mathrm{d}a = \int f_1(k)\beta(k)\mathrm{d}_r k = \iint f_1(\zeta\delta)\beta(\zeta\delta)\mathrm{d}\delta \mathrm{d}\zeta$$
$$= \iiint f(\zeta\delta z)\beta(\delta)\mathrm{d}\delta \mathrm{d}\zeta \mathrm{d}z,$$

and (4) is proved. Further,

$$\int f(a)\mathrm{d}a = \int f(s^{-1}a)\mathrm{d}a = \iiint f(s^{-1}\zeta\delta z)\beta(\delta)\mathrm{d}\delta \mathrm{d}\zeta \mathrm{d}z$$
$$= \iiint f(s^{-1}\zeta s \cdot s\delta z_2)\beta(\delta)\mathrm{d}\delta \mathrm{d}\zeta \mathrm{d}z_1. \quad (7)$$

Setting $s^{-1}\zeta s = z^{-1}$; we easily see that $\mathrm{d}\zeta = \mathrm{d}z$, and (7) yields (5).

5. Some auxiliary functions and relations between them

Now we describe how the transition from $x(a)$ to the kernel $K(z_1, z_2)$ can be realized by successive Fourier transforms and a point transformation. We introduce the parameters z, z_1, λ, letting

$$x(a) = x(z^{-1}s\delta z_1) = x(z, z_1, \lambda) \quad (1)$$

where

$$\delta = \begin{Vmatrix} \lambda & 0 \\ 0 & \lambda^{-1} \end{Vmatrix}.$$

From (5) Subsection 4 it follows that

$$\int |x(a)|^2 \mathrm{d}a = \iiint |x(z^{-1}s\delta z_1)|^2 \beta(\delta) \mathrm{d}z \mathrm{d}z_1 \mathrm{d}\delta$$
$$= \iiint |x(z, z_1, \lambda)|^2 |\lambda|^{-6} \mathrm{d}z \mathrm{d}z_1 \mathrm{d}\lambda, \tag{2}$$

where

$$\mathrm{d}\lambda = \mathrm{d}\sigma \mathrm{d}\tau \quad \text{when} \quad \lambda = \sigma + i\tau. \tag{3}$$

We denote by X' the set of all functions $x(z, z_1, \lambda)$ which are twice continuously differentiable with respect to the variables

$$x, y, \quad x_1, y_1, \quad \sigma, \tau (z = x+iy, \quad z_1 = x_1 + iy_1, \quad \lambda = \sigma + i\tau)$$

and are equal to zero outside some set (depending on x) defined by inequalities of the form

$$|z| \leqslant C, \quad |z_1| \leqslant C_1, \quad 0 < C_2 \leqslant |\lambda| \leqslant C_3.$$

Let $x(z, z_1, \lambda) \in X'$. We consider the Fourier transform

$$\tilde{x}(w, w_1, \lambda) = \frac{1}{(2\pi)^2} \iint x(z, z_1, \lambda) e^{i\mathrm{Re}(\bar{z}w - \bar{z}_1 w_1)} \mathrm{d}z \mathrm{d}z_1 \tag{4}$$

of the function $x(z, z_1, \lambda)$ with respect to z and z_1; on the basis of the usual Plancherel formula we deduce from (2) that

$$\int |x(a)|^2 \mathrm{d}a = \iiint |\tilde{x}(w, w_1, \lambda)|^2 |\lambda|^{-6} \mathrm{d}w \mathrm{d}w_1 \mathrm{d}\lambda, \tag{5}$$

where

$$\mathrm{d}w = \mathrm{d}u \mathrm{d}v, \mathrm{d}w_1 = \mathrm{d}u_1 \mathrm{d}v_1 \quad \text{when} \quad w = u + iv, w_1 = u_1 + iv_1. \tag{6}$$

Now let us agree to denote by $\hat{K}(z, z_1, m, \rho)$ the kernel of the operator T_x of the representation $\mathfrak{S}_{m,\rho}$ of the principal series, so as to emphasize its dependence on m and ρ.

According to formula (13) § 13, Subsection 7 we have

$$\hat{K}(z, z_1, m, \rho) = \int x(z^{-1}kz_1) \alpha(k) \mathrm{d}_l k$$
$$= \int x(z^{-1}\delta\zeta z_1) |\lambda|^{-m+i\rho-2} \lambda^m \mathrm{d}\zeta \mathrm{d}\delta \tag{7}$$

when

$$\delta = \begin{Vmatrix} \lambda^{-1} & 0 \\ 0 & \lambda \end{Vmatrix}.$$

We set

$$\phi(z, z_1, \lambda) = |\lambda|^{-2} \int x(z^{-1}\delta\zeta z_1) \mathrm{d}\zeta; \tag{8}$$

then (7) can be rewritten in the form

$$\hat{K}(z, z_1, m, \rho) = \int \phi(z, z_1\lambda)\,|\lambda|^{-m+i\rho}\lambda^m \frac{d\lambda}{|\lambda|^2}. \tag{9}$$

We will find an expression for $\phi(z, z_1, \lambda)$ in terms of $x(z, z_1, \lambda)$. Letting

$$\delta\zeta = \hat{z}^{-1}s\hat{\delta}\hat{z}_1, \qquad \hat{\delta} = \begin{Vmatrix} \hat{\lambda} & 0 \\ 0 & \hat{\lambda}^{-1} \end{Vmatrix}, \tag{10}$$

we have:

$$\phi(z, z_1, \lambda) = |\lambda|^{-2} \int x(z^{-1}\hat{z}^{-1}s\hat{\delta}\hat{z}_1 z_1)d\zeta$$
$$= |\lambda|^{-2} \int x(z+\hat{z}, z_1+\hat{z}_1, \hat{\lambda})d\zeta. \tag{11}$$

On the other hand, it follows from (10) that

$$s^{-1}\delta\zeta = \hat{\zeta}\hat{\delta}\hat{z}_1, \quad \text{where} \quad \hat{\zeta} = s^{-1}\hat{z}^{-1}s; \tag{12}$$

applying formulae (4) § 10, Subsection 2, we obtain:

$$\hat{z} = -\frac{\lambda^2}{\zeta}, \quad \hat{z}_1 = \frac{1}{\zeta}, \quad \hat{\lambda} = \frac{\lambda}{\zeta}, \tag{13}$$

and (11) takes the form

$$\phi(z, z_1, \lambda) = |\lambda|^{-2} \int x\left(z - \frac{\lambda^2}{\zeta}, z_1 + \frac{1}{\zeta}, \frac{\lambda}{\zeta}\right)d\zeta. \tag{14}$$

In this integral we make the substitution $\zeta_1 = \frac{\lambda}{\zeta}$; we obtain:

$$\phi(z, z_1, \lambda) = \int x\left(z - \lambda\zeta_1, z_1 + \frac{1}{\lambda}\zeta_1, \zeta_1\right)|\zeta_1|^{-4}d\zeta_1. \tag{15}$$

Now we consider the Fourier transform

$$\tilde{\phi}(w, w_1, \lambda) = \frac{1}{(2\pi)^2}\iint \phi(z, z_1, \lambda)e^{i\mathrm{Re}(w\bar{z}-w_1\bar{z}_1)}dz\,dz_1 \tag{16}$$

of the function $\phi(z, z_1, \lambda)$ with respect to z and z_1; and (15) from (4) we deduce that

$$\tilde{\phi}(w, w_1, \lambda) = \int \tilde{x}(w, w_1, \zeta_1)e^{i\mathrm{Re}((\bar{w}\lambda+\bar{w}_1\lambda^{-1})\zeta_1)}|\zeta_1|^{-4}d\zeta_1. \tag{17}$$

Now we take the Fourier transform

$$\hat{x}(w, w_1, p) = \frac{1}{2\pi}\int \tilde{x}(w, w_1, \lambda)|\lambda|^{-4} e^{i\mathrm{Re}(\bar{p}\lambda)} d\lambda; \tag{18}$$

then (17) means that

$$\tilde{\phi}(w, w_1, \lambda) = 2\pi\hat{x}(w, w_1, w\bar{\lambda} + w_1\bar{\lambda}^{-1}). \tag{19}$$

Formula (19) also represents a fundamental relation between $x(a)$ and $\hat{K}(z, z_1, m, \rho)$ expressed by means of the auxiliary functions $\tilde{\phi}$ and $\hat{x}$. By virtue of this relation the transition $x \to K$ can be represented as a chain of transitions $x \to \tilde{x} \to \hat{x} \to \tilde{\phi} \to \phi \to \hat{K}$, each of which is a Fourier transform or a point transformation.

From (19) it follows immediately that the function $\tilde{\phi}$ satisfies the relation

$$\tilde{\phi}\left(w, w_1, \frac{\bar{w}_1}{\lambda\bar{w}}\right) = \tilde{\phi}(w, w_1, \lambda) \tag{20}$$

and that $\hat{x}$ is expressed in terms of $\tilde{\phi}$ by means of the formula

$$\hat{x}(w, w_1, p) = \frac{1}{2\pi}\tilde{\phi}\left(w, w_1, \frac{\bar{p} + \sqrt{(\bar{p}^2 - 4\bar{w}\bar{w}_1)}}{2\bar{w}}\right); \tag{21}$$

here, by virtue of relation (20), the choice of the value of the root $\sqrt{(\bar{p}^2 - 4\bar{w}\bar{w}_1)}$ plays no part.

Relation (20) corresponds to a relation between the kernels $\hat{K}(z, z_1, m, \rho)$ and $\hat{K}(z, z_1, -m, -\rho)$. In order to obtain this, we pass from these kernels to their Fourier transforms with respect to z and z_1, letting

$$\tilde{K}(w, w_1, m, \rho) = \frac{1}{(2\pi)^2}\iint \hat{K}(z, z_1, m, \rho) e^{i\mathrm{Re}(\bar{w}z - \bar{w}_1 z_1)} dz\, dz_1. \tag{22}$$

Then, we have by virtue of (9):

$$\tilde{K}(w, w_1, m, \rho) = \int \tilde{\phi}(w, w_1, \lambda)|\lambda|^{-m+i\rho}\lambda^m \frac{d\lambda}{|\lambda|^2}, \tag{23}$$

and from (20) it follows immediately that

$$\tilde{K}(w, w_1, -m, -\rho) = \left|\frac{w}{w_1}\right|^{m+i\rho}\left(\frac{w}{w_1}\right)^{-m}\tilde{K}(w, w_1, m, \rho). \tag{24}$$

6. The derivation of an analogue of Plancherel's formula

First let $x(z, z_1, \lambda) \in X'$; then, differentiating both sides of (18) Subsection 5, we obtain:

$$\frac{\partial \hat{x}}{\partial p} = \frac{i}{4\pi} \int \tilde{x}(w, w_1, \lambda) |\lambda|^{-4} \bar{\lambda} e^{i\mathrm{Re}(\bar{p}\lambda)} d\lambda; \tag{1}$$

in this $\frac{\partial \hat{x}}{\partial p}$ is given by the expression

$$\frac{\partial \hat{x}}{\partial p} = \frac{1}{2}\left(\frac{\partial \hat{x}}{\partial p_1} - i \frac{\partial \hat{x}}{\partial p_2}\right), \quad p = p_1 + ip_2.$$

Thus, $\frac{2}{i}\frac{\partial \hat{x}}{\partial p}$ is the Fourier transform of the function

$$\tilde{x}(w, w_1, \lambda) |\lambda|^{-4} \bar{\lambda}.$$

Hence, on the basis of the usual Plancherel formula we have

$$4 \iiint \left| \frac{\partial}{\partial p} \hat{x}(w, w_1, p) \right|^2 dw\, dw_1\, dp$$
$$= \iiint |\tilde{x}(w, w_1, \lambda)|^2 |\lambda|^{-6} dw\, dw_1\, d\lambda. \tag{2}$$

Combining (2) with formula (5) Subsection 5, we conclude that

$$\int |x(a)|^2 da = 4 \iiint \left| \frac{\partial}{\partial p} \hat{x}(w, w_1, p) \right|^2 dw\, dw_1\, dp. \tag{3}$$

We go over in the last integral from the variable p to the variable λ by means of the formula

$$p = w\bar{\lambda} + w_1 \bar{\lambda}^{-1}; \tag{4}$$

we have

$$\left| \frac{\partial \hat{x}}{\partial p} \right|^2 dp = \left| \frac{\partial \hat{x}}{\partial \bar{\lambda}} \right|^2 \left| \frac{d\bar{\lambda}}{dp} \right|^2 \left| \frac{dp}{d\bar{\lambda}} \right|^2 d\lambda = \left| \frac{\partial \hat{x}}{\partial \bar{\lambda}} \right|^2 d\lambda. \tag{5}$$

Substituting this expression in (3) and taking into account the fact that the mapping $p \to \bar{\lambda}$ by means of formula (4) is two-fold, we arrive at the relation

$$\int |x(a)|^2 da = 2 \iiint \left| \frac{\partial}{\partial \bar{\lambda}} \hat{x}(w, w_1, w\bar{\lambda} + w_1 \bar{\lambda}^{-1}) \right|^2 dw\, dw_1\, d\lambda;$$

hence, by virtue of (19) Subsection 5,

$$\int |x(a)|^2 \mathrm{d}a = \frac{1}{2\pi^2} \iiint \left| \frac{\partial}{\partial \bar{\lambda}} \tilde{\phi}(w, w_1, \lambda) \right|^2 \mathrm{d}w \mathrm{d}w_1 \mathrm{d}\lambda. \tag{6}$$

Taking into account definition (16) Subsection 5 of the function $\tilde{\phi}(w, w_1, \lambda)$ and again applying the usual Plancherel formula, we obtain:

$$\int |x(a)|^2 \mathrm{d}a = \frac{1}{2\pi^2} \iiint \left| \frac{\partial}{\partial \bar{\lambda}} \phi(z, z_1, \lambda) \right|^2 \mathrm{d}z \mathrm{d}z_1 \mathrm{d}\lambda. \tag{7}$$

If we set

$$\bar{\lambda} = \mathrm{e}^{\xi}, \ \xi = t - i\theta, \ -\pi \leqslant \theta \leqslant \pi, \ \phi(z, z_1, \lambda) = \phi(z, z_1, t, \theta); \tag{8}$$

then

$$\left| \frac{\partial \phi}{\partial \bar{\lambda}} \right|^2 \mathrm{d}\lambda = \left| \frac{\partial \phi}{\partial \xi} \right|^2 \left| \frac{\mathrm{d}\xi}{\mathrm{d}\bar{\lambda}} \right|^2 \mathrm{d}\lambda = \left| \frac{\partial \phi}{\partial \xi} \right|^2 \mathrm{d}\xi = \left| \frac{\partial \phi}{\partial \xi} \right|^2 \mathrm{d}t \mathrm{d}\theta,$$

and formula (7) takes the form

$$\int |x(a)|^2 \mathrm{d}a = \frac{1}{2\pi^2} \int_{-\pi}^{\pi} \mathrm{d}\theta \int_{-\infty}^{\infty} \mathrm{d}t \iint \left| \frac{\partial}{\partial \xi} \phi(z, z_1, t, \theta) \right|^2 \mathrm{d}z \mathrm{d}z_1. \tag{9}$$

Moreover, formula (9) Subsection 5 gives:

$$\hat{K}(z, z_1, m, \rho) = \int_{-\pi}^{\pi} \mathrm{d}\theta \int_{-\infty}^{\infty} \phi(z, z_1, t, \theta) \mathrm{e}^{it\rho} \mathrm{e}^{im\theta} \mathrm{d}t, \tag{10}$$

whence

$$\begin{aligned} &\int_{-\pi}^{\pi} \mathrm{d}\theta \int_{-\infty}^{\infty} \frac{\partial}{\partial \xi} \phi(z, z_1, t, \theta) \mathrm{e}^{it\rho} \mathrm{e}^{im\theta} \mathrm{d}t \\ &= \frac{1}{2} \int_{-\pi}^{\pi} \mathrm{d}\theta \int_{-\infty}^{\infty} \left(\frac{\partial}{\partial t} + i \frac{\partial}{\partial \theta} \right) \phi(z, z_1, t, \theta) \mathrm{e}^{it\rho} \mathrm{e}^{im\theta} \mathrm{d}t \\ &= -\frac{1}{2}(i\rho + m) \hat{K}(z, z_1, m, \rho). \end{aligned}$$

This means that

$$-\frac{1}{4\pi}(i\rho+m)\hat{K}(z, z_1, m, \rho)$$

is the Fourier transform with respect to t and θ of the function $\partial\phi/\partial\xi$; therefore applying to the right hand side of (9) the usual Plancherel formula and Parseval's equation, we obtain:

$$\int |x(a)|^2 \mathrm{d}a = \frac{1}{32\pi^4}\sum_{m=-\infty}^{\infty}\int_{-\infty}^{\infty}\left[\iint |\hat{K}(z, z_1, m, \rho)|^2 \mathrm{d}z\,\mathrm{d}z_1\right]\times$$
$$\times (m^2+\rho^2)\mathrm{d}\rho .$$

This is the analogue of Plancherel's formula.† We have therefore proved:

THEOREM 11. *For any function* $x(a) = x(z, z_1, \lambda)$ *from* X' *the formula*

$$\int |x(a)|^2 \mathrm{d}a$$
$$= \frac{1}{32\pi^4}\sum_{m=-\infty}^{\infty}\int_{-\infty}^{\infty}\left[\iint |\hat{K}(z, z_1, m, \rho)|^2 \mathrm{d}z\,\mathrm{d}z_1\right](m^2+\rho^2)\mathrm{d}\rho, \qquad (11)$$

holds, where $\hat{K}(z, z_1, m, \rho)$ *is the kernel of the operator* T_x *of the representation* $\mathfrak{S}_{m,\rho}$ *of the principal series.*‡

We denote by $V_x^{(m,\rho)}$ the operator of the representation $\mathfrak{S}_{m,\rho}$ of the principal series. The integral in the square brackets in (11) is the trace of the operator $V_{x^*x}^{(m,\rho)}$; therefore (11) can be

† This formula was first obtained by I. M. Gelfand and the author [12b] and then extended by them in [12e] to complex unimodular groups of arbitrary order.

Subsequently Harish–Chandra [38c, d] extended this formula to arbitrary complex semi-simple groups. The most simple method of deriving it was then proposed by I. M. Gelfand and M. I. Graev [11].

‡ See the remark at the end of § 13.

rewritten in the form

$$\int |x(a)|^2 \mathrm{d}a = \frac{1}{32\pi^4} \sum_{m=-\infty}^{\infty} \int_{-\infty}^{\infty} S(V_{x^*x}^{(m,\rho)})(m^2+\rho^2)\mathrm{d}\rho. \tag{12}$$

The representations $\mathfrak{S}_{m,\rho}$ and $\mathfrak{S}_{-m,-\rho}$ are equivalent; therefore

$$S(V_{x^*x}^{(m,\rho)}) = S(V_{x^*x}^{(-m,-\rho)}), \tag{13}$$

i.e.†

$$\iint |\hat{K}(z, z_1, m, \rho)|^2 \mathrm{d}z\, \mathrm{d}z_1 = \iint |\hat{K}(z, z_1, -m, -\rho)|^2 \mathrm{d}z\, \mathrm{d}z_1. \tag{14}$$

Hence, instead of formulae (11) and (12) we have:

$$\int |x(a)|^2 \mathrm{d}a = \frac{1}{(2\pi)^4} \sum_{m=-\infty}^{\infty} \int_0^{\infty} \left[\iint |\hat{K}(z, z_1, m, \rho)|^2 \mathrm{d}z\, \mathrm{d}z_1\right](m^2+\rho^2)\mathrm{d}\rho \tag{15}$$

and

$$\int |x(a)|^2 \mathrm{d}a = \frac{1}{(2\pi)^4} \sum_{m=-\infty}^{\infty} \int_0^{\infty} S(V_{x^*x}^{(m,\rho)})(m^2+\rho^2)\mathrm{d}\rho. \tag{16}$$

We denote by $K(u, u_1, m, \rho)$ the kernel of the operator $V_x^{(m,\rho)}$ in the space $L_2^m(\mathfrak{U})$ (see § 11); then (see (7) and (8) § 3, Subsection 7)

$$S(V_{x^*x}^{(m,\rho)}) = \iint |K(u, u_1, m, \rho)|^2 \mathrm{d}u\, \mathrm{d}u_1. \tag{17}$$

Therefore also

$$\int |x(a)|^2 \mathrm{d}a = \frac{1}{(2\pi)^4} \sum_{m=-\infty}^{\infty} \int_0^{\infty} \left[\iint |K(u, u_1, m, \rho)|^2 \mathrm{d}u\, \mathrm{d}u_1\right] \times (m^2+\rho^2)\mathrm{d}\rho. \tag{18}$$

† Formula (14) also follows from (24) Subsection 5.

7. The inverse formulae

We denote by $L^2(\mathfrak{A})$ the Hilbert space of all measurable functions $x(a) = x(z, z_1, \lambda)$, satisfying the condition

$$\int |x(a)|^2 \mathrm{d}a < \infty, \tag{1}$$

where the scalar product in $L^2(\mathfrak{A})$ is defined by the formula

$$(x_1, x_2) = \int x_1(a)\overline{x_2(a)}\mathrm{d}a. \tag{2}$$

Further, we let $\mathfrak{H}_{\hat{K}}$ denote the Hilbert space of all measurable functions

$$\hat{K}(z, z_1, m, \rho) \; (m = 0, \pm 1, \pm 2, \ldots; 0 \leqslant \rho \leqslant \infty),$$

satisfying the condition

$$\sum_{m=-\infty}^{\infty} \int_0^{\infty} [\iint |\hat{K}(z, z_1, m, \rho)|^2 \mathrm{d}z\,\mathrm{d}z_1](m^2+\rho^2)\mathrm{d}\rho < \infty, \tag{3}$$

where the scalar product in $\mathfrak{H}_{\hat{K}}$ is defined by the formula

$$(\hat{K}, \hat{K}_1) = \frac{1}{(2\pi)^4} \sum_{m=-\infty}^{\infty} \int_0^{\infty} \left[\iint \hat{K}(z, z_1, m, \rho)\overline{\hat{K}_1(z, z_1, m, \rho)}\mathrm{d}z\,\mathrm{d}z_1\right] \times (m^2+\rho^2)\mathrm{d}\rho. \tag{4}$$

The analogue of Plancherel's formula means that the mapping $x \to \hat{K}$, defined by the formula

$$\hat{K}(z, z_1, m, \rho) = \int x(z^{-1}kz_1)\alpha(k)\mathrm{d}_l k = \iint x(z^{-1}\delta\zeta z_1)|\lambda|^{-m+i\rho-2}\lambda^m \mathrm{d}\zeta\,\mathrm{d}\delta, \tag{5}$$

is an isometric mapping of the set $X' \subset L^2(\mathfrak{A})$ into the space $\mathfrak{H}_{\hat{K}}$. But from formula (2) Subsection 5 and the definition of the set X' (see Subsection 5) it follows that X' is dense in $L^2(\mathfrak{A})$; hence this isometric mapping $x \to \hat{K}$ can be extended in a unique way, to an isometric mapping of the whole of $L^2(\mathfrak{A})$ into $\mathfrak{H}_{\hat{K}}$. It is easy to see that this mapping can be described as the result of successive applications of the mappings $x \to \tilde{x} \to \hat{x} \to \hat{\phi} \to \phi \to \hat{K}$, provided only that the convergence of each of the integrals, defining the functions $\tilde{x}, \hat{x}, \hat{\phi}, \phi, \hat{K}$, is understood in the sense of one norm or another. In particular, the convergence of the integral (5) holds in the sense of the norm in $\mathfrak{H}_{\hat{K}}$, and moreover for any function $x(a) \in L^2(\mathfrak{A})$. By this mapping $x \to \hat{K}$ the whole space $\mathfrak{H}_{\hat{K}}$ is obtained. In fact, we consider the functions

$$\hat{K}(z, z_1, m, \rho), \quad (m = 0, \pm 1, \pm 2, \dots, \quad 0 \leqslant \rho < \infty),$$

satisfying the condition

$$\sum_{m=-\infty}^{\infty} \int_0^{\infty} [\int\int |\hat{K}(z, z_1, m, \rho)|^2 \, dz \, dz_1] (m^2+\rho^2+1) d\rho < \infty .$$

Clearly, these functions $\hat{K}$ form a set $\mathfrak{H}'_{\hat{K}}$, dense in $\mathfrak{H}_{\hat{K}}$; therefore it is sufficient to show that our mapping $x \to \hat{K}$ yields all the functions from $\mathfrak{H}'_{\hat{K}}$.

For the function $\hat{K} \in \mathfrak{H}'_{\hat{K}}$ one can construct, in a unique way, a function $\tilde{K}(w, w_1, m, \rho)$, $-\infty < \rho < \infty$, $m = 0, \pm 1, \pm 2, \dots$, satisfying relation (24) Subsection 5, and this means also a function $\tilde{\phi}(w, w_1, \lambda)$, satisfying (20) Subsection 5. But then, using formula (21) Subsection 5, one can define $\hat{x}(w, w_1, p)$ for $\tilde{\phi}(w, w_1, \lambda)$ and further $\tilde{x}(w, w_1, \lambda)$ and $x(z, z_1, \lambda)$. The reasoning of Subsection 6 shows that formula (15) Subsection 6 holds here, so that the function $x(a) = x(z, z_1, \lambda)$ obtained belongs to $L^2(\mathfrak{A})$; from the same reasoning it follows that, in the mapping $x \to \hat{K}$, the original function $\hat{K} \in \mathfrak{H}'_{\hat{K}}$ corresponds to this function $x(a)$.

Now we will find the inverse mapping $\hat{K} \to x$ of the space $\mathfrak{H}_{\hat{K}}$ into $L^2(\mathfrak{A})$. First let $\hat{K}$ be a function from $\mathfrak{H}_{\hat{K}}$, equal to zero outside a set Q of the form

$$|z| \leqslant C, |z_1| \leqslant C_1, -m_1 \leqslant m \leqslant m_2, 0 \leqslant \rho \leqslant \rho_0; \tag{6}$$

it corresponds to some function $x(a)$ from $L^2(\mathfrak{A})$. We set

$$y(a) = \frac{1}{(2\pi)^4} \sum_{m=-\infty}^{\infty} \int_0^{\infty} \left[\int \hat{K}(z, z\bar{a}, m, \rho) \overline{\alpha(za)} dz \right] (m^2+\rho^2) d\rho . \tag{7}$$

where

$$\alpha(a) = |a_{22}|^{-m+i\rho-2} a_{22}^m .$$

Here the summation and integration are in fact over the set (6), and so the question of convergence does not arise. We will prove that $x(a) = y(a)$. Let $x'(a) \in X'$; we consider the integral

$$\int y(a)\overline{x'(a)}\,\mathrm{d}a$$

$$= \frac{1}{(2\pi)^4} \sum_{m=-\infty}^{\infty} \int_0^{\infty} \left[\iint \overline{x'(a)\alpha(za)\hat{K}(z, z\bar{a}, m, \rho)}\,\mathrm{d}z\,\mathrm{d}a \right] (m^2+\rho^2)\,\mathrm{d}\rho; \tag{8}$$

the integral

$$\int \overline{x'(a)\alpha(z_1 a)\hat{K}(z, z_1\bar{a}, m, \rho)}\,\mathrm{d}a$$

is the result of applying the operator $T_{\varkappa'}$ of the representation $\mathfrak{S}_{m,\rho}$; to the function $\overline{\hat{K}(z, z_1, m, \rho)}$, considered as a function of z_1: hence, denoting by $\hat{K}'(z_1, z_2, m, \rho)$ the kernel of this operator, we have:

$$\int x'(a)\alpha(z_1 a)\overline{\hat{K}(z, z_1\bar{a}, m, \rho)}\,\mathrm{d}a = \int \hat{K}'(z_1, z_2, m, \rho) \times \\ \times \overline{\hat{K}(z, z_2, m, \rho)}\,\mathrm{d}z_2.$$

Letting $z_1 = z$ and taking the complex conjugate quantities, we obtain:

$$\int \overline{x'(a)\alpha(za)}\hat{K}(z, z\bar{a}, m, \rho)\,\mathrm{d}a = \int \overline{\hat{K}'(z, z_2, m, \rho)} \times \\ \times \hat{K}(z, z_2, m, \rho)\,\mathrm{d}z_2,$$

and so (8) takes the form

$$\int y(a)\overline{x'(a)}\,\mathrm{d}a$$

$$= \frac{1}{(2\pi)^4} \sum_{m=-\infty}^{\infty} \int_0^{\infty} \left[\iint \overline{\hat{K}'(z, z_2, m, \rho)}\hat{K}(z, z_2, m, \rho)\,\mathrm{d}z\,\mathrm{d}z_2 \right] \times \\ \times (m^2+\rho^2)\,\mathrm{d}\rho = (\hat{K}, \hat{K}').$$

On the other hand, by virtue of the isometric mapping $x \to \hat{K}$, we also have

$$\int x(a)\overline{x'(a)}\,\mathrm{d}a = (\hat{K}, \hat{K}').$$

Hence

$$\int y(a)\overline{x'(a)}da = \int x(a)\overline{x'(a)}da,$$

and since the functions $x' \in X'$ form a dense subset in $L^2(\mathfrak{A})$, then $y(a) = x(a)$.

Now let $\hat{K}(z, z_1, m, \rho)$ be an arbitrary function from $\mathfrak{H}_{\hat{K}}$. We set

$$\hat{K}_Q(z, z_1, m, \rho) = \begin{cases} \hat{K}(z, z_1, m, \rho) \text{ when } |z| \leqslant C,\ |z_1| \leqslant C,\ -m_1 \leqslant m \leqslant m_2, \\ 0 \text{ otherwise} \qquad\qquad 0 \leqslant \rho \leqslant \rho_0, \end{cases}$$

and we denote by x_Q the corresponding function from $L^2(\mathfrak{A})$. Clearly

$$\hat{K}_Q \to K \quad \text{as} \quad C, C_1, m_1, m_2, \rho_0 \to \infty$$

in the sense of the norm in $\mathfrak{H}_{\hat{K}}$; by virtue of the isometric mapping $x \to K$ we also have

$$x_Q \to x \quad \text{as} \quad C, C_1, m_1, m_2, \rho_0 \to \infty$$

in the sense of the norm in $L^2(\mathfrak{A})$. But, by the above proof:

$$x_Q(a) = \frac{1}{(2\pi)^4} \sum_{m=-\infty}^{\infty} \int_0^{\infty} \left[\int \hat{K}_Q(z, z\bar{a}, m, \rho)\overline{\alpha(za)}dz \right](m^2+\rho^2)d\rho$$

$$= \frac{1}{(2\pi)^4} \sum_{n=-n_1}^{n_2} \int_0^{\rho_0} \left[\int_{|z| \leqslant C} \hat{K}_Q(z, z\bar{a}, m, \rho)\overline{\alpha(za)}dz \right](m^2+\rho^2)d\rho, \quad (9)$$

so that the last expression converges to $x(a)$ in the sense of the norm in $L^2(\mathfrak{A})$. This means that

$$x(a) = \frac{1}{(2\pi)^4} \sum_{m=-\infty}^{\infty} \int_0^{\infty} \left[\int \hat{K}(z, z\bar{a}, m, \rho)\overline{\alpha(za)}dz \right](m^2+\rho^2)d\rho$$

where the integral and the series on the right side converge in the sense of the norm in $L^2(\mathfrak{A})$. Combining our results we arrive at the following theorem:

THEOREM 12. *For any function $x(a)$ from $L^2(\mathfrak{A})$ the integral*

$$\hat{K}(z, z_1, m, \rho) = \int x(z^{-1}kz_1)\alpha(k)\mathrm{d}_l k, \tag{10}$$

$$\alpha(k) = |k_{22}|^{-m+i\rho-2}k_{22}^m \tag{11}$$

converges in the sense of the norm in $\mathfrak{H}_{\hat{K}}$ and represents a function from $\mathfrak{H}_{\hat{K}}$. Conversely, for any function $\hat{K}$ from $\mathfrak{H}_{\hat{K}}$ the expression

$$x(a) = \frac{1}{(2\pi)^4}\sum_{m=-\infty}^{\infty}\int_0^{\infty}\left[\int \hat{K}(z, z\bar{a}, m, \rho)\overline{\alpha(za)}\mathrm{d}z\right](m^2+\rho^2)\mathrm{d}\rho \tag{12}$$

converges in the sense of the norm in $L^2(\mathfrak{A})$ and represents a function from $L^2(\mathfrak{A})$.

Formulae (10) *and* (12) *define mutually inverse isometric mappings of $L^2(\mathfrak{A})$ on $\mathfrak{H}_{\hat{K}}$ and $\mathfrak{H}_{\hat{K}}$ on $L^2(\mathfrak{A})$ respectively, so that corresponding functions $x(a)$ and $\hat{K}$ satisfy*

$$\int |x(a)|^2 \mathrm{d}a$$

$$= \frac{1}{(2\pi)^4}\sum_{m=-\infty}^{\infty}\int_0^{\infty}\left[\iint |\hat{K}(z, z_1, m, \rho)|^2 \mathrm{d}z\mathrm{d}z_1\right](m^2+\rho^2)\mathrm{d}\rho. \tag{13}$$

We note that when written out in detail formula (12) takes the form

$$x(a) = \frac{1}{(2\pi)^4}\sum_{m=-\infty}^{\infty}\int_0^{\infty}\left[\int \hat{K}\left(z, \frac{a_{11}z+a_{21}}{a_{12}z+a_{22}}, m, \rho\right)\times\right.$$

$$\left.\times |a_{12}z+a_{22}|^{-m+i\rho-2}\overline{(a_{12}z+a_{22})}^m \mathrm{d}z\right](m^2+\rho^2)\mathrm{d}\rho. \tag{14}$$

Remark. Theorem 12 remains true if the kernel $\hat{K}(z, z_1, m, \rho)$ is replaced in its formulation by the kernel $K(u, u_1, m, \rho)$ (see § 13, Subsection 7). This follows from the fact that $\iint |\hat{K}(z, z_1, m, \rho)|^2 \mathrm{d}z\mathrm{d}z_1 = \iint |K(u, u_1, m, \rho)|^2 \mathrm{d}u\mathrm{d}u_1$. Here the part of $\mathfrak{H}_{\hat{K}}$ is played by the Hilbert space $\mathfrak{H}_K$ of measurable functions $K(u,$

$u_1, m, \rho)$, $m = 0, \pm 1, \pm 2, \ldots, 0 \leqslant \rho < \infty$, satisfying the condition

$$\sum_{m=-\infty}^{\infty} \int_0^{\infty} [\iint |K(u, u_1, m, \rho)|^2 \mathrm{d}u \, \mathrm{d}u_1](m^2+\rho^2)\mathrm{d}\rho < \infty, \qquad (15)$$

and formula (12) becomes

$$x(a) = \frac{1}{(2\pi)^4} \sum_{m=-\infty}^{\infty} \int_0^{\infty} \left[\int K(u, u\bar{a}, m, \rho) \frac{\alpha(ua)}{\overline{\alpha(u\bar{a})}} \mathrm{d}u \right] (m^2+\rho^2)\mathrm{d}\rho. \qquad (16)$$

8. The decomposition of the regular representation of the group $\mathfrak{A}$ into irreducible representations

We define in $L^2(\mathfrak{A})$ an operator T_a, putting for $f(a) \in L^2(\mathfrak{A})$

$$T_{a_0} f(a) = f(aa_0).$$

The correspondence $a \to T_a$ is a representation of the group $\mathfrak{A}$, for

$$T_e f(a) = f(ae) = f(a), \qquad T_{a_1} T_{a_2} f(a) = T_{a_1} f(aa_2) = f(aa_1 a_2);$$

since

$$|T_{a_0} f| = \int |f(aa_0)|^2 \mathrm{d}a = \int |f(a)|^2 \mathrm{d}a = |f|^2,$$

this representation is unitary. It is called the *right regular representation of the group* $\mathfrak{A}$. Analogously the formula

$$T'_{a_0} f(a) = f(a_0^{-1} a)$$

defines the so-called *left regular* unitary representation of the group $\mathfrak{A}$.

We will show that these regular representations decompose into the direct sum of irreducible representations, indeed representations of the principal series.

For this purpose we note that according to formula (10) Subsection 7, every function $x(a)$ from $L^2(\mathfrak{A})$ corresponds to an element

$$f_{m,\rho,z_1}(z) = \hat{K}(z, z_1, m, \rho) \qquad (1)$$

of the space $L^2(Z)$, depending on the parameters z_1, m, ρ. Formula (13), written in the form

$$|x|^2 = \int |x(a)|^2 \mathrm{d}a = \frac{1}{(2\pi)^4} \sum_{m=-\infty}^{\infty} \int_0^{\infty} \left[\int |f_{m,\rho,z_1}|^2 \mathrm{d}z_1 \right] (m^2+\rho^2)\mathrm{d}\rho \quad (2)$$

shows that in this correspondence the space $L^2(\mathfrak{A})$ is mapped isometrically into the (discrete-continuous) direct sum of images of the space $L^2(Z)$ (in this connection see Subsection 1). We prove that *in this mapping the operator of the left regular representation is transformed into the orthogonal direct sum of operators of representations of the principal series, and indeed that every component* f_{m,ρ,z_1} *is transformed into the same component by the operators of the representation* $\mathfrak{S}_{m,\rho}$ *of the principal series.*

In other words, we will prove that *in the transition from* $x(a)$ *to* $T'_{a_0}x(a) = x(a_0^{-1}\, a)$ *the kernel* $f_{m,\,\rho,\,z_1}(z) = \hat{K}(z, z_1, m, \rho)$ *goes into*

$$V_{a_0}^{(m,\rho)} f_{m,\rho,z_1}(z) = \alpha(za_0)\hat{K}(z\bar{a}_0, z_1, m, \rho), \quad (3)$$

where

$$\alpha(a) = |a_{22}|^{-m+i\rho-2} a_{22}^m. \quad (4)$$

One can immediately convince oneself of the validity of this assertion by direct verification. In fact, by virtue of (10) Subsection 7, the function $x_{a_0}(a) = x(a_0^{-1}\, a)$ corresponds to the kernel

$$\hat{K}_{a_0}(z, z_1, m, \rho) = \int x_{a_0}(z^{-1}kz_1)\alpha(k)\mathrm{d}_l k = \int x(a_0^{-1}z^{-1}kz_1) \times \\ \times \alpha(k)\mathrm{d}_l k. \quad (5)$$

We set

$$za_0 = k_1 z',$$

then, $z\bar{a} = z'$, and

$$\alpha(za_0) = \alpha(k_1). \quad (6)$$

Substituting in (5) we obtain:

$$\hat{K}_{a_0}(z, z_1, m, \rho) = \int x(z'^{-1}k_1^{-1}kz_1)\alpha(k)\mathrm{d}_l k = \int x(z'^{-1}kz_1)\alpha(k_1 k) \\ \times \mathrm{d}_l k = \alpha(k_1)\int x(z'^{-1}kz_1)\alpha(k)\mathrm{d}_l k = \alpha(k_1)\hat{K}(z', z_1, m, \rho) \\ = \alpha(za_0)\hat{K}(z\bar{a}_0, z_1, m, \rho).$$

We have therefore proved the following theorem:

THEOREM 13. *The left regular representation of the group* $\mathfrak{A}$ *decomposes into the orthogonal direct sum of representations of the principal series; this decomposition is given by the formulae* (1), (2), *and* (3).

An analogous theorem holds also for the right regular representation; the decomposition is given by the formula

$$f_{m,\rho,z}(z_1) = \hat{K}(z, z_1, m, \rho), \tag{7}$$

where the operator $T_{a_0}x(a) = x(aa_0)$ corresponds to

$$V_{a_0}^{(-m,-\rho)} f_{m,\rho,z}(z_1) = \overline{\alpha(za_0)}\hat{K}(z, z_1\bar{a}_0, m, \rho). \tag{8}$$

We note also that the kernel $\hat{K}(z, z_1, m, \rho)$ can be replaced in the preceding theorem by the kernel $K(u, u_1, m, \rho)$. Every function $x(a)$ from $L^2(\mathfrak{A})$ corresponds to a vector-valued function

$$\phi_{m,\rho,u_1}(u) = K(u, u_1, m, \rho) \tag{9}$$

with values from $L_2^m(\mathfrak{U})$, which also realizes a decomposition. Here, the operator $T'_{a_0}x(a) = x(a_0^{-1}a)$ of the left regular representation corresponds to

$$V_a^{(m,\rho)} \phi_{m,\rho,u_1}(u) = \frac{\alpha(ua)}{\alpha(u\bar{a})} K(u\bar{a}, u_1, m, \rho). \tag{10}$$

An analogous assertion holds for the right regular representation.

§ 15. A Description of all the Completely Irreducible Representations of the Proper Lorentz Group

Now we proceed to a precise statement and solution of *the problem of determining all irreducible representations, to within equivalence, of the group* $\mathfrak{A}$ (hence also of the proper Lorentz group). For this, it is convenient to change somewhat the concept of irreducibility, so that in fact the term will be used to describe the so-called *completely irreducible* representations, whose definition will be given below in Subsection 4.

Moreover, we give in Subsection 3 the general definition of equivalence, which plays an essential part in what follows.

As a preliminary we need the concept of a *conjugate representation.*

1. Conjugate representations

Let R be a Banach space, and R' the conjugate space, i.e. the space of all bounded linear functionals $f = f(\xi)$ in R (see § 6, Subsection 4); in what follows it will be convenient to write (ξ, f) instead of $f(\xi)$. Further, let A be a bounded linear operator in R; for any functional $f \in R'$ we set

$$f'(\xi) = f(A\xi) = (A\xi, f).$$

The functional $f'(\xi)$ is linear and bounded, since

$$\begin{aligned} f'(\alpha_1\xi_1 + \alpha_2\xi_2) &= f(A(\alpha_1\xi_1 + \alpha_2\xi_2)) = f(\alpha_1 A\xi_1 + \alpha_2 A\xi_2) \\ &= \alpha_1 f(A\xi_1) + \alpha_2 f(A\xi_2) = \alpha_1 f'(\xi_1) + \alpha_2 f'(\xi_2), \end{aligned}$$

$$|f'(\xi)| = |f(A\xi)| \leqslant |f|\,|A\xi| \leqslant |f|\,|A|\,|\xi|. \tag{1}$$

Hence, $f' \in R'$. It follows from (1) that

$$|f'| \leqslant |A|\,|f|. \tag{2}$$

We define an operator A' in R', letting $A'f = f'$. Clearly the operator A' is linear and, by virtue of (2), bounded; it is called the *conjugate* operator to A. With this definition of the conjugate operator we have

$$(A\xi, f) = (\xi, A'f) \quad \text{for all} \quad \xi \in R, f \in R'. \tag{3}$$

If R is a Hilbert space, then every functional $f \in R'$ is given by the formula $f(\xi) = (\xi, \eta)$, where (ξ, η) is the scalar product in R, and we can identify η with f and R' with R; then the operator A' coincides with the adjoint operator A^*. As in the case of the adjoint operator in a Hilbert space, the operation of transition from A to A' possesses the following properties, whose validity is easy to verify†

$$(\alpha A)' = \bar{\alpha} A'; \quad (A_1 + A_2)' = A_1' + A_2', \quad (A_1 A_2)' = A_2' A_1';$$
$$A'' = A; \tag{4}$$

† We recall that the space R is supposed to be reflexive, so that $R'' = R$; the relation $A'' = A$ is correct only in this case.

moreover, it follows from (2) that $|A'| \leqslant |A|$; applying this to A' instead of A, we see that $|A| \leqslant |A'|$, and so†

$$|A'| = |A|. \tag{5}$$

Hence we conclude that *the transition from A to A' is continuous in the sense of the norm of the operator.*

Now let there be given a linear representation $a \to T_a$ of the group $\mathfrak{A}$ in the Banach space R. We set

$$\hat{T}_a = T'_{a^{-1}}; \tag{6}$$

the correspondence $a \to \hat{T}_a$ is again a representation of the group $\mathfrak{A}$. In fact‡

$$\hat{T}_e = \hat{T}'_e = \mathbf{1}' = \mathbf{1}$$

and

$$\hat{T}_{a_1 a_2} = T'^{-1}_{a_2^{-1} a_1^{-1}} = \left(T_{a_2^{-1}} T_{a_1^{-1}}\right)' = T'_{a_1^{-1}} T'_{a_2^{-1}} = \hat{T}_{a_1} \hat{T}_{a_2}.$$

The representation $a \to \hat{T}_a$ is said to be *conjugate* to the representation $a \to T_a$.

Clearly, the conjugate to the conjugate representation is the original representation, so that

$$\hat{\hat{T}}_a = T_a, \quad \hat{\hat{T}}_x = T_x.$$

If $a \to T_a$ is a unitary representation in the Hilbert space R, then $R' = R$ and $\hat{T}_a = (T_{a^{-1}})^* = T_a$, i.e. *a unitary representation coincides with its conjugate representation.*

With this definition of the conjugate representation we have

$$(T_a\xi, \hat{T}_a f) = (T_a\xi, T'^{-1}_a f) = (T_a^{-1} T_a \xi, f) = (\xi, f),$$

i.e.

$$(T_a\xi, \hat{T}_a f) = (\xi, f). \tag{7}$$

---

† In fact $|A'| = |A|$ holds in a non-reflexive space, but we do not need this. We leave the proof of the equation $|A'| = |A|$ in the general case as a useful exercise for the reader.

‡ We denote identity operators in different spaces by the same symbol if this does not lead to misunderstanding.

Formula (7) replaces the relation

$$(T_a\xi, T_a\eta) = (\xi, \eta)$$

for a unitary representation.

By means of the conjugate representation $a \to \hat{T}_a$ of the group $\mathfrak{A}$ one can construct a conjugate representation $x \to \hat{T}_x$ of its group ring, letting

$$\hat{T}_x = \int x(a)\hat{T}_a da. \tag{8}$$

We have

$$\hat{T}_{x^*} = T'_x, \tag{9}$$

for

$$\hat{T}_{x^*} = \int x^*(a)\hat{T}_a da = \int \overline{x(a^{-1})}\, T'_{a^{-1}} da = \int \overline{x(a)}\, T'_a da = T'_x.$$

We will now establish a relation between the infinitesimal operators of a given representation and its conjugate representation. We denote by $\hat{\mathfrak{D}}$ the set $\mathfrak{D}$ for the conjugate representation (see the remark in § 13, Subsection 5). Let $a(t)$ be a one-parameter group in $\mathfrak{A}$; we set $A(t) = T_{a(t)}$; $\hat{A}(t) = \hat{T}_{a(t)}$. Then $\hat{A}(-t) = T'_{a(t)} = A(t)'$, and so

$$(A(t)\xi, \eta) = (\xi, \hat{A}(-t)\eta) \quad \text{for} \quad \xi \in \mathfrak{D}, \eta \in \hat{\mathfrak{D}}.$$

Hence

$$\left(\frac{A(t)-1}{t}\xi, \eta\right) = -\left(\xi, \frac{\hat{A}(-t)-1}{-t}\eta\right).$$

Passing to the limit in this equation we see that

$$(A\xi, \eta) = -(\xi, \hat{A}\eta) \quad \text{for} \quad \xi \in \mathfrak{D}, \eta \in \hat{\mathfrak{D}},$$

where A, $\hat{A}$ are infinitesimal operators of the one-parameter groups $A(t)$, $\hat{A}(t)$ respectively. In this formula taking $a = a_j(t)$, $a = b_j(t)$, $j = 1, 2, 3$, we arrive at the relations:

$$(A_j\xi, \eta) = -(\xi, \hat{A}_j\eta), \quad (B_j\xi, \eta) = -(\xi, \hat{B}_j\eta),$$
$$j = 1, 2, 3, \quad \xi \in \mathfrak{D}, \eta \in \hat{\mathfrak{D}}. \tag{10}$$

Hence

$$(H_+\xi, \eta) = (\xi, \hat{H}_-\eta), \quad (H_-\xi, \eta) = (\xi, \hat{H}_+\eta),$$
$$(H_3\xi, \eta) = (\xi, \hat{H}_3\eta), \tag{11}$$

$$(F_+\xi, \eta) = (\xi, \hat{F}_-\eta), \quad (F_-\xi, \eta) = (\xi, \hat{F}_+\eta),$$
$$(F_3\xi, \eta) = (\xi, \hat{F}_3\eta) \quad (12)$$

for $\xi \in \mathfrak{D}$, $\eta \in \hat{\mathfrak{D}}$

The relations (10–12) are a generalization of the relations (2) and (3) § 8, Subsection 4 for unitary representations.

2. The operators E^k_{jl}

An important role in the solution of our problem is played by some auxiliary operators, to which we devote Subsections 2,5.

Let $g \to T_g$ be a representation of some group G, and H a subgroup of G. The operators T_g can be considered in particular, for $g = h \in H$; then we obtain a representation $h \to T_h$ of the group H. This representation $h \to T_h$ is called *the restriction to the subgroup* H of the original representation $g \to T_g$.

If, in particular, there is given a representation $a \to T_a$ of the group $\mathfrak{A}$, then one can consider the restriction $u \to T_u$ of this representation to the unitary subgroup $\mathfrak{U}$; hence, for this representation one can construct the operators

$$E^k_{jl} = (2k+1) \int \overline{c^k_{jl}(u)}\, T_u \, du \quad (1)$$

(see § 6, Subsection 6). With the help of these operators, as in § 6, Subsection 6, one can single out the subspaces $\mathfrak{M}^k_j$ ($\mathfrak{M}^k_j = E^k_{jj}R$); as before, R is the closed direct sum of all the $\mathfrak{M}^k_j$, $k_0 \leqslant k < \infty$, $-k \leqslant j \leqslant k$. We denote the corresponding operators for the conjugate representation by $\hat{E}^k_{jl}$. Then

$$\hat{E}^k_{jl} = (2k+1) \int \overline{c^k_{jl}(u)}\, \hat{T}_u \, du = (2k+1) \int \overline{c^k_{jl}(u)}\, T'_{u^{-1}} \, du$$
$$= \left((2k+1) \int c^k_{jl}(u^{-1})\, T_u \, du\right)' = \left((2k+1) \int c^k_{lj}(u)\, T_u \, du\right)' = (E^k_{lj})',$$

so that

$$\hat{E}^k_{jl} = (E^k_{lj})'. \quad (2)$$

3. Equivalence of representations

Let $a \to T_a$ be a linear representation of the group $\mathfrak{A}$ in the Banach space R. We denote by Ω the set of all finite linear combinations of the vectors $\eta = T_x\xi$, where ξ runs through all the vectors from all the subspaces $\mathfrak{M}_j^k$, and $x \in X$ (we recall that X denotes the group ring of the group $\mathfrak{A}$; see § 13, Subsection 4).

Thus to every representation $a \to T_a$ in R corresponds its own completely defined set Ω. If several representations $a \to T_a^{(1)}$, $a \to T_a^{(2)}$ are considered, then the corresponding sets Ω will be denoted by Ω_1, Ω_2, ...; moreover, the set Ω corresponding to the conjugate representation to $a \to T_a$ will be denoted by $\hat{\Omega}$. Clearly, Ω is invariant with respect to the operators T_x, $x \in X$. Moreover:

I. *The set Ω is dense in R.* For otherwise there would exist a functional $f \in R, f \neq 0$, such that $f(T_x\xi) = 0$, i.e. $\int x(a) f(T_a \xi) da = 0$ for all $\xi \in \mathfrak{M}_j^k$ and $x \in X$.

This is possible only when $f(T_a\xi) = 0$ for all $a \in \mathfrak{A}$, $\xi \in \mathfrak{M}_j^k$. Letting $a = e$, we see that $f(\xi) = 0$ for all $\xi \in \mathfrak{M}_j^k$. Since the finite linear combinations of the vectors ξ, belonging to all possible $\mathfrak{M}_j^k$, generate a set dense in R (see VI § 6, Subsection 6), this contradicts the condition, $f \neq 0$.

Now let there be given two representations $a \to T_a^{(1)}$, $a \to T_a^{(2)}$ of the group $\mathfrak{A}$ in the spaces R_1 and R_2. The representation $a \to T_a^{(1)}$ is said to be *equivalent* to the representation $a \to T_a^{(2)}$, if there exists a linear operar to$A$ from R_1 to† R_2 and a linear operator B from R_2' to R_1', possessing the following properties;

(α) The domains of definition of the operators A, B are Ω_1, $\hat{\Omega}_2$, and the domains of variation Ω_2, $\hat{\Omega}_1$ respectively;

(β)$(A\xi, \eta) = (\xi, B\eta)$ for all $\xi \in \Omega_1$, $\eta \in \hat{\Omega}_2$;

(γ) if $A\xi = 0$, $B\eta = 0$ for some vectors $\xi \in \Omega_1$, $\eta \in \hat{\Omega}_2$, then $\xi = 0$, $\eta = 0$;

(δ) for any vectors $\xi \in \Omega_1, \eta \in \hat{\Omega}_2$

$$AT_x^{(1)}\xi = T_x^{(2)}A\xi, \quad B\hat{T}_x^{(2)}\eta = \hat{T}_x^{(1)}B\eta.$$

† An operator A from R_1 to R_2 is any function $y = Ax$, whose domain of definition lies in R_1, and whose domain of variation lies in R_2. Such an operator is called *linear*, if its domain of definition is a subspace in R_1 and if $A(\lambda_1\xi_1 + \lambda_2\xi_2) = \lambda_1 A\xi_1 + \lambda_2 A\xi_2$ for any vectors ξ_1, ξ_2 from the domain of definition of the operator A.

This definition of equivalence possesses all the usual properties of equivalence, namely:

(1) every representation $a \to T_a$ is equivalent to itself;

(2) if the representation $a \to T_a^{(1)}$ is equivalent to the representation $a \to T_a^{(2)}$, then the representation $a \to T_a^{(2)}$ is equivalent to the representation $a \to T_a^{(1)}$;

(3) if the representation $a \to T_a^{(1)}$ is equivalent to the representation $a \to T_a^{(2)}$, and the representation $a \to T_a^{(2)}$ is equivalent to the representation $a \to T_a^{(3)}$, then the representation $a \to T_a^{(1)}$ is equivalent to the representation $a \to T_a^{(3)}$.

In fact, in order to verify property (1), it is sufficient to set $A\xi = \xi$ for $\xi \in \Omega$, $B\eta = \eta$ for $\eta \in \hat{\Omega}$. Further, if the operators A, B satisfy the conditions (α–δ) for the representations $a \to T_a^{(1)}$, $a \to T_a^{(2)}$, then the inverse operators† A^{-1}, B^{-1} (which exist by virtue of condition (γ) satisfy the conditions (α–δ) for the representations $a \to T_a^{(2)}$, $a \to T_a^{(1)}$; hence property (2) also holds.

Finally, if A_1, B_1 are operators satisfying conditions (α–δ) for the representations $a \to T_a^{(1)}$, $a \to T_a^{(2)}$, and A_2, B_2 are operators satisfying conditions (α–δ) for the representations $a \to T_a^{(2)}$, $a \to T_a^{(3)}$, then the operators $A\xi = A_2(A_1\xi)$, $B\eta = B_1(B_2\xi)$, $\xi \in \Omega_1$, $\eta \in \hat{\Omega}_3$, will satisfy conditions (α–δ) for the representations $a \to T_a^{(1)}$, $a \to T_a^{(3)}$; hence property (3) will also hold.

If the representations $a \to T_a^{(1)}$, $a \to T_a^{(2)}$ are finite-dimensional, then $\Omega_1 = R_1$, $\Omega_2 = R_2$; the first of the relations (δ) means that the linear operator A mapping R_1 on R_2 in a one-one manner, carries $T_a^{(1)}$ into $T_a^{(2)}$, i.e. that the representations $a \to T_a^{(1)}$, $a \to T_a^{(2)}$ are equivalent in the sense of the definition given in § 3, Subsection 3. The remaining conditions are satisfied for this automatically,

---

† Let A be a linear operator from R_1 to R_2 with domain of definition $\mathfrak{D}_A$ and of variation Δ_A. The operator A_1 is called *inverse* to A, if $\mathfrak{D}_{A_1} = \Delta_A, \Delta_{A_1} = \mathfrak{D}_A$ and $A_1\eta = \xi$ when $A\xi = \eta$. The inverse operator to A is denoted by A^{-1}. Clearly for the existence of an inverse operator it is necessary and su fficient that the mapping $\eta = A\xi$ be one-one. For this in turn it is sufficient that the equation $A\xi = 0$, $\xi \in \mathfrak{D}_A$ should imply $\xi = 0$. In fact the equation $A\xi_1 = A\xi_2$, ξ_1, $\xi_2 \in \mathfrak{D}_A$ implies that $A(\xi_1 - \xi_2) = 0$, and so $\xi_1 - \xi_2 = 0$, i.e. the mapping $\eta = A\xi$ is one-one.

if one defines the operator B by means of the formula $(A\xi, \eta) = (\xi, B\eta)$, $\xi \in R_1$, $\eta \in R_2'$.

Thus:

II. *In the case of finite-dimensional representations our definition of equivalence coincides with the definition of equivalence given in* § 3, *Subsection* 3.

Further:

III. *Two unitary representations are equivalent if and only if they are unitarily equivalent.* The validity of this assertion follows immediately from Theorem 1 § 7, Subsection 1 in Ref. [28a] (see also Refs. [28e] and [12c]), since by virtue of condition (β) the operator A admits closure (see Appendix V).

In conclusion we note that in our definition of equivalence the operators A, B can be unbounded and, consequently, the spaces R_1, R_2 can be non-isometric; this removes the unbounded nature of the representations, which results from too fine a distinction of the spaces of these representations. In fact the norms play no part, in the definition of equivalence so that this definition is easily carried over to representations in locally convex topological spaces.

Remark. Let $a \to T_a$ be a representation of the group $\mathfrak{A}$ in the space R and let X_1 be a subring with involution of the ring X. Suppose that the spaces R and R' have closed subspaces $\mathfrak{M}$ and $\mathfrak{M}'$, possessing the following properties:

(a) $\mathfrak{M}$ is invariant with respect to all the operators T_x, $x \in X_1$, and $\mathfrak{M}'$ is invariant with respect to all the operators $\hat{T}_x$, $x \in X_1$;

(b) every linear functional f in $\mathfrak{M}$ is given by a formula

$$f(\xi) = (\xi, \eta), \quad \eta \in \mathfrak{M}',$$

where

$$|f| \leqslant |\eta| \leqslant c|f|,$$

and c is some constant;

(c) every linear functional ϕ in $\mathfrak{M}'$ is given by formula $\phi(\eta) = (\eta, \xi)$, where $|\phi| \leqslant |\xi| \leqslant c|\phi|$, where c is some constant;

(d) $\mathfrak{M} \cap \Omega$ is dense in $\mathfrak{M}$ and $\mathfrak{M}' \cap \hat{\Omega}$ is dense in $\mathfrak{M}'$.

By virtue of conditions (b) and (c) the representations $x \to T_x$ and $x \to \hat{T}_x$ of the ring X_1, considered only on $\mathfrak{M}$ and $\mathfrak{M}'$ respectively, can be regarded as mutually conjugate representations. Clearly, the preceding definitions and results are applicable to them, if in place of Ω and $\hat{\Omega}$ one takes $\mathfrak{M} \cap \Omega$ and $\mathfrak{M}' \cap \hat{\Omega}$.

4. Completely irreducible representations

Let there be given a representation $a \to T_a$ of the group $\mathfrak{A}$ in the space R; a bounded linear operator C in R will be called *admissible* (with respect to the given representation $a \to T_a$), if it has the form

$$C\xi = f_1(\xi)e_1 + \dots + f_n(\xi)e_n,$$

where $f_1, \dots, f_n \in \hat{\Omega}$, and $e_1, \dots, e_n \in \Omega$.

The representation $a \to T_a$ is called *completely irreducible*,† if for every admissible operator C in R there exists a sequence $x_n \in X$ such that

$$(T_{x_n}\xi, \eta) \to (C\xi, \eta) \quad \text{as} \quad n \to \infty \quad \text{for all} \quad \xi \in \Omega, \ \eta \in \hat{\Omega}. \tag{1}$$

I. *If the representations $a \to T_a^{(1)}$, $a \to T_a^{(2)}$ are equivalent and one of them (for instance, $a \to T_a^{(1)}$) is completely irreducible, then the second representation is also completely irreducible.*

Proof. Let C_2 be an admissible operator in R_2 with respect to the representation $a \to T_a^{(2)}$ and let A, B be operators satisfying conditions (α–δ) Subsection 2 for the representations $a \to T_a^{(1)}$, $a \to T_a^{(2)}$.

Thus

$$C_2\xi_2 = f_1(\xi_2)e_1 + \dots + f_n(\xi_2)e_n, \tag{2}$$

where $f_1, \dots, f_n \in \hat{\Omega}_2$, $e_1, \dots, e_n \in \Omega_2$. We define an operator C_1 in R_1, letting $C_1A^{-1}\xi_2 = A^{-1} C_2\xi_2$.

Then, by (2):

$$C_1A^{-1}\xi_2 = f_1(\xi_2)A^{-1}e_1 + \dots + f_n(\xi_2)A^{-1}e_n,$$

or, letting $A^{-1}\xi_2 = \xi_1, A^{-1} e_k = e_k', k = 1, 2, \dots, n,$

$$C_1\xi_1 = f_1(A\xi_1)e_1' + \dots + f_n(A\xi_1)e_n'. \tag{3}$$

† This concept is a generalization of a concept introduced by Godement [16].

We set $Bf_k = f'_k$; by virtue of conditions (α) and (β) Subsection 2 we have $f'_k \in \hat{\Omega}_1$ and

$$f_k(A\xi_1) = (A\xi_1, f_k) = (\xi_1, Bf_k) = (\xi_1, f'_k) = f'_k(\xi_1),$$

so that formula (3) takes the form

$$C_1\xi_1 = f_1'(\xi_1)e_1' + \dots + f_n'(\xi_1)e_n' \quad \text{for} \quad \xi_1 \in \Omega_1. \tag{4}$$

But the right-hand side of (4) is defined for all $\xi_1 \in R_1$ and represents a bounded linear operator in R_1; we extend the definition of $C_1\xi_1$ considering it equal to the right-hand side of (4) for all $\xi \in R_1$. Then C_1 will become admissible with respect to the representation $a \to T_a^{(1)}$; by virtue of the assumed complete irreducibility of this representation, there exists a sequence $x_m \in X$ such that

$$(T_{x_m}^{(1)}\xi_1, \eta_1) \to (C_1\xi_1, \eta_1) \quad \text{as} \quad m \to \infty \quad \text{for all} \quad \xi_1 \in \Omega_1, \quad \eta_1 \in \hat{\Omega}_1.$$

Letting $\eta_1 = B\eta_2$, $\eta_2 \in \hat{\Omega}_2$, we obtain:

$$(T_{x_m}^{(1)}\xi_1, B\eta_2) \to (C_1\xi_1, B\eta_2), \quad \text{i.e.} \quad (AT_{x_m}^{(1)}\xi_1, \eta_2) \to (AC_1\xi_1, \eta_2);$$

hence, letting $A\xi_1 = \xi_2$ and taking conditions (α) and (δ) into account, we conclude that

$$(T_{x_m}^{(2)}\xi_2, \eta_2) = (T_{x_m}^{(2)}A\xi_1, \eta_2) = (AT_{x_m}^{(1)}\xi_1, \eta_2) \to (AC_1\xi_1, \eta_2)$$
$$= (C_2A\xi_1, \eta_2) = (C_2\xi_2, \eta_2).$$

Hence the representation $a \to T_a^{(2)}$ is completely irreducible.

II. *If the representation $a \to T_a$ is completely irreducible, then the conjugate representation $a \to \hat{T}_a$ is also completely irreducible.*

Proof. Let $\hat{C}$ be a bounded linear operator in R', admissible with respect to the representation $a \to \hat{T}_a$, so that†

$$\check{C}\eta = \phi_1(\eta)\eta_1 + \dots + \phi_n(\eta)\eta_n,$$

where $\eta_1, \dots, \eta_n \in \hat{\Omega}$, and $\phi_1, \dots, \phi_n \in \hat{\hat{\Omega}} = \Omega$ (see Subsection 1).

Thus:

$$\hat{C}\eta = \overline{(\phi_1, \eta)}\eta_1 + \dots + \overline{(\phi_n, \eta)}\eta_n,$$

† We note that the space R of the representation is assumed to be reflexive i.e. that $R'' = R$.

and so

$$(\xi, \hat{C}\eta) = (\phi_1, \eta)(\xi, \eta_1) + \dots + (\phi_n, \eta)(\xi, \eta_n)$$
$$= \eta_1(\xi)(\phi_1, \eta) + \dots + \eta_n(\xi)(\phi_n, \eta).$$

We set $C\xi = \eta_1(\xi)\phi_1 + \dots + \eta_n(\xi)\phi_n$ for $\xi \in R$; the preceding relation means that

$$(C\xi, \eta) = (\xi, \hat{C}\eta) \quad \text{for all} \quad \xi \in R, \quad \eta \in R'.$$

But the operator C is admissible with respect to the representation $a \to T_a$; hence there exists a sequence $x_m \in X$ such that as $m \to \infty$,

$$(T_{x_m}\xi, \eta) \to (C\xi, \eta),$$

i.e.

$$(\xi, \hat{T}_{x_m}\eta) \to (\xi, \hat{C}\eta) \quad \text{for all} \quad \xi \in \hat{\hat{\Omega}}, \quad \eta \in \hat{\Omega}.$$

This means that the representation $a \to \hat{T}_a$ is completely irreducible.

III. *Every completely irreducible representation* $a \to T_a$ *of the group* $\mathfrak{A}$ *is irreducible.*

Proof. Let the representation $a \to T_a$ be completely irreducible and let $\mathfrak{M}$ be a closed subspace of R, which is invariant with respect to all operators T_x, $x \in X$, and is distinct from (0) and the whole of R. We denote by $\Omega_{\mathfrak{M}}$ the set of all finite linear combinations of the vectors $T_x E^k_{jj}\xi$, where ξ runs through $\mathfrak{M}$, $x \in X$, and the indices k and j take all possible values. By virtue of I Subsection 3 $\Omega_{\mathfrak{M}}$ is a dense subset of $\mathfrak{M}$ because $\mathfrak{M}$ is invariant with respect to the operators E^k_{jj}. Clearly, $\Omega_{\mathfrak{M}} \subset \Omega$ and $\Omega_{\mathfrak{M}} \neq \Omega$ since Ω is dense in R. We choose a functional $f_0 \in R'$, $f_0 \neq 0$ such that $(\xi, f_0) = 0$ for all $\xi \in \mathfrak{M}$; in particular, $(\xi, f_0) = 0$ for all $\xi \in \Omega_{\mathfrak{M}}$. Hence also

$$(\xi, \hat{T}_x f_0) = (T_{x^*}\xi, f_0) = 0 \quad \text{for all} \quad \xi \in \Omega_{\mathfrak{M}}, \quad x \in X,$$

because $\Omega_{\mathfrak{M}}$ is invariant with respect to all operators T_x, $x \in X$. Choosing $x_0 \in X$ so that $\hat{T}_{x_0} f_0 \in \hat{\Omega}$, $\hat{T}_{x_0} f_0 \neq 0$ we obtain a vector $\eta_0 = \hat{T}_{x_0} f_0 \in \hat{\Omega}$, such that

$$(\xi, \eta_0) = 0 \quad \text{for all} \quad \xi \in \Omega_{\mathfrak{M}};$$

hence also

$$(T_x\xi, \eta_0) = 0 \quad \text{for all} \quad \xi \in \Omega_{\mathfrak{M}}, \quad x \in X. \tag{5}$$

On the other hand, because $\eta_0 \neq 0$, and Ω is dense in R, then there exists a vector $\xi_1 \in \Omega$ such that

$$(\xi_1, \eta_0) \neq 0. \tag{6}$$

Clearly, $\xi_1 \overline{\in} \Omega_{\mathfrak{M}}$.

We choose a vector $\xi_0 \in \Omega_{\mathfrak{M}}$ distinct from zero; because $\hat{\Omega}$ is dense in R', there exists an $\eta_1 \in \hat{\Omega}$ such that

$$(\xi_0, \eta_1) \neq 0. \tag{7}$$

Now we define an operator C in R, letting

$$C\xi = (\xi, \eta_1)\xi_1. \tag{8}$$

This operator is admissible; hence there exists a sequence $x_n \in X$ such that

$$(T_{x_n}\xi, \eta) \to (C\xi, \eta) \quad \text{for all} \quad \xi \in \Omega, \quad \eta \in \hat{\Omega},$$

i.e., by virtue of (8)

$$(T_{x_n}\xi, \eta) \to (\xi, \eta_1)(\xi_1, \eta) \quad \text{for all} \quad \xi \in \Omega, \quad \eta \in \hat{\Omega}.$$

Putting $\xi = \xi_0$, $\eta = \eta_0$ and taking condition (5) into account, we obtain $0 = (\xi_0, \eta_1)(\xi_1, \eta_0)$, which contradicts conditions (6) and (7) Hence, such a subspace $\mathfrak{M}$ cannot exist, and the representation is irreducible

In the case of a finite-dimensional representation the converse proposition is also true:

IV. *Every irreducible finite-dimensional representation is completely irreducible.* In fact, it follows from Burnside's theorem (see Appendix III) that the set of all operators T_x, $x \in X$, coincides in this case with the set of all linear operators in R. Hence for any linear operator C in R there exists a function $x \in X$ such that $T_x = C$, and condition (1) is satisfied in a trivial manner with $x_n = x$.

Further we have

V. *Every irreducible unitary representation* in a separable† *Hilbert space is completely irreducible.*

† A normed space R is called *separable* if R contains a dense countable subset. It is easy to prove that the representation space of every irreducible representation of $\mathfrak{U}$ is separable. Proposition V remains true also for non-separable spaces if in the definition of complete irreducibility, one replaces limits by weak limit points of the operators T_x.

Proof. Let M be the set of all bounded linear operators C in the Hilbert space R, for which

$$(T_{x_n}\xi, \eta) \to (C\xi, \eta) \quad \text{for} \quad \xi, \eta \in R$$

and for some sequence $x_n \in X$, and let B be the set of all bounded linear operators in R. We denote by M' the set of all operators from B, which commute with all operators from M, and by M'' the set of all operators from B, which commute with all operators from M'. Then $M'' = M$ (see Ref. [28e]). On the other hand, M' consists only of those operators which are multiples of the identity operator (see the remark in the lemma Subsection 7 § 10), and so $M'' = B$, i.e. $M = B$. Hence the given unitary representation is completely irreducible.

We leave open the interesting question of when complete irreducibility follows from irreducibility. However, we note that the definitions of equivalence and of complete irreducibility given above and the results of Subsection 2, 3 carry over to the representations of any semisimple Lie group; there is a very interesting extension of these definitions and results to arbitrary locally compact groups. The proper choice of the set Ω presents the major difficulty in the general case. (In this connection see G. W. Mackey, *Infinite dimensional group representations*, Colloquium Lecture at Stillwater, Oklahoma, 1961)

Remark. It is easy to see that the preceding definition of complete irreducibility and propositions I, II carry over to the representations of an arbitrary subring with involution of the ring X, satisfying the conditions of the remark at the end of Subsection 3.

VI. *Let $x \to T_x$ be a representation in the space $\mathfrak{M}$ of the subring X_1 with involution of the ring X, satisfying the condition of the remark in Subsection* 3, *and let all the operators T_x commute with one another; if this representation $x \to T_x$ is completely irreducible, then the space R is one-dimensional.*

Proof. We suppose that $\mathfrak{M}$ is not one-dimensional, and introduce the notation $\Omega_1 = \mathfrak{M} \cap \Omega$; $\hat{\Omega}_1 = \mathfrak{M}' \cap \hat{\Omega}$.

Since Ω_1 is dense in $\mathfrak{M}$, Ω_1 is also not one-dimensional. Hence Ω_1 contains at least two linearly independent vectors ξ_1, ξ_2. Since $\hat{\Omega}_1$ is dense in $\mathfrak{M}'$, there exists a functional $\eta_1 \in \hat{\Omega}_1$ such that

$\eta_1(\xi_1) \neq 0$. By normalizing η_1, one can ensure that $\eta_1(\xi_1) = 1$. We denote by $\mathfrak{N}$ the set of all functionals $\zeta \in \hat{\Omega}_1$, for which $\zeta(\xi_1) = 0$.

Let η be an arbitrary functional from $\hat{\Omega}_1$. Letting $\zeta = \eta - c\eta_1$, where $c = \eta(\xi_1)$, we have:

$$\zeta(\xi_1) = \eta(\xi_1) - c\eta_1(\xi_1) = \eta(\xi_1) - c = 0;$$

hence, $\zeta \in \mathfrak{N}$. In $\mathfrak{N}$ there exists a functional η_2 such that $\eta_2(\xi_2) \neq 0$. For otherwise $\zeta(\xi_2) = 0$ for all $\zeta \in \mathfrak{N}$ and in particular,

$$\eta(\xi_2) - c\eta_1(\xi_2) = \eta(\xi_2) - \eta(\xi_1)\eta_1(\xi_2) = 0$$

for all $\eta \in \hat{\Omega}_1$. Letting $\eta_1(\xi_2) = c_1$ we see that $\eta(\xi_2 - c_1\xi_1) = 0$ for all $\eta \in \hat{\Omega}_1$. As $\hat{\Omega}_1$ is dense in $\mathfrak{M}'$, then $\eta(\xi_2 - c_1\xi_1) = 0$ for all $\eta \in \mathfrak{M}'$, which is possible only when $\xi_2 - c_1\xi_1 = 0$, contrary to hypothesis.

Therefore there exists a functional $\eta_2 \in \mathfrak{N}$ such that $\eta_2(\xi_2) \neq 0$. By normalizing η_2, one can ensure that $\eta_2(\xi_2) = 1$. Here, by the definition of $\mathfrak{N}$, $\eta_2(\xi_1) = 0$, so that finally we have:

$$\eta_1(\xi_1) = 1, \quad \eta_2(\xi_2) = 1, \quad \eta_2(\xi_1) = 0. \tag{9}$$

Now we define operators C_1 and C_2 in $\mathfrak{M}$, letting

$$C_1\xi = \eta_1(\xi)\xi_2, \quad C_2\xi = \eta_2(\xi)\xi_1.$$

These operators are admissible and it is easy to verify that

$$C_1 C_2\xi = \eta_2(\xi)\xi_2, \quad C_2 C_1\xi = \eta_1(\xi)\xi_1. \tag{10}$$

In particular we have by (9)

$$C_1 C_2\xi_1 = 0, \quad C_2 C_1\xi_1 = \xi_1.$$

Hence it is seen that the operators C_1, C_2 do not commute. Since C_1, C_2 are admissible, there exist sequences x_n, $y_n \in X_1$ such that as $n \to \infty$

$$(T_{x_n}\xi, \eta) \to (C_1\xi, \eta), \quad (T_{y_n}\xi, \eta) \to (C_2\xi, \eta)$$

for all $\xi \in \Omega_1$, $\eta \in \hat{\Omega}_1$. On the other hand, the condition, $T_{x_n} \times T_{y_m} = T_{y_m} T_{x_n}$ gives $(T_{x_n} T_{y_m}\xi, \eta) = (T_{y_m} T_{x_n}\xi, \eta)$, or

$$(T_{y_m}\xi, \hat{T}^*_{x_n}\eta) = (T_{y_m} T_{x_n}\xi, \eta).$$

Passing to the limit as $m \to \infty$ for fixed n, we see that $(C_2\xi, \hat{T}_{x_n^*}\eta) = (C_2 T_{x_n}\xi, \eta)$, or $(T_{x_n}C_2\xi, \eta) = (C_2 T_{x_n}\xi, \eta)$ for all $\xi \in \Omega_1, \eta \in \hat{\Omega}_1$. Now passing to the limit as $n \to \infty$, we conclude that $(C_1 C_2 \xi, \eta) = (C_2 C_1 \xi, \eta)$, or, by virtue of (10):

$$\eta_2(\xi)\eta(\xi_2) = \eta_1(\xi)\eta(\xi_1).$$

When $\xi = \xi_1$, $\eta = \eta_1$ this yields a contradiction of conditions (9). Hence R is one-dimensional, and proposition VI is proved.

5. The operators e^k_{jl}

We can construct the operators E^k_{jl} for the left regular representation of the group $\mathfrak{A}$ (see § 14, Subsection 8); we denote the operators corresponding to the operators E^k_{jl} by e^k_{jl}.

Thus, by the definition of this operator and of the left regular representation

$$e^k_{jl}x(a) = (2k+1)\int \overline{c^k_{jl}(u)}x(u^{-1}a)\,du. \tag{1}$$

Together with the operator e^k_{jl}, we shall need another operator, which will also be denoted by e^k_{jl}, but which will be written on the right of x; this operator is defined by the formula

$$(xe^k_{jl})(a) = (2k+1)\int c^k_{lj}(u)\,x(au)\,du. \tag{2}$$

Clearly, all the results of Subsections 6–7 are applicable to the left operator e^k_{jl}; in particular, it satisfies relations (3), (6) and (7) § 6, Subsection 6. It is easy to verify that these relations remain valid also for the right operator e^k_{jl}.

Since the left regular representation is unitary, the left operator e^k_{jl} satisfies the relation

$$(e^k_{jl})^* = e^k_{lj} \tag{3}$$

(see § 6, Subsection 7); in particular, e^k_{jj} is an operator of projection into $L^2(\mathfrak{U})$; it is easy to verify that analogous assertions also hold for the right operator e^k_{jl}.

I. *The operators e^k_{jl} satisfy the relation*

$$(e^k_{jl}x)\,e^r_{pq} = e^k_{jl}(xe^r_{pq}). \tag{4}$$

In fact, letting $e^k_{jl}x = y$, we have:

$$y(a) = (e^k_{jl}\, x)(a) = (2k+1)\int \overline{c^k_{jl}(u)}\, x(u^{-1}a)\, du,$$

and so

$$(e^k_{jl}x)\, e^r_{pq}(a) = (ye^r_{pq})(a) = (2r+1)\int c^r_{qp}(u')\, y(au')\, du'$$
$$= (2r+1)(2k+1)\iint \overline{c^k_{jl}(u)}\, c^r_{qp}(u')\, x(u^{-1}au')\, du\, du'.$$

The same expression is similarly derived for $e^k_{jl}\ (xe^r_{pq})(a)$, and so the two sides of (4) are equal.

II. *If* $x \in X$, *then also* $e^k_{jl}x,\ xe^k_{jl} \in X$.

The assertion follows immediately from formulae (1) and (2).

III. *If* $x \in X$, *then*

$$(e^k_{jl}x)^* = x^* e^k_{lj}, \quad (xe^k_{jl})^* = e^k_{lj}x^*. \tag{5}$$

Proof. We set $y = e^k_{jl}\, x$; then

$$y(a) = (2k+1)\int \overline{c^k_{jl}(u)}\, x(u^{-1}a)\, du$$

and

$$y^*(a) = \overline{y(a^{-1})} = (2k+1)\int c^k_{jl}(u)\, \overline{x(u^{-1}a^{-1})}\, du$$
$$= (2k+1)\int c^k_{jl}(u)\, x^*(au)\, du = (x^* e^k_{lj})(a),$$

and the first relation of (5) is proved; the second relation is proved similarly.

IV. *If* $x \in X$ *and* $x' = e^k_{jl}\, x,\ x'' = xe^k_{jl}$, *then*

$$T_{x'} = E^k_{jl}\, T_x, \quad T_{x''} = T_x E^k_{jl}. \tag{6}$$

In fact,

$$E^k_{jl}\, T_x = (2k+1)\int \overline{c^k_{jl}(u)}\, T_u du \int x(a)\, T_a da$$
$$= (2k+1)\iint \overline{c^k_{jl}(u)}\, x(a)\, T_{ua} da du$$
$$= (2k+1)\iint \overline{c^k_{jl}(u)}\, x(u^{-1}a)\, T_a da du = \int x'(a)\, T_a da = T'_x;$$

analogously it is proved that $T_x E^k_{jl} = T_{x''}$.

6. The ring X^k_j

We denote by X^k_j the set of all functions $x(a) \in X$, satisfying the condition

$$e^k_{jj}x = xe^k_{jj} = x. \tag{1}$$

I. X^k_j *is a subring with involution of the ring* X.

Proof. From condition (1) it is evident that X_j^k is a linear set; we will prove that it is a ring. Let $x_1, x_2 \in X_j^k$, so that

$$e_{jj}^k x_1 = x_1 e_{jj}^k = x_1, \quad e_{jj}^k x_2 = x_2 e_{jj}^k = x_2;$$

then

$$e_{jj}^k x_1 x_2 = x_1 e_{jj}^k x_2 = x_1 x_2 e_{jj}^k = x_1 x_2,$$

so that $x_1 x_2 \in X_j^k$, and X_j^k is a ring. We will prove that it is a ring with involution. Let $x \in X_j^k$, so that (1) holds; applying the operation of involution to both sides of (1) and using relation (5) Subsection 5, we see that $x^* e_{jj}^k = e_{jj}^k x^* = x^*$; hence also $x^* \in X_j^k$.

II. *Every function $x(a)$ from $L^2(\mathfrak{A})$ satisfying condition* (1), *has the form*

$$x(a) = x(u_1^{-1} \varepsilon u_2) = \sum_{p=-k}^{k} x_p(\varepsilon) c_{pj}^k(u_1) \overline{c_{pj}^k(u_2)}; \tag{2}$$

if, moreover, $x \in X$, then the function $x_p(\varepsilon)$ is infinitely differentiable and vanishes outside some bounded subset of the group E.

Proof. From (1) it follows that $x = e_{jj}^k x e_{jj}^k$, i.e.

$$x(a) = (2k+1)^2 \iint \overline{c_{jj}^k(v_1)} c_{jj}^k(v_2) x(v_1^{-1} a v_2) dv_1 dv_2;$$

hence

$$x(u_1^{-1} \varepsilon u_2) = (2k+1)^2 \iint \overline{c_{jj}^k(v_1)} c_{jj}^k(v_2) x(v_1^{-1} u_1^{-1} \varepsilon u_2 v_2) dv_1 dv_2$$

$$= (2k+1)^2 \iint \overline{c_{jj}^k(u_1^{-1} v_1)} c_{jj}^k(u_2^{-1} v_2) x(v_1^{-1} \varepsilon v_2) dv_1 dv_2 \tag{3}$$

$$= (2k+1)^2 \sum_{p,q=-k}^{k} \iint \overline{c_{jp}^k(u_1^{-1})} \overline{c_{pj}^k(v_1)} c_{jq}^k(u_2^{-1}) c_{qj}^k(v_2) x(v_1^{-1} \varepsilon v_2) dv_1 dv_2.$$

We set

$$x_{pq}(\varepsilon) = (2k+1)^2 \iint \overline{c_{pj}^k(v_1)} c_{qj}^k(v_2) x(v_1^{-1} \varepsilon v_2) dv_1 dv_2; \tag{4}$$

then (3) can be rewritten in the form

$$x(u_1^{-1} \varepsilon u_2) = \sum_{p,q=-k}^{k} x_{pq}(\varepsilon) c_{pj}^k(u_1) \overline{c_{qj}^k(u_2)}. \tag{5}$$

We will prove that $x_{pq}(\varepsilon) = 0$ for $p \neq q$. For this we note that

$$x_{pq}(\varepsilon) = (2k+1)^2 \iint \overline{c_{pj}^k(\gamma v_1)} c_{qj}^k(\gamma v_2) x(v_1^{-1} \gamma^{-1} \varepsilon \gamma v_2) dv_1 dv_2$$

$$= e^{2i(q-p)\omega}(2k+1)^2 \iint \overline{c_{pj}^k(v_1)} c_{qj}^k(v_2) x(v_1^{-1} \varepsilon v_2) dv_1 dv_2$$

$$= e^{2i(q-p)\omega} x_{pq}(\varepsilon);$$

if $p \neq q$ this is possible only when $x_{pq}(\varepsilon) = 0$. Letting $x_{pp}(\varepsilon) = x_p(\varepsilon)$ in (5), we obtain (2).

If $x \in X$, then $x(u_1^{-1}\, \varepsilon\, u_2)$ is an infinitely differentiable function of the parameters of the matrices u_1, u_2, ε, equal to zero outside some bounded set $Q \subset \mathfrak{A}$; therefore $x_p(\varepsilon) = x_{pp}(\varepsilon)$ in formula (4) is an infinitely differentiable function of ε, equal to zero outside the bounded set $E \cap \mathfrak{U} Q \mathfrak{U}$.

7. The relation between the representations of the rings X and X_j^k

In this subsection, S_k will denote an arbitrary irreducible representation of the group $\mathfrak{U}$, contained in a given representation $a \rightarrow T_a$, so that $E_{jl}^k \neq 0$. By virtue of VI § 6, Subsection 6 such representations S_k exist.

I. *If $x \in X_j^k$, then $\mathfrak{M}_j^k$ is invariant with respect to T_x.*

Proof. Let $\xi \in \mathfrak{M}_j^k$ and $x \in X_j^k$. Then $x = e_{jj}^k x$. Hence, by virtue of IV Subsection 5, $T_x \xi = E_{jj}^k T_x \xi$, and so $T_x \xi \in \mathfrak{M}_j^k$.

To every function $x \in X_j^k$ we assign an operator A_x in $\mathfrak{M}_j^k$, letting

$$A_x \xi = T_x \xi \quad \text{when} \quad \xi \in \mathfrak{M}_j^k. \tag{1}$$

By virtue of I, A_x is an operator in $\mathfrak{M}_j^k$ and, clearly, a bounded operator. The correspondence $x \rightarrow A_x$ is a representation of the ring X_j^k in the space $\mathfrak{M}_j^k$; we will call it *the representation of the ring X_j^k induced in the space $\mathfrak{M}_j^k$.*

We find the conjugate representation of an induced representation. First of all we will find the space $(\mathfrak{M}_j^k)'$, conjugate to $\mathfrak{M}_j^k$. Let $f \in (\mathfrak{M}_j^k)'$; i.e. f is a bounded linear functional in $\mathfrak{M}_j^k$; letting $f'(\xi) = f(E_{jj}^k\, \xi)$ when $\xi \in R$, we obtain a bounded linear functional f' in R, i.e. $f' \in R'$. Here

$$f'(E_{jj}^k \xi) = f(E_{jj}^k E_{jj}^k \xi) = f(E_{jj}^k \xi) = f'(\xi);$$

hence it is seen that:

(1) $f'(\xi) = f(\xi)$ when $\xi \in \mathfrak{M}_j^k$;

(2) $\hat{E}_{jj}^k f' = f'$, i.e. $f' \in \hat{\mathfrak{M}}_j^k$.

Conversely, if $f' \in \hat{\mathfrak{M}}_j^k$, then

$$\hat{E}_{jj}^k f' = f',$$

i.e.

$$f'(E^k_{jj}\xi) = f'(\xi);$$

hence, letting $f(\xi) = f'(\xi)$ when $\xi \in \mathfrak{M}^k_j$, we obtain a functional $f \in (\mathfrak{M}^k_j)'$, where $f'(\xi) = f'(E^k_{jj}\,\xi) = f(E^k_{jj}\,\xi)$.

The correspondence $f \to f'$ between the functionals $f \in (\mathfrak{M}^k_j)'$, and $f' \in \hat{\mathfrak{M}}^k_j$ defined in this way is one-one and continuous in both directions; therefore one can write $(\mathfrak{M}^k_j)' = \hat{\mathfrak{M}}^k_j$.

In fact we have

$$|f| = \sup_{\xi \in \mathfrak{M}^k_j} \frac{|f(\xi)|}{|\xi|} = \sup_{\xi \in R} \frac{|f(E^k_{jj}\xi)|}{|E^k_{jj}\xi|} \geqslant \sup_{\xi \in R} \frac{|f'(\xi)|}{c|\xi|} = \frac{1}{c}|f'|,$$

$$\text{where} \quad c = |E^k_{jj}|;$$

on the other hand it is clear that $|f| \leqslant |f'|$, and so

$$|f| \leqslant |f'| \leqslant \frac{1}{c}|f|.$$

Hence $|f_1 - f_2| \leqslant |f_1' - f_2'| \leqslant \frac{1}{c}|f_1 - f_2|$. Consequently $f_1 = f_2$ if and only if $f_1' = f_2'$, and $|f_n - f| \to 0$ if and only if $|f_n' - f'| \to 0$.

Thus we can assume that

$$(\mathfrak{M}^k_j)' = \hat{\mathfrak{M}}^k_j. \tag{2}$$

It is now easy to find the representation conjugate to $x \to A_x$. Let $\xi \in \mathfrak{M}^k_j$, $\eta \in \hat{\mathfrak{M}}^k_j$; then for $x \in X^k_j$,

$$(A_x\xi, \eta) = (T_x\xi, \eta) = (\xi, T_x'\eta) = (\xi, \hat{T}_{x*}\eta).$$

Hence, the operator $\hat{T}_{x*}$, considered only on $\hat{\mathfrak{M}}^k_j$, is conjugate to the operator A_x. In other words:

II. *The conjugate representation of the induced representation in $\mathfrak{M}^k_j$ for the original representation $a \to T_a$ is the induced representation in $\hat{\mathfrak{M}}^k_j$ for the conjugate representation $a \to \hat{T}_a$.* Now we set†

$$\Omega^k_j = E^k_{jj}\Omega, \quad \hat{\Omega}^k_j = \hat{E}^k_{jj}\hat{\Omega};$$

clearly,

$$\Omega^k_j = \Omega \cap \mathfrak{M}^k_j, \quad \hat{\Omega}^k_j = \hat{\Omega} \cap \hat{\mathfrak{M}}^k_j. \tag{3}$$

---

† If A is a linear operator in R, and $\mathfrak{D}$ is some set in R, then $A\mathfrak{D}$ denotes the set of all vectors $A\xi$, $\xi \in \mathfrak{D}$.

III. *If the representation $a \to T_a$ of the group $\mathfrak{A}$ is completely irreducible, then the corresponding induced representation $x \to A_x$ of the ring X_j^k in the space $\mathfrak{M}_j^k \neq (0)$ is also completely irreducible.*

Proof. First we prove that the sets Ω_j^k, $\hat{\Omega}_j^k$ are dense in $\mathfrak{M}_j^k$ and $\hat{\mathfrak{M}}_j^k$ respectively and, consequently, the remarks of Subsections 3 and 4 are applicable to the representation $x \to A_x$; by virtue of II, it is sufficient to prove this assertion for the set Ω_j^k. We denote by Ω' the set of all vectors of the form $T_x\xi_0$, where ξ_0 is a fixed vector from $\mathfrak{M}_j^k$ distinct from zero; clearly,

$$\Omega' \subset \Omega. \tag{4}$$

Moreover, Ω' is invariant with respect to all the operators T_x, $x \in X$, hence its closure $\bar{\Omega}'$ is also invariant with respect to these operators. By virtue of the complete irreducibility, and this means (see III Subsection 4) also the irreducibility of the representation $a \to T_a$, this is possible only when $\bar{\Omega}' = R$, i.e. when Ω' is dense in R. Therefore $E_{jj}^k \Omega'$ is dense in $E_{jj}^k R = \mathfrak{M}_j^k$. On the other hand, $E_{jj}^k \Omega' \subset E_{jj}^k \Omega = \Omega_j^k$, and so Ω_j^k is dense in $\mathfrak{M}_j^k$.

Now let C be an arbitrary bounded linear operator in $\mathfrak{M}_j^k$, admissible with respect to the representation $x \to A_x$, $x \in X_j^k$, i.e.

$$C\xi = (\xi, \eta_1)e_1 + \ldots + (\xi, \eta_n)e_n \quad \text{for} \quad \xi \in \mathfrak{M}_j^k, \tag{5}$$

where

$$\eta_1, \ldots, \eta_n \in \hat{\Omega}_j^k, \quad e_1, \ldots, e_n \in \Omega_j^k.$$

The right hand side of (5) is meaningful for all $\xi \in R$ and defines a bounded linear operator in R, admissible with respect to the representation $x \to T_x$ of the ring X. By virtue of the complete irreducibility of this representation there exists a sequence $x_m \in X$ such that as $m \to \infty$,

$$(T_{x_m}\xi, \eta) \to (C\xi, \eta) \quad \text{for all} \quad \xi \in \Omega, \quad \eta \in \hat{\Omega}. \tag{6}$$

In particular, (6) is true for $\xi \in \Omega_j^k$, $\eta \in \hat{\Omega}_j^k$.

Since $E_{jj}^k \xi = \xi$, $\hat{E}_{jj}^k \eta = \eta$ for $\xi \in \Omega_j^k$, $\eta \in \hat{\Omega}_j^k$, then

$$(T_{x_m} E_{jj}^k \xi, \hat{E}_{jj}^k \eta) \to (C\xi, \eta) \quad \text{for all} \quad \xi \in \Omega_j^k, \quad \eta \in \hat{\Omega}_j^k. \tag{7}$$

But

$$(T_{x_m} E_{jj}^k \xi, \hat{E}_{jj}^k \eta) = (E_{jj}^k T_{x_m} E_{jj}^k \xi, \eta) = (T_{x_m'} \xi, \eta),$$

where

$$x'_n = e^k_{jj} x_n e^k_{jj} \in X^k_j;$$

therefore relation (7) takes the form

$$(T_{x'_m} \xi, \eta) \to (C\xi, \eta) \quad as \quad m \to \infty, \quad \xi \in \Omega^k_j, \quad \eta \in \hat{\Omega}^k_j,$$

where $x'_m \in X^k_j$. This means that the representation $x \to A_x$ of the ring X^k_j is completely irreducible, and proposition III is proved.

By virtue of proposition III the problem of determining all the completely irreducible representations of the group $\mathfrak{A}$ is reduced to the problem of finding all the completely irreducible representations of the ring X^k_j. That is, by giving all the completely irreducible representations of the ring X^k_j, we do not omit a single completely irreducible representation of the group $\mathfrak{A}$.

8. The commutativity of the rings X^k_j

Essential in what follows is the fact that the rings X^k_j are commutative. The proof of their commutativity is based on an investigation of the kernel $K(u_1, u_2, m, \rho)$ of the operator $V^{(m, \rho)}_x$ of the principal series.

I. *If $x \in X^k_j$, then the corresponding kernel $K(u_1, u_2, m, \rho)$ has the form*

$$\mathrm{K}(u_1, u_2, m, \rho) = \begin{cases} 0 & for\ |m| < 2k \\ (2k+1) K_\nu(\rho) c^k_{\nu j}(u_1) \overline{c^k_{\nu j}(u_2)}, & for\ |m| \leqslant 2k \end{cases}$$

$$where \quad \nu = \tfrac{1}{2} m \tag{1}$$

and

$$\int |x(a)|^2 da = \frac{1}{(2\pi)^4} \sum_{\nu=-k}^{k} \int_0^\infty |K_\nu(\rho)|^2 (4\nu^2 + \rho^2) d\rho. \tag{2}$$

Proof. By the definition of this kernel, we have

$$K(u_1, u_2, m, \rho) = \pi \int x(u_1^{-1} k u_2) \alpha(k) d_l k,$$

$$\text{where} \quad \alpha(k) = |k_{22}|^{-m+i\rho-2} k_{22}^m \tag{3}$$

(see (5) § 13, Subsection 7). We set here

$$k = v_1^{-1} \varepsilon v_2$$

and make use of formula (2) Subsection 6; we obtain:

$$K(u_1, u_2, m, \rho) = \pi \int x(u_1^{-1} v_1^{-1} \varepsilon v_2 u_2) \alpha(k) \mathrm{d}_l k$$

$$= \pi \sum_{p=-k}^{k} \int x_p(\varepsilon) c_{pj}^k(v_1 u_1) \overline{c_{pj}^k(v_2 u_2)} \alpha(k) \mathrm{d}_l k$$

$$= \pi \sum_{p,\mu,\nu=-k}^{k} \int x_p(\varepsilon) c_{p\mu}^k(v_1) c_{\mu j}^k(u_1) \overline{c_{p\nu}^k(v_2) c_{\nu j}^k(u_2)} \alpha(k) \mathrm{d}_l k$$

$$= (2k+1) \sum_{\mu,\nu=-k}^{k} K_{\mu\nu}(m, \rho) c_{\mu j}^k(u_1) \overline{c_{\nu j}^k(u_2)}, \tag{4}$$

where

$$K_{\mu\nu}(m, \rho) = \frac{\pi}{2k+1} \sum_{p=-k}^{k} \int x_p(\varepsilon) c_{p\mu}^k(v_1) \overline{c_{p\nu}^k(v_2)} \alpha(k) \mathrm{d}_l k. \tag{5}$$

We will prove that $K_{\mu\nu}(m, \rho) = 0$ when $\mu \neq \nu$ and $m \neq 2\nu$. For this we note that the transition from k to γk in formula (5) is equivalent to the transition from v_1 to $v_1 \gamma^{-1}$; taking into account the left invariance of the integral with respect to $\mathrm{d}_l k$, we have:

$$K_{\mu\nu}(m, \rho) = \frac{\pi}{2k+1} \sum_{p=-k}^{k} \int x_p(\varepsilon) c_{p\mu}^k(v_1 \gamma^{-1}) \overline{c_{p\nu}^k(v_2)} \alpha(\gamma k) \mathrm{d}_l k$$

$$= \mathrm{e}^{-2i\mu\omega} \mathrm{e}^{im\omega} \frac{\pi}{2k+1} \sum_{p=-k}^{k} \int x_p(\varepsilon) c_{p\mu}^k(v_1) \overline{c_{p\nu}^k(v_2)} \alpha(k) \mathrm{d}_l k$$

$$= \mathrm{e}^{i\omega(m-2\mu)} K_{\mu\nu}(m, \rho).$$

When $m \neq 2\mu$ this is possible only when $K_{\mu\nu}(m,\rho) = 0$. Analogously, going over from k to $k\gamma$, and this means also from v_2 to $v_2\gamma$, and using the fact that $\mathrm{d}_l k$ goes into $\beta(\gamma)\mathrm{d}_l k = \mathrm{d}_l k$, we find that $K_{\mu\nu}(m, \rho) = 0$ for $m \neq 2\nu$. Thus, in formula (4), there is only one summand, corresponding to $\mu = \nu = \frac{1}{2}\mathrm{m}$; therefore, putting $K_\nu(\rho) = K_{\nu\nu}(m, \rho)$ when $2\nu = m$, in (4) we obtain formula (1). Here, by virtue of (5),

$$K_\nu(\rho) = \frac{\pi}{2k+1} \sum_{p=-k}^{k} \int x_p(\varepsilon) c_{p\nu}^k(v_1) \overline{c_{p\nu}^k(v_2)} \alpha(k) \mathrm{d}_l k, \tag{6}$$

where

$$k = v_1^{-1} \varepsilon v_2, \quad 2\nu = m, \quad \alpha(k) = |k_{22}|^{-m+i\rho-2} k_{22}^m. \tag{7}$$

In order to obtain formula (2), we note that by (1) and the relations of orthogonality for $2\nu = m$,

$$\iint |K(u_1, u_2, m, \rho)|^2 du_1 du_2$$
$$= (2k+1)^2 |K_\nu(\rho)|^2 \int |c^k_{\nu j}(u_1)|^2 du_1 \cdot \int |c^k_{\nu j}(u_2)|^2 du_2 = |K_\nu(\rho)|^2.$$

As ν must be one of the numbers $-k, -k+1, \ldots, k$, the integral $\iint |K(u_1, u_2, m, \rho)|^2\, du_1\, du_2$ can be distinct from zero only when $\frac{1}{2}m$ is equal to one of these numbers. From this and from the analogue of Plancherel's formula namely,

$$\int |x(a)|^2\, da$$
$$= \frac{1}{(2\pi)^4} \sum_{m=-\infty}^{\infty} \int_0^\infty \left[\iint |K(u_1, u_2, m, \rho)|^2 du_1 du_2 \right] (m^2 + \rho^2)\, d\rho$$

(see (18) § 14, Subsection 6) (2) follows.

II. *The correspondence $x \to K_\nu(\rho)$ between the elements x of the ring X^k_j and the functions $K_\nu(\rho)$ is one-one and possesses the following properties:*

(a) *if $x' \to K'_\nu(\rho)$, $x'' \to K''_\nu(\rho)$, then*

$$\lambda x' + \mu x'' \to \lambda K'_\nu(\rho) + \mu K''_\nu(\rho) \tag{8}$$

and

$$x'x'' \to K'_\nu(\rho) K''_\nu(\rho); \tag{9}$$

(b) *if $x \to K_\nu(\rho)$, then*

$$x^* \to \overline{K_\nu(\rho)}. \tag{10}$$

Proof. The linearity of the correspondence $x \to K_\nu(\rho)$ is evident, i.e. relation (8) is satisfied. Therefore the property of being one-one will follow if we show that $K_\nu(\rho) = 0$, implies $x(a) = 0$; this, however, follows immediately from formula (2). It remains to prove relations (9) and (10).

For this we note that the product corresponds to the composition of the corresponding kernels:

$$K(u_1, u_2, m, \rho) = \int K'(u_1, u, m, \rho) K''(u, u_2, m, \rho) du, \tag{11}$$

and the function x^* corresponds to the Hermitian adjoint kernel

$$K^*(u_1, u_2, m, \rho) = \overline{K(u_2, u_1, m, \rho)} \tag{12}$$

(see III § 13, Subsection 7). Substituting expressions (1) in both sides of (11) for K, K', K'', we obtain:

$$(2k+1)K_\nu(\rho)c^k_{\nu j}(u_1)\overline{c^k_{\nu j}(u_2)} = (2k+1)^2 K'_\nu(\rho)K''_\nu(\rho)c^k_{\nu j}(u_1)\overline{c^k_{\nu j}(u_2)} \times$$
$$\times \int c^k_{\nu j}(u)\overline{c^k_{\nu j}(u)}du = (2k+1)K'_\nu(\rho)K''_\nu(\rho)c^k_{\nu j}(u_1)\overline{c^k_{\nu j}(u_2)};$$

hence $K_\nu(\rho) = K'_\nu(\rho)K''_\nu(\rho)$, and relation (9) is proved.

Analogously, substituting from (1) in both sides of (12), we obtain relation (10).

III. *The rings X^k_j are commutative.* In fact, if $x', x'' \in X^k_j$, then, by (9), both products $x'x''$ and $x''x'$ correspond to one and the same function $K_\nu(\rho) = K'_\nu(\rho)K''_\nu(\rho)$; in view of the one-one nature of the correspondence $x \to K_\nu(\rho)$ it follows from this that $x'x'' = x''x'$.

We can now prove the following theorem:

THEOREM 14. *If the representation $a \to T_a$ of the group $\mathfrak{A}$ is completely irreducible, then every irreducible representation S_k of the group $\mathfrak{U}$ is contained in the representation $a \to T_a$ at most once.*

Proof. Let S_k be an irreducible representation of the group $\mathfrak{U}$ which is contained in the representation $a \to T_a$.

We consider the induced representation $x \to A_x$ of the ring X^k_j in the space $\mathfrak{M}^k_j$, corresponding to the representation $a \to T_a$.

By virtue of II and III Subsection 7, the representation $x \to A_x$ is a completely irreducible representation of the commutative ring with involution X^k_j, satisfying the conditions of the remark in Subsection 3. On the basis of proposition VI Subsection 4 this is possible only when $\mathfrak{M}^k_j$ is one-dimensional, and the theorem is proved.

Remark. Theorem 14 means that for completely irreducible representations of the group $\mathfrak{A}$ condition B § 7, Subsection 3 is satisfied. We proved above (see the remarks in § 13, Subsection 5), that condition A § 7, Subsection 3 is also satisfied, where for $\mathfrak{D}$ one can take the set of all linear combinations of the vectors $T_x\xi$, $\xi \in R$, where x runs through $\hat{\mathrm{X}}$. We note that $E^k_{jj}T_x\xi = T_{x'}\xi$, where $x' = e^k_{jj}x \in \mathrm{X}$ Therefore $E^k_{jj}\mathfrak{D}$ is a subset of $\mathfrak{D}$, dense in $\mathfrak{M}^k_j$. Because $\mathfrak{M}^k_j$ is one-dimensional, we have $E^k_{jj}\mathfrak{D} = \mathfrak{M}^k_j$ and $\mathfrak{M}^k_j \subset \mathfrak{D}$. In this way it is proved that for completely irreducible representations of the group $\mathfrak{A}$ condition C § 7, Subsection 3 is also satisfied, and the results of §§ 7 and 8 apply to all completely irreducible representations of the group $\mathfrak{A}$.

By virtue of Theorem 14, the induced representation $x \to A_x$ of the ring x^k_j is one-dimensional and so has the form

$$A_x\xi = \lambda(x)\xi, \quad \xi \in \mathfrak{M}^k_j, \tag{13}$$

where $\lambda(x)$ is a linear functional in X^k_j. Because the correspondence $x \to A_x$ is a representation, then necessarily

$$\lambda(x_1x_2) = \lambda(x_1)\lambda(x_2). \tag{14}$$

Linear functionals satisfying condition (14), will be called *linear multiplicative functionals*.

Thus, *every completely irreducible representation of the group* $\mathfrak{A}$ *induces in every ring* X^k_j *some linear multiplicative functional.*

The question arises, to what extent a completely irreducible representation of the group $\mathfrak{A}$ is defined by such a functional. Below we will give an answer to this question.

9. A criterion of equivalence

THEOREM 15. *Let* $a \to T^{(1)}_a$, $a \to T^{(2)}_a$ *be two completely irreducible representations of the group* $\mathfrak{A}$, *containing one and the same representation* S_k *of the group* $\mathfrak{U}$; *if for fixed corresponding subspaces* $\mathfrak{M}^{(1)k}_j$, $\mathfrak{M}^{(2)k}_j$ *the functionals* $\lambda_1(x)$, $\lambda_2(x)$, *induced by the representations* $a \to T^{(1)}_a$, $a \to T^{(2)}_a$, *coincide, then these representations are equivalent. Conversely, if these representations are equivalent, then* $\lambda_1(x) = \lambda_2(x)$.

Proof. Let $\xi^{(1)}_0$, $\xi^{(2)}_0$ be fixed vectors from $\mathfrak{M}^{(1)k}_j$, $\mathfrak{M}^{(2)k}_j$ respectively, distinct from zero. We denote by Ω'_1 the set of all vectors $T^{(1)}_x\xi^{(1)}_0$, $x \in X$, and by Ω'_2 the set of all vectors $T^{(2)}_x\xi^{(2)}_0$, $x \in X$.

Because the representations $x \to T^{(1)}_x$, $x \to T^{(2)}_x$ are completely irreducible, then Ω'_1, Ω'_2 are dense in R_1, R_2 respectively, where R_1, R_2 are the spaces of these representations (see the proof of proposition III Subsection 7).

Now we consider the conjugate operators $a \to \hat{T}^{(1)}_a$, $a \to \hat{T}^{(2)}_a$. We choose vectors $\eta^{(1)}_0 \in \hat{\mathfrak{M}}^{(1)k}_j$, $\eta^{(2)}_0 \in \hat{\mathfrak{M}}^{(2)k}_j$ distinct from zero so that

$$(\xi^{(1)}_0, \eta^{(1)}_0) = (\xi^{(2)}_0, \eta^{(2)}_0) \tag{1}$$

and we denote by $\hat{\Omega}'_1$ the set of all vectors $\hat{T}^{(1)}_x \eta^{(1)}_0$, $x \in X$, and by $\hat{\Omega}'_2$ the set of all vectors $\hat{T}^{(2)}_x \eta^{(2)}_0$, $x \in X$. Because the conjugate representations $a \to \hat{T}^{(1)}_a$, $a \to \hat{T}^{(2)}_a$ are also completely irreducible, then $\hat{\Omega}'_1, \hat{\Omega}'_2$ are dense in R'_1, R'_2 respectively.

We will prove that

$$\Omega'_j = \Omega_j, \quad \hat{\Omega}'_j = \hat{\Omega}_j, \quad j = 1, 2. \tag{2}$$

For this we note that $E^{(1)k'}_{j'j'}\Omega'_1$ is dense in $E^{(1)k'}_{j'j'} R_1 = \mathfrak{M}^{(1)k'}_{j'}$; since $\mathfrak{M}^{(1)k'}_{j'}$ is one-dimensional or zero, then $E^{(1)k'}_{j'j'}\Omega'_1 = \mathfrak{M}^{(1)k'}_{j'}$, and so the whole of $\mathfrak{M}^{(1)k'}_{j'} \subset \Omega'_1$. But then Ω'_1 contains all the vectors $T^{(1)}_x \xi$, $\xi \in \mathfrak{M}^{(1)k'}_{j'}$, and this means also all linear combinations of these vectors, because Ω'_1 is invariant with respect to the operators $T^{(1)}_x$, $x \in X$, and is linear. Therefore $\Omega'_1 \supset \Omega_1$ and, consequently $\Omega'_1 = \Omega_1$. The remaining relations (2) are proved similarly.

Let $x \in X$; for brevity we set $x' = e^k_{jj}\, x e^k_{jj}$. Then $x' \in X^k_j$, and so (see IV Subsection 5)

$$(T^{(1)}_x \xi^{(1)}_0, \eta^{(1)}_0) = (T^{(1)}_x E^{(1)k}_{jj} \xi^{(1)}_0, \hat{E}^{(1)k}_{jj} \eta^{(1)}_0) = (E^{(1)k}_{jj} T^{(1)}_x E^{(1)k}_{jj} \xi^{(1)}_0, \eta^{(1)}_0)$$
$$= (T^{(1)}_{x'} \xi^{(1)}_0, \eta^{(1)}_0) = \lambda_1(x')(\xi_0{}^{(1)}, \eta^{(1)}_0) \tag{3}$$

and similarly

$$(T^{(2)}_x \xi^{(2)}_0, \eta^{(2)}_0) = \lambda_2(x')(\xi^{(2)}_0, \eta^{(2)}_0). \tag{4}$$

Assume now that $\lambda_1(x') = \lambda_2(x')$ for all $x \in X^k_j$; by virtue of (1), (3), (4) we have

$$(T^{(1)}_x \xi^{(1)}_0, \eta^{(1)}_0) = (T^{(2)}_x \xi^{(2)}_0, \eta^{(2)}_0) \tag{5}$$

for all $x \in X$. Replacing x by y^*x in (5), where $x, y \in X$, we find that

$$(T^{(1)}_{y^*x} \xi^{(1)}_0, \eta^{(1)}_0) = (T^{(2)}_{y^*x} \xi^{(2)}_0, \eta^{(2)}_0).$$

But

$$(T^{(1)}_{y^*x} \xi^{(1)}_0, \eta^{(1)}_0) = (T^{(1)}_{y^*} T^{(1)}_x \xi^{(1)}_0, \eta^{(1)}_0) = (T^{(1)}_x \xi^{(1)}_0, \hat{T}^{(1)}_y \eta^{(1)}_0)$$

and similarly

$$(T^{(2)}_{y^*x} \xi^{(2)}_0, \eta^{(2)}_0) = (T^{(2)}_x \xi^{(2)}_0, \hat{T}^{(2)}_y \eta^{(2)}_0);$$

hence:

$$(T^{(1)}_x \xi^{(1)}_0, \hat{T}^{(1)}_y \eta^{(1)}_0) = (T^{(2)}_x \xi^{(2)}_0, \hat{T}^{(2)}_y \eta^{(2)}_0) \tag{6}$$

for all $x, y \in X$.

Now we define an operator A from R_1 to R_2, letting

$$AT_x^{(1)}\xi_0^{(1)} = T_x^{(2)}\xi_0^{(2)} \quad \text{for all} \quad x \in X, \tag{7}$$

so that the domain of definition of the operator A is Ω_1, and the domain of variation Ω_2. In order that this definition be single-valued, we must show that if $T_{x_1}^{(1)}\ \xi_0^{(1)} = T_{x_2}^{(1)}\ \xi_0^{(1)}$, then also $T_{x_1}^{(2)}\ \xi_0^{(2)} = T_{x_2}^{(2)}\ \xi_0^{(2)}$.

Letting $x_1 - x_2 = x$, we see that it is sufficient to verify that the equation $T_x^{(1)}\ \xi_0^{(1)} = 0$ implies $T_x^{(2)}\ \xi_0^{(2)} = 0$.

But if $T_x^{(1)}\ \xi_0^{(1)} = 0$, then from (6) it follows that

$$(T_x^{(2)}\xi_0^{(2)},\ \hat{T}_y^{(2)}\eta_0^{(2)}) = 0 \quad \text{for all} \quad \eta = \hat{T}_y^{(2)}\eta_0^{(2)}, \quad \text{where} \quad y \in X$$

i.e. $(T_x^{(2)}\ \xi_0^{(2)}, \eta) = 0$ for all $\eta \in \hat{\Omega}_2$.

Since $\hat{\Omega}_2$ is dense in R'_2, we deduce from this that

$$T_x^{(2)}\xi_0^{(2)} = 0.$$

Analogously it can be proved that if

$$A\xi = 0, \quad \xi \in \Omega, \quad \text{then} \quad \xi = 0.$$

Hence equation (7) defines the operator A unambiguously. We replace x by xy in (7), where $x, y \in X$, and we set $\xi = T_y^{(1)}\ \xi_0^{(1)}$; we find:

$$AT_x^{(1)}\xi = AT_x^{(1)}T_y^{(1)}\xi_0^{(1)} = AT_{xy}^{(1)}\xi_0^{(1)} = T_{xy}^{(2)}\xi_0^{(1)}$$
$$= T_x^{(2)}T_y^{(2)}\xi_0^{(2)} = T_x^{(2)}AT_y^{(1)}\xi_0^{(1)} = T_x^{(2)}A\xi,$$

i.e.

$$AT_x^{(1)}\xi = T_x^{(2)}A\xi \quad \text{for all} \quad \xi \in \Omega_1. \tag{8}$$

Similarly we define an operator B from R'_2 to R'_1, letting

$$B\hat{T}_x^{(2)}\eta_0^{(2)} = \hat{T}_x^{(1)}\eta_0^{(1)}, \tag{9}$$

so that the domain of definition of the operator B is $\hat{\Omega}'_2$, and the domain of variation is $\hat{\Omega}'_1$.

Reasoning as above, we conclude that this definition of the operator B is unambiguous and that:

(a) $B\hat{T}_x^{(2)}\eta = \hat{T}_x^{(1)}B\eta$ for all $\eta \in \hat{\Omega}'_2$, (10)

(b) if $B\eta = 0$, $\eta \in \hat{\ }'_2$, then $\eta = 0$. (11)

Relation (6) here takes the form

$$(T_x^{(1)}\xi_0^{(1)}, B\hat{T}_x^{(2)}\eta_0^{(2)}) = (AT_x^{(1)}\xi_0^{(1)}, \hat{T}_y^{(2)}\eta_0^{(2)}),$$

i.e.

$$(A\xi, \eta) = (\xi, B\eta) \tag{12}$$

for all $\xi \in \Omega_1'$, $\eta \in \hat{\Omega}_2'$.

Thus, the operators A, B satisfy all the conditions of the definition of equivalence (conditions (α–δ) Subsection 3); hence, the representations $a \to T_a^{(1)}$ $a \to T_a^{(2)}$ are equivalent.

Conversely, let the representations $a \to T_a^{(1)}$, $a \to T_a^{(2)}$ be equivalent and let A, B be operators satisfying for these representations conditions (α–δ) Subsection 3. Then for $\xi \in \mathfrak{M}_j^{(1)k}$, $\xi \neq 0$ and $x \in X_j^k$,

$$AT_x^{(1)}\xi = A\lambda_1(x)\xi = \lambda_1(x)A\xi, \quad T_x^{(2)}A\xi = \lambda_2(x)A\xi.$$

Since $AT_x^{(1)}\xi = T_x^{(2)}A\xi$, then $\lambda_1(x)A\xi = \lambda_2(x)A\xi$; hence $\lambda_1(x) = \lambda_2(x)$, because $A\xi \neq 0$, and the theorem is completely proved.

The theorem just proved means that a completely irreducible representation is completely defined (to within equivalence) by the induced linear multiplicative functional $\lambda(x)$ in the fixed ring X_j^k. Therefore the problem arises of finding all the linear multiplicative functionals in X_j^k.

10. The functional $\lambda(x)$ in the case of an irreducible representation of the principal series

We will find $\lambda(x)$ in the case of a representation $\mathfrak{S}_{m,\rho}$ of the principal series. First of all we note that in this case $c_{\nu j}^k(u) \in \mathfrak{M}_j^k$, where $\nu = \frac{1}{2}m$. In fact, $c_{\nu j}^k(u) \in L_2^m(\mathfrak{U})$ (see § 11, Subsection 4); moreover, in the case of the representation $\mathfrak{S}_{m,\rho}$,

$$T_{u'}c_{\nu j}^k(u) = c_{\nu j}^k(uu')$$

and, by virtue of the relations of orthogonality,

$$\begin{aligned} E_{jj}^k c_{\nu j}^k(u) &= (2k+1)\int \overline{c_{jj}^k(u')}\, c_{\nu j}^k(uu')du' \\ &= (2k+1)\sum_{p=-k}^{k} \int \overline{c_{jj}^k(u')}\, c_{\nu p}^k(u)\, c_{pj}^k(u')du' = c_{\nu j}^k(u). \end{aligned}$$

When $x \in X_j^k$ the operator T_x is given by the kernel

$$K(u, u', m, \rho) = (2k+1)K_\nu(\rho)c_{\nu j}^k(u)\overline{c_{\nu j}^k(u')}$$

(see Subsection 8), and so

$$T_x c_{\nu j}^k(u) = \int K(u, u', m, \rho)c_{\nu j}^k(u')\mathrm{d}u'$$
$$= (2k+1)K_\nu(\rho)c_{\nu j}^k(u)\int \overline{c_{\nu j}^k(u')}c_{\nu j}^k(u')\mathrm{d}u' = K_\nu(\rho)c_{\nu j}^k(u);$$

hence,

$$\lambda(x) = K_\nu(\rho).$$

Thus:

I. *In the case of the representation* $\mathfrak{S}_{m,\rho}$ *of the principal series*

$$\lambda(x) = K_\nu(\rho), \quad \text{where} \quad \nu = \tfrac{1}{2}m. \tag{1}$$

Hence we deduce:

II. *The function* $K_\nu(\rho)$ *satisfies the relation*

$$K_{-\nu}(-\rho) = K_\nu(\rho). \tag{2}$$

In fact, the representations $\mathfrak{S}_{-m,-\rho}$ and $\mathfrak{S}_{m,\rho}$ are equivalent (indeed unitarily equivalent, see III § 11, Subsection 6). On the basis of Theorem 15 Subsection 9 the functionals $\lambda'(x) = K_{-\nu}(-\rho)$ and $\lambda''(x) = K_\nu(\rho)$ corresponding to them must coincide.

11. The functions $B_\nu(\varepsilon)$

The solution of the problem posed at the end of Subsection 9, is based on the consideration of some auxiliary functions, which are obtained in the following way.

In formula (6) Subsection 8 we pass from integration with respect to $\mathrm{d}_l k$ to integration with respect to $\mathrm{d}\varepsilon$, $\mathrm{d}\gamma$ and $\mathrm{d}\zeta$ (see I § 14, Subsection 4); we obtain:

$$K_\nu(\rho) = \frac{\pi}{2k+1}\sum_{p=-k}^{k}\iiint x_p(\varepsilon)c_{p\nu}^k(v_1)\overline{c_{p\nu}^k(v_2)}\alpha(\varepsilon')\alpha(\gamma)\mathrm{d}\varepsilon'\,\mathrm{d}\gamma\,\mathrm{d}\zeta, \tag{1}$$

where

$$\gamma\varepsilon'\zeta = k = v_1^{-1}\varepsilon v_2, \quad \alpha(k) = |k_{22}|^{-m+i\rho-2}k_{22}^m. \tag{2}$$

We set

$$B_\nu(\varepsilon') = \frac{\pi}{2k+1}\beta^{-\frac{1}{2}}(\varepsilon')\sum_{p=-k}^{k}\iint x_p(\varepsilon)c_{p\nu}^k(v_1)\overline{c_{p\nu}^k(v_2)}\alpha(\gamma)\mathrm{d}\gamma\,\mathrm{d}\zeta; \tag{3}$$

then formula (1) can be rewritten in the form

$$K_\nu(\rho) = \int B_\nu(\varepsilon)\varepsilon_{22}^{i\rho}d\varepsilon, \quad \text{where} \quad \varepsilon = \begin{Vmatrix} \varepsilon_{22}^{-1} & 0 \\ 0 & \varepsilon_{22} \end{Vmatrix}. \tag{4}$$

To every function $x \in X_j^k$ we assign a function $B = B_\nu(\varepsilon)$ by means of formula (3); clearly, $B_\nu(\varepsilon)$ is an infinitely differentiable function of ε, equal to zero outside some bounded subset† of the group E.

I. *The correspondence* $x \to B$ *between the functions* $x \in X_j^k$ *and the functions* B *is one-one and linear; moreover:*

(a) *if* $x \to B_\nu(\varepsilon)$, *then* $x^* \to B_\nu^*(\rho) = \overline{B_\nu(\varepsilon^{-1})}$;

(b) *if* $x' \to B_\nu'(\varepsilon)$, $x'' \to B_\nu''(\varepsilon)$, *then*

$$x'x'' \to B_\nu(\varepsilon) = \int B_\nu'(\varepsilon')B_\nu''(\varepsilon\varepsilon'^{-1})d\varepsilon'. \tag{5}$$

Proof. The linearity of the correspondence $x \to B$ is evident, therefore the property of being one-one will be established by proving that the equation $B_\nu(\varepsilon) = 0$ implies $x = 0$. But if $B_\nu(\varepsilon) = 0$, then, by (4), $K_\nu(\rho) = 0$ also; according to proposition II Subsection 8 we deduce from this that $x = 0$.

In order to prove assertion (a), we denote by $B_\nu^*(\varepsilon)$ the function B corresponding to x^*; then, by virtue of II Subsection 8:

$$\int B_\nu^*(\varepsilon)\varepsilon_{22}^{i\rho}d\varepsilon = \overline{K_\nu(\rho)};$$

on the other hand,

$$\int \overline{B_\nu(\varepsilon^{-1})}\varepsilon_{22}^{i\rho}d\varepsilon = \int \overline{B_\nu(\varepsilon)\varepsilon_{22}^{-i\rho}}d\varepsilon = \overline{K_\nu(\rho)}.$$

In view of the arbitrary nature of the number ρ we deduce from this that $B_\nu^*(\varepsilon) = \overline{B_\nu(\varepsilon^{-1})}$. Finally, for the proof of formula (5), let $B_\nu(\varepsilon)$ denote the function B corresponding to $x'x''$; by virtue of II Subsection 8 we have

$$\int B_\nu(\varepsilon)\varepsilon_{22}^{i\rho}d\varepsilon = K_\nu(\rho) = K_\nu'(\rho)K_\nu''(\rho);$$

† Below, in formula (34), an explicit connection between the variables ε_{22} and ε_{22}' is indicated, from which it follows that $|\ln\varepsilon_{22}| \geqslant |\ln \varepsilon_{22}'|$. Therefore for sufficiently large $|\ln \varepsilon_{22}'|$, the function $x_p(\varepsilon)$, occuring in the integral in (3) vanishes.

on the other hand,

$$\int [\int B_\nu'(\varepsilon')B_\nu''(\varepsilon\varepsilon'^{-1})d\varepsilon']\varepsilon_{22}^{i\rho}d\varepsilon = \int B_\nu'(\varepsilon')d\varepsilon' \int B_\nu''(\varepsilon\varepsilon'^{-1})\varepsilon_{22}^{i\rho}d\varepsilon$$
$$= \int B_\nu'(\varepsilon')d\varepsilon' \int B_\nu''(\varepsilon'')\varepsilon_{22}'^{i\rho}\varepsilon_{22}''^{i\rho}d\varepsilon'' = K_\nu'(\rho)K_\nu''(\rho),$$

whence

$$\int [\int B_\nu'(\varepsilon')B_\nu''(\varepsilon\varepsilon'^{-1})d\varepsilon']\varepsilon_{22}^{i\rho}d\varepsilon = \int B_\nu(\varepsilon)\varepsilon_{22}^{i\rho}d\varepsilon.$$

In view of the arbitrary nature of the number ρ we deduce from this equation that

$$\int B_\nu'(\varepsilon')B_\nu''(\varepsilon\varepsilon'^{-1})d\varepsilon' = B_\nu(\varepsilon),$$

and formula (5) is proved.

II. *The functions* $B_\nu(\varepsilon)$ *satisfy the relation*

$$B_{-\nu}(\varepsilon^{-1}) = B_\nu(\varepsilon). \tag{6}$$

Proof. Since

$$\int B_\nu(\varepsilon)\varepsilon_{22}^{i\rho}d\varepsilon = K_\nu(\rho),$$

then

$$\int B_{-\nu}(\varepsilon^{-1})\varepsilon_{22}^{i\rho}d\varepsilon = \int B_{-\nu}(\varepsilon)\varepsilon_{22}^{-i\rho}d\varepsilon = K_{-\nu}(-\rho);$$

but $K_\nu(\rho) = K_{-\nu}(-\rho)$ (see (2) Subsection 10), i.e.

$$\int B_\nu(\varepsilon)\varepsilon_{22}^{i\rho}d\varepsilon = \int B_{-\nu}(\varepsilon^{-1})\varepsilon_{22}^{i\rho}d\varepsilon.$$

By virtue of the arbitrary nature of the number ρ, (6) follows.

We denote by $\mathfrak{B}_j^k$ the set of all functions $B = B_\nu(\varepsilon)$, corresponding to all possible functions $x \in X_j^k$; $\mathfrak{B}_j^k$ is a ring with involution, in which the operations of addition and multiplication by a number are defined in the usual way, where the operation of multiplication is defined by formula (5), and the involution by means of the formula

$$B_\nu^*(\varepsilon) = \overline{B_\nu(\varepsilon^{-1})}. \tag{7}$$

Proposition I means that our correspondence $x \to B$ is an isomorphism† of the rings X_j^k and $\mathfrak{B}_j^k$, preserving involution. There-

† A *homomorphism* of the ring R_1 into the ring R_2 is a linear mapping $x_1 \to x_2$ of the ring R_1 into the ring R_2, preserving the operation of multiplication, so that if $x_1 \to x_2$, $y_1 \to y_2$ then $\alpha x_1 + \beta y_1 \to \alpha x_2 + \beta y_2$, $x_1 y_1 \to x_2 y_2$; a one-one homomorphism is called an *isomorphism*. Two rings R_1, R_2 are called *isomorphic*, if there exists an isomorphism of R_1 onto R_2. In the abstract theory of rings isomorphic rings are not considered to be essentially different.

fore a linear multiplicative functional $\lambda(x)$ in the ring X_j^k can also be considered as a linear multiplicative functional $\lambda(B)$ in the ring $\mathfrak{B}_j^k$, by writing

$$\lambda(B) = \lambda(x) \quad \text{if} \quad x \to B. \tag{8}$$

Our problem is thus reduced to a determination of all linear multiplicative functionals $\lambda(B)$ in the ring $\mathfrak{B}_j^k$, in which the rule of multiplication is defined by the simple formula (5). For the solution of this last problem we must know what functions belong to the ring $\mathfrak{B}_j^k$; for this purpose we derive a formula expressing x in terms of $B_\nu(\varepsilon)$.

III. *The function $x_p(\varepsilon)$ is expressed in terms of the function $B_\nu(\varepsilon)$ by the formula*

$$x_p(\varepsilon) = \frac{1}{16\pi^3}(2k+1)\sum_{\nu=-k}^{k}\int C_\nu(\varepsilon')c_{\nu p}(u)\overline{c_{\nu p}(v)}du, \tag{9}$$

where

$$C_\nu(\varepsilon) = \varepsilon_{22}^{-2}\left[4\nu^2-\left(\varepsilon_{22}\frac{\partial}{\partial\varepsilon_{22}}\right)^2\right]B_\nu(\varepsilon) \tag{10}$$

and

$$u\varepsilon = \varepsilon'\zeta v. \tag{11}$$

Proof. According to formula (16) § 14, Subsection 7 we have

$$x(a) = \frac{1}{(2\pi)^4}\sum_{m=-\infty}^{\infty}\int_0^\infty\left[\int K(u, u\bar{a}, m, \rho)\frac{\overline{\alpha(ua)}}{\alpha(u\bar{a})}du\right](m^2+\rho^2)d\rho, \tag{12}$$

and so

$$x(u_1^{-1}\varepsilon u_2) = \frac{1}{(2\pi)^4}\times$$

$$\times\sum_{m=-\infty}^{\infty}\int_0^\infty\left[\int K(u,(uu_1^{-1})\bar{\varepsilon}u_2, m, \rho)\frac{\overline{\alpha(uu_1^{-1}\varepsilon u_2)}}{\alpha((uu_1^{-1})\bar{\varepsilon}u_2)}du\right](m^2+\rho^2)d\rho$$

$$= \frac{1}{(2\pi)^4}\sum_{m=-\infty}^{\infty}\int_0^\infty\left[\int K(uu_1, u\bar{\varepsilon}u_2, m, \rho)\frac{\overline{\alpha(u\varepsilon u_2)}}{\alpha(u\bar{\varepsilon}u_2)}du\right](m^2+\rho^2)d\rho. \tag{13}$$

We set $u\varepsilon = \varepsilon'\zeta v$; then

$$v = u\bar{\varepsilon}, \tag{14}$$

$$\alpha(u\varepsilon u_2) = \alpha(\varepsilon'\zeta v u_2) = \alpha(\varepsilon')\alpha(v u_2) = \alpha(\varepsilon')\alpha(u\bar{\varepsilon} u_2), \tag{15}$$

and formula (13) is rewritten in the form

$$x(u_1^{-1}\varepsilon u_2) = \frac{1}{(2\pi)^4}\sum_{m=-\infty}^{\infty}\int_0^{\infty}\left[\int K(uu_1, vu_2, m, \rho)\overline{\alpha(\varepsilon')}du\right]\times \\ \times (m^2+\rho^2)d\rho. \tag{16}$$

Substituting instead of $x(u_1^{-1}\,\varepsilon\, u_2)$ and $K(u_1, u_2, m, \rho)$ their expressions from formulae (2) Subsection 6 and (1) Subsection 8, we obtain:

$$\sum_{p=-k}^{k} x_p(\varepsilon)\, c_{pj}^k(u_1)\overline{c_{pj}^k(u_2)} \\ = \frac{1}{(2\pi)^4}(2k+1)\sum_{\nu=-k}^{k}\int_0^{\infty}\left[\int K_\nu(\rho)\, c_{\nu j}^k(uu_1)\overline{c_{\nu j}^k(vu_2)}\,\overline{\alpha(\varepsilon')}du\right]\times \\ \times(4\nu^2+\rho^2)d\rho = \frac{1}{(2\pi)^4}(2k+1)\times \\ \times\sum_{\nu=-k}^{k}\sum_{p,q=-k}^{k}\int_0^{\infty}[K_\nu(\rho)\, c_{\nu p}^k(u)\, c_{pj}^k(u_1)\overline{c_{\nu q}^k(v)}\,\overline{c_{qj}^k(u_2)}\,\overline{\alpha(\varepsilon')}du]\times \\ \times(4\nu^2+\rho^2)d\rho,$$

whence

$$x_p(\varepsilon) = \frac{1}{(2\pi)^4}(2k+1)\sum_{\nu=-k}^{k}\int_0^{\infty}K_\nu(\rho)\left[\int c_{\nu p}^k(u)\overline{c_{\nu p}^k(v)\alpha(\varepsilon')}du\right]\times \\ \times(4\nu^2+\rho^2)d\rho. \tag{17}$$

By virtue of the relation $K_{-\nu}(-\rho) = K_\nu(\rho)$ this formula can also be written in the form

$$x_p(\varepsilon) = \frac{1}{32\pi^4}(2k+1)\sum_{\nu=-k}^{k}\int_{-\infty}^{\infty}K_\nu(\rho)\left[\int c_{\nu p}^k(u)\overline{c_{\nu p}^k(v)}\,\overline{\alpha(\varepsilon')}du\right]\times \\ \times(4\nu^2+\rho^2)d\rho. \tag{18}$$

We set

$$B_\nu(t) = B_\nu(\varepsilon) \quad \text{when} \quad \varepsilon_{22} = e^t; \tag{19}$$

then formula (4), namely

$$K_\nu(\rho) = \int B_\nu(\varepsilon)\varepsilon_{22}^{i\rho}\,d\varepsilon$$

can be rewritten in the form

$$K_\nu(\rho) = \int_{-\infty}^{\infty} B_\nu(t)e^{it\rho}\,dt. \tag{20}$$

Hence

$$B_\nu(\varepsilon) = B_\nu(t) = \frac{1}{2\pi}\int_{-\infty}^{\infty} K_\nu(\rho)e^{-it\rho}\,d\rho = \frac{1}{2\pi}\int_{-\infty}^{\infty} K_\nu(\rho)\varepsilon_{22}^{-i\rho}\,d\rho \tag{21}$$

and

$$\frac{d^2B_\nu(t)}{dt^2} = -\frac{1}{2\pi}\int_{-\infty}^{\infty} \rho^2K_\nu(\rho)e^{-it\rho}\,d\rho,$$

i.e.

$$\left(\varepsilon_{22}\frac{d}{d\varepsilon_{22}}\right)^2 B_\nu(\varepsilon) = -\frac{1}{2\pi}\int_{-\infty}^{\infty} \rho^2K_\nu(\rho)\varepsilon_{22}^{-i\rho}\,d\rho. \tag{22}$$

Therefore

$$\frac{1}{2\pi}\int_{-\infty}^{\infty} K_\nu(\rho)\overline{\alpha(\varepsilon')}(4\nu^2+\rho^2)\,d\rho = \frac{1}{2\pi}\int_{-\infty}^{\infty} K_\nu(\rho)\varepsilon_{22}'^{-i\rho-2}(4\nu^2+\rho^2)\,d\rho$$

$$= \varepsilon_{22}'^{-2}\left[4\nu^2B_\nu(\varepsilon') - \left(\varepsilon_{22}'\frac{d}{d\varepsilon_{22}'}\right)^2 B_\nu(\varepsilon')\right] = C_\nu(\varepsilon');$$

substituting this expression in (18), we obtain formula (9).

IV. *Let $B_\nu(\varepsilon)$ be an arbitrary infinitely differentiable function of ε_{22}, which vanishes outside some bounded subset of the group E and satisfies the conditions*

$$B_{-\nu}(\varepsilon^{-1}) = B_\nu(\varepsilon), \tag{23}$$

$$\int B_\nu(\varepsilon)\varepsilon_{22}^{p}\,d\varepsilon = 0 \quad \text{when} \quad p = -2k, -2k+2, \ldots, 2k. \tag{24}$$

Then $B_\nu(\varepsilon) \in \mathfrak{B}_j^k$.

Proof. We set

$$K_\nu(\rho) = \int B_\nu(\varepsilon)\varepsilon_{22}^{i\rho}\,d\varepsilon \tag{25}$$

and

$$K(u_1, u_2, m, \rho) = \begin{cases} 6 & \text{for } |m| > 2k \\ (2k+1)K_\nu(\rho)c_{\nu j}^k(u_1)\overline{c_{\nu j}^k(u_2)} & \text{for } \nu = \dfrac{m}{2},\ |m| \leqslant 2k. \end{cases} \tag{26}$$

The function $K(u_1, u_2, m, \rho)$, considered only for $0 \leqslant \rho < \infty$, belongs to the space $\mathfrak{H}_K$; in the isometric mapping $x \to K$, the function $x_0(a) \in L^2(\mathfrak{A})$ corresponds to it (see Theorem 12 in § 14, Subsection 7); it follows from (26) that $e_{jj}^k x_0 = x_0 e_{jj}^k = x_0$, and so

$$x_0(u_1^{-1}\varepsilon u_2) = \sum_{p=-k}^{k} x_p(\varepsilon)c_{pj}^k(u_1)\overline{c_{pj}^k(u_2)}, \tag{27}$$

where $x_p(\varepsilon)$ is defined by formula (17). But, by condition (23), $K_{-\nu}(-\rho) = K_\nu(\rho)$, and so formula (18) also holds, which in turn implies formula (9).

Thus, our function $B_\nu(\varepsilon)$ corresponds to the function $x_0(a)$ in the correspondence $x \to B$, and it remains only to establish that $x_0(a) \in X$ or, which is the same, that $x_0(a)$ is infinitely differentiable and vanishes outside some bounded subset of the group E.

The first assertion follows immediately from formula (9); therefore it is sufficient to prove the second assertion.

From the spinor representation of the group $\mathfrak{U}$ (see (7) § 5, Subsection 4) we conclude that $c_{\nu p}^k(u)$ is a homogeneous polynomial in $u_{21}, u_{22}, \bar{u}_{21}, \bar{u}_{22}$ of degree $2k$; therefore it is sufficient to prove that for

$$p_1+p_2+q_1+q_2 = 2k, \quad m_1+m_2+n_1+n_2 = 2k \tag{28}$$

the function

$$I(\varepsilon) = \int C_\nu(\varepsilon')u_{21}^{p_1}u_{22}^{p_2}\bar{u}_{21}^{q_1}\bar{u}_{22}^{q_2}v_{21}^{m_1}v_{22}^{m_2}\bar{v}_{21}^{n_1}\bar{v}_{22}^{n_2}\,du \tag{29}$$

vanishes outside some bounded subset of the group E.

We introduce into the group $\mathfrak{U}$ the usual parameters

$$t = |u_{22}|^2, \quad \theta = \arg u_{22}, \quad \theta' = \arg u_{21}; \tag{30}$$

then

$$du = \frac{1}{4\pi^2}\,dt\,d\theta\,d\theta', \tag{31}$$

$$u_{21} = (1-t)^{\frac{1}{2}}e^{i\theta'}, \quad u_{22} = t^{\frac{1}{2}}e^{i\theta}. \tag{32}$$

Moreover, applying formulae (4) §11, Subsection 1 to the relation $u\varepsilon = \varepsilon'\zeta v$ (where $a = u\varepsilon$, $\lambda = \varepsilon_{22}$), we obtain:

$$v_{22} = \frac{u_{22}\varepsilon_{22}}{\varepsilon'_{22}}, \qquad v_{21} = \frac{u_{21}}{\varepsilon_{22}\varepsilon'_{22}}, \tag{33}$$

and

$$\varepsilon'^2_{22} = \varepsilon_{22}^{-2}|u_{21}|^2 + \varepsilon_{22}^2|u_{22}|^2 = \varepsilon_{22}^{-2}(1-t) + \varepsilon_{22}^2 t. \tag{34}$$

We set

$$C_\nu(\varepsilon) = \hat{C}_\nu(\varepsilon_{22}^2); \tag{35}$$

substituting in formula (29) this expression and expressions (31–34), we deduce that

$$I(\varepsilon) = \frac{1}{4\pi^2}\varepsilon_{22}^m \int_0^{2\pi} e^{in\theta} \int_0^{2\pi} e^{in'\theta'} d\theta' \times$$

$$\times \int_0^1 \hat{C}_\nu(\varepsilon_{22}^{-2}(1-t) + \varepsilon_{22}^2 t)(1-t)^{\frac{p'}{2}} t^{\frac{q'}{2}} \varepsilon'^{-r}_{22} dt, \tag{36}$$

where

$$m = m_2 + n_2 - m_1 - n_1, \qquad n = p_2 - q_2 + m_2 - n_2,$$
$$n' = p_1 - q_1 + m_1 - n_1, \tag{37}$$

$$p' = p_1 + q_1 + m_1 + n_1, \qquad q' = p_2 + q_2 + m_2 + n_2,$$
$$r = m_1 + m_2 + n_1 + n_2. \tag{38}$$

This integral is distinct from zero only when $n = n' = 0$; from formulae (37), (38) it follows that in this case p' and q' are even numbers.

Letting $p' = 2p''$, $q' = 2q''$, we see that for $n = n' = 0$

$$I(\varepsilon) = \varepsilon_{22}^m \int_0^1 \hat{C}_\nu(\varepsilon_{22}^{-2}(1-t) + \varepsilon_{22}^2 t)(1-t)^{p''} t^{q''} \varepsilon'^{-r}_{22} dt. \tag{39}$$

We will introduce the variable of integration

$$\xi = \varepsilon_{22}^{-2}(1-t) + \varepsilon_{22}^2 t; \tag{40}$$

then formula (39) becomes

$$I(\varepsilon) = \varepsilon_{22}^m(\varepsilon_{22}^2 - \varepsilon_{22}^{-2})^{-s} \int_{\varepsilon_{22}^{-2}}^{\varepsilon_{22}^2} \hat{C}_\nu(\xi)(\varepsilon_{22}^2 - \xi)^{p''}(\xi - \varepsilon_{22}^{-2})^{q''} \xi^{-\frac{r}{2}} d\xi, \tag{41}$$

where $s = p''+q''+1$. Since the function $\hat{C}_\nu(\xi)$ vanishes for sufficiently large or sufficiently small ξ, then for sufficiently large or sufficiently small ε_{22} formula (41) can be rewritten in the form

$$I(\varepsilon) = \varepsilon_{22}^m(\varepsilon_{22}^2 - \varepsilon_{22}^{-2})^{-s} \int_0^\infty \hat{C}_\nu(\xi)(\varepsilon_{22}^2 - \xi)^{p''}(\xi - \varepsilon_{22}^{-2})^{q''} \xi^{-\frac{r}{2}} d\xi; \quad (42)$$

hence, eliminating the brackets on the right side of (42), we see that if

$$\int_0^\infty \hat{C}_\nu(\xi)\xi^{\mu - \frac{r}{2}} d\xi = 0 \quad \text{for} \quad \mu = 0, 1, \ldots, p''+q'', \quad (43)$$

then I (ε) vanishes outside some bounded subset of the group E. We set $\xi = \varepsilon_{22}^2$ in (43); then this condition can be rewritten in the form

$$\int C_\nu(\varepsilon)\varepsilon_{22}^{2\mu - r + 2} d\varepsilon = 0,$$

or, by virtue of (10), in the form

$$\int \left[4\nu^2 - \left(\varepsilon_{22}\frac{\partial}{\partial \varepsilon_{22}}\right)^2\right] B_\nu(\varepsilon)\varepsilon_{22}^{2\mu - r} d\varepsilon = 0$$

$$\text{when} \quad \mu = 0, 1, \ldots, p''+q''. \quad (44)$$

Integrating by parts we conclude that condition (44) will be satisfied if

$$\int B_\nu(\varepsilon)\varepsilon_{22}^p d\varepsilon = 0, \quad (45)$$

where $p = 2\mu - r$. Now we find the values which p can take. By virtue of (28) and (38), $r = 2k$, hence $p = 2\mu - 2k$; further:

$$2\mu \leqslant 2(p''+q'') = p'+q'$$
$$= p_1 + q_1 + m_1 + n_1 + p_2 + q_2 + m_2 + n_2;$$

hence, by virtue of (28), $0 \leqslant 2\mu < 4k$. Hence

$$-2k \leqslant 2\mu - r \leqslant 2k, \quad \text{i.e.} \quad -2k \leqslant p \leqslant 2k.$$

In other words, condition (24) insures the vanishing of the function $x_p(\varepsilon)$ outside some bounded set of the group E and proposition IV is proved.

Remark. Let the function $B_\nu(\varepsilon)$ satisfy the conditions of proposition IV and vanish outside a set $Q \subset E$ defined by

$$\frac{1}{C} \leqslant \varepsilon_{22} < C; \tag{46}$$

then the function $x_p(\varepsilon)$ also vanishes outside the set Q, consequently, $x_0(a)$ vanishes outside the set $\tilde{Q} = \mathfrak{U}Q\mathfrak{U}$.

In fact, if, for instance, $\varepsilon_{22} > C$, then in the integral (41) the limits of integration ε_{22}^{-1}, ε_{22} can be replaced by the limits $0, \infty$, and so $I(\varepsilon) = 0$ by virtue of condition (24); analogously $I(\varepsilon) = 0$ when $\varepsilon_{22} < \frac{1}{C}$.

V. *Let $B_\nu(\varepsilon)$, $x_0(\varepsilon)$, Q and $\tilde{Q}$ be the same as in the preceding remark; then*

$$\left(\int |x_0(a)|\,\mathrm{d}a\right)^2 = \left(\int_{\tilde{Q}} |x_0(a)|\,\mathrm{d}a\right)^2$$

$$\leqslant \frac{1}{16\pi^3}\left(\int_{\tilde{Q}} \mathrm{d}a\right)\sum_{\nu=-k}^{k}\int_{Q}\overline{B_\nu(\varepsilon)}\left[4\nu^2 - \left(\varepsilon_{22}\frac{\mathrm{d}}{\mathrm{d}\varepsilon_{22}}\right)^2\right]B_\nu(\varepsilon)\,\mathrm{d}\varepsilon. \tag{47}$$

Proof. Applying Bunyakovskii's inequality and taking into account formula (2), Subsection 8, we have:

$$\left(\int |x_0(a)|\,\mathrm{d}a\right)^2 = \left(\int_{\tilde{Q}} |x_0(a)|\,\mathrm{d}a\right)^2 \leqslant \int_{\tilde{Q}} \mathrm{d}a \int_{\tilde{Q}} |x_0(a)|^2 \mathrm{d}a$$

$$\leqslant \int_{\tilde{Q}} \mathrm{d}a\, \frac{1}{32\pi^4}\sum_{\nu=-k}^{k}\int_{-\infty}^{\infty}\overline{K_\nu(\rho)}K_\nu(\rho)(4\nu^2+\rho^2)\,\mathrm{d}\rho. \tag{48}$$

Now taking into account that

$$B_\nu(\varepsilon) = \frac{1}{2\pi}\int_{-\infty}^{\infty} K_\nu(\rho)\varepsilon_{22}^{-i\rho}\mathrm{d}\rho,$$

$$\left(\varepsilon_{22}\frac{\mathrm{d}}{\mathrm{d}\varepsilon_{22}}\right)^2 B_\nu(\varepsilon) = -\frac{1}{2\pi}\int_{-\infty}^{\infty} \rho^2 K_\nu(\rho)\varepsilon_{22}^{-i\rho}\mathrm{d}\rho$$

(see (21) and (22)), and applying Plancherel's formula for the usual Fourier integral, we obtain:

$$\int_{-\infty}^{\infty} \overline{K_\nu(\rho)} K_\nu(\rho)(4\nu^2+\rho^2)\mathrm{d}\rho$$

$$= 2\pi \int_Q \overline{B_\nu(\varepsilon)}\left[4\nu^2-\left(\varepsilon_{22}\frac{\mathrm{d}}{\mathrm{d}\varepsilon_{22}}\right)^2\right]B_\nu(\varepsilon)\mathrm{d}\varepsilon; \quad (49)$$

from this together with (48), (47) follows.

12. The ring $\tilde{\mathfrak{B}}_j^k$

We denote by $\tilde{\mathfrak{B}}_j^k$ the set of all functions from $\mathfrak{B}_j^k$, satisfying the conditions

$$\int B_\nu(\varepsilon)\varepsilon_{22}^p \mathrm{d}\varepsilon = 0 \quad \text{for} \quad p = -2k, -2k+2, \ldots, 2k. \quad (1)$$

From proposition IV Subsection 11 we conclude that:

I. *$\tilde{\mathfrak{B}}_j^k$ is the set of all infinitely differentiable functions $B_\nu(\varepsilon)$ which vanish outside some bounded set (depending on the function) and satisfying* (1) *and the condition*

$$B_{-\nu}(\varepsilon^{-1}) = B_\nu(\varepsilon). \quad (2)$$

Clearly, $\tilde{\mathfrak{B}}_j^k$ is a subring of the ring $\mathfrak{B}_j^k$, and the functional $\lambda(B)$ can also be considered as a functional on $\tilde{\mathfrak{B}}_j^k$.

It can happen that $\lambda(B) = 0$ throughout $\tilde{\mathfrak{B}}_j^k$; for the time being, we assume that this is not the case, i.e. we suppose that there exists a function $\tilde{B} \in \tilde{\mathfrak{B}}_j^k$ for which $\lambda(\tilde{B}) \neq 0$.

Every function $B \in \tilde{\mathfrak{B}}_j^k$ can be represented in the form†

$$B = B^{(0)}+B^{(1)}+ \ldots +B^{(k)}, \quad (3)$$

where

$$B_\nu^{(p)}(\varepsilon) = \begin{cases} 0 & \text{when } |\nu| \neq p, \\ B_\nu(\varepsilon) & \text{when } |\nu| = p, \end{cases} \quad (4)$$

† For definiteness we have considered the case of integral k; in the case of semi-integral k the reasoning remains as before; it is only necessary to replace the indices $0, 1, 2, \ldots, k$ by the indices $\frac{1}{2}, \frac{3}{2}, \ldots, k$.

where, by I, $B^{(p)} \in \tilde{\mathfrak{B}}_j^k, p = 0, 1, \ldots, k$. In particular

$$\tilde{B} = \tilde{B}^{(0)} + \tilde{B}^{(1)} + \ldots + \tilde{B}^{(k)},$$

and, according to the condition

$$\lambda(\tilde{B}) = \lambda(\tilde{B}^{(0)}) + \lambda(\tilde{B}^{(1)}) + \lambda(\tilde{B}^{(2)}) + \ldots + \lambda(\tilde{B}^{(k)}) \neq 0,$$

at least one of the values ν is such that

$$\lambda(\tilde{B}^{(\nu)}) \neq 0. \tag{5}$$

Clearly, $\tilde{B}^{(j)}\tilde{B}^{(\nu)} = 0$ when $j \neq \nu$, and so $\lambda(\tilde{B}^{(j)}\tilde{B}^{(\nu)}) = 0$, i.e. $\lambda(\tilde{B}^{(j)})\lambda(\tilde{B}^{(\nu)}) = 0$. By virtue of (5), we deduce from this that $\lambda(B^{(j)}) = 0$ when $j \neq \nu$. We arrive at the following result:

II. *Every linear multiplicative functional in* $\tilde{\mathfrak{B}}_j^k$ *has the form*

$$\lambda(B) = \lambda(B^{(\nu)}) \tag{6}$$

for some fixed ν, $|\nu| \leqslant k$. We denote by $\mathfrak{b}$ the set of all functions $b(\varepsilon)$ which are infinitely differentiable, equal to zero outside a bounded subset of the group E and satisfy the conditions:

$$\int b(\varepsilon)\varepsilon_{22}^{p}\, d\varepsilon = 0 \quad \text{when} \quad p = -2k, -2k+1, \ldots, 2k, \tag{7}$$

let $\mathfrak{b}_0$ be the set of all functions from $\mathfrak{b}$, such that

$$b(\varepsilon^{-1}) = b(\varepsilon). \tag{8}$$

The sets $\mathfrak{b}$ and $\mathfrak{b}_0$ become rings with involution if one defines the operations of addition and multiplication by a number in the usual way, and multiplication and involution by the formulae

$$b'b''(\varepsilon) = \int b'(\varepsilon')b''(\varepsilon'^{-1}\varepsilon)\, d\varepsilon', \tag{9}$$

$$b^*(\varepsilon) = \overline{b(\varepsilon^{-1})}. \tag{10}$$

As B runs through the whole ring $\tilde{\mathfrak{B}}_j^k$, then, by virtue of IV Subsection 11, the functions $B_\nu(\varepsilon)$ for fixed $\nu \neq 0$ run through the whole ring $\mathfrak{b}$, and for $\nu = 0$ through the whole ring $\mathfrak{b}_0$; here, with the same definition of the operations in $\tilde{\mathfrak{B}}_j^k$, $\mathfrak{b}$ and $\mathfrak{b}_0$, the correspondence $B \to B_\nu(\varepsilon)$ is a homomorphism of the ring $\tilde{\mathfrak{B}}_j^{(k)}$ on the ring $\mathfrak{b}$ for $\nu \neq 0$ and on the ring $\mathfrak{b}_0$ for $\nu = 0$. By virtue of (6), the formula

$$\lambda(b) = \lambda(B) \quad \text{for} \quad b(\varepsilon) = B_\nu(\varepsilon) \tag{11}$$

defines a linear multiplicative functional $\lambda(b)$ in the ring $\mathfrak{b}$ for $v \neq 0$ and in the ring $\mathfrak{b}_0$ for $v = 0$. We thus arrive at the problem of finding all the linear multiplicative functionals in the rings $\mathfrak{b}$ and $\mathfrak{b}_0$.

13. The general form of the functional $\lambda(b)$

(a) *The case* $v > 0$. Let $b_0(\varepsilon)$ be a fixed function from $\mathfrak{b}$, for which $\lambda(b_0) \neq 0$. Multiplying $b_0(\varepsilon)$ by some constant, one can arrange that

$$\lambda(b_0) = 1. \tag{1}$$

Now we consider the function

$$b_{\varepsilon_0}(\varepsilon) = b_0(\varepsilon\varepsilon_0). \tag{2}$$

Since $b_0 \in \mathfrak{b}$ the function $b^{\varepsilon}_{\circ}(\varepsilon)$ is also infinitely differentiable, equal to zero outside a bounded set and satisfies condition (7) Subsection 12, i.e. $b_{\varepsilon_0}(\varepsilon)$ also belongs to the ring $\mathfrak{b}$. We set

$$f(\varepsilon_0) = \lambda(b_{\varepsilon_0}) \tag{3}$$

and determine the general form of the function $f(\varepsilon)$.

I. *The function $f(\varepsilon)$ satisfies the relation*

$$f(\varepsilon_1 \varepsilon_2) = f(\varepsilon_1) f(\varepsilon_2). \tag{4}$$

For the proof we note that

$$b_{\varepsilon_1} b_{\varepsilon_2} = b_{\varepsilon_1\varepsilon_2} b_0. \tag{5}$$

Indeed, letting $\varepsilon' = \varepsilon_2 \varepsilon''$, we have:

$$(b_{\varepsilon_1} b_{\varepsilon_2})(\varepsilon) = \int b_{\varepsilon_1}(\varepsilon') b_{\varepsilon_2}(\varepsilon'^{-1}\varepsilon) d\varepsilon' = \int b_0(\varepsilon_1 \varepsilon') b_0(\varepsilon_2 \varepsilon'^{-1}\varepsilon) d\varepsilon'$$
$$= \int b_0(\varepsilon_1 \varepsilon_2 \varepsilon'') b_0(\varepsilon''^{-1}\varepsilon) d\varepsilon'' = (b_{\varepsilon_1\varepsilon_2} b_0)(\varepsilon).$$

Applying the functional λ to both sides of (5), we obtain:

$$\lambda(b_{\varepsilon_1}) \lambda(b_{\varepsilon_2}) = \lambda(b_{\varepsilon_1\varepsilon_2}) \lambda(b_0),$$

i.e., by virtue of (1) and (3):

$$f(\varepsilon_1) f(\varepsilon_2) = f(\varepsilon_1 \varepsilon_2).$$

II. *The function $f(\varepsilon)$ is continuous.*

Proof. Let V be a bounded neighbourhood of the element ε_0 and let $\varepsilon_n \in V$, $\varepsilon_n \to \varepsilon_0$. We must prove that $\lambda(b_{\varepsilon_n}) \to \lambda(b_{\varepsilon_0})$ as $n \to \infty$.

Let $x_0(a)$ and $x_n(a)$ be functions $x(a)$ from the ring X_j^k, corresponding to the functions $B^{(0)} = B_p^{(0)}(\varepsilon)$ and $B^{(n)} = B_p^{(n)}(\varepsilon)$, defined by the conditions:

$$B_p^{(0)}(\varepsilon) = \begin{cases} 0 & \text{when } |p| \neq \nu, \\ b_{\varepsilon 0}(\varepsilon) & \text{when } p = \nu, \\ b_{\varepsilon 0}(\varepsilon^{-1}) & \text{when } p = -\nu, \end{cases} \tag{6}$$

$$B_p^{(n)}(\varepsilon) = \begin{cases} 0 & \text{when } |p| \neq \nu, \\ b_{\varepsilon_n}(\varepsilon) & \text{when } p = \nu, \\ b_{\varepsilon_n}(\varepsilon^{-1}) & \text{when } p = -\nu. \end{cases} \tag{7}$$

Then $\lambda(x_0) = \lambda(b_{\varepsilon 0})$, $\lambda(x_n) = \lambda(b_{\varepsilon_n})$, and it is sufficient to show that $\lambda(x_0 - x_n) \to 0$ as $n \to \infty$, i.e. that for $\xi \in \mathfrak{M}_j^k$ and $n \to \infty$

$$T_{x_0 - x_n}\xi = \lambda(x_0 - x_n)\xi \to 0. \tag{8}$$

There exists a bounded set $Q \subset E$ such that all the functions $b_{\varepsilon_n}(\varepsilon) = b_0(\varepsilon\varepsilon_n)$vanish outside Q. From the properties of the function $b_0(\varepsilon)$ it follows that as $n \to \infty$ the sequence $b_0(\varepsilon\varepsilon_n)$ and the sequence of derivatives with respect to ε_{22} of the functions $b_0(\varepsilon\varepsilon_n)$ (up to and including the second order) converge uniformly in Q to $b_0(\varepsilon\varepsilon_0)$ and the corresponding derivatives of this function.

This together with the estimate (47) Subsection 11 implies that

$$\int_{\tilde{Q}} |x_0(a) - x_n(a)|\, da \to 0 \quad \text{as} \quad n \to \infty, \tag{9}$$

where $\tilde{Q} = \mathfrak{U}Q\mathfrak{U}$. Let

$$c = \sup_{a \in \tilde{Q}} |T_a|;$$

then

$$|T_{x_0 - x_n}\xi| = |\int [x_0(a) - x_n(a)]\, T_a \xi\, da|$$
$$\leqslant c|\xi| \int |x_0(a) - x_n(a)|\, da \to 0 \quad \text{as} \quad n \to \infty.$$

Hence (8) follows, and the continuity of the function $f(\varepsilon)$ is proved.

III. *The function $f(\varepsilon)$ has the form*

$$f(\varepsilon) = \varepsilon_{22}^{-i\rho}, \tag{10}$$

where ρ is some complex number.

Proof. We set

$$\phi(t) = f(\varepsilon) \quad \text{where} \quad \varepsilon_{22} = e^t. \tag{11}$$

Propositions I and II mean that

$$\phi(t_1+t_2) = \phi(t_1)\phi(t_2) \tag{12}$$

and that $\phi(t)$ is a continuous function. But every non-zero continuous function, satisfying condition (12), has the form $\phi(t) = e^{-i\rho t}$, where ρ is a complex number. Thus,

$$f(\varepsilon) = \phi(t) = e^{-i\rho t} = \varepsilon_{22}^{-i\rho}.$$

IV. *Every linear multiplicative functional $\lambda(b)$ in the ring $\mathfrak{b}$ has the form*

$$\lambda(b) = \int b(\varepsilon)\varepsilon_{22}^{i\rho}\,d\varepsilon, \tag{13}$$

where ρ is a complex number.

Proof. Since $\lambda(b_0) = 1$, then

$$\lambda(bb_0) = \lambda(b)\lambda(b_0) = \lambda(b); \tag{14}$$

on the other hand

$$(bb_0)(\varepsilon) = \int b(\varepsilon'^{-1})b_0(\varepsilon'\varepsilon)\,d\varepsilon' = \int b(\varepsilon'^{-1})b_{\varepsilon'}(\varepsilon)\,d\varepsilon'. \tag{15}$$

Let Q be a bounded set outside which b, b_0 and bb_0 vanish; we decompose Q into the sets Q_k; then the last integral is the limit, as $\Delta\varepsilon_k \to 0$, of a sum of the form

$$S_\varepsilon = \sum_k b(\varepsilon_k'^{-1})b_{\varepsilon_k'}(\varepsilon)\Delta\varepsilon_k', \tag{16}$$

where $\Delta\varepsilon_k' = \int_{Q_k} d\varepsilon'$. Here the sum S_ε and its first and second derivatives with respect to ε_{22} converge uniformly in Q to the integral in (15) and its derivatives first and second respectively. Hence, reasoning as in the proof of proposition II, we conclude that

$$\lambda(S_\varepsilon) \to \lambda(bb_0) = \lambda(b) \quad \text{as} \quad \Delta\varepsilon_k' \to 0. \tag{17}$$

On the other hand,

$$\lambda(S_\varepsilon) = \sum_k b(\varepsilon_k'^{-1})\lambda(b_{\varepsilon_k'})\Delta\varepsilon_k' = \sum_k b(\varepsilon_k'^{-1})f(\varepsilon_k')\Delta\varepsilon_k';$$

passing to the limit on both sides of this equation, we obtain:

$$\lambda(b) = \int b(\varepsilon'^{-1})f(\varepsilon')\,d\varepsilon' = \int b(\varepsilon'^{-1})\varepsilon_{22}'^{-i\rho}\,d\varepsilon = \int b(\varepsilon)\varepsilon_{22}^{i\rho}\,d\varepsilon.$$

(b) *The case* $\nu = 0$. In this case the functions $b(\varepsilon)$ of the ring $\mathfrak{b}_0$ satisfy the condition

$$b(\varepsilon^{-1}) = b(\varepsilon). \tag{18}$$

Again let $b_0 \in \mathfrak{b}_0$ and $\lambda(b_0) = 1$. We set

$$\tilde{b}_{\varepsilon_0}(\varepsilon) = \tfrac{1}{2}[b_0(\varepsilon\varepsilon_0) + b_0(\varepsilon\varepsilon_0^{-1})] = \tfrac{1}{2}(b_{\varepsilon_0} + b_{\varepsilon_0^{-1}}). \tag{19}$$

Then

$$\tilde{b}_{\varepsilon_0}(\varepsilon^{-1}) = \tfrac{1}{2}[b_0(\varepsilon^{-1}\varepsilon_0) + b_0(\varepsilon^{-1}\varepsilon_0^{-1})]$$
$$= \tfrac{1}{2}[b_0(\varepsilon\varepsilon_0^{-1}) + b_0(\varepsilon_0\varepsilon)] = \tilde{b}_{\varepsilon_0}(\varepsilon),$$

and therefore $\tilde{b}_{\varepsilon_0}(\varepsilon) \in \mathfrak{b}_0$ also.

We set

$$\tilde{f}(\varepsilon_0) = \lambda(\tilde{b}_{\varepsilon_0}); \tag{20}$$

reasoning as above, we convince ourselves of the fact that the function $f(\varepsilon)$ is continuous and that

$$\lambda(b) = \int b(\varepsilon'^{-1})\tilde{f}(\varepsilon')d\varepsilon'. \tag{21}$$

It remains to determine the form of the function $f(\varepsilon)$.

V. *The function* $\tilde{f}(\varepsilon)$ *satisfies the relations*:

$$\tilde{f}(\varepsilon^{-1}) = \tilde{f}(\varepsilon), \tag{22}$$

$$\tilde{f}(\varepsilon')\tilde{f}(\varepsilon'') = \tfrac{1}{2}[\tilde{f}(\varepsilon'\varepsilon'') + \tilde{f}(\varepsilon'\varepsilon''^{-1})]. \tag{23}$$

Proof. By virtue of (19):

$$\tilde{b}_{\varepsilon^{-1}} = \tilde{b}_\varepsilon;$$

applying $\lambda(b)$ to both sides of this equation, we obtain (22). Further:

$$\tilde{b}_{\varepsilon'}\tilde{b}_{\varepsilon''} = \tfrac{1}{2}(\tilde{b}_{\varepsilon'\varepsilon''}b_0 + \tilde{b}_{\varepsilon'\varepsilon''^{-1}}b_0). \tag{24}$$

In fact, by (5) we have

$$\tilde{b}_{\varepsilon'}\tilde{b}_{\varepsilon''} = \tfrac{1}{4}(b_{\varepsilon'} + b_{\varepsilon'^{-1}})(b_{\varepsilon''} + b_{\varepsilon''^{-1}})$$
$$= \tfrac{1}{4}(b_{\varepsilon'\varepsilon''}b_0 + b_{\varepsilon'\varepsilon''^{-1}}b_0 + b_{\varepsilon'^{-1}\varepsilon''}b_0 + b_{\varepsilon'^{-1}\varepsilon''^{-1}}b_0)$$
$$= \tfrac{1}{2}(\tilde{b}_{\varepsilon'\varepsilon''}b_0 + \tilde{b}_{\varepsilon'\varepsilon''^{-1}}b_0).$$

Applying the functional $\lambda(b)$ to both sides of (24), we obtain (23).

VI. *The function* $\tilde{f}(\varepsilon)$ *has the form*

$$\tilde{f}(\varepsilon) = \tfrac{1}{2}(\varepsilon_{22}^{i\rho} + \varepsilon_{22}^{-i\rho}), \tag{25}$$

where ρ *is a complex number.*

Proof. We set

$$\tilde{\phi}(t) = \tilde{f}(\varepsilon) \quad \text{when} \quad \varepsilon_{22} = \mathrm{e}^{t};$$

then the function $\tilde{\phi}(t)$ is continuous and, by virtue of (22) and (23), it satisfies the relations:

$$\tilde{\phi}(t')\tilde{\phi}(t'') = \tfrac{1}{2}[\tilde{\phi}(t'+t'') + \tilde{\phi}(t'-t'')], \tag{26a}$$

$$\tilde{\phi}(-t) = \tilde{\phi}(t), \quad \tilde{\phi}(0) = 1. \tag{26b}$$

But every such relation has the form†

$$\tilde{\phi}(t) = \cos \rho t = \tfrac{1}{2}(\mathrm{e}^{i\rho t} + \mathrm{e}^{-i\rho t}).$$

Hence

$$\tilde{f}(\varepsilon) = \tilde{\phi}(t) = \tfrac{1}{2}(\varepsilon_{22}^{i\rho} + \varepsilon_{22}^{-i\rho}).$$

VII. *Every linear multiplicative functional* $\lambda(b)$ *in* $\mathfrak{b}_0$ *has the form*

$$\lambda(b) = \int b(\varepsilon)\varepsilon_{22}^{i\rho}\mathrm{d}\varepsilon, \tag{27}$$

where ρ *is a complex number. Here* ρ *and* $-\rho$ *define one and the same functional* $\lambda(b)$.

Proof. Combining (21) and (25), we have:

$$\lambda(b) = \tfrac{1}{2}\int b(\varepsilon)\varepsilon_{22}^{i\rho}\mathrm{d}\varepsilon + \tfrac{1}{2}\int b(\varepsilon)\varepsilon_{22}^{-i\rho}\mathrm{d}\varepsilon. \tag{28}$$

But $b(\varepsilon^{-1}) = b(\varepsilon)$; therefore

$$\int b(\varepsilon)\varepsilon_{22}^{-i\rho}\mathrm{d}\varepsilon = \int b(\varepsilon^{-1})\varepsilon_{22}^{i\rho}\mathrm{d}\varepsilon = \int b(\varepsilon)\varepsilon_{22}^{i\rho}\mathrm{d}\varepsilon,$$

---

† In fact, integrating with respect to t' both sides of (26a), (26b) and letting $\phi_1(t) = \int_0^t \tilde{\phi}(t')\,\mathrm{d}t'$, we have:

$$\phi_1(-t) = -\phi_1(t), \quad \phi_1(t)\tilde{\phi}(t'') = \tfrac{1}{2}[\phi_1(t+t'') + \phi_1(t-t'')].$$

The right hand side of this equation is differentiable with respect to t''; hence, $\tilde{\phi}(t'')$ is differentiable with respect to t''. But then $\phi_1(t)$ is twice differentiable, hence $\tilde{\phi}$ is also twice differentiable. Differentiating both sides of (26a) twice with respect to t'' and then putting $t'' = 0$, we deduce that the function $\tilde{\phi}$ satsfies the condition $\tilde{\phi}'' = -\rho^2\tilde{\phi}$, where $\rho^2 = -\tilde{\phi}''(0)$. The solution of this equation, satisfying conditions (26b), is $\cos \rho t$.

and (28) gives

$$\lambda(b) = \int b(\varepsilon)\varepsilon_{22}^{i\rho}d\varepsilon = \int b(\varepsilon)\varepsilon_{22}^{-i\rho}d\varepsilon.$$

14. The general form of the linear multiplicative functional $\lambda(B)$ in the ring $\mathfrak{B}_j^k$

LEMMA. *Let there be given in a ring $\mathfrak{R}$ linear multiplicative functionals $f(x) \not\equiv 0, \tilde{f}(x), f_j(x), j = 1, 2, ..., n$, and a subring $\mathfrak{R}_0$, possessing the following properties*:

(1) *$\mathfrak{R}_0$ is the set of all elements x of the ring $\mathfrak{R}$, for which*

$$f_j(x) = 0, \quad j = 1, 2, ..., n; \tag{1}$$

(2) $$f(x) = \tilde{f}(x) \text{ for } x \in \mathfrak{R}_0. \tag{2}$$

Then in the whole ring $\mathfrak{R}$, either $f(x) = \tilde{f}(x)$, or $f(x) = f_j(x)$ for some j.

Proof. Without loss of generality, we can assume that the functionals $f_j(x)$, $j = 1, 2, ..., n$, are linearly independent. Otherwise, one can reject those of them which are linear combinations of the rest, without violating the conditions of the lemma. But then there exist elements $x_1, x_2, ..., x_n$ in $\mathfrak{R}$ such that

$$f_k(x_j) = \begin{cases} 0 \text{ when } k \neq j, \\ 1 \text{ when } k = j. \end{cases} \tag{3}$$

Indeed this assertion is evident for $n = 1$, because for a functional f, distinct from zero, there exists a vector x such that $f(x) = 1$. Assuming the assertion already proved for $n-1$ functionals, we will prove that it is valid for n functionals. For $f_2, ..., f_n$, choose elements $e_2, ..., e_n$ so that

$$f_k(e_j) = \begin{cases} 0 \text{ when } k \neq j, \\ 1 \text{ when } k = j. \end{cases} \tag{4}$$

We denote $\mathfrak{N}_1$ the set of all vectors $y \in \mathfrak{R}$ such that $f_2(y) = 0, ..., f_n(y) = 0$; clearly, $\mathfrak{N}_1$ is a subspace in $\mathfrak{R}$.

If x is an arbitrary element of the ring $\mathfrak{R}$, then letting

$$y = x - f_2(x)e_2 - \dots - f_n(x)e_n \tag{5}$$

and taking (4) into account, we have $f_j(y) = 0$ for $j = 2, ..., n$, i.e. $y \in \mathfrak{N}_1$. In $\mathfrak{N}_1$ there exists an element x_1 such that $f_1(x_1) \neq 0$.

In fact, if $f_1(y) = 0$ for all $y \in \mathfrak{N}_1$, then taking, in particular, an element y of the form (5) and letting $c_k = f_1(e_k)$, $k = 2, \ldots, n$, we find that $f_1(x) - c_2 f_2(x) - \ldots - c_n f_n(x) = 0$ for all $x \in \mathfrak{R}$; this contradicts the linear independence of the functionals $f_1, f_2, \ldots, f_n$. Thus there exists an element $x_1 \in \mathfrak{N}_1$ such that $f_1(x_1) \neq 0$. Replacing x_1 by $\frac{1}{f_1(x_1)} x_1$, we can arrange that $f_1(x_1) = 1$. Then, by definition of the subspace $\mathfrak{N}_1$:

$$f_1(x_1) = 1, \quad f_2(x_1) = \ldots = f_n(x_1) = 0. \tag{6}$$

Now denote by $\mathfrak{M}_1$ the set of all elements y of the ring $\mathfrak{R}$, for which $f_1(y) = 0$; clearly, $\mathfrak{M}_1$ is a subspace of $\mathfrak{R}$. If x is an arbitrary element of the ring $\mathfrak{R}$, then, letting

$$y = x - f_1(x)x_1, \tag{7}$$

we have $f_1(y) = 0$; hence $y \in \mathfrak{M}_1$.

The functionals $f_2, \ldots, f_n$, considered only on $\mathfrak{M}_1$, are linearly independent. In fact, let $c_2 f_2(y) + \ldots + c_n f_n(y) = 0$ for all $y \in \mathfrak{M}_1$. Substituting the element y in the form (7) and making use of relations (6), we see that $c_2 f_2(x) + \ldots + c_n f_n(x) = 0$ for all $x \in \mathfrak{R}$; hence it follows that $c_2 = \ldots = c_n = 0$, because the functionals $f_2, \ldots, f_n$ are linearly independent on $\mathfrak{R}$. By induction, in $\mathfrak{M}_1$ there exist elements $x_2, \ldots, x_n$ such that

$$f_k(x_j) = \begin{cases} 1 \text{ for } k = j, \\ 0 \text{ for } k \neq j, \ k, j = 2, \ldots, n. \end{cases}$$

By virtue of formula (6) and the definition of the subspace $\mathfrak{M}_1$, the elements $x_1, x_2, \ldots, x_n$ satisfy conditions (3).

Now let x be an arbitrary element of $\mathfrak{R}$, and put

$$y = x - \sum_{j=1}^{n} f_j(x) x_j,$$

we have, by virtue of (3): $f_k(y) = 0$ for all $k = 1, 2, \ldots, n$. Thus, $y \in \mathfrak{R}_0$, and we have proved that all the elements $x \in \mathfrak{R}$ can be represented in the form

$$x = y + \sum_{j=1}^{n} f_j(x) x_j, \quad y \in \mathfrak{R}_0. \tag{8}$$

Hence

$$f(x) = f(y) + \sum_{j=1}^{n} f(x_j) f_j(x) \tag{9}$$

and

$$\tilde{f}(x) = \tilde{f}(y) + \sum_{j=1}^{n} \tilde{f}(x_j) f_j(x); \tag{10}$$

using the condition $f(y) = \tilde{f}(y)$, subtracting equation (10) from (9) and letting

$$\alpha_j = f(x_j) - \tilde{f}(x_j), \tag{11}$$

we obtain

$$f(x) - \tilde{f}(x) = \sum_{j=1}^{n} \alpha_j f_j(x),$$

i.e.

$$f(x) = \tilde{f}(x) + \sum_{j=1}^{n} \alpha_j f_j(x). \tag{12}$$

Now we make use of the multiplicative nature of our functionals.

We first make the following remark: *If* $f(x) \neq 0$ *and* $g(x)$ *are two multiplicative linear functionals and if* $f(x) = \lambda g(x)$ for all $x \in R$, then $\lambda = 1$.

In fact, $\lambda^2 [g(x)]^2 = [f(x)]^2 = f(x^2) = \lambda g(x^2) = \lambda [g(x)]^2$, hence $\lambda^2 = \lambda$, $\lambda = 1$ $(g\ x) \neq 0$ and $\lambda \neq 0$, since otherwise we would have $f(x) = \lambda g(x) = 0$.

Now only the following three cases are possible:

1. There exist at least two elements x_k, x_l, $k \neq l$ such that $f(x_k) \neq 0$ and $f(x_l) \neq 0$, Then in virtue of (12) we have

$$f(x) f(x_k x_l) = f(x x_k x_l) = \tilde{f}(x x_k x_l) + \sum_{j=1}^{n} \alpha_j f_1(x x_k x_l) = \tilde{f}(x) \tilde{f}(x_k x_l) \tag{13}$$

since by (3) $f_j(x x_k x_l) = f_j(x) f_1(x_k) f_1(x_l) = 0$. It follows from (13), that $f(x) = \lambda \tilde{f}(x)$ with hence by the remark above $\lambda = 1$, $f(x) = \tilde{f}(x)$.

2. There exists only one element x_k, such that $f(x_k) \neq 0$, so that $f(x_j) = 0$ for $j \neq k$. Then we have in virtue of (12) and (3)

$$f(x) f(x_k) = f(x x_k) = \tilde{f}(x x_k) + \sum_{j=1}^{n} \alpha_j f_j(x x_k) = \tilde{f}(x) \tilde{f}(x_k) + \alpha_k f_k(x) \tag{14}$$

thus

$$f(x) = \gamma \tilde f(x) + \delta f_k(x) \tag{15}$$

where

$$\gamma = \frac{\tilde f(x_k)}{f(x_k)}, \quad \delta = \frac{\alpha_k}{f(x_k)}. \tag{16}$$

Putting in (15) $x = x_j$, $j \neq k$, we get in virtue of (3)

$$0 = f(x_j) = \gamma f(x_j). \tag{17}$$

If $\gamma = 0$, then (15) implies $f(x) = \delta f_k(x)$ and by the remark we have $f(x) = f_k(x)$ proving the Lemma for this case.
Now let $\gamma \neq 0$. Then by (17) $f(x_j) = 0$, hence $\alpha_j = f(x_j) - \tilde f(x_j) = 0$ for $j \neq k$. Equation (12) takes the form

$$f(x) = f(x) + \alpha_k \tilde f_k(x). \tag{18}$$

If $\gamma = 1$, then (16) implies $f(x_k) = \tilde f(x_k)$, hence $\alpha_k = f(x_k) - \tilde f(x_k = 0$. Thus by virtue of (18) $f(x) = \tilde f(x)$. But if $\gamma \neq 1$, then (15) and (18) imply $\tilde f(x) = \lambda f_k(x)$ with $\lambda = \dfrac{\alpha_k - \delta}{\gamma - 1}$ and by the remark either $\tilde f(x) \equiv 0$ or $\tilde f(x) = f_k(x)$. Then (18) takes the form $f(x) = \lambda f_k(x)$ with $\lambda = \alpha_k$ or $\lambda = 1 + \alpha_k$, hence by the remark $f(x) = f_k(x)$ concluding the proof of the Lemma for this case.

3. $\tilde f(x_j) = 0$ for all $j = 1, \ldots, n$. Then

$$\alpha_j = f(x_j) - \tilde f(x_j) = -\tilde f(x_j) \tag{19}$$

hence by (12) for $j \neq k$

$$0 = f(x_k) f(x_j) = f(x_k x_j) = \tilde f(x_k x_j) = \alpha_k \alpha_j, \tag{20}$$

hence there exists at most one $\alpha_k \neq 0$. If all $\alpha_j = 0$, then $f(x) = \tilde f(x)$. We consider therefore the case $\alpha_k \neq 0$, $\alpha_j = 0$ for $j \neq k$. Then by (12) $0 = f(x_k) f(x_k) = (f x_k^2) = \tilde f(x^2) + \alpha_k = \alpha_k^2 + \alpha_k$. Combining this with (19) we get $\alpha_k = -1$, $\tilde{f}(x_k) = 1$, thus by virtue of (12) $f(x) = \tilde{f}(x) - f_k(x)$. But then we have

$$0 = f(x)f(x_k) = f(xx_k) = \tilde{f}(xx_k) - f_k(xx_k) = f(x)\tilde{f}(x_k) - f_k(x)f_k(x_k)$$
$$= \tilde{f}(x) - f_k(x) = f(x),$$

i.e. $f(x) = 0$ contradicting the hypothesis. This concludes the proof of the Lemma.

Now we apply this lemma to the ring $\mathfrak{B}_j^k$.

Let $\lambda(B)$ be an arbitrary linear multiplicative functional, $\lambda_0(B)$ its restriction to $\tilde{\mathfrak{B}}_j^k$, i.e. the functional defined only in $\tilde{\mathfrak{B}}_j^k$ by the formula $\lambda_0(B) = \lambda(B)$ when $B \in \tilde{\mathfrak{B}}_j^k$; according to the results of Subsections 12 and 13 either $\lambda_0(B) = 0$, or

$$\lambda_0(B) = \int B_\nu(\varepsilon)\,\varepsilon_{22}^{i\rho}\,d\varepsilon, \tag{21}$$

where ν is fixed, and ρ is some complex number. We define a linear multiplicative functional $\tilde{\lambda}(B)$ in the whole ring $\mathfrak{B}_j^k$, letting $\tilde{\lambda}(B) = 0$, if $\tilde{\lambda}_0(B) = 0$, and

$$\tilde{\lambda}(B) = \int B_\nu(\varepsilon)\,\varepsilon_{22}^{i\rho}\,d\varepsilon, \tag{22}$$

if formula (21) holds. Then

$$\lambda(B) = \tilde{\lambda}(B) \text{ when } B \in \tilde{\mathfrak{B}}_j^k. \tag{23}$$

Further, we set

$$\left.\begin{aligned} \lambda_{p,\nu}(B) &= \int B_\nu(\varepsilon)\,\varepsilon_{22}^{p}\,d\varepsilon,\; p = -2k,\; -2k+2,\; \ldots,\; 2k, \\ \nu &= -k,\; -k+1,\; \ldots,\; k. \end{aligned}\right\} \tag{24}$$

Then the $\lambda_{p,\nu}$ are linear multiplicative functionals in $\mathfrak{B}_j^k$, and $\tilde{\mathfrak{B}}_j^k$, as originally defined, is the set of all elements $B \in \mathfrak{B}_j^k$, for which

$$\lambda_{p,\nu}(B) = 0,\; p = -2k,\; -2k+1,\; \ldots,\; 2k,$$
$$p = -k,\; -k+1,\; \ldots,\; k. \tag{25}$$

Thus, we have the conditions of the applicability of the preceding lemma, and so in the whole ring $\mathfrak{B}_j^k$ either $\lambda = \tilde{\lambda}$, or $\lambda = \lambda_{p,\nu}$ for some p and ν.

Because the case $\lambda(B) = 0$ is impossible, we arrive at the following result:
either

$$\lambda(B) = \int B_\nu(\varepsilon)\varepsilon_{22}^{i\rho}d\varepsilon, \tag{26}$$

or

$$\lambda(B) = \int B_\nu(\varepsilon)\varepsilon_{22}^{\rho}d\varepsilon. \tag{27}$$

But the second case in fact coincides with the first when $\rho = -ip$; hence:

Every non-zero linear multiplicative functional $\lambda(B)$ in the ring $\mathfrak{B}_j^k$ is defined for a pair of numbers (ν, ρ) by means of the formula

$$\lambda(B) = \int B_\nu(\varepsilon)\varepsilon_{22}^{i\rho}d\varepsilon; \tag{28}$$

here ρ is a complex number, and ν is a fixed number of the form $\nu = -k, -k+1, \ldots, k$. The pairs (ν, ρ) and $(-\nu, -\rho)$ define one and the same functional $\lambda(B)$.

On the basis of Theorem 15 Subsection 9 every completely irreducible representation of the group $\mathfrak{A}$ is defined to within equivalence by a functional† $\lambda(x) = \lambda(B)$; if therefore we construct, for every functional $\lambda(B)$ of the form (28), a completely irreducible representation inducing this functional on $\mathfrak{B}_j^k$, then we will obtain all the completely irreducible representations (to within equivalence) of the group $\mathfrak{A}$.

We turn to the construction of such representations.

---

† We note that $\lambda(B) = \lambda(x) \neq 0$. Otherwise we would have $T_x\xi = \lambda(x)\xi = 0$ for all $\xi \in \mathfrak{m}_j^k$, $x \in X_j^k$. Putting $x = e_{jj}^k x' e_{jj}^k$ for $x' \in X$ we get $\int x'(a)E_{jj}^k \; TaE_{jj}^k \, da = E_{jj}^k T_{x'} E_{jj}^k = T_x = 0$ and as $x'(a)$ is arbitrary in X this implies $E_{jj}^k T_a E_{jj}^k = 0$ for all $a \in \mathfrak{A}$. Particulary $E_{jj}^k T_u E_{jj}^k = 0$ for all $u \in \mathfrak{A}$ hence

$$0 = (2k+1) \int \overline{C_{jj}^k(u)} \, E_{jj}^k \, T_u E_{jj}^k \, du$$
$$= E_{jj}^k(2k+1)' \int C_{jj}^k(u) \, T_u \, du \, E_{jj}^k = E_{jj}^k E_{jj}^k E_{jj}^k = E_{jj}^k$$

contradicting our hypothesis.

15. The complete series of completely irreducible representations of the group $\mathfrak{A}$

We now attempt to solve the problem raised at the end of Subsection 14, the parameters ρ in the formulae for the representations of the principal series being allowed complex values.

Thus we define the operator T_a, in the space $L_2^m(\mathfrak{U})$, writing for $\phi \in L_2^m(\mathfrak{U})$

$$T_a\phi(u) = \frac{\alpha(ua)}{\alpha(u\bar{a})}\phi(u\bar{a}), \tag{1}$$

$$\alpha(a) = |a_{22}|^{-m+i\rho-2}a_{22}^m, \tag{2}$$

where m is a fixed integer, and ρ is a fixed complex number (for the notation employed in formula (1), see § 11, Subsection 3).

I. *The operator T_a is bounded.* In fact,

$$|T_{a^{-1}}\phi|^2 = \int\left|\frac{\alpha(u'a^{-1})}{\alpha(u'\bar{a}^{-1})}\right|^2|\phi(u'\bar{a}^{-1})|^2du'; \tag{3}$$

we make a change of variable of integration, namely

$$u = u'\bar{a}^{-1} \tag{4}$$

and we make use of the formula

$$du = \frac{\beta(u'\bar{a}^{-1})}{\beta(u'a^{-1})}du' \tag{5}$$

(see (10) § 11, Subsection 3). We obtain:

$$|T_{a^{-1}}\phi|^2 = \int\left|\frac{\alpha(u\bar{a}\cdot a^{-1})}{\alpha(u)}\right|^2|\phi(u)|^2\frac{\beta(u\bar{a}\cdot a^{-1})}{\beta(u)}du. \tag{6}$$

We set

$$ua = ku'; \quad \text{whence } u\bar{a} = u'; \tag{7}$$

then

$$\alpha(u\bar{a}\cdot a^{-1}) = \alpha(u'a^{-1}) = \alpha(k^{-1}u) = \alpha(k^{-1})\alpha(u);$$

consequently

$$\frac{\alpha(u\bar{a}\cdot a^{-1})}{\alpha(u)} = \alpha(k^{-1}) = |k_{22}|^{m-i\rho+2}k_{22}^{-m}. \tag{8}$$

Similarly,

$$\frac{\beta(u\bar{a}\cdot a^{-1})}{\beta(u)} = \beta(k^{-1}) = |k_{22}|^{-4}. \tag{9}$$

Substituting these expressions in (6), we find

$$|T_{a^{-1}}\phi|^2 = \int |k_{22}|^{2\sigma} |\phi(u)|^2 du, \tag{10}$$

where $\sigma = \operatorname{Im}\rho$.

On the other hand, it follows from (7) that, for fixed a, the matrix $k = uau'^{-1}$ runs through a bounded set $\subset \mathfrak{U}a\mathfrak{U}$; in particular, its elements k_{22} and k_{22}^{-1} are bounded:

$$|k_{22}| \leqslant C, \quad |k_{22}^{-1}| \leqslant C,$$

where C is some constant. We deduce that $|k_{22}|^{2\sigma} \leqslant C^{2|\sigma|}$, and so by (10),

$$|T_{a^{-1}}\phi|^2 \leqslant C^{2|\sigma|} \int |\phi(u)|^2 du = C^{2|\sigma|} |\phi|^2,$$

and $T_{a^{-1}}$ is bounded; replacing a^{-1} by a, we see that T_a is bounded.

Repeating the usual argument (see, for instance, § 10, Subsection 6), it is easy to convince oneself that $T_e = 1$, $T_{a_1 a_2} = T_{a_1} T_{a_2}$ and that $(T_a \xi, \eta)$ is a continuous function on $\mathfrak{A}$ for any $\xi, \eta \in L_2^m(\mathfrak{U})$; hence, *the correspondence $a \to T_a$ is a representation of the group $\mathfrak{A}$ in the space $L_2^m(\mathfrak{U})$*. We denote this representation by $\mathfrak{S}_{m,\rho}$.

II. *The representation $\mathfrak{S}_{m,\bar{\rho}}$ is conjugate to $\mathfrak{S}_{m,\rho}$.*

Proof. The space of the representation $\mathfrak{S}_{m,\rho}$ is the Hilbert space $L_2^m(\mathfrak{U})$; hence, the conjugate space is also $L_2^m(\mathfrak{U})$.

Now we find the operator $\hat{T}_a = T'_{a^{-1}}$, where T_a is an operator of the representation $\mathfrak{S}_{m,\rho}$. By the definition of the conjugate operator we have for all $\phi_1, \phi_2 \in L_2^m(\mathfrak{U})$

$$(\phi_1, \hat{T}_a\phi_2) = (\phi_1, T'_{a^{-1}}\phi_2) = (T_{a^{-1}}\phi_1, \phi_2)$$

$$= \int \frac{\alpha(u'a^{-1})}{\alpha(u'\bar{a}^{-1})} \phi_1(u'\bar{a}^{-1}) \overline{\phi_2(u')} du'.$$

We make the following change of variable of integration

$$u' = u\bar{a};$$

Since $du' = \dfrac{\beta(u\bar{a})}{\beta(ua)} du$ (see (10) § 11, Subsection 3), we obtain

$$(\phi_1, \hat{T}_a\phi_2) = \int \frac{\alpha((u\bar{a})a^{-1})}{\alpha(u)} \frac{\beta(u\bar{a})}{\beta(ua)} \phi_1(u)\overline{\phi_2(u\bar{a})} du .$$

Applying formulae (7) and (8), we deduce that

$$(\phi_1, \hat{T}_a\phi_2) = \int |k_{22}|^{m-i\rho+2} k_{22}^{-m} |k_{22}|^{-4} \phi_1(u)\overline{\phi_2(u\bar{a})} du$$
$$= \int \phi_1(u) \overline{|k_{22}|^{-m+i\bar{\rho}-2} k_{22}^{m} \phi_2(u\bar{a})} du .$$

This means that

$$\hat{T}_a\phi_2(u) = |k_{22}|^{-m+i\bar{\rho}-2} k_{22}^{m} \phi_2(u\bar{a}) = \frac{\alpha_1(u\bar{a})}{\alpha_1(u\bar{a})} \phi_2(u\bar{a}),$$

where $\alpha_1(a) = |a_{22}|^{-m+i\bar{\rho}-2} a_{22}^{m}$; hence, the correspondence $a \to \hat{T}_a$ is the representation $\mathfrak{S}_{m, \bar{\rho}}$.

III. *For* $\rho^2 \neq -(|m|+2n)^2$, $n = 1, 2, 3, \ldots$, *the representation* $\mathfrak{S}_{m,\rho}$ *is completely irreducible.*

Proof. We set $\nu = \frac{1}{2}|m|$,

$$e_n = \sum_{k=\nu}^{\nu+n} \sum_{j=-k}^{k} e_{jj}^{k}, \quad E_n = \sum_{k=\nu}^{\nu+n} \sum_{j=-k}^{k} E_{jj}^{k} \tag{11}$$

and we denote by X_n the set of all functions $x \in X$, satisfying the conditions

$$e_n x = x e_n = x . \tag{12}$$

We note that the E_{jj}^k are operators of projection into $L_2^m(\mathfrak{U})$, since by formulae (1) and (2), $T_{u_0}\phi(u) = \phi(uu_0)$ so that the restriction to the group $\mathfrak{U}$ of the representation $\mathfrak{S}_{m,\rho}$ is unitary (see II § 6, Subsection 7). Hence, applying Theorem 8 and formula (11) § 6, Subsection 7, we deduce that

$$\lim_{n\to\infty} E_n\xi = \xi \quad \text{for all} \quad \xi \in R; \tag{13}$$

moreover, when $x \in X_n$

$$E_n T_x = T_x E_n = T_x . \tag{14}$$

Let $\mathfrak{P}_n$ be the subspace onto which E_n projects; then

$$\mathfrak{P}_n = \sum_{k=\nu}^{\nu+n} \sum_{j=-k}^{k} \mathfrak{M}_j^k, \tag{15}$$

and by virtue of (14), $\mathfrak{P}_n$ is invariant with respect to all the operators

$$T_x, \quad x \in X_n.$$

Here, as in the case of the principal series, every subspace $\mathfrak{M}_j^k$ is one-dimensional or equal to zero; this is proved in the same way as for the principal series (see Theorem 8 §11, Subsection 4). Hence it follows that $\mathfrak{P}_n$ is finite-dimensional.

The operators $E_n T_a E_n$ form an irreducible set† *in* $\mathfrak{P}_n$. In fact, let $\mathfrak{M}$ be a subspace in $\mathfrak{P}_n$, distinct from zero and invariant with respect to all the operators $E_n T_a E_n$; in particular, it is invariant with respect to all the operators $E_n T_u E_n$, coinciding with T_u on $\mathfrak{P}_n$. Because $\mathfrak{M}_j^k$ is one-dimensional or equal to zero, we deduce from this that $\mathfrak{M}$ is the direct sum of subspaces $\mathfrak{M}^k = \sum_{j=-k}^{k} \mathfrak{M}_j^k$.

If we had $\mathfrak{M} \neq \mathfrak{P}_n$, then $\mathfrak{P}_n$ contains a subspace $\mathfrak{M}^l$, orthogonal to $\mathfrak{M}$.

There are two possibilities: $k \leqslant l$ or $k > l$. We consider first the case $k \leqslant l$. In this case $\mathfrak{M}^k$ contains a function $c_{\nu k}^k(u)$, and $\mathfrak{M}^l$ a function $c_{\nu k}^l(u)$, where $\nu = \frac{1}{2} m$. By the invariance of the space $\mathfrak{M}$, it follows that $E_n T_\varepsilon E_n c_{\nu k}^k(u) \in \mathfrak{M}$, and so $E_n T_\varepsilon E_n c_{\nu k}^k(u) \perp c_{\nu k}^l(u)$, i.e.

$$0 = (E_n T_\varepsilon E_n c_{\nu k}^k(u),\ c_{\nu k}^l(u)) = (T_\varepsilon c_{\nu k}^k(u),\ E_n c_{\nu k}^l(u))$$
$$= (T_\varepsilon c_{\nu k}^k(u), c_{\nu k}^l(u)), \tag{16}$$

i.e., by virtue of (1):

$$\int \frac{\alpha(u\varepsilon)}{\alpha(u\bar{\varepsilon})} c_{\nu k}^k(u\bar{\varepsilon}) \overline{c_{\nu k}^l(u)}\, du = 0, \quad \text{if} \quad k \leqslant l. \tag{17a}$$

Analogously we find that

$$\int \frac{\alpha(u\varepsilon)}{\alpha(u\bar{\varepsilon})} c_{\nu l}^k(u\bar{\varepsilon}) \overline{c_{\nu l}^l(u)}\, du = 0, \quad \text{if} \quad k > l. \tag{17b}$$

† A set of operators in a finite-dimensional space R is called *irreducible* if R has no subspace, other than (0) and the whole of R, which is invariant with respect to all the operators of this set.

We will prove that this is impossible when $\rho^2 \neq -(|m|+2n)^2$; by the preceding remarks this would mean that the operators $E_n T_a E_n$ form an irreducible set in $\mathfrak{P}_n$. In conditions (17a), (17b), put

$$u\varepsilon = \varepsilon' \zeta v. \tag{18}$$

Then

$$v = u\bar{\varepsilon}, \quad \alpha(u\varepsilon) = \alpha(\varepsilon'\zeta v) = \alpha(\varepsilon')\alpha(\zeta)\alpha(v) = \alpha(\varepsilon')\alpha(u\bar{\varepsilon});$$

hence, by virtue of (2):

$$\frac{\alpha(u\varepsilon)}{\alpha(u\bar{\varepsilon})} = \alpha(\varepsilon') = \varepsilon_{22}'^{i\rho-2}.$$

Substituting these expressions in conditions (17a) and (17b), we get

$$\int \varepsilon_{22}'^{i\rho-2} c_{\nu k}^{k}(v)\overline{c_{\nu k}^{l}(u)}\,du = 0 \quad \text{when} \quad k \leqslant l, \tag{19a}$$

$$\int \varepsilon_{22}'^{i\rho-2} c_{\nu l}^{k}(v)\overline{c_{\nu l}^{l}(u)}\,du = 0 \quad \text{when} \quad k > l, \tag{19b}$$

where $u\varepsilon = \varepsilon'\zeta v$.

It is sufficient to consider the case (19a); the case (19b) is reduced to it by the transition from the variable of integration u to the variable of integration v by means of the formula $u\varepsilon = \varepsilon'\zeta v$. In fact, doing this we have

$$v\varepsilon^{-1} = \varepsilon'^{-1}\zeta_1 u, \quad v = u\bar{\varepsilon}, \quad \text{where} \quad \zeta_1 = \varepsilon'\zeta^{-1}\varepsilon'^{-1};$$

hence (see (10) § 11, Subsection 3),

$$dv = \frac{\beta(u\bar{\varepsilon})}{\beta(u\varepsilon)}du = \frac{\beta(v)}{\beta(\varepsilon'\zeta v)}du = \beta^{-1}(\varepsilon')du = \varepsilon_{22}'^{-4}du.$$

Then (19b) takes the form

$$\int (\varepsilon_{22}'^{-1})^{-i\rho+2}\varepsilon_{22}'^{4} c_{\nu l}^{k}(v)\overline{c_{\nu l}^{l}(u)}\,dv = 0$$

or, taking conjugates and putting $\varepsilon'' = \varepsilon'^{-1}$,

$$\int \varepsilon_{22}''^{i\bar{\rho}-2} c_{\nu l}^{l}(u)\overline{c_{\nu l}^{k}(v)}\,dv = 0 \quad \text{when} \quad v\varepsilon^{-1} = \varepsilon''\zeta_1 u, \quad l < k.$$

This last relation coincides with (19a) with l and k changing parts, and where the part of ε is played by ε^{-1}, and the part of ρ is played by $\bar{\rho}$. But if ρ satisfies the condition $\rho^2 \neq -(|m|+2n)^2$, then $\bar{\rho}$ also satisfies this condition; therefore it is sufficient to consider the relation (19a).

Thus, let (19a) hold. From formula (7) § 5, Subsection 4 for the matrix elements $c^k_{\nu p}(u)$ it follows that

$$c^k_{\nu k}(v) = \kappa_1 v_{22}^{k+\nu} \bar{v}_{21}^{k-\nu} \tag{20}$$

$$\overline{c^l_{\nu k}(u)} = c^l_{k\nu}(u)^* = \kappa_2 \sum_{q=0}^{l-k} (-1)^q C^q_{l+\nu} C^{k+q-\nu}_{l-\nu} \bar{u}_{21}^q u_{21}^{k+q-\nu} \bar{u}_{22}^{l+\nu-q} u_{22}^{l-k-q}, \tag{21}$$

where κ_1, κ_2 are some constants,

For brevity we let I denote the integral on the left side of (19a). Substituting expressions (20), (21) for $c^k_{\nu k}(v)$, $c^l_{\nu k}(u)$ in this integral and making a change of variables by means of the formulae $t = |u_{22}|^2$, $\theta = \arg u_{22}$, $\theta' = \arg u_{21}$, we obtain, as in Subsection 11 (see page 268):

$$I = \kappa_1\kappa_2 \sum_{q=0}^{l-k} (-1)^q C^q_{l+\nu} C^{k+q-\nu}_{l-\nu} \varepsilon_{22}^{2\nu} \int_0^1 [\varepsilon_{22}^{-2}(1-t)+\varepsilon_{22}^2 t]^{-k-1+i\frac{\rho}{2}} \times$$
$$\times (1-l)^{k+q-\nu} t^{l+\nu-q} dt. \tag{22}$$

Here we set $\varepsilon_{22}^4 = x$ and make the substitution

$$\eta = 1-t+\varepsilon_{22}^4 t = 1-t+xt; \tag{23}$$

we see that for all x

$$\sum_{q=0}^{l-k} (-1)^q C^q_{l+\nu} C^{k+q-\nu}_{l-\nu} \int_1^x \phi(\eta)(x-\eta)^{k+q-\nu}(\eta-1)^{l+\nu-q} d\eta = 0, \tag{24}$$

where

$$\phi(\eta) = \eta^{-k-1+i\frac{\rho}{2}}. \tag{25}$$

But condition (24) means that the coefficient of $\alpha^{\nu-k}$ in the expression

$$\int_1^x (\eta-1+\alpha)^{l+\nu} \left[1-\frac{1}{\alpha}(x-\eta)\right]^{l-\nu} \phi(\eta) d\eta \tag{26}$$

is zero, i.e. that the coefficient of α^{l-k} in the expression

$$I_\alpha = \int_1^x (\eta-1+\alpha)^{l+\nu}(\alpha+\eta-x)^{l-\nu}\phi(\eta) d\eta \tag{27}$$

vanishes ; consequently

$$\frac{\partial^{l-k} I_\alpha}{\partial \alpha^{l-k}} = 0 \quad \text{when} \quad \alpha = 0. \tag{28}$$

We set

$$F(y, x) = (y-1)^{l+\nu}(y-x)^{l-\nu}; \tag{29}$$

then condition (28) takes the form

$$\int_1^x \left[\frac{\partial^{l-k} F(\eta+\alpha, x)}{\partial \alpha^{l-k}}\right]_{\alpha=0} \phi(\eta) d\eta = 0. \tag{30}$$

But

$$\left[\frac{\partial^{l-k} F(\eta+\alpha, x)}{\partial \alpha^{l-k}}\right]_{\alpha=0} = \left[\frac{\partial^{l-k} F(\eta+\alpha, x)}{\partial \eta^{l-k}}\right]_{\alpha=0} = \frac{\partial^{l-k} F(\eta, x)}{\partial \eta^{l-k}},$$

and so condition (30) can be rewritten in the form

$$\int_1^x \frac{\partial^{l-k} F(\eta, x)}{\partial \eta^{l-k}} \phi(\eta) d\eta = 0. \tag{31}$$

Since $|\nu| \leqslant k$, then the function $F(\eta, x) = (\eta - 1)^{l+\nu}(\eta - x)^{l-\nu}$ and all its derivatives up to and including the $(l - k)$ th order vanish when $\eta = 1$ and $\eta = x$; therefore, integrating by parts in (31), we obtain:

$$\int_1^x F(\eta, x) \phi^{(l-k)}(\eta) d\eta = 0,$$

i.e.

$$\int_1^x (\eta-1)^{l+\nu}(\eta-x)^{l-\nu}\phi^{(l-k)}(\eta) d\eta = 0. \tag{32}$$

Differentiating both sides of this equation $l - \nu+1$ times with respect to x, we see that $(x - 1)^{l+\nu}\phi^{(l-k)}(x) = 0$; hence,

$$\phi^{(l-k)}(x) = 0,$$

.e., by virtue of (25),

$$\left(-k-1+i\frac{\rho}{2}\right)\left(-k-2+i\frac{\rho}{2}\right)\ldots\left(-l+i\frac{\rho}{2}\right) x^{-l-1+i\frac{\rho}{2}} = 0.$$

This is possible only when one of the numbers

$$-k-1+i\frac{\rho}{2}, \quad -k-2+i\frac{\rho}{2}, \quad \ldots, \quad -l+i\frac{\rho}{2}$$

is equal to zero, i.e. when $\rho = -i(2k+2n) = -i(|m|+2n_1)$ for some natural n and n_1. But then $\rho^2 = -(|m|+2n_1)^2$, which contradicts the condition.

Thus, the relations (17a) and (17b) are impossible for $\rho^2 \neq -(|m|+2n)^2$, hence the operators $E_n T_a E_n$ form an irreducible set in the finite-dimensional space $\mathfrak{P}_n$. It follows that *the operators* $E_n T_x E_n$, $x \in X$, *also form an irreducible set in* $\mathfrak{P}_n$. In fact, suppose that $\mathfrak{P}_n$ has a subspace $\mathfrak{M}$, distinct from zero and the whole of $\mathfrak{P}_n$ and invariant with respect to all the operators $E_n T_x E_n$. Then for $\xi \in \mathfrak{M}$, $\eta \in \mathfrak{P}_n - \mathfrak{M}$ and all $x \in X$,

$$(T_x\xi, \eta) = (T_x E_n\xi, E_n\eta) = (E_n T_x E_n \xi, \eta) = 0, \tag{33}$$

since $E_n T_x E_n \xi \in \mathfrak{M}$, $\eta \perp \mathfrak{M}$.

Let a' be a fixed matrix from the group $\mathfrak{A}$ and let Q_m be a sequence of neighbourhoods of the matrix a', given by the inequalities $\sum_{j,k=1}^{2} |a_{jk} - a'_{jk}| < \frac{1}{m}$. By virtue of the continuity of the representation $a \to T_a$, we have

$$\sup_{a \in Q_m} |(T_a\xi, \eta) - (T_{a'}\xi, \eta)| \to 0 \quad \text{as} \quad m \to \infty. \tag{34}$$

We choose a sequence of functions $x_m \in X$ so that

$$x_m(a) \geqslant 0, \quad x_m(a) = 0 \quad \text{outside} \quad Q_m, \quad \int x_m(a)\,da = 1. \tag{35}$$

Then

$$\begin{aligned} |(T_{a'}\xi, \eta) - (T_{x_m}\xi, \eta)| &= \left| \int x_m(a)(T_{a'}\xi, \eta)\,da - \int x_m(a)(T_a\xi, \eta)\,da \right| \\ &\leqslant \int x_m(a) |(T_{a'}\xi, \eta) - (T_a\xi, \eta)|\,da \\ &\leqslant \sup_{a \in Q_m} |(T_{a'}\xi, \eta) - (T_a\xi, \eta)| \int x_m(a)\,da \\ &= \sup_{a \in Q_m} |(T_{a'}\xi, \eta) - (T_a\xi, \eta)| \to 0 \quad \text{as} \quad m \to \infty. \end{aligned}$$

By virtue of (33) this is possible only when $(T_{a'}\ \xi, \eta)=0$ for all $\xi \in \mathfrak{M}$, $\eta \in \mathfrak{P}_n - \mathfrak{M}$, i.e. when $\mathfrak{M}$ is invariant with respect to all the operators $E_n T_{a'} E_n$, $a' \in \mathfrak{A}$, which is impossible.

Thus the operators $E_n T_x E_n$, $x \in X$, form a completely irreducible set in $\mathfrak{P}_n$. But the operators $E_n T_x E_n$ also form a ring; according to Burnside's theorem (see Appendix III) this ring coincides with the ring of all linear operators in $\mathfrak{P}_n$.

Now let A be an arbitrary bounded operator in $L_2^m(\mathfrak{U})$; by what has been said there exists a function $x_n \in X_n$ such that $T_{x_n} = E_n T_{x_n} E_n = E_n A E_n$ on $\mathfrak{P}_n$. But in the orthogonal complement $L_2^m(\mathfrak{U}) - \mathfrak{P}_n$ both of the operators T_{x_n} and $E_n A E_n$ are equal to zero; therefore $T_{x_n} = E_n A E_n$ in the whole of $L_2^m(\mathfrak{U})$. Hence for any $f_1, f_2 \in L_2^m(\mathfrak{U})$

$$(T_{x_n} f_1, f_2) = (E_n A E_n f_1, f_2) = (A E_n f_1, E_n f_2) \to (A f_1, f_2) \quad (36)$$

as $n \to \infty$.

In view of the arbitrary nature of the operator A this means that the given representation $\mathfrak{S}_{m,\rho}$ is completely irreducible.†

The set of all representations $\mathfrak{S}_{m,\rho}$, corresponding to all pairs (m,ρ) where $\rho^2 \neq -(|m|+2n)^2$, will be called *the complete series of representations of the group* $\mathfrak{A}$. When $\rho^2 = -(|m|+2n)^2$ the representation $\mathfrak{S}_{m,\rho}$ will not be irreducible, and therefore definitely not completely irreducible. In fact supposing firstly that $\rho = -i(|m|+2n)$, let $\mathfrak{P}$ be the set of all homogeneous polynomials in u_{21}, $\bar{u}_{21}$, u_{22}, $\bar{u}_{22}$:

$$p(u) = \sum_{\alpha,\beta,\gamma,\delta,} c_{\alpha\beta\gamma\delta} u_{21}^{\alpha} \bar{u}_{21}^{\beta} u_{22}^{\gamma} \bar{u}_{22}^{\delta}, \quad (37)$$

satisfying the conditions:

$$\alpha-\beta+\gamma-\delta = m, \quad (38)$$

$$\alpha+\beta+\gamma+\delta = |m|+2n-2. \quad (39)$$

† See Subsection 4; in fact we have proved a stronger assertion, namely that (36) holds for any bounded linear operator in $L_2^m(\mathfrak{U})$, not only for an admissible operator.

By virtue of condition (38), $p(\gamma u) = e^{im\omega} p(u)$ where $\gamma = \begin{Vmatrix} e^{-i\omega} & 0 \\ 0 & e^{i\omega} \end{Vmatrix}$; hence $\mathfrak{P} \subset L_2^m(\mathfrak{U})$. Further we have by virtue of condition (39) and formula (33) Subsection 11 when $u\varepsilon = \varepsilon' \zeta v$,

$$\begin{aligned} T_\varepsilon p(u) &= \varepsilon_{22}'^{i\rho-2} p(v) \\ &= \varepsilon_{22}'^{i\rho-2-(|m|+2n-2)} \sum_{\alpha,\beta,\gamma,\delta} c_{\alpha\beta\gamma\delta} \varepsilon_{22}^{\gamma+\delta-\alpha-\beta} u_{21}^{\alpha} \bar{u}_{21}^{\beta} u_{22}^{\gamma} \bar{u}_{22}^{\delta} \\ &= \sum_{\alpha,\beta,\gamma,\delta} c_{\alpha\beta\gamma\delta} \varepsilon_{22}^{\gamma+\delta-\alpha-\beta} u_{21}^{\alpha} \bar{u}_{21}^{\beta} u_{22}^{\gamma} \bar{u}_{22}^{\delta} \in \mathfrak{P}, \end{aligned}$$

hence, $\mathfrak{P}$ is invariant with respect to all the operators T_ε. On the other hand, it is evident that it is invariant also with respect to all the operators T_u, because $T_{u_0} f(u) = f(uu_0)$; hence $\mathfrak{P}$ is invariant with respect to all the operators $T_a = T_{u_1} T_\varepsilon T_{u_2}$ where $a = u_1 \varepsilon u_2$, and so the given representation $a \to T_a$ is not irreducible.

By virtue of the results of § 11, Subsection 7, this representation, considered only in $\mathfrak{P}$, is a spinor representation S_{pq}, where

$$p = \frac{m}{2} + i\frac{\rho}{2} - 1,$$

$$q = -\frac{m}{2} + i\frac{\rho}{2} - 1.$$

Now we consider the case $\rho = i(|m|+2n)$. The representation conjugate to $\mathfrak{S}_{m,\rho}$ is $\mathfrak{S}_{m,\rho'}$, where $\rho' = \bar{\rho} = -\rho$ (ρ in our case is pure imaginary). The representation $\mathfrak{S}_{m,\rho'}$ is not irreducible, because the relation between m and ρ' has the form $\rho' = -i(|m|+2n)$, and we obtain the case considered above. But then the original representation $\mathfrak{S}_{m,\rho}$ also cannot be completely irreducible since mutually conjugate representations must be completely irreducible simultaneously.

Remark. One can also realize the complete series by means of operators in the space of functions $f(z)$, $z \in Z$.

Let $\sigma = \operatorname{Im} \rho \geqslant 0$.

We denote by $R_\sigma(Z)$ the set of all measurable functions $f(z)$ satisfying the condition

$$\int (1 + |z^2|)^{-\sigma} |f(z)|^2 \, dz < \infty.$$

Then $R\sigma(Z)$ is a Hilbert space, and the operator

$$T_a f(z) = |a_{12}z+a_{22}|^{-m+i\rho-2}(a_{12}z+a_{22})^m f\left(\frac{a_{11}z+a_{21}}{a_{12}z+a_{22}}\right)$$

is bounded in $R\sigma(Z)$. The correspondence $a \to T_a$ is a representation of the group $\mathfrak{A}$. It is easy to convince oneself that this representation is equivalent to the representation $\mathfrak{S}_{m,\rho}$ of the complete series.

16. A fundamental theorem

Now we can prove the following fundamental theorem:

THEOREM 16. *Every completely irreducible representation of the group $\mathfrak{A}$ is defined by a pair of numbers (m, ρ) where m is some integer, and ρ is some complex number; here, the pairs (m, ρ) and $(-m, -\rho)$ define one and the same completely irreducible representation.*

When $\rho^2 \neq -(|m|+2n)^2$, $n = 1, 2, 3, \ldots$, the representation is equivalent to the representation $\mathfrak{S}_{m,\rho}$ of the complete series; when $\rho^2 = -(|m|+2n)^2$, $n = 1, 2, 3, \ldots$, the representation is equivalent to the finite-dimensional, spinor representation S_{pq} of the group $\mathfrak{A}$, where $p = \frac{m}{2}+i\frac{\rho}{2}-1$, $q = -\frac{m}{2}+i\frac{\rho}{2}-1$.

Proof. Let $\lambda_0(B)$ be a linear multiplicative functional in $\mathfrak{B}_j^k$, induced by a given completely irreducible representation of the group $\mathfrak{A}$. According to the result of Subsection 14, the functional $\lambda_0(B)$ is defined by the formula

$$\lambda_0(B) = \int B_\nu(\varepsilon)\varepsilon_{22}^{i\rho}\, d\varepsilon. \tag{1}$$

On the other hand, calculations analogous to those carried out in Subsection 10 show that in the case of a representation of the complete series

$$\lambda(B) = \int B_\mu(\varepsilon)\varepsilon_{22}^{i\rho} d\varepsilon, \quad \text{where} \quad \mu = \frac{m}{2}, \tag{2}$$

and in the case of the spinor representation $S_{p,q}$,

$$\lambda(B) = \int B_\mu(\varepsilon)\varepsilon_{22}^{i\rho} d\varepsilon, \quad \text{where} \quad \mu = \frac{p-q}{2}, \quad i\rho = p+q+2. \tag{3}$$

In formula (1) let $\rho^2 \neq -(|m|+2n)^2$, $n = 1, 2, 3, \ldots$, then when $m/2 = \mu = \nu$ the functional $\lambda(B)$ induced by the representation $\mathfrak{S}_{m,\rho}$ of the complete series coincides with the functional $\lambda_0(B)$; according to Theorem 15 Subsection 9 we deduce from this that the given completely irreducible representation is equivalent to the representation $\mathfrak{S}_{m,\rho}$.

Now let† $\rho = -i(|m|+2n)$, $n = 1, 2, 3, \ldots$, then if $p = \frac{m}{2} + i\frac{\rho}{2} - 1$, $q = -\frac{m}{2} + i\frac{\rho}{2} - 1$ the functional $\lambda(B)$ induced by the spinor representation $S_{p,q}$, coincides with $\lambda_0(B)$; hence in this case the given completely irreducible representation is equivalent to the spinor representation $S_{p,q}$. The theorem is proved.

Remark. Repeating the reasoning of § 11, Subsection 6, we may convince ourselves of the fact that the infinitesimal operators of the representation $\mathfrak{S}_{m,\rho}$, are given by formulae (51–55) § 8, Subsection 3, where the parameters (m, ρ) and (k_0, c) are connected by formulae (9), (10) § (11), Subsection 6.

We deduce that *for any integral or semi-integral non-negative number* k_0 *and any complex number* c, *formulae* (51–55) § 8, *Subsection* 3 *define the infinitesimal operators of some completely irreducible representation of the group, namely, the representations* $\mathfrak{S}_{m,\rho}$ *for* $c^2 \neq (k_0+n)^2$, $n = 1, 2, \ldots$, *and the spinor representations for* $c^2 = (k_0+n)^2$, $n = 1, 2, 3, \ldots$.

From Theorem 15, Subsection 9 it also follows that *completely irreducible representations* (of the complete series) *defined by different pairs* (m, ρ) *and* (m', ρ'), *are equivalent if and only if* $m' = -m$ *and* $\rho' = -\rho$.

We denote the completely irreducible representation defined by the pair (k_0, c) by $S_c^{k_0}$, so that $S_c^{k_0}$ is either a representation $\mathfrak{S}_{m,\rho}$ of the complete series or a spinor representation S_{pq}.

---

† Since the pairs (ν, ρ), $(-\nu, -\rho)$ define one and the same functional $\lambda_0(B)$, one can assume that $\mathrm{Im}\, \rho < 0$.

§ 16. Description of all the Completely Irreducible Representations of the Complete Lorentz Group

1. Statement of the problem

The complete Lorentz group $\mathfrak{G}_0$ has as one of its subgroups the proper Lorentz group $\mathfrak{G}_+$, and every transformation $g \in \mathfrak{G}_0$, not contained in $\mathfrak{G}_+$, can be represented in the form $g = sg_1$, where $g_1 \in \mathfrak{G}_+$, and s is the reflection with respect to the axes Ox_1, Ox_2, Ox_3:

$$x_1' = -x_1, \quad x_2' = -x_2, \quad x_3' = -x_3, \quad x_4' = x_4$$

(see § 2, Subsection 2). Therefore every representation $g \to T_g$ of the group $\mathfrak{G}_0$ is also a representation of the group $\mathfrak{G}_+$; it differs from an arbitrary representation of the group $\mathfrak{G}_+$ by the fact that the space R of the representation must permit an operator $S = T_s$, corresponding to the reflection s. On the other hand, instead of the representation $g \to T_g$ of the group $\mathfrak{G}_+$ one can consider the representation $a \to T_a$ of the group $\mathfrak{A}$ or the corresponding representation $x \to T_x$ of its group ring X.

Thus, the original representation $g \to T_g$ of the group $\mathfrak{G}_0$ is completely defined by a representation $x \to T_x$ of the ring X and an operator $S = T_s$.

The aim of this section is the description of all the completely irreducible representations of the complete Lorentz group $\mathfrak{G}_0$ to within equivalence; here the definitions of equivalence and complete irreducibility of representations of the group $\mathfrak{G}_0$ are analogous to the corresponding definitions for the group $\mathfrak{G}_+$(or $\mathfrak{A}$) (see Subsection 3 below). For the solution of this problem we will make use of the results and notations of § 15.

2. The fundamental properties of the operator S

It is clear from the definition of the transformation s that $s^2 = e$, where e is the identity transformation, and so

$$S^2 = \mathbf{1}, \tag{1}$$

where **1** is the identity operator. Moreover, for any matrix

$$g = \begin{Vmatrix} g_{11} & g_{12} & g_{13} & g_{14} \\ g_{21} & g_{22} & g_{23} & g_{24} \\ g_{31} & g_{32} & g_{33} & g_{34} \\ g_{41} & g_{42} & g_{43} & g_{44} \end{Vmatrix}$$

we have:

$$sgs^{-1} = sgs = \hat{g}, \tag{2}$$

where

$$g = \begin{Vmatrix} g_{11} & g_{12} & g_{13} & -g_{14} \\ g_{21} & g_{22} & g_{23} & -g_{24} \\ g_{31} & g_{32} & g_{33} & -g_{34} \\ -g_{41} & -g_{42} & -g_{43} & g_{44} \end{Vmatrix}.$$

If, in particular,

$$g = \begin{Vmatrix} g_{11} & g_{12} & g_{13} & 0 \\ g_{21} & g_{22} & g_{23} & 0 \\ g_{31} & g_{32} & g_{33} & 0 \\ 0 & 0 & 0 & 1 \end{Vmatrix}$$

is an element of the group G_0 (the group of rotations of three-dimensional space), then $sg = gs$ for $g \in G_0$.

Passing from the group $\mathfrak{G}_+$ to the group $\mathfrak{A}$, we deduce from this that

$$ST_u = T_uS \quad \text{for all} \quad u \in \mathfrak{U}. \tag{3}$$

Further, letting in (2),

$$g = b_3(t) = \begin{Vmatrix} 1 & 0 & 0 & 0 \\ 0 & 1 & 0 & 0 \\ 0 & 0 & \cosh t & \sinh t \\ 0 & 0 & \sinh t & \cosh t \end{Vmatrix},$$

we obtain

$$sb_3(t)s^{-1} = sb_3(t)s = \begin{Vmatrix} 1 & 0 & 0 & 0 \\ 0 & 1 & 0 & 0 \\ 0 & 0 & \cosh t & -\sinh t \\ 0 & 0 & -\sinh t & \cosh t \end{Vmatrix} = b_3(-t),$$

(see § 7, Subsection 1), and so

$$ST_{b_3(t)}S = T_{b_3(-t)}. \tag{4}$$

Again passing from $\mathfrak{G}_+$ to $\mathfrak{A}$, we can rewrite (4) in the form

$$ST_\varepsilon S^{-1} = T_\varepsilon^{-1} \tag{5}$$

(see (2) § 9, Subsection 4). But, by virtue of II § 11, Subsection 5, every matrix $a \in \mathfrak{A}$ can be represented in the form $a = u_1 \varepsilon u_2$; therefore, applying relations (3) and (5) we obtain:

$$ST_a S = ST_{u_1\varepsilon u_2}S = ST_{u_1}T_\varepsilon T_{u_2}S = T_{u_1}ST_\varepsilon ST_{u_2} = T_{u_1}T_{\varepsilon^{-1}}T_{u_2}$$
$$= T_{u_1\varepsilon^{-1}u_2}. \tag{6}$$

For brevity we introduce the notation

$$a^\wedge = a^{*-1}; \quad x^\wedge(a) = x(a^\wedge); \tag{7}$$

then

$$a^\wedge = (u_1\varepsilon u_2)^{*-1} = u_1\varepsilon^{-1}u_2,$$

and so (6) can be rewritten in the form

$$ST_a S^{-1} = ST_a S = T_{a^\wedge}. \tag{8}$$

Conversely, let there be given a representation $a \to T_a$ of the group $\mathfrak{A}$ and an operator S, satisfying conditions (1), (3) and (5), and therefore also condition (8).

We set

$$T_g = T_a \quad \text{if} \quad g \in \mathfrak{G}_+ \quad \text{and} \quad g \to a,$$
$$T_g = ST_{a'} \quad \text{if} \quad g = sg' \quad \text{and} \quad g' \to a'$$

(see § 9, Subsection 1). Then the correspondence $g \to T_g$ will be a representation of the group $\mathfrak{G}_0$.

In fact, it is only necessary to verify that $T_{g_1}T_{g_2} = T_{g_1g_2}$. This is evident if $g_1, g_2 \in \mathfrak{G}_+$. Therefore it is necessary to consider the following cases: (1) $g_1 \in \mathfrak{G}_0 - \mathfrak{G}_+$, $g_2 \in \mathfrak{G}_+$; (2) $g_1 \in \mathfrak{G}_+$, $g_2 \in \mathfrak{G}_0 - \mathfrak{G}_+$ and (3) $g_1 \in \mathfrak{G}_0 - \mathfrak{G}_+$, $g_2 \in \mathfrak{G}_0 - \mathfrak{G}_+$. Assume, for instance, that case (1) holds. Then $g_1 = sg_1'$, and $T_{g_1}T_{g_2} = ST_{a_1'}T_{a_2} = ST_{a_1'a_2} = ST_{g_1'g} = T_{g_1g_2}$ as $g_1' \to a_1'$, $g_2 \to a_2$, imply that $g_1'g_2 \to a_1'a_2$ Next, suppose case (2) holds. Then $g_2 = sg_2'$ and

$T_{g_1}T_{g_2} = T_{a_1}ST_{a_2'} = ST_{a_1^\wedge}T_{a_2'} = ST_{a_1^\wedge a_2'} = T_{sg_1^\wedge g_2'} = T_{g_1g_2}$, where $g_1 \to a_1$, $g_2' \to a_2'$, because then $a_1^\wedge a_2' \to g_1^\wedge g_2'$. Case (3) is dealt with similarly

The definition of a representation $g \to T_g$ of the group $\mathfrak{G}_0$ is thus reduced to the definition of the representation $a \to T_a$ of the group $\mathfrak{A}$ and the operator S, satisfying condition (8).

We note the following useful properties of the operation of transition from a to $a^\wedge$ and from x to $x^\wedge$:

$$a^{\wedge\wedge} = a, \quad (a_1a_2)^\wedge = a_1^\wedge a_2^\wedge, \tag{9}$$

$$x^{\wedge\wedge} = x, \quad (\lambda x)^\wedge = \lambda x^\wedge, \quad (x_1+x_2)^\wedge = x_1^\wedge + x_2^\wedge, \tag{10}$$

$$\int x(a)da = \int x(a^\wedge)da = \int x^\wedge(a)da, \tag{11}$$

$$(x_1x_2)^\wedge = x_1^\wedge x_2^\wedge. \tag{12}$$

Here properties (9) and (10) are evident, and properties (11) and (12) are obtained from the following chains of equations:

$$\int x(a)da = \int x(a^{-1})da = \int x(a^{*-1})da = \int x(a^\wedge)da$$
$$= \int x^\wedge(a)da,$$

$$(x_1x_2)^\wedge(a) = \int x_1(a_1)x_2(a_1^{-1}a^\wedge)da_1 = \int x_1(a_1^\wedge)x_2(a_1^{\wedge -1}a^\wedge)da_1$$
$$= \int x_1^\wedge(a_1)x_2^\wedge(a_1^{-1}a)da_1 = (x_1^\wedge x_2^\wedge)(a).$$

From (8) and (11) we deduce that

$$ST_xS^{-1} = ST_xS = S(\int x(a)\,T_a da)\,S$$
$$= \int x(a)\,ST_aSda = \int x(a)\,T_{a^\wedge}da$$
$$= \int x(a^\wedge)\,T_a da = \int x^\wedge(a)\,T_a da = T_{x^\wedge},$$

so that

$$ST_xS^{-1} = ST_xS = T_{x^\wedge}. \tag{13}$$

From the relation $ST_u = T_uS$ it follows that the corresponding operators E_{je}^k commute with S, and so all the subspaces $\mathfrak{M}_j^k$ are invariant with respect to the operator S.

3. The group ring of the group $\mathfrak{G}_0$

The results of Subsection 2 suggest the possibility of defining the group ring of the group $\mathfrak{G}_0$; this definition resembles to some degree the definition of complex numbers. Thus, we consider the set $\mathfrak{C}$ of all possible formal sums $c = x+sy$, $x, y \in X$, and we define operations with these sums by means of the following formulae:

$$\lambda c = \lambda x + s\lambda y, \quad c_1 + c_2 = (x_1+x_2)+s(y_1+y_2),$$

$$c_1 c_2 = (x_1 x_2 + \hat{y_1} y_2) + s(y_1 x_2 + \hat{x_1} y_2)$$

where $c_1 = x_1+sy_1$, $c_2 = x_2+sy_2$.

It is easy to verify that this definition of the operations turns $\mathfrak{C}$ into a ring, which we will call *the group ring of the group* $\mathfrak{G}_0$.

To every element $c = x+sy$ of the group ring we assign an operator $T_c = T_x+ST_y$. Clearly, $T_{\lambda c} = \lambda T_c$; $T_{c_1+c_2} = T_{c_1}+T_{c_2}$; moreover, from formula (13) Subsection 2 it follows that $T_{c_1 c_2} = T_{c_1} T_{c_2}$, so that the correspondence $c \to T_c$ is a representation of the ring $\mathfrak{C}$. Hence, every representation $g \to T_g$ of the group $\mathfrak{G}_0$ corresponds to a representation $c \to T_c$ of its group ring $\mathfrak{C}$.

We can now define the concepts of equivalence and complete irreducibility of the representations of the group $\mathfrak{G}_0$ in a manner similar to that used in § 15, Subsection 3 and 4 for the representations of the group $\mathfrak{A}$, replacing the ring X and the operators T_x by the ring $\mathfrak{C}$ and the operators T_c; in particular, the set Ω is now defined as the set of all finite linear combinations of the vectors $T_c\xi$, where c runs through all the elements of the ring $\mathfrak{C}$, and ξ through the vectors from all possible subspaces $\mathfrak{M}_j^k$. It is easy to convince oneself that all the results of § 15, Subsection 3 and 4 carry over to the representations of the group $\mathfrak{G}_0$.

4. Induced representations

We denote by $\mathfrak{C}_j^k$ the set of all elements $c = x+sy$, where x, $y \in X_j^k$ (see § 15, Subsection 6); since X_j^k is a subring of the ring X, then $\mathfrak{C}_j^k$ is a subring of the ring $\mathfrak{C}$. By virtue of the properties of the operators S and T_x, $x \in X_j^k$, the subspace $\mathfrak{M}_j^k$ is invariant with respect to the operators T_c, $c \in \mathfrak{C}_j^k$. If therefore one sets $A_c\,\xi = T_c\xi$ for $\xi \in \mathfrak{M}_j^k$ then A_c is an operator in $\mathfrak{M}_j^k$ and the correspondence $c \to A^c$ is a representation of the ring $\mathfrak{C}_j^k$ in the space $\mathfrak{M}_j^k$. This representation will be called the *representation of the ring* $\mathfrak{C}_j^k$ *induced in the space* $\mathfrak{M}_j^k$.

Repeating the reasoning in § 15, Subsections 7 and 9, one can show that.[†]

I. *If the original representation* $g \to T_g$ *of the group* $\mathfrak{G}_0$ *is completely irreducible, then the corresponding induced representation* $c \to A_c$ *of the ring* $\mathfrak{C}_j^k$ *in* $\mathfrak{M}_j^k$ *is also completely irreducible.*

II. *Two completely irreducible representations* $g \to T'_g$, $g \to T''_g$ *of the group* $\mathfrak{G}_0$, *containing one and the same representation* S_k, *are equivalent if and only if the corresponding induced representations of the ring* $\mathfrak{C}_j^k$ *are equivalent.*

Therefore, by determining all the completely irreducible representations (to within equivalence) of the ring $\mathfrak{C}_j^k$, we can be sure that we have not omitted any completely irreducible representation of the group $\mathfrak{G}_0$, containing the representation S_k.

5. Description of the completely irreducible representations of the ring $\mathfrak{C}_j^k$

We set

$$P = \tfrac{1}{2}(\mathbf{1}-S) \quad Q = \tfrac{1}{2}(\mathbf{1}+S). \tag{1}$$

Since $S^2 = \mathbf{1}$, it is easy to verify, that

$$P^2 = P, \quad Q^2 = Q; \tag{2}$$

moreover,

$$P+Q = \mathbf{1} \tag{3}$$

and

$$PQ = QP = 0. \tag{4}$$

We denote the set of all vectors $\xi \in \mathfrak{M}_j^k$, satisfying the condition $P\xi = \xi$ by $\mathfrak{P}_j^k$, and the set of all vectors $\xi \in \mathfrak{M}_j^k$, satisfying the condition $Q\xi = \xi$ by $\mathfrak{Q}_j^k$.

Since P, Q are bounded linear operators, then $\mathfrak{P}_j^k$, $\mathfrak{Q}_j^k$ are closed subspaces of $\mathfrak{M}_j^k$. By virtue of (2) $\mathfrak{P}_j^k$ is the set of all vectors $P\xi$,

† For the proof of proposition II it is necessary to make use of the finite-dimensionality of $\mathfrak{M}_j^k$ proved below in Subsection 5 (independently of II) (see VI, Subsection 5).

$\xi \in \mathfrak{M}_j^k$, and $\mathfrak{Q}_j^k$ is the set of all vectors $Q\xi$, $\xi \in \mathfrak{M}_j^k$. Therefore, taking (4) into account, we have:

$$P\xi = 0 \quad \text{for all} \quad \xi \in \mathfrak{Q}_j^k; \quad Q\xi = 0 \quad \text{for all} \quad \xi = \mathfrak{P}_j^k. \tag{5}$$

Moreover, letting $\eta = P\xi$, $\zeta = Q\xi$ for $\xi \in \mathfrak{M}_j^k$ and taking (3) into account, we have $\xi = \eta + \zeta$, $\eta \in \mathfrak{P}_j^k$, $\zeta = \mathfrak{Q}_j^k$, where it follows easily from (5) that this decomposition is unique. Hence:

I. *$\mathfrak{M}_j^k$ is the direct sum of the subspaces $\mathfrak{P}_j^k$ and $\mathfrak{Q}_j^k$*

$$\mathfrak{M}_j^k = \mathfrak{P}_j^k + \mathfrak{Q}_j^k. \tag{6}$$

Finally we note that relations (5) are equivalent to the relations

$$S\xi = \xi \quad \text{on} \quad \mathfrak{Q}_j^k; \quad S\xi = -\xi \quad \text{on} \quad \mathfrak{P}_j^k. \tag{7}$$

Conversely, if for a vector $\xi \in \mathfrak{M}_j^k$ one of the relations $S\xi = \xi$, $S\xi = -\xi$ is satisfied, then $\xi \in \mathfrak{Q}_j^k$ or $\xi \in \mathfrak{P}_j^k$. In fact, in the first case $Q\xi = \frac{1}{2}(1+S)\xi = \xi$, and in the second case $P\xi = \frac{1}{2}(1-S)\xi = \xi$.

Now we denote by X_{j+}^k the set of all functions $x(a)$ from X_j^k, satisfying the condition $x^{\wedge} = x$, and by X_{j-}^k the set of all functions $x(a)$ from X_j^k, satisfying the condition $x^{\wedge} = -x$. From the relations (10) and (12) Subsection 2 we conclude that X_{j+}^k is a subring of the ring X_j^k. Moreover, every function $x \in X_j^k$ can be represented in the form $x = x_1 + x_2$, where $x_1 \in X_{j+}^k$, $x_2 \in X_{j-}^k$; indeed, it is sufficient to set

$$x_1 = \tfrac{1}{2}(x + x^{\wedge}), \quad x_2 = \tfrac{1}{2}(x - x^{\wedge}).$$

II. *The subspaces $\mathfrak{P}_j^k$, $\mathfrak{Q}_j^k$ are invariant with respect to the operators T_x, $x \in X_{j+}^k$; if however $x \in X_{j-}^k$, then T_x maps $\mathfrak{P}_j^k$ into $\mathfrak{Q}_j^k$ and $\mathfrak{Q}_j^k$ into $\mathfrak{P}_j^k$.*

Proof. Let, for instance, $\xi \in \mathfrak{Q}_j^k$; then by (7) $S\xi = \xi$. Hence, making use of formula (13) Subsection 2, we see that if $x \in X_{j+}^k$,

$$ST_x\xi = ST_xS\xi = T_{x^{\wedge}}\xi = T_x\xi;$$

so that $T_x\xi \in \mathfrak{Q}_j^k$, i.e. $\mathfrak{Q}_j^k$ is invariant with respect to T_x, $x \in X_{j+}^k$. The remaining assertions are proved analogously.

We denote by $\mathfrak{C}_{j+}^k$ the set of all sums $c = x + sy$, for which $x, y \in X_{j+}^k$; as X_{j+}^k is a subring of X_j^k, then $\mathfrak{C}_{j+}^k$ is a subring of

$\mathfrak{C}_j^k$. By virtue of II, the subspaces $\mathfrak{P}_j^k$, $\mathfrak{Q}_j^k$ are invariant with respect to the operators T_c, $c \in \mathfrak{C}_{j+}^k$. Therefore, letting

$$\Lambda_c \xi = T_c \xi \quad \text{for} \quad \xi \in \mathfrak{Q}_j^k, \quad c \in \mathfrak{C}_{j+}^k,$$

we obtain a representation $c \to \Lambda_c$ of the ring $\mathfrak{C}_{j+}^k$ in the space $\mathfrak{Q}_j^k$. Analogously one can obtain a representation of the ring $\mathfrak{C}_{j+}^k$ in the space $\mathfrak{P}_j^k$.

It is easy to find the representation conjugate to the representation $c \to \Lambda_c$. For this we note that the formula $f'(\xi) = f(Q\xi)$ establishes a one-one bicontinuous correspondence between the functionals $f \in (\mathfrak{Q}_j^k)'$ and the functionals f' from $\hat{\mathfrak{M}}_j^k$, satisfying the condition $\hat{Q}f' = f'$, i.e. the functionals $f' \in \hat{\mathfrak{Q}}_j^k$(see the analogous reasoning in § 15, Subsection 7). Therefore one can write $(\mathfrak{Q}_j^k)' = \hat{\mathfrak{Q}}_j^k$ and similarly $(\mathfrak{P}_j^k)' = \hat{\mathfrak{P}}_j^k$.

III. *If the original representation $g \to T_g$ of the group $\mathfrak{G}_0$ is completely irreducible, then the corresponding representation $c \to \Lambda_c$ of the ring $\mathfrak{C}_{j+}^k$ is also completely irreducible.*

Proof. First of all we note that $\Omega \cap \mathfrak{Q}_j^k$ and $\hat{\Omega} \cap \hat{\mathfrak{Q}}_j^k$ are dense in $\mathfrak{Q}_j^k$ and $\hat{\mathfrak{Q}}_j^k$ respectively, so that the representation $c \to \Lambda_c$ satisfies the conditions of the remark in § 15, Subsection 3. In fact, let ξ_0 be a fixed non-zero vector from $\mathfrak{M}_j^k$. The vectors $T_c\xi_0$ form a dense set in R, because the original representation is completely irreducible; hence, the vectors $QE_{jj}^k T_c \xi_0$ form a dense set in $\mathfrak{Q}_j^k$. However, all of these vectors belong to Ω.

Analogously it can be proved that $\hat{\Omega} \cap \hat{\mathfrak{Q}}_j^k$ is dense in $\hat{\mathfrak{Q}}_j^k$.

Let C be a bounded linear operator in $\mathfrak{Q}_j^k$ which is admissible with respect to $c \to \Lambda_c$, $c \in \mathfrak{C}_{j+}^k$; then it is admissible also with respect to the representation† $c \to A_c$, $c \in \mathfrak{C}_j^k$. By virtue of I Subsection 4, there exists a sequence $c_n \in \mathfrak{C}_j^k$ such that as $n \to \infty$

$$(\Lambda_{c_n}\xi, \eta) \to (C\xi, \eta) \quad \text{for all} \quad \xi \in \Omega \cap \mathfrak{M}_j^k, \eta \in \hat{\Omega} \cap \hat{\mathfrak{M}}_j^k.$$

† We recall (see Subsection 4) that $c \to A_c$ is the induced representation of the ring $\mathfrak{C}_j^k$.

In particular, this relation is valid for $\xi \in \Omega \cap \mathfrak{Q}_j^k$, $\eta \in \hat{\Omega} \cap \hat{\mathfrak{Q}}_j^k$. But for all vectors ξ, η

$$(A_{c_n}\xi, \eta) = (A_{c_n}\xi, \hat{Q}\eta) = (QA_{c_n}\xi, \eta) = (A_{c'_n}\xi, \eta) = (\Lambda_{c'_n}\xi, \eta),$$

where $c'_n \in \mathfrak{S}_{j+}^k$. In fact, letting $c_n = (x'_n + x''_n) + s(y'_n + y''_n)$, $c'_n = x'_n + sy'_n$ where $x'_n, y'_n \in X_j^k+$, $x''_n, y''_n \in X_j^k-$, and taking into account that $\xi \in \mathfrak{Q}_j^k$, we have

$$QA_{c_n}\xi = QT_{c_n}\xi = Q(T_{x'_n}\xi + T_{x''_n}\xi + ST_{y'_n}\xi + ST_{y''_n}\xi)$$
$$= (T_{x'_n}\xi + ST_{y'_n}\xi) = T_{c'_n}\xi = \Lambda_{c'_n}\xi,$$

because $T_{x'_n}\xi$, $T_{y'_n}\xi \in \mathfrak{Q}_j^k$, $T_{x''_n}\xi$, $T_{y''_n}\xi \in \mathfrak{P}_j^k$. Thus $(\Lambda_{c'_n}\xi, \eta) \to (C\xi, \eta)$ for all $\xi \in \Omega \cap \mathfrak{Q}_j^k$, $\eta \in \hat{\Omega} \cap \hat{\mathfrak{Q}}_j^k$, where $c'_n \in \mathfrak{S}_{j+}^k$ and this means that the representation $c \to \Lambda_c$ is completely irreducible.

IV. *The operators* Λ_c, $c \in \mathfrak{S}_{j+}^k$ *commute with each other.* In fact, if $c = x + sy$, $x, y \in X_j^k+$, then $\Lambda_c = T_x + ST_y = T_x + T_y$ on $\mathfrak{Q}_j^k$, because $S = \mathbf{1}$ on $\mathfrak{Q}_j^k$; on the other hand, all the operators T_x, $x \in X_j^k+$, commute with each other.

V. *If the representation* $g \to T_g$ *of the group* $\mathfrak{S}_0$ *is completely irreducible, then each of the spaces* $\mathfrak{P}_j^k$, $\mathfrak{Q}_j^k$ *is either one-dimensional or* $= (0)$.

Proof. By virtue of III and IV, the operators Λ_c, $c \in \mathfrak{S}_{j+}^k$, commute with each other, and the representation $c \to \Lambda_c$ is completely irreducible; this is possible only when $\mathfrak{Q}_j^k$ either $= (0)$, or is one-dimensional (see VI § 15, Subsection 4). Similarly it can be proved that $\mathfrak{P}_j^k$ either $= (0)$, or is one-dimensional.

VI. *If the representation* $g \to T_g$ *of the group* $\mathfrak{G}_0$ *is completely irreducible, then each of the subspaces* $\mathfrak{M}_j^k$ *is at most two-dimensional.* The assertion follows immediately from V and the relation $\mathfrak{M}_j^k = \mathfrak{P}_j^k + \mathfrak{Q}_j^k$. In order to make use of these last results, we must express the sets X_j^k+, X_j^k- in terms of the functions $B_\nu(\varepsilon)$ (see § 15, Subsection 11).

VII. *In the transition from* $x(a)$ *to* $x^{\wedge}(a)$ *the functions* $B_\nu(\varepsilon)$ *go into* $B_\nu^{\wedge}(\varepsilon) = B_\nu(\varepsilon^{-1})$. *In particular,* $x(a)$ *belongs respectively to* X_j^k+, X_j^k-, *if and only if respectively* $B_\nu(\varepsilon^{-1}) = B_\nu(\varepsilon)$, $B_\nu(\varepsilon^{-1}) = -B_\nu(\varepsilon)$.

Proof. We have by the definition of the function $B_v(\varepsilon)$:

$$B_v(\varepsilon) =$$

$$= \pi 2k + 1 \beta^{-\frac{1}{2}}(\varepsilon) \int x(u_1^{-1}\gamma\varepsilon\zeta u_2) c_{vj}^k(u_1) \overline{c_{vj}^k(u_2)} \alpha(\gamma) du_1 du_2 d\zeta d\gamma, \qquad (8)$$

where $\alpha(\gamma) = e^{2v\omega}$ when $\gamma = \left\| \begin{matrix} e^{-i\omega} & 0 \\ 0 & e^{i\omega} \end{matrix} \right\|$ (see (1), and (4) § 15,

Subsection 8 and (4) § 15, Subsection 11). Hence

$$B_v^{\wedge}(\varepsilon) = \pi 2k + 1 \beta^{-\frac{1}{2}}(\varepsilon) \int x^{\wedge}(u_1^{-1}\gamma\varepsilon\zeta u_2) \overline{c_{vj}^k(u_1)} c_{vj}^k(u_2) \alpha(\gamma) du_1 du_2 d\zeta d\gamma$$

$$= \pi 2k + 1 \beta^{-\frac{1}{2}}(\varepsilon) \int x(u_1^{-1}\gamma\varepsilon^{-1}\zeta^{\wedge}u_2) \overline{c_{vjc}^k u_1)} c_{vj}^k(u_2) \alpha(\gamma) du_1 du_2 d\zeta d\gamma. \qquad (9)$$

But if $\zeta = \left\| \begin{matrix} 1 & \zeta \\ 0 & 1 \end{matrix} \right\|$, then $\zeta^{\wedge} = \zeta^{*-1} = \left\| \begin{matrix} 1 & 0 \\ -\zeta & 1 \end{matrix} \right\|$, and so, taking[†]

$s = \left\| \begin{matrix} 0 & 1 \\ -1 & 0 \end{matrix} \right\|$ and $s^{-1}\zeta^{\wedge}s = \zeta_1$, we have:

$$\zeta_1 = s^{-1}\zeta^{\wedge}s = \left\| \begin{matrix} 1 & \overline{\zeta} \\ 0 & 1 \end{matrix} \right\| \in Z.$$

Clearly this implies that $d\zeta = d\zeta_1$.

Since, moreover, $s^{-1}\varepsilon^{-1}s = \varepsilon$, $s^{-1}\gamma s = \gamma^{-1}$; then (9) can be written in the form

$$B_v^{\wedge}(\varepsilon) = \pi 2k + 1 \beta^{-\frac{1}{2}}(\varepsilon) \int x((s^{-1}u_1)^{-1}\gamma^{-1}\varepsilon\zeta_1 s^{-1}u_2) \overline{c_{vj}^k(u_1)} c_{vj}^k(u_2) \times$$

$$\times \alpha(\gamma) du_1 du_2 d\zeta_1 d\gamma = \pi 2k + 1 \beta^{-\frac{1}{2}}(\varepsilon) \int x(u_1^{-1}\gamma\varepsilon\zeta u_2) \overline{c_{vj}^k(su_1)} c_{vj}^k(su_2) \times$$

$$\times \alpha(\gamma^{-1}) du_1 du_2 d\zeta d\gamma$$

$$= \pi 2k + 1 \beta^{-\frac{1}{2}}(\varepsilon) \sum_{p,\,q=-k}^{k} \int x(u_1^{-1}\gamma\varepsilon\zeta u_2) \overline{c_{vp}^k(s)c_{pj}^k(u_1)} \times$$

$$\times c_{vq}^k(s) c_{qj}^k(u_2) \alpha(\gamma^{-1}) du_1 du_2 d\zeta d\gamma. \qquad (10)$$

But

$$c_{vp}^k(s) = \begin{cases} 0 & \text{if} \quad p \neq -v, \\ (-1)^{k+v} & \text{if} \quad p = -v. \end{cases} \qquad (11)$$

---

† We use the same letter s to denote the reflection in the axes Ox_1, Ox_2, Ox_3 as well as the matrix $\left\| \begin{smallmatrix} 0 & 1 \\ -1 & 0 \end{smallmatrix} \right\|$; however, this will never lead to confusion in het sequel.

In fact, consider the spinor representation of the group $\mathfrak{U}$ of weight k. In this representation the elements of the canonical basis are the functions

$$f_\nu(z) = (-1)^{k-\nu} \frac{z^{k-\nu}}{\sqrt{[(k-\nu)!(k+\nu)!]}},$$

and the representation is given by the formula

$$T_u f(z) = (u_{12}z+u_{22})^{2k} f\left(\frac{u_{11}z+u_{21}}{u_{12}z+u_{22}}\right)$$

(see (6) § 5, Subsection 4 and (7) § 5, Subsection 3). In particular

$$T_s f_\nu(z) = z^{2k} f_\nu\left(-\frac{1}{z}\right) = \frac{z^{k+\nu}}{\sqrt{[(k-\nu)!(k+\nu)!]}} = (-1)^{k+\nu} f_{-\nu}(z).$$

Hence formula (11) follows. Substituting in (10) the value of $c^k_{\nu p}(s)$ given by (11), we obtain:

$$B^{\wedge}_\nu(\varepsilon) =$$

$$= \pi(2k+1)\beta^{-\frac{1}{2}}(\varepsilon) \int x(u_1^{-1}\gamma\varepsilon\zeta u_2) c^k_{-\nu j}(u_1) \overline{c^k_{-\nu j}(u_2)} \alpha^{-1}(\gamma) du_1 du_2 d\zeta d\gamma = B_{-\nu}(\varepsilon).$$

On the other hand, $B_{-\nu}(\varepsilon) = B_\nu(\varepsilon^{-1})$ (see II § 15, Subsection 11), and so $B^{\wedge}_\nu(\varepsilon) = B_\nu(\varepsilon^{-1})$.

The remaining assertions of proposition VII are consequences of this last equation.

Now we consider a fixed subspace $\mathfrak{M}^k_j \neq (0)$. By virtue of VI, only the following two cases are possible:

(1) $\mathfrak{M}^k_j$ IS ONE-DIMENSIONAL, HENCE, ONE OF THE SUBSPACES $\mathfrak{P}^k_j$, $\mathfrak{Q}^k_j$ IS ONE-DIMENSIONAL, AND THE OTHER $= (0)$.

In order to be specific, let $\mathfrak{P}^k_j = (0)$, and $\mathfrak{Q}^k_j$ be one-dimensional; the other alternative is considered analogously. Then $S = \mathbf{1}$ on $\mathfrak{M}^k_j$. The representation $c \to A_c$ of the ring $\mathfrak{C}^k_j$ in $\mathfrak{M}^k_j$ also defines a representation of the ring X^k_j, which is given by the multiplicative linear functional

$$\lambda(x) = \int B_\nu(\varepsilon)\varepsilon^{i\rho}_{22} d\varepsilon$$

(see § 15, Subsection 14); here, by II, $\lambda(x) = 0$ when $x \in X^k_{j-}$, and so $\lambda(x^{\wedge} - x) = 0$, $\lambda(x^{\wedge}) = \lambda(x)$ for any function $x \in X^k_j$.

According to proposition VII this means that

$$\int B_\nu(\varepsilon^{-1})\varepsilon_{22}^{i\rho}\,d\varepsilon = \int B_\nu(\varepsilon)\varepsilon_{22}^{i\rho}\,d\varepsilon,$$

i.e.

$$\int B_\nu(\varepsilon)\varepsilon_{22}^{-i\rho}\,d\varepsilon = \int B_\nu(\varepsilon)\varepsilon_{22}^{i\rho}\,d\varepsilon. \tag{12}$$

Equation (12), satisfied for all $x \in X_j^k$, signifies that the functionals $\lambda(B)$ induced by the completely irreducible representations with parameters $(2\nu, -\rho)$ and $(2\nu, \rho)$ coincide. From this follows the equivalence of these representations, which is possible only in two cases (see the end of § 15): $\nu = 0$ or $\rho = 0$.

If the two representations $c \to A_c'$, $c \to A_c''$ of the ring $\mathfrak{S}_j^k$ are equivalent, then, by virtue of the one-dimensionality of the space $\mathfrak{M}_j^k$, the corresponding functionals $\lambda(x)$, and therefore also the corresponding pairs (ν, ρ), are equal;† hence the corresponding operators S in $\mathfrak{M}_j^k$ coincide.

Thus:

VIII. *A completely irreducible representation of the group* $\mathfrak{G}_0$ *with one-dimensional* $\mathfrak{M}_j^k$ *is possible only when* $\nu = 0$, *or* $\rho = 0$. *In either of these cases the representation* $c \to A_c$ *of the ring* $\mathfrak{S}_j^k$ *is given by the condition*

$$A_{x+sy} = [\lambda(x)+\lambda(y)]\mathbf{1} \text{ or } A_{x+sy} = [\lambda(x)-\lambda(y)]\mathbf{1},\ x, y \in X_j^k, \tag{13}$$

where

$$\lambda(x) = \int B_\nu(\varepsilon)\varepsilon_{22}^{i\rho}\,d\varepsilon. \tag{14}$$

Two such representations of the group $\mathfrak{G}_0$ *are equivalent if and only if the corresponding pairs* (ν, ρ) *and the operators* S *in* $\mathfrak{M}_j^k$ *coincide.*

(2) $\mathfrak{M}_j^k$ IS TWO-DIMENSIONAL, HENCE, $\mathfrak{P}_j^k$, $\mathfrak{Q}_j^k$ ARE ONE-DIMENSIONAL.

We choose in $\mathfrak{P}_j^k$ and $\mathfrak{Q}_j^k$ vectors $\xi_1 \neq 0$, $\xi_2 \neq 0$. If $y \in X_{j-}^k$, then, by virtue of proposition II, $T_y\xi_1 \in \mathfrak{Q}_j^k$. We cannot have $T_y\xi_1 = 0$ for all $y \in X_{j-}^k$, because this implies, by virtue of the relations $T_x\xi_1 \in \mathfrak{P}_j^k$ when $x \in X_{j+}^k$, $S\xi_1 = -\xi_1$, that the subspace $\mathfrak{P}_j^k$ would be invariant with respect to all the operators A_c, $c \in \mathfrak{S}_j^k$, contrary to the supposed complete irreducibility of the representation $c \to A_c$.

† Here the pairs (ν, ρ) and $(\nu-, -\rho)$ are not dintinguished from one an other.

Thus there exists a function $y_1 \in X^k_{j-}$ such that $T_{y_1}\xi_1 \neq 0$, and so $T_{y_1}\xi_1 = \alpha_1\xi_2$ where $\alpha_1 \neq 0$. Replacing y_1 by $\alpha_1 y_1$, we may assume that $T_{y_1}\xi_1 = \xi_2$.

Similarly there exists a function $y_2 \in X^k_{j-}$ such that $T_{y_2}\xi_2 = \xi_1$. Here $T_{y_2}\xi_1 = \beta_1\xi_2$, $T_{y_1}\xi_2 = \beta_2\xi_1$, because $T_{y_2}\xi_1 \in \mathfrak{Q}^k_j$, $T_{y_1}\xi_2 \in \mathfrak{P}^k_j$. Only the two following cases are possible:

(α) $\beta_1 = \beta_2 = 0$. Letting $y_0 = y_1 + y_2$, we obtain a function $y_0 \in X^k_{j-}$, satisfying the conditions:

$$T_{y_0}\xi_1 = \xi_2, \quad T_{y_0}\xi_2 = \xi_1. \tag{15}$$

(β) At least one of the numbers β_1, β_2 is distinct from zero. Let for instance, $\beta_2 \neq 0$. Then replacing ξ_2 by $\beta_2^{\frac{1}{2}}\,\xi_2$ and letting $y_0 = \beta_2^{-\frac{1}{2}}y_1$, we again obtain a function $y_0 \in X^k_{j-}$, satisfying conditions (15); here the argument of $\sqrt{\beta_2}$ can be chosen to be arbitrary, but the same for ξ_2 and y_0.

Hence, in either case there exists a function $y_0 \in X^k_{j-}$, satisfying conditions (15).

Now we consider the operators T_x, $x \in X^k_{j+}$. Since $\mathfrak{P}^k_j$ is invariant with respect to these operators, $T_x\xi_1 = \lambda_1(x)\xi_1$, where $\lambda_1(x)$ is a multiplicative linear functional in X^k_{j+}. Similarly, $T_x\xi_2 = \lambda_2(x)\xi_2$, where $\lambda_2(x)$ is a multiplicative linear functional in X^k_{j+}.

Further, by virtue of II, $T_y\xi_1 \in \mathfrak{Q}^k_j$ when $y \in X^k_{j-}$; therefore $T_y\xi_1 = \mu_1(y)\xi_2$ where $\mu_1(y)$ is some linear functional in X^k_{j-}; analogously $T_y\xi_2 = \mu_2(y)\,\xi_1$.

From (15) it follows that

$$\mu_1(y_0) = \mu_2(y_0) = 1. \tag{16}$$

But, by (12) Subsection 2 and the commutativity of the rings X^k_j, $y'y'' = y''y' \in X^k_{j+}$, $xy = yx \in X^k_{j-}$ for any $y, y', y'' \in X^k_{j-}$, $x \in X^k_{j+}$; therefore

$$T_{y'}T_{y''}\xi_1 = T_{y''}T_{y'}\xi_1 = \lambda_1(y'y'')\xi_1,$$

$$T_{y'}T_{y''}\xi_2 = T_{y''}T_{y'}\xi_2 = \lambda_2(y'y'')\xi_2,$$

$$T_{xy}\xi_1 = T_{yx}\xi_1 = \mu_1(xy)\xi_2, \quad T_{xy}\xi_2 = T_{yx}\xi_2 = \mu_2(xy)\xi_1.$$

These relations mean that

$$\mu_1(y')\mu_2(y'') = \mu_1(y'')\mu_2(y') = \lambda_1(y'y'') = \lambda_2(y'y''), \tag{17}$$

$$\lambda_2(x)\mu_1(y) = \lambda_1(x)\mu_1(y) = \mu_1(xy), \tag{18}$$

$$\lambda_1(x)\mu_2(y) = \lambda_2(x)\mu_2(y) = \mu_2(xy). \tag{19}$$

Letting $y = y_0$ in (18) and (19) and taking relations (16) into account, we obtain:

$$\lambda_1(x) = \lambda_2(x) = \mu_1(xy_0) = \mu_2(xy_0); \tag{20}$$

we therefore write $\lambda(x) = \lambda_1(x) = \lambda_2(x)$.

Further letting $y' = y$, $y'' = y_0$ in (17), we obtain:

$$\mu_1(y) = \mu_2(y) = \lambda(yy_0); \tag{21}$$

we write $\mu(y) = \mu_1(y) = \mu_2(y)$.

Relations (17–21) then take the form

$$\mu(y) = \lambda(yy_0), \quad \mu(xy_0) = \lambda(x), \tag{22}$$

$$\mu(y')\mu(y'') = \lambda(y'y_0)\lambda(y''y_0) = \lambda(y'y''), \tag{23}$$

$$\lambda(x)\mu(y) = \lambda(x)\lambda(yy_0) = \mu(xy) \tag{24}$$

for all $x \in X^k_{j+}$, $y, y', y'' \in X^k_{j-}$.

Here, by definition of the functionals $\lambda_1, \lambda_2, \mu_1, \mu_2$ and by virtue of relations (16),

$$T_x\xi_1 = \lambda(x)\xi_1, \quad T_x\xi_2 = \lambda(x)\xi_2 \quad \text{for} \quad x \in X^k_{j+}, \tag{25}$$

$$T_y\xi_1 = \mu(y)\xi_2, \quad T_y\xi_2 = \mu(y)\xi_1 \quad \text{for} \quad y \in X^k_{j-} \tag{26}$$

and

$$\mu(y_0) = 1. \tag{27}$$

Now we define a functional $\tilde{\lambda}(x)$ in X^k_j, letting

$$\tilde{\lambda}(x) = \tilde{\lambda}(x'+x'') = \lambda(x')+\mu(x'') = \lambda(x')+\lambda(x''y_0), \tag{28}$$

where $x = x'+x''$, $x' \in X^k_{j+}$, $x'' \in X^k_{j-}$. Applying relations (23), (24), it can casily be verified that $\tilde{\lambda}(x)$ is a multiplicative linear functional in X^k_j; hence, it can be represented in the form

$$\tilde{\lambda}(x) = \int B_\nu(\varepsilon)\varepsilon^i_{22}d\varepsilon \tag{29}$$

(see § 15 Subsection 14). In particular,

$$\lambda(x) = \int B_\nu(\varepsilon)\varepsilon_{22}^{i\rho}\,d\varepsilon \quad \text{when} \quad x \in X_{j+}^k, \tag{30}$$

$$\mu(x) = \int B_\nu(\varepsilon)\varepsilon_{22}^{i\rho}\,d\varepsilon \quad \text{when} \quad x \in X_{j-}^k. \tag{31}$$

Here $\nu \neq 0$ and $\rho \neq 0$. For, otherwise $\tilde{\lambda}(x^\wedge) = \tilde{\lambda}(x)$ for all $x \in X_j^k$; on the other hand, $y^\wedge = -y$ for $y \in X_{j-}^k$, and so for all $y \in X_{j-}^k$, $\mu(y) = \tilde{\lambda}(y) = \tilde{\lambda}(y^\wedge) = -\tilde{\lambda}(y) = -\mu(y)$, i.e. $\mu(y) = 0$, contrary to the condition $\mu(y_0) = 1$.

Formulae (30), (31) completely define the representation $c \to A_c$ of the ring $\mathfrak{S}_j^k$.

In fact if

$$c = (x_1 + y_1) + s(x_2 + y_2),\ x_1, x_2 \in X_{j+}^k,\ y_1, y_2 \in X_{j-}^k,$$

then, by virtue of (25), (26) and the equations $S\xi_1 = -\xi_1$, $S\xi_2 = \xi_2$ we have

$$A_c\xi_1 = [\lambda(x_1) - \lambda(x_2)]\xi_1 + [\mu(y_1) + \mu(y_2)]\xi_2,$$

$$A_c\xi_2 = [\lambda(x_1) + \lambda(x_2)]\xi_2 + [\mu(y_1) - \mu(y_2)]\xi_1.$$

Now we assume that the two representations $c \to A_c'$, $c \to A_c''$ of the ring $\mathfrak{S}_j^k$ in the spaces $\mathfrak{M}_j'^k$, $\mathfrak{M}_j''^k$ are equivalent. This means that there exists a linear operator V, mapping $\mathfrak{M}_j'^k$ on $\mathfrak{M}_j''^k$ such that

$$A_c'' = VA_c'V^{-1} \quad \text{for all} \quad c \in \mathfrak{S}_j^k. \tag{32}$$

Let ξ_1', ξ_2' be the corresponding basis vectors in $\mathfrak{M}_j'^k$, so that

$$A_x'\xi_1' = \lambda'(x)\xi_1', \quad A_x'\xi_2' = \lambda'(x)\xi_2' \quad \text{for} \quad x \in X_{j+}^k,$$

$$A_y'\xi_2' = \mu'(y)\xi_2', \quad A_y'\xi_2' = \mu'(y)\xi_1' \quad \text{for} \quad y \in X_{j-}^k.$$

We set $\xi_1'' = V\xi_1'$, $\xi_2'' = V\xi_2'$. Then

$$A_x''\xi_1'' = VA_c'V^{-1}V\xi_1' = \lambda'(x)V\xi_1' = \lambda'(x)\xi_1'' \quad \text{for} \quad x \in X_{j+}^k$$

and analogously

$$A_x''\xi_2'' = \lambda'(x)\xi_2 \quad \text{for} \quad x \in X_{j+}^k,$$

$$A_y''\xi_1'' = \mu'(y)\xi_2'', \quad A_y''\xi_2'' = \mu'(y)\xi_1'' \quad \text{for} \quad y \in X_{j-}^k,$$

$$S''A_y''\xi_1'' = \mu'(y)\xi_2'', \quad S''A_y''\xi_2'' = -\mu'(y)\xi_1'' \quad \text{for} \quad y \in X_{j-}^k.$$

Hence we deduce that $\xi_1'' \in \mathfrak{P}_j''^k$, $\xi_2'' \in \mathfrak{Q}_j''^k$ and that the corresponding functionals $\lambda''(x)$ and $\mu''(x)$ coincide with $\lambda'(x)$ and $\mu'(x)$.

Thus:

IX. *A completely irreducible representation of the group* $\mathfrak{G}_0$ *with two-dimensional* $\mathfrak{M}_j^k$ *is defined by a positive integral or semi-integral number* ν *and a complex number* $\rho \neq 0$. *The corresponding representation* $c \to A_c$ *of the ring* $\mathfrak{C}_j^k$ *is given by the formulae:*

$$A_c\xi_1 = [\lambda(x_1)-\lambda(x_2)]\xi_1+[\mu(y_1)+\mu(y_2)]\xi_2,$$
$$A_c\xi_2 = [\mu(y_1)-\mu(y_2)]\xi_1+[\lambda(x_1)+\lambda(x_2)]\xi_2$$

for $c = (x_1+y_1)+s(x_2+y_2)$, $x_1, x_2 \in X_{j+}^k$, $y_1, y_2 \in X_{j-}^k$, *where*

$$\lambda(x) = \int B_\nu(\varepsilon)\varepsilon_{22}^{i\rho}\, d\varepsilon \quad \text{when} \quad x \in X_{j+}^k,$$
$$\mu(x) = \int B_\nu(\varepsilon)\varepsilon_{22}^{i\rho}\, d\varepsilon \quad \text{when} \quad x \in X_{j-}^k.$$

Two representations $c \to A_c'$, $c \to A_c''$ *of the ring* $\mathfrak{C}_j^k$ *(and therefore also two completely irreducible representations* $g \to T_g'$, $g \to T_g''$ *of the group* $\mathfrak{G}_0$*) with two-dimensional* $\mathfrak{M}_j'^k$, $\mathfrak{M}_j''^k$ *are equivalent if and only if a proper choice of the basis vectors* ξ_1', ξ_2', ξ_1'', ξ_2'' *ensures that the corresponding pairs* (ν', ρ'), (ν'', ρ'') *coincide.*

6. Realizations of the completely irreducible representations of the group $\mathfrak{G}_0$

Now we show how in fact to realize all the cases analysed in Subsection 5. According to the results of Subsection 5, a completely irreducible representation $g \to T_g$ of the group $\mathfrak{G}_0$ is given by a pair of numbers (ν, ρ), where ν is an integral or semi-integral number, and ρ is an arbitrary complex number. If $\nu = 0$ or $\rho = 0$, then the pair (ν, ρ) can correspond to two mutually non-equivalent representations of the group $\mathfrak{G}_0$, and the corresponding $\mathfrak{M}_j^k$ are one-dimensional; if however $\nu \neq 0$ and $\rho \neq 0$, then the pair (ν, ρ) corresponds to a unique representation (up to equivalence) of the group $\mathfrak{G}_0$, where the corresponding $\mathfrak{M}_j^k$ is two-dimensional.

We examine these cases separately:

(1) $\nu = 0$. In order to be specific, assume that ρ^2 is not one of the numbers $-4n^2$, $n = 1, 2, 3, \ldots$.

We consider the completely irreducible representation $\mathfrak{S}_{0,\rho}$ of the group $\mathfrak{A}$. It is realized in the space $L_2^0(\mathfrak{U})$ of measurable functions $f(u)$, satisfying the conditions:

$$\int |f(u)|^2 du < +\infty, \quad f(\gamma u) = f(u) \quad \text{for all} \quad \gamma \in \Gamma, \tag{1}$$

and so:

$$T_g f(u) = \frac{\alpha(ua)}{\alpha(u\bar{a})} f(u\bar{a}), \tag{2}$$

where

$$\alpha(a) = |a_{22}|^{i\rho-2} \tag{3}$$

(see § 15, Subsection 15). We define an operator S in $L_2^0(\mathfrak{U})$, letting

$$Sf(u) = f(su), \tag{4}$$

where

$$s = \begin{Vmatrix} 0 & 1 \\ -1 & 0 \end{Vmatrix};$$

S is an operator in $L_2^0(\mathfrak{U})$, indeed an isometric operator, because

$$\int |f(su)|^2 du = \int |f(u)|^2 du$$

and

$$f(s\gamma u) = f(s\gamma s^{-1} su) = f(\gamma^{-1} su) = f(su).$$

We show that this operator S together with the operators T_a, $a \in \mathfrak{A}$, of the representation $\mathfrak{S}_{0,\rho}$ defines a representation of the group $\mathfrak{G}_0$. For this it is sufficient to establish that: (α) $S^2 = 1$; (β) S commutes with all the operators T_u, $u \in \mathfrak{U}$; (γ) $ST_\varepsilon S = T_\varepsilon^{-1}$ (see Subsection 2).

But

$$S^2 f(u) = f(s^2 u) = f(\gamma_0 u) = f(u),$$

where

$$\gamma_0 = \begin{Vmatrix} -1 & 0 \\ 0 & -1 \end{Vmatrix} = s^2,$$

so that $S^2 = 1$. Further, $T_{u_0} f(u) = f(uu_0)$, and so $ST_{u_0} f(u) = T_{u_0} Sf(u) = f(suu_0)$, so that T_{u_0} and S commute. Finally,

$$ST_\varepsilon S^{-1} f(u) = ST_\varepsilon f(s^{-1}u) = S\left[\frac{\alpha(u\varepsilon)}{\alpha(u\bar{\varepsilon})} f(s^{-1}(u\bar{\varepsilon}))\right]$$

$$= \frac{\alpha(su\varepsilon)}{\alpha((su)\bar{\varepsilon})} f(s^{-1}((su)\bar{\varepsilon})), \tag{5}$$

$$T_{\varepsilon^{-1}}f(u) = \frac{\alpha(u\varepsilon^{-1})}{\alpha(u\bar{\varepsilon}^{-1})} f(u\bar{\varepsilon}^{-1}). \tag{6}$$

We set

$$su\varepsilon = \varepsilon'\zeta'u' \tag{7}$$

$$u\varepsilon^{-1} = \varepsilon''\zeta''u''; \tag{8}$$

then formulae (5) and (6) take the form

$$ST_\varepsilon S^{-1}f(u) = \alpha(\varepsilon')f(s^{-1}u'), \quad T_{\varepsilon^{-1}}f(u) = \alpha(\varepsilon'')f(u'') \tag{9}$$

(see (9) § 11, Subsection 5). But, applying the operation ^ to both sides of (7) and making use of the properties of this operation (see (9) Subsection 2), we obtain:

$$su\varepsilon^{-1} = \varepsilon'^{-1}\zeta'^{\wedge}u',$$

and so

$$u\varepsilon^{-1} = s^{-1}\varepsilon'^{-1}ss^{-1}\zeta'^{\wedge}ss^{-1}u' = \varepsilon'\zeta'''s^{-1}u', \tag{10}$$

where

$$\zeta''' = s^{-1}\zeta'^{\wedge}s \in Z.$$

Comparison of formulae (8) and (10) shows that $\varepsilon'' = \varepsilon'$, $\zeta'' = \zeta'''$ and $u'' = s^{-1}u'$; therefore the right sides, and this means also the left sides, of formulae (9) coincide. In this way it follows that $ST_\varepsilon S^{-1} = T_{\varepsilon^{-1}}$.

We have considered the case when ρ^2 is not of the form $-4n^2$. If, however, $\rho^2 = -4n^2$ for some natural number n, then the preceding reasoning remains in force, where the part of $\mathfrak{S}_{0,\rho}$ is played by the corresponding spinor representation, which we again denote by† $\mathfrak{S}_{0,\rho}$, and where the part of the space $L_2^0(\mathfrak{U})$ will be played by a finite-dimensional subspace of the space $L_2^0(\mathfrak{U})$—the space of the spinor representation.

Thus, in either case *the operators* T_a *of the representation* $\mathfrak{S}_{0,\rho}$ *together with the operator* $Sf(u) = f(su)$ *define a representation of the group* $\mathfrak{G}_0$ *in the space* $L_2^0(\mathfrak{U})$. This representation is denoted by $D^+_{0,\rho}$. We obtain a second representation, corresponding to the pair $(0, \rho)$, letting

$$Sf(u) = -f(su);$$

† Here we deviate from the notation of § 15, Subsection 15.

it is easy to see that conditions (α), (β), (γ) will also be satisfied; the corresponding representation of the group $\mathfrak{G}_0$ is denoted by $D^-_{0,\rho}$.

I. *The representations* $D^+_{0,\rho}$, $D^-_{0,\rho}$ *are completely irreducible,* because the restriction of each of these representations to the group $\mathfrak{G}_+$ is a completely irreducible representation $\mathfrak{S}_{0,\rho}$.

We will now indicate how the operators S act on the vectors ξ^k_p of the canonical basis. Since these vectors are proportional to the functions $c^k_{0p}(u)$ (see Theorem 8 § 11, Subsection 4), it is sufficient to describe how S acts on these functions. But in the case of the representation $D^+_{0,\rho}$, we have applying formula (4),

$$Sc^k_{0p}(u) = c^k_{0p}(su) = \sum_{j=-k}^{k} c^k_{0j}(s)c^k_{jp}(u) = (-1)^k c^k_{0p}(u)$$

(see (11) Subsection 5); therefore

$$S\xi^k_p = (-1)^k\xi^k_p \text{ in case of representation } D^+_{0,\rho}, \tag{11}$$

hence,

$$S\xi^k_p = (-1)^{k+1}\xi^k_p \text{ in case of representation } D^-_{0,\rho}. \tag{12}$$

(2) $\nu > 0$, $\rho = 0$. We will consider the representations of the principal series $\mathfrak{S}_{m,0}$, $\mathfrak{S}_{-m,0}$ of the group $\mathfrak{G}_+$, where $m = 2\nu$ (see § 11, Subsection 3). These representations are realized in the spaces $L^m_2(\mathfrak{U})$, $L^{-m}_2(\mathfrak{U})$ of measurable functions $f(u)$, satisfying respectively the conditions:

$$\int |f(u)|^2 \, du < \infty, \quad f(\gamma u) = e^{im\phi}f(u), \tag{13a}$$

$$\int |f(u)|^2 \, du < \infty, \quad f(\gamma u) = e^{-im\phi}f(u), \tag{13b}$$

where the operators T'_a, T''_a of the representations $\mathfrak{S}_{m,0}$ $\mathfrak{S}_{-m,0}$ are given essentially by the same formula

$$T'_a f(u) = \frac{\alpha(u\alpha)}{\alpha(u\bar{a})} f(u\bar{a}), \quad f \in L^m_2(\mathfrak{U}), \tag{14a}$$

$$T''_a f(u) = \frac{\alpha(ua)}{\alpha(u\bar{a})} f(u\bar{a}), \quad f \in L^{-m}_2(\mathfrak{U}). \tag{14b}$$

The representations $\mathfrak{S}_{m,0}$ and $\mathfrak{S}_{-m,0}$ are unitary and unitarily equivalent (see III § 11, Subsection 6). Let W be an operator mapping $L_2^m(\mathfrak{U})$ isometrically on $L_2^{-m}(\mathfrak{U})$, such that

$$T''_a = WT'_aW^{-1} \quad \text{for all} \quad a \in \mathfrak{U}. \tag{15}$$

This operator W is uniquely defined by the condition

$$W\xi'^k_p = \xi''^k_p, \tag{16}$$

where $\{\xi'^k_p\}$, $\{\xi''^k_p\}$ are canonical bases of the representations $a \to T'_a$, $a \to T''_a$ in the spaces $L_2^m(\mathfrak{U})$, $L_2^{-m}(\mathfrak{U})$ respectively (see III § 11, Subsection 6). But ξ'^k_p, ξ''^k_p only differ from the functions $c^k_{\nu p}(u)$, $c^k_{-\nu p}(u)$ by a factor $\kappa^k_{\nu 0}\sqrt{(2k+1)}$ (§ 11, Subsection 4); therefore condition (16) can also be written in the form

$$Wc^k_{\nu p}(u) = c^k_{-\nu p}(u). \tag{17}$$

Now we set

$$A_s f(u) = \kappa f(su) \quad \text{for} \quad f \in L_2^m(\mathfrak{U}), \tag{18}$$

where $\kappa = (-1)^\nu$ when ν is integral and $\kappa = (-1)^{\nu-\frac{1}{2}}$ when ν is semi-integral.

Then A_s is a linear operator mapping $L_2^m(\mathfrak{U})$ isometrically on $L_2^{-m}(\mathfrak{U})$. In fact, the isometry of the operator A_s follows from the relation

$$\int |A_s f(u)|^2 du = \int |f(su)|^2 du = \int |f(u)|^2 du.$$

Further,

$$f(s\gamma u) = f(s\gamma s^{-1} \cdot su) = f(\gamma^{-1} su) = e^{-im\phi} f(su);$$

hence, $A_s f(u) = \kappa f(su) \in L_2^{-m}(\mathfrak{U})$, i.e. A_s maps $L_2^m(\mathfrak{U})$ isometrically into $L_2^{-m}(\mathfrak{U})$. However, this mapping is *onto* $L_2^{-m}(\mathfrak{U})$, because there exists an inverse operator A_s^{-1}, defined in $L_2^{-m}(\mathfrak{U})$ by

$$A_s^{-1} f(u) = \kappa f(s^{-1}u) \quad \text{for} \quad f \in L_2^{-m}(\mathfrak{U}). \tag{19}$$

Now we define an operator S in $L_2^m(\mathfrak{U})$, letting

$$S = A_s W. \tag{20}$$

By virtue of the properties of the operators A_s and W, S is a unitary operator in $L_2^m(\mathfrak{U})$.

We describe how this operator acts on the functions $c^k_{\nu p}(u)$. By virtue of (11) Subsection 5 and formula (17), we have

$$Sc^k_{\nu p}(u) = A_s W c^k_{\nu p}(u) = A_s c^k_{-\nu p}(u) = \kappa c^k_{-\nu p}(su) = (-1)^{[k]} c^k_{\nu p}(u),$$

where $[k]$ denotes the integral part of the number k; hence,

$$Sc^k_{\nu p}(u) = (-1)^{[k]} c^k_{\nu p}(u). \tag{21}$$

By virtue of the relation $c^k_{\nu p}(u) = \kappa^k_{\nu 0} \sqrt{(2k+1)}\, \xi^k_p$ formula (21) can be written in the form

$$S\xi^k_p = (-1)^{[k]} \xi^k_p. \tag{22}$$

We will prove that the operator S and the operators T'_a of the representation $\mathfrak{S}_{m,0}$ define a representation $g \to T_g$ of the group $\mathfrak{G}_0$. For this it is sufficient to establish that the operator S together with the operators T'_a satisfy conditions (α), (β), (γ) (see page 312). From formula (21) it follows that

$$S^2 c^k_{\nu p}(u) = c^k_{\nu p}(u),$$

hence we deduce that $S^2 = \mathbf{1}$, because the functions $c^k_{\nu p}(u)$ (for fixed ν) form a complete system in $L^m_2(\mathfrak{U})$.

Further, applying formula (21) again, we have:

$$T_{u_0} S c^k_{\nu p}(u) = S T_{u_0} c^k_{\nu p}(u) = (-1)^{[k]} c^k_{\nu p}(u u_0).$$

Hence, using again the completeness in $L^m_2(\mathfrak{U})$ of the functions $c^k_{\nu p}(u)$ (for fixed ν), we deduce that $T_{u_0} S = S T_{u_0}$. Finally, reasoning in the same way as in case (1), we find that $A_s T''_\varepsilon A_s^{-1} = T'_{\varepsilon^{-1}}$, and so $ST'_\varepsilon S^{-1} = A_s W T'_\varepsilon W^{-1} A_s^{-1} = A_s T''_\varepsilon A_s^{-1} = T'_{\varepsilon^{-1}}$. Hence, *the operators T'_a of the representation $\mathfrak{S}_{m,0}$, $m = 2\nu$, together with the operator $S = A_s W$ define a representation $g \to T_g$ of the group $\mathfrak{G}_0$*; we denote this representation by $D^+_{\nu,0}$.

We obtain a second representation corresponding to the pair $(\nu, 0)$, letting $S = -A_s W$; conditions (α) (β), (γ) will again be satisfied here. We denote this second representation by $D^-_{\nu,0}$; clearly, in the case of the representation $D^-_{\nu,0}$, we have instead of formula (22)

$$S\xi^k_p = (-1)^{[k]+1} \xi^k_p. \tag{23}$$

II. *The representations* $D^+_{\nu,0}$, $D^-_{\nu,0}$ *are completely irreducible,* because their restriction to the group $\mathfrak{G}_+$ is a completely irreducible representation $\mathfrak{S}_{m,0}$.

(3) $\nu > 0$, $\rho \neq 0$. Firstly assume that ρ^2 is not equal to a number of the form $-(2\nu+2n)^2$, $n = 1, 2, 3, \ldots$. We consider the representations $\mathfrak{S}_{m,\rho}$ and $\mathfrak{S}_{-m,\rho}$, where $m = 2\nu$. These representations are realized in the spaces $L_2^m(\mathfrak{U})$, $L_2^{-m}(\mathfrak{U})$ by means of the formulae:

$$T'_a f(u) = \frac{\alpha'(ua)}{\alpha'(u\bar{a})} f(u\bar{a}) \quad \text{when} \quad f \in L_2^m(\mathfrak{U}), \tag{24}$$

$$T''_a f(u) = \frac{\alpha''(ua)}{\alpha''(u\bar{a})} f(u\bar{a}) \quad \text{when} \quad f \in L_2^{-m}(\mathfrak{U}), \tag{25}$$

where $\alpha'(a) = |a_{22}|^{-m+i\rho-2}\, a_{22}^m$, $\alpha''(a) = |a_{22}|^{m+i\rho-2}\, a_{22}^{-m}$, so that

$$\frac{\alpha'(ua)}{\alpha'(u\bar{a})} = \frac{\alpha''(ua)}{\alpha''(u\bar{a})} = \varepsilon_{22}^{i\rho-2} \tag{26}$$

when $ua = \varepsilon\zeta u'$, $\varepsilon = \left\| \begin{matrix} \varepsilon_{22}^{-1} & 0 \\ 0 & \varepsilon_{22} \end{matrix} \right\|$.

We let $\bar{L}_2^m(\mathfrak{U})$ denote the set of all vector-valued functions $f(u) = \{f_1(u), f_2(u)\}$, where $f_1(u) \in L_2^m(\mathfrak{U})$, $f_2(u) \in L_2^{-m}(\mathfrak{U})$; $\bar{L}_2^m(\mathfrak{U})$ becomes a Hilbert space, if one defines the operations and scalar products in it by means of the formulae:

$$\alpha f(u) = \{\alpha f_1(u), \alpha f_2(u)\},$$

$$f(u) + \phi(u) = \{f_1(u) + \phi_1(u), f_2(u) + \phi_2(u)\},$$

$$(f, \phi) = \int [f_1(u)\overline{\phi_1(u)} + f_2(u)\overline{\phi_2(u)}]\, du$$

where $f = \{f_1, f_2\}$, $\phi = \{\phi_1, \phi_2\}$. We define an operator T_a in $\bar{L}_2^m(\mathfrak{U})$, letting

$$T_a f(u) = \varepsilon_{22}^{i\rho-2} f(u\bar{a}) \quad \text{when} \quad f(u) \in \bar{L}_2^m(\mathfrak{U}), \tag{27}$$

where

$$ua = \varepsilon\zeta v, \qquad \varepsilon = \left\| \begin{matrix} \varepsilon_{22}^{-1} & 0 \\ 0 & \varepsilon_{22} \end{matrix} \right\|.$$

Written out in detail formula (27) means that

$$T_a\{f_1(u), f_2(u)\} = \left\{ \frac{\alpha'(ua)}{\alpha'(u\bar{a})} f_1(u\bar{a}),\ \frac{\alpha''(ua)}{\alpha''(u\bar{a})} f_2(u\bar{a}) \right\}$$

$$= \{T'_a f_1(u),\ T''_a f_2(u)\}. \qquad (28)$$

Hence it is seen that the operator T_a is bounded and that the correspondence $a \to T_a$ is a representation of the group $\mathfrak{A}$, which is the orthogonal direct sum of the representations $\mathfrak{S}_{m,\rho}$, and $\mathfrak{S}_{-m,\rho}$.

We now set

$$S\{f_1(u), f_2(u)\} = \kappa\{f_2(su), (-1)^{2\nu} f_1(su)\}, \qquad (29)$$

where again $\kappa = (-1)^\nu$ when ν is integral and $\kappa = (-1)^{\nu - \frac{1}{2}}$ when ν is semi-integral; S is a unitary operator in $\bar{L}_2^m$, satisfying the condition $S^2 = 1$.

In fact, if

$$f_1(u) \in L_2^m(\mathfrak{U}), f_2(u) \in L_2^{-m}(\mathfrak{U}),$$

$$\text{then} \quad f_2(su) \in L_2^m(\mathfrak{U}), f_1(su) \in L_2^{-m}(\mathfrak{U})$$

(see case (2)); this means that if $\{f_1, f_2\} \in \bar{L}_2^m(\mathfrak{U})$, then also $S\{f_1, f_2\} \in \bar{L}_2^m(\mathfrak{U})$. Moreover, letting

$$f = \{f_1, f_2\}, \phi = \{\phi_1, \phi_2\}, f_1, \phi_1 \in L_2^m(\mathfrak{U}), f_2, \phi_2 \in L_2^{-m}(\mathfrak{U}),$$

we have:

$$(Sf, S\phi) = \int [f_1(su)\overline{\phi_1(su)} + f_2(su)\overline{\phi_2(su)}]\,du$$

$$= \int [f_1(u)\overline{\phi_1(u)} + f_2(u)\overline{\phi_2(u)}]\,du = (f, \phi), \qquad (30)$$

hence, the operator S is isometric. Letting

$$\gamma_0 = \begin{Vmatrix} -1 & 0 \\ 0 & -1 \end{Vmatrix},$$

we have:

$$S^2\{f_1(u), f_2(u)\} = (-1)^m\{f_1(s^2u), f_2(s^2u)\} = (-1)^m\{f_1(\gamma_0 u),$$

$$f_2(\gamma_0 u)\} = (-1)^m(-1)^m\{f_1(u), f_2(u)\} = \{f_1(u), f_2(u)\}.$$

Hence we deduce that $S^2 = \mathbf{1}$, and so S^2 is unitary. Further:

$$ST_{u_0}\{f_1(u), f_2(u)\} = T_{u_0}S\{f_1(u), f_2(u)\} = \kappa\{f_2(suu_0), (-1)^m f_1(suu_0)\},$$

so that $ST_{u_0} = T_{u_0}S$ for all $u_0 \in \mathfrak{U}$. Finally, reasoning in the same way as in case (1), we conclude that $ST_\varepsilon S^{-1} = T_{\varepsilon^{-1}}$. Hence, the operators T_a, $a \in \mathfrak{A}$, together with the operator S define a representation $g \to T_g$ of the group $\mathfrak{G}_0$, which we denote by $D_{\nu,\rho}$.

We have considered the case when ρ^2 does not coincide with any one of the numbers $-4(\nu+n)^2$, $n = 1, 2, 3, \ldots$. If however $\rho^2 = -4(\nu+n)^2$ for some natural n, then all the preceding reasoning remains in force, where the part of $\mathfrak{S}_{m,\rho}$, $\mathfrak{S}_{-m,\rho}$, is played by the corresponding spinor representations of the group $\mathfrak{A}$ (which we again denote by $\mathfrak{S}_{m,\rho}$, $\mathfrak{S}_{-m,\rho}$), and where it is necessary to replace the spaces $L_\nu^m(\mathfrak{U})$, $L_\nu^{-m}(\mathfrak{U})$ by their finite-dimensional subspaces, which we denote $\mathfrak{N}^m$, $\mathfrak{N}^{-m}$, namely the spaces of these spinor representations; at the same time it will be necessary to replace the space $\overline{L}_\nu^m(\mathfrak{U})$ by its subspace $\overline{\mathfrak{N}}^m$, composed of all vector-valued functions $f = \{f_1, f_2\}$, for which $f_1 \in \mathfrak{N}^m$, $f_2 \in \mathfrak{N}^{-m}$. The formulae for the operators T_a and S will be the same as in the preceding case. The corresponding representation $g \to T_g$ of the group $\mathfrak{G}_0$ is again denoted by $D_{\nu,\rho}$. Again it is easy to indicate how the operator S acts on the elements of the canonical basis of the representation $D_{\nu,\rho}$. For brevity, we denote by R, R', R'' the spaces of the representations $D_{\nu,\rho}$, $\mathfrak{S}_{m,\rho}$, $\mathfrak{S}_{-m,\rho}$ respectively, so that

$$R = \overline{L}_2^m(\mathfrak{U}), \quad R' = L_2^m(\mathfrak{U}), \quad R'' = L_2^{-m}(\mathfrak{U})$$

in the case of infinite-dimensional representations and $R = \overline{\mathfrak{N}}^m$, $R' = \mathfrak{N}^m$, $R'' = \mathfrak{N}^{-m}$ in the case of spinor representations.

Let us agree not to distinguish the pair $\{f_1, 0\}$ from f_1 nor the pair $\{0, f_2\}$ from f_2; then the spaces R', R'' can be considered as mutually orthogonal subspaces of the space R, and R as the direct sum of these subspaces.

Let ξ_p^k and η_p^k be canonical bases of the representations $\mathfrak{S}_{m,\rho}$, $\mathfrak{S}_{-m,\rho}$, so that $\xi_p^k = \kappa_{\nu\rho}^k \sqrt{(2k+1)}\, c_{\nu p}^k(u)$, $\eta_p^k = \kappa_{\nu\rho}^k \sqrt{(2k+1)}\, c_{-\nu p}^k(u)$;

then ξ_p^k and η_p^k form a basis in the space of the representation $D_{\nu,\rho}$. By virtue of the above statement this means in fact that the vector-valued functions

$$\xi_p^k = \kappa_{\nu\rho}^k \sqrt{(2k+1)}\{c_{\nu p}^k(u), 0\}; \quad \eta_p^k = \kappa_{\nu\rho}^k \sqrt{(2k+1)}\{0, c_{-\nu p}^k(u)\}$$

form a basis in the space of the representation $D_{\nu,\rho}$. But by the definition of the operator S

$$S\xi_p^k = \kappa\kappa_{\nu\rho}^k\sqrt{(2k+1)}\{0, (-1)^{2\nu}c_{\nu p}^k(su)\}$$
$$= \kappa\kappa_{\nu\rho}^k\sqrt{(2k+1)}(-1)^{k-\nu}\{0, c_{-\nu p}^k(u)\} = (-1)^{k-\nu}\kappa\eta_p^k = (-1)^{[k]}\eta_p^k,$$

so that

$$S\xi_p^k = (-1)^{[k]}\eta_p^k \tag{31}$$

and analogously

$$S\eta_p^k = (-1)^{[k]}\xi_p^k. \tag{32}$$

III. *Every representation* $D_{\nu,\rho}$ $(\nu > 0,\ \rho \neq 0)$ *is completely irreducible.*

Proof. Let us again agree to consider the space R as the direct sum of the mutually orthogonal subspaces R', R''. Let E_{jj}^k, $E_{jj}'^k$, $E_{jj}''^k$ and $\mathfrak{M}_j^k$, $\mathfrak{M}_j'^k$, $\mathfrak{M}_j''^k$ be the operators E_{jj}^k and the subspaces $\mathfrak{M}_j^k$, corresponding to the representations $a \to T_a$, $a \to T_a'$, $a \to T_a''$ of the group $\mathfrak{G}_0$ in $D_{\nu,\rho}$, $\mathfrak{S}_{m,\rho}$ and $\mathfrak{S}_{-m,\rho}$ respectively.

We set, as in the proof of proposition III § 15, Subsection 15:

$$e_n = \sum_{k=\nu}^{\nu+n}\sum_{j=-k}^{k} e_{jj}^k, \quad E_n = \sum_{k=\nu}^{\nu+n}\sum_{j=-k}^{k} E_{jj}^k,$$

$$E_n' = \sum_{k=\nu}^{\nu+n}\sum_{j=-k}^{k} E_{jj}'^k, \quad E_n'' = \sum_{k=\nu}^{\nu+n}\sum_{j=-k}^{k} E_{jj}''^k;$$

then

$$E_n = E_n' + E_n'', \quad E_n'E_n'' = 0 \tag{33}$$

and

$$E_n f \to f, \quad E_n' f' \to f', \quad E_n'' f'' \to f'' \tag{34}$$

as $n \to \infty$ and $f \in R, f' \in R', f'' \in R''$.

We denote by $\mathfrak{M}_n$, $\mathfrak{M}_n'$, $\mathfrak{M}_n''$ the subspaces onto which E, E_n', E_n'' project; by virtue of (33) we have

$$\mathfrak{M}_n' \perp \mathfrak{M}_n'' \quad \text{and} \quad \mathfrak{M}_n = \mathfrak{M}_n' + \mathfrak{M}_n''. \tag{35}$$

Moreover, $\mathfrak{M}_n$, $\mathfrak{M}'_n$, $\mathfrak{M}''_n$ are orthogonal direct sums of the subspaces

$$\mathfrak{M}_j^k,\ \mathfrak{M}_j'^k,\ \mathfrak{M}_j''^k,\ -k \leqslant j \leqslant k, \quad \nu \leqslant k \leqslant \nu+n$$

respectively.

Further, we denote by X_n the set of all functions $x \in X$, satisfying the condition

$$e_n x = x e_n = x. \tag{36}$$

Then X_n is a subring of the ring X and the subspace $\mathfrak{M}'_n$ is invariant with respect to the operators T'_x, $x \in X_n$, and the subspace $\mathfrak{M}''_n$ is invariant with respect to the operators T''_x, $x \in X_n$, where the representations $x \to T'_x$, $x \to T''_x$ of the ring X_n in the spaces $\mathfrak{M}'_n$, $\mathfrak{M}''_n$ are irreducible (see the proof of Proposition III § 15, Subsection 15). Moreover, these representations are non-equivalent. For otherwise the representations $x \to T'_x$, $x \to T''_x$ of the subring X_ν^k of the ring X_n in the one-dimensional spaces $\mathfrak{M}_\nu'^k$, $\mathfrak{M}_\nu''^k$ would also be equivalent, and consequently, by Theorem 15 Subsection 9 Section 15 the representations $\mathfrak{S}_{m,\rho}$, and $\mathfrak{S}_{-m,\rho}$ would be equivalent, which is impossible when $m \neq 0$ and $\rho \neq 0$.

Now we consider an arbitrary linear operator A in the space $\mathfrak{M}_n$; corresponding to the decomposition (35), this operator can be represented in the form of a matrix

$$A \sim \begin{Vmatrix} A_{11} & A_{12} \\ A_{21} & A_{22} \end{Vmatrix}, \tag{37}$$

where A_{11}, A_{22} are linear operators in $\mathfrak{M}'_n$, $\mathfrak{M}''_n$, and A_{12}, A_{21} are linear operators from $\mathfrak{M}''_n$ to $\mathfrak{M}'_n$ and from $\mathfrak{M}'_n$ to $\mathfrak{M}''_n$ respectively.

Here by virtue of (31) and (32) the operator S, considered only on $\mathfrak{M}_n$, is represented by a matrix of the form

$$S \sim \begin{Vmatrix} 0 & S_1 \\ S_2 & 0 \end{Vmatrix}; \tag{38}$$

the condition $S^2 = 1$ means that

$$S_1 S_2 = \mathbf{1}', \quad S_2 S_1 = \mathbf{1}'', \tag{39}$$

where $\mathbf{1}'$, $\mathbf{1}''$ are the identity operators in $\mathfrak{M}'_n$, $\mathfrak{M}''_n$ respectively.

Since the representations $x \to T'_x$, $x \to T''_x$ of the ring X_n in the spaces $\mathfrak{M}'_n$, $\mathfrak{M}''_n$ are irreducible and non-equivalent, then there exist functions x, $y \in X_n$ such that

$$T'_x \sim \begin{Vmatrix} A_{11} & 0 \\ 0 & 0 \end{Vmatrix}, \qquad T''_x \sim \begin{Vmatrix} 0 & 0 \\ 0 & A_{22} \end{Vmatrix},$$

$$T'_y \sim \begin{Vmatrix} S_1 A_{21} & 0 \\ 0 & 0 \end{Vmatrix}, \qquad T''_y \sim \begin{Vmatrix} 0 & 0 \\ 0 & S_2 A_{12} \end{Vmatrix}$$

(see Appendix IV). Hence,

$$T_x = T'_x + T''_x \sim \begin{Vmatrix} A_{11} & 0 \\ 0 & A_{22} \end{Vmatrix},$$

$$T_y = T'_y + T''_y \sim \begin{Vmatrix} S_1 A_{21} & 0 \\ 0 & S_2 A_{12} \end{Vmatrix}.$$

But then, making use of formulae (38) and (39) and letting $c = x + sy$, we have:

$$T_c = T_x + ST_y \sim \begin{Vmatrix} A_{11} & A_{12} \\ A_{21} & A_{22} \end{Vmatrix} \text{ on } \mathfrak{M}_n,$$

i.e. $T_c = A$ on $\mathfrak{M}_n$.

Thus, for every linear operator A in $\mathfrak{M}_n$ there exists an element $c = x + sy$, x, $y \in X_n$, of the ring $\mathfrak{C}$ such that $T_c = A$ on $\mathfrak{M}_n$.

But then, reasoning as at the end of the proof of Proposition III Subsection 15 Section 15, we conclude that the representation $g \to T_g$ of the group $\mathfrak{G}_0$ is completely irreducible.

Remark. In each of the representations $D^{+}_{0,\rho}$, $D^{-}_{0,\rho}$, $D^{+}_{\nu,0}$, $D^{-}_{\nu,0}$, $D_{\nu,\rho}$ ($\nu > 0$, $\rho \neq 0$) the operator S is unitary; hence, *these representations* are unitary if and only if the corresponding representation $\mathfrak{S}_{m,\rho}$ is unitary; it is evident also that these representations are finite-dimensional if and only if the corresponding representations $\mathfrak{S}_{m,\rho}$ are finite-dimensional.

The representations $D^{+}_{0,\rho}$, $D^{-}_{0,\rho}$, $D^{+}_{\nu,0}$, $D^{-}_{\nu,0}$, $D_{\nu,\rho}$ can also be given by means of the parameters k_0 and c (see the remark in Subsection 16 Section 15); in that case these representations are denoted by $\hat{D}^{+}_{0,c}$, $\hat{D}^{-}_{0,c}$, $\hat{D}^{+}_{k_0,0}$, $\hat{D}^{-}_{k_0,0}$, $\hat{D}_{k_0 c}$.

7. A fundamental theorem

We can now prove the following fundamental theorem:

THEOREM 17. *Every completely irreducible representation of the complete Lorentz group* $\mathfrak{G}_0$ *is equivalent to one of the represen-*

tations $D^+_{0,\rho}$, $D^-_{0,\rho}$, $D^+_{\nu,0}$, $D^-_{\nu,0}$, $D_{\nu,\rho}$ $(\nu > 0, \rho \neq 0)$, *and these representations, corresponding to all possible* ν *and* ρ, *are mutually non-equivalent.*

Proof. Let $g \to T_g$ be a completely irreducible representation of the group $\mathfrak{G}_0$; we choose some subspace $\mathfrak{M}^k_j$ distinct from zero, corresponding to the restriction of this representation to the group $\mathfrak{G}_+$. Let $c \to A_c$ be the corresponding representation of the ring $\mathfrak{C}^k_j$ in $\mathfrak{M}^k_j$. According to the results of Subsection 5, this representation corresponds to a pair of numbers (ν, ρ), where ν is an integral or semi-integral positive number, and ρ is a complex number. Here only the following cases are possible:

(1) $\nu = 0$; then $\mathfrak{M}^k_j$ is one-dimensional and the representation $c \to A_c$ is given by one of the formulae

$$A_{x+sy} = [\lambda(x) + \lambda(y)]\mathbf{1}, \tag{1a}$$

or

$$A_{x+sy} = [\lambda(x) - \lambda(y)]\mathbf{1} \tag{1b}$$

with x, $y \in X^k_j$, where

$$\lambda(x) = \int B_0(\varepsilon)\varepsilon_{22}^{i\rho}\, d\varepsilon \tag{2}$$

(see VIII Subsection 5). Assume, for example, that formula (1a) holds and, in order to be specific, let k be even. We consider the representation $D^+_{0,\rho}$ of the group $\mathfrak{G}_0$. The functional $\lambda(x)$ for this representation is also given by formula (2); therefore, making use of formula (11) Subsection 6, we see that the operator A_{x+sy} of the representation $D^+_{0,\rho}$ is also given by formula (1a). Hence, the given representation $g \to T_g$ is equivalent to the representation $D^+_{0,\rho}$.

Considering in an analogous way the case of odd k, and also the case of formula (1b), we deduce that in any of these cases the given representation is equivalent to one of the representations $D^+_{0,\rho}$, $D^-_{0,\rho}$.

(2) $\nu > 0$, $\rho = 0$. Then $\mathfrak{M}^k_j$ is again one-dimensional and the corresponding representation $c \to A_c$ of the ring $\mathfrak{C}^k_j$ is again given by one of the formulae (1a), (1b). Reasoning as in case (1), we conclude that the given representation $g \to T_g$ is equivalent to one of the representations $D^+_{\nu,0}$, $D^-_{\nu,0}$.

(3) $\nu > 0$, $\rho \neq 0$. Then $\mathfrak{M}_j^k$ is two-dimensional and the corresponding representation $c \to A_c$ of the ring $\mathfrak{S}_j^k$ is given, relative to a proper choice of basis ξ_1, ξ_2 in $\mathfrak{M}_j^k$, by the formulae:

$$\left.\begin{aligned} A_c\xi_1 &= [\lambda(x_1)-\lambda(x_2)]\xi_1+[\mu(y_1)+\mu(y_2)]\xi_2, \\ A_c\xi_2 &= [\mu(y_1)-\mu(y_2)]\xi_1+[\lambda(x_1)+\lambda(x_2)]\xi_2, \end{aligned}\right\} \tag{3}$$

where $c = (x_1+y_1)+s(x_2+y_2)$, $x_1, x_2 \in X_{j+}^k, y_1, y_2 \in X_{j-}^k$, and where

$$\left.\begin{aligned} \lambda(x) &= \int B_\nu(\varepsilon)\varepsilon_{22}^{i\rho}\,d\varepsilon \quad \text{when} \quad x \in X_{j+}^k, \\ \mu(x) &= \int B_\nu(\varepsilon)\varepsilon_{22}^{i\rho}\,d\varepsilon \quad \text{when} \quad x \in X_{j-}^k \end{aligned}\right\} \tag{4}$$

(see IX Subsection 5). We consider the representation $D_{\nu,\rho}$, with a view to determining the corresponding representation $c \to A_c$ of the ring $\mathfrak{S}_j^k$. The space $\mathfrak{M}_j^k$ for this representation is the set of all vector-valued functions of the form $f = \{\alpha c_{\nu j}^k(u),\ \beta c_{-\nu j}^k(u)\}$, where

$$\begin{aligned} Sf &= \kappa\{\beta c_{-\nu j}^k(su), \quad \alpha(-1)^{2\nu}c_{\nu j}^k(su)\} \\ &= \kappa\{(-1)^{k-\nu}\beta c_{\nu j}^k(u), \quad (-1)^{k-\nu}\alpha c_{-\nu j}^k(u)\} = (-1)^{[k]}\{\beta c_{\nu j}^k(u), \\ &\qquad \alpha c_{-\nu j}^k(u)\} \end{aligned}$$

(see (29) Subsection 6). Hence it is seen that $\mathfrak{P}_j^k$ consists of all the functions $f \in \mathfrak{M}_j^k$, for which $\beta = (-1)^{[k]+1}\alpha$, and $\mathfrak{Q}_j^k$ consists of all functions $f \in \mathfrak{M}_j^k$, for which $\beta = (-1)^{[k]}\alpha$. We set

$$\xi_1 = \{c_{\nu j}^k(u), \quad (-1)^{[k]+1}c_{-\nu j}^k(u)\}, \qquad \xi_2 = \{c_{\nu j}^k(u), \quad (-1)^{[k]}c_{-\nu j}^k(u)\} \tag{5}$$

and we will find the matrix of the operator A_c, corresponding to the representation $D_{\nu,\rho}$ in the basis $\{\xi_1, \xi_2\}$.

Let $x \to T'_x$, $x \to T''_x$ be representations of the ring X_j^k, corresponding to the representations $\mathfrak{S}_{m,\rho}$, $\mathfrak{S}_{-m,\rho}$ of the group $\mathfrak{A}$. Then for all $x \in X_j^k$

$$T'_x c_{\nu j}^k(u) = \lambda'(x)c_{\nu j}^k(u), \quad T''_x c_{-\nu j}^k(u) = \lambda''(x)c_{-\nu j}^k(u), \tag{6}$$

where

$$\lambda'(x) = \int B_\nu(\varepsilon)\varepsilon_{22}^{i\rho}\,d\varepsilon, \quad \lambda''(x) = \int B_{-\nu}(\varepsilon)\varepsilon_{22}^{i\rho}\,d\varepsilon.$$

From this and from (4) we deduce that

$$\lambda''(x) = \lambda'(x) = \lambda(x) \qquad \text{when} \qquad x \in X^k_{j+} \tag{7}$$

and

$$\lambda''(x) = -\lambda'(x) = -\mu(x) \qquad \text{when} \qquad x \in X^k_{j-}. \tag{8}$$

By the definition of the operator T_a of the representation $D_{\nu,\rho}$, (see (28) Subsection 6) we have

$$T_x\{f_1, f_2\} = \{T'_x f_1, T''_x f_2\};$$

hence, making use of formulae (5–8), we obtain:

$$T_x\xi_1 = \lambda(x)\xi_1 \qquad T_x\xi_2 = \lambda(x)\xi_2 \qquad \text{when} \qquad x \in X^k_{j+}, \tag{9}$$

$$T_x\xi_1 = \mu(x)\xi_2, \qquad T_x\xi_2 = \mu(x)\xi_2 \qquad \text{when} \qquad x \in X^k_{j-}. \tag{10}$$

On the basis of proposition IX Subsection 5, we conclude from (3) that the given representation of the group $\mathfrak{G}_0$ is equivalent to the representation $D_{\nu,\rho}$.

The remaining assertion of the theorem is proved in the same way.

From the above reasoning it is seen that the different representations $D^+_{0,\rho}$, $D^-_{0,\rho}$, $D^+_{\nu,0}$, $D^-_{\nu,0}$, $D_{\nu,\rho}$, $(\nu > 0,\ \rho \neq 0)$ correspond to non-equivalent representations $c \to \Lambda_c$ of the ring $\mathfrak{C}^k_j$; hence, these representations are mutually non-equivalent and the theorem is completely proved.

The results of §§ (10–14) are due to I. M. GELFAND and the author [12a, b]; those of §§ 15 and 16 are the author's [28c, d, f]; a detailed exposition of the results of §§ 15 and 16 is here published for the first time.

A rough derivation of the formulae for the representations of the complete Lorentz group in *infinitesimal form* was given in the paper [14a] by I. M. GELFAND and A. M. YAGLOM.

CHAPTER IV

INVARIANT EQUATIONS

§ 17. Equations Invariant with Respect to Rotations of Three-dimensional Space

1. A general definition of quantities

The quantities considered in physics are usually referred to a definite system of coordinates and classified according to the way they are transformed by a transition from one system of coordinates to another. Thus, a scalar quantity is characterized by the fact that it is not altered by a transformation of coordinates; a vector (in the usual non-relativistic treatment) is a system of three numbers x_1, x_2, x_3 (the projections of the vector on the coordinate axes) referred to a given system of coordinates, which is transformed by a rotation of the coordinate axes by means of the formulae

$$x'_i = \sum_{j=1}^{3} g_{ij} x_j, \quad i = 1, 2, 3, \tag{1}$$

where g is the matrix of the rotation performed.

Further, a tensor of the second rank is a system of nine numbers x_{jk}, j, $k = 1, 2, 3$, which is transformed by a rotation g of the coordinate axes by means of the formulae

$$x'_{jk} = \sum_{j_1, k_1 = 1}^{3} g_{jj_1} g_{kk_1} x_{j_1 k_1}, \quad j, k = 1, 2, 3; \tag{2}$$

analogously we define *a tensor of the third rank* and so on.

Every such class of quantities is characterized by the general property that a rotation g of the coordinate axes makes their components undergo a linear transformation T_g, dependent on g.

If one first performs a rotation g_2, and then g_1, then the components undergo a transformation T_{g_2}, and then T_{g_1}, so that $T_{g_1 g_2} = T_{g_1} T_{g_2}$; moreover, it is evident that $T_e = 1$. This means that the correspondence $g \to T_g$ is a representation of the group of rotations of three-dimensional space, and the set of all quantities of the class considered forms the space of this representation. In relativistic physics the quantities are defined in an analogous way with the difference that now the indices $i, j, k, \ldots$ take four values 1, 2, 3, 4, and the transformations in formulae (1), (2) are Lorentz transformations; each class of quantities now defines some representation of the Lorentz group.

We see that all these examples can be united in the following general scheme.

Let there be given some group G of transformations of coordinates in a fixed space P (the group of rotations of three-dimensional space or the Lorentz group in our examples) and a continuous linear representation $g \to T_g$ of the group G in some space R; a vector $x \in R$, referred to a given system of coordinates in P and carried into $T_g x$ by the transformation g of the coordinates in P, is called *a quantity, corresponding to the representation* $g \to T_g$.

We can also adopt another point of view, namely, we can fix in P a definite system of coordinates and consider the group G as a group of transformations in P. Thus, the group G can be considered as the group of all orthogonal transformations of the cartesian coordinates of a point and as the group of rotations of three-dimensional space.

Clearly, in such a treatment of a quantity, corresponding to a given representation $g \to T_g$, there will be a vector $x \in R$, which goes into the vector $T_g x$ under the transformation g of the space P.

2. The concept of an equation invariant with respect to a representation of the group G_0

Let $g \to T_g$ be some representation of the group G_0 of rotations of three-dimensional space, R the space of this representation, and E^k_{jl} the operators constructed for this representation by means of the formulae in § 6, Subsection 6. We consider the differential equation

$$L_1\frac{\partial\psi}{\partial x_1}+L_2\frac{\partial\psi}{\partial x_2}+L_3\frac{\partial\psi}{\partial x_3}+i\kappa\psi=0, \tag{1}$$

where ψ is an unknown function of x_1, x_2, x_3, whose values are quantities corresponding to the representation $g\to T_g$, where L_1, L_2, L_3 are given closed† linear operators in R, and κ is a real number, different from zero. With regard to these operators it is assumed that R contains a dense subspace $\mathfrak{D}$, possessing the following properties:

(1) L_1, L_2, L_3 are defined on $\mathfrak{D}$;

(2) $\mathfrak{D}$ is invariant with respect to the operators L_1, L_2, L_3 and E^k_{jl};

(3) the closures of the operators L_1, L_2, L_3, considered only on finite sums of vectors of the form $E^k_{jj}x$, $x\in\mathfrak{D}$, coincide with the original operators L_1, L_2, L_3.

Equation (1) is called *an invariant equation, corresponding to the given representation* $g\to T_g$ *of the group of rotations of three-dimensional space* (or, briefly, *an invariant equation with respect to the group* G_0), if $\mathfrak{D}$ can be chosen so that:

(1) $T_g\mathfrak{D}=\mathfrak{D}$ for all $g\in G_0$;

(2) equation (1) is not altered by any of the transformations $g\in G_0$ of the point (x_1, x_2, x_3) and a simultaneous transformation T_g of the quantity ψ for all vector-valued functions $\psi(x_1, x_2, x_3)$ with values in $\mathfrak{D}$, having continuous partial derivatives of the first order with respect to x_1, x_2, x_3.

If R is finite-dimensional, we may take $\mathfrak{D}=R$ and equation (1) becomes a system of linear partial differential equations for the components ψ_i of the quantity ψ.

The aim of this section consists in finding the general form of all equations invariant with respect to the group G_0.

---

† See Appendix V.

3. Conditions of invariance

By a rotation g the point (x_1, x_2, x_3) goes into the point (x'_1, x'_2, x'_3), where

$$x'_j = \sum_{k=1}^{3} g_{jk} x_k, \quad j = 1, 2, 3, \tag{1}$$

and ψ goes into $\psi' = T_g \psi$. Then $\psi = T_g^{-1}\psi'$ and

$$\frac{\partial}{\partial x_k} = \sum_{j=1}^{3} g_{jk} \frac{\partial}{\partial x'_j}, \quad k = 1, 2, 3. \tag{2}$$

Substituting these expressions in equation (1) Subsection 2, we obtain:

$$\sum_{j=1}^{3}\left[g_{j1} L_1 \frac{\partial}{\partial x'_j}(T_g^{-1}\psi') + g_{j2} L_2 \frac{\partial}{\partial x'_j}(T_g^{-1}\psi') + g_{j3} L_3 \frac{\partial}{\partial x'_j}(T_{g^{-1}}\psi')\right] + i\kappa T_g^{-1}\psi' = 0;$$

hence

$$\sum_{j=1}^{3}(g_{j1} T_g L_1 T_g^{-1} + g_{j2} T_g L_2 T_g^{-1} + g_{j3} T_g L_3 T_g^{-1})\frac{\partial \psi'}{\partial x'_j} + i\kappa\psi' = 0. \tag{3}$$

Since equation (1) Subsection 2 is assumed to be invariant, then it must coincide with equation (4), i.e. we must have:†

$$\sum_{k=1}^{3} g_{jk} T_g L_k T_g^{-1} = L_j, \quad j = 1, 2, 3. \tag{4}$$

This is also *a necessary and sufficient condition for the invariance* of equation (1).

4. Conditions of invariance in infinitesimal form

Let A_1, A_2, A_3 be the infinitesimal operators of a given representation $g \to T_g$ of the group G_0 (see § 4, Subsection 3).

Without loss of generality, we may assume that the operators A_1, A_2, A_3 *are applicable to each of the vectors* $\xi \in \mathfrak{D}$ *and that* $\mathfrak{D}$ *is invariant with respect to these operators.*

---

† Here and in what follows, all equations between operators are understood in the sense that these operators coincide on $\mathfrak{D}$.

In fact, let $\mathfrak{D}'$ denote the set of all finite linear combinations of vectors of the form

$$\eta = \int f(g)\, T_g \xi \,dg, \tag{1}$$

where $f(g)$ runs through all infinitely differentiable functions on G_0, and ξ runs through $\mathfrak{D}$. This set is dense in R; for otherwise there exists a functional $F \in R'$, $F \neq 0$, such that

$$F(\eta) = \int f(g) F(T_g \xi) dg = 0$$

for all infinitely differentiable functions $f(g)$. This is possible only when $F(T_g \xi) = 0$ for all $g \in G_0$. Letting $g = e$, we see that $F(\xi) = 0$ for all $\xi \in \mathfrak{D}$; since $\mathfrak{D}$ is dense in R, it follows from this that $F = 0$.

Since

$$T_{g_0} \eta = \int f(g)\, T_{g_0 g} \xi \,dg = \int f(g_0^{-1} g)\, T_g \xi \,dg, \tag{2}$$

then $T_{g_0} \mathfrak{D}' = \mathfrak{D}'$ for all $g_0 \in G_0$.

Making use of formula (2) and reasoning as in § 4, Subsection 1 and 3, we conclude that the operators A_1, A_2, A_3 are applicable to all the vectors of $\mathfrak{D}'$ and that $\mathfrak{D}'$ is invariant with respect to these operators.

We now prove that $\mathfrak{D}'$ also satisfies conditions (1–3) Subsection 2. Let

$$\eta' = \sum_{\nu} f(g_\nu)\, T_{g_\nu} \xi \Delta_\nu g$$

be an integral sum for the integral in (1). From (4) Subsection 3 it follows that

$$L_j \eta' = \sum_{\nu} f(g_\nu) L_j T_{g_\nu} \xi \Delta_\nu g = \sum_{k=1}^{3} \sum_{\nu} (g_\nu)_{jk} f(g_\nu)\, T_{g_\nu} L_k \xi \Delta_\nu g$$

hence, we have the relation:

$$\eta' \to \eta = \int f(g)\, T_g \xi \,dg, \quad L_j \eta' \to \sum_{k=1}^{3} \int g_{jk} f(g)\, T_g L_k \xi \,dg. \tag{3}$$

By virtue of the closed nature of the operators L_j we deduce from these relations that the operator L_j is defined on η and

$$L_j \eta = \sum_{k=1}^{3} \int g_{jk} f(g)\, T_g L_k \xi \,dg \in \mathfrak{D}'. \tag{4}$$

Hence, the operators L_1, L_2, L_3 are defined on $\mathfrak{D}'$, i.e. $\mathfrak{D}'$ satisfies conditions (1) and (2) Subsection 2.

Finally, condition (3) Subsection 2 is satisfied in an obvious way, because the set of all finite sums of elements of the form $E^k_{jj}x$, $x \in \mathfrak{D}$, coincides with the set of all finite sums of elements of the form $E^k_{jj}x$, $x \in \mathfrak{D}'$; one can convince oneself of this by letting $f(g) = (2k+1)c^k_{jl}(g)$ in (1).

Thus, $\mathfrak{D}'$ satisfies all the conditions laid down, and we can replace $\mathfrak{D}$ by the set $\mathfrak{D}'$. In what follows we will assume that this replacement is performed at the very beginning, so that $\mathfrak{D}$ already possesses all the properties of the set $\mathfrak{D}'$.

In condition (4) Subsection 3 set $g = a_1(t) = 1+ta_1+ \dots$, hence,

$$T_g = A_1(t) = \mathbf{1}+tA_1+o(t), \quad T_g^{-1} = \mathbf{1}-tA_1+o(t)$$

(see § 4, Subsection 2 and 3). We substitute these expressions in condition (4) Subsection 3 and write the resulting equation in the form

$$\sum_{k=1}^{3} a_{1jk}(t)\,A_1(t)\,L_k = L_j A_1(t);$$

differentiating both sides of this equation with respect to t at $t = 0$ and making use of the properties of the set $\mathfrak{D}$ and the closed nature of the operators L_j, we arrive at the relation

$$A_1 L_j - L_j A_1 = -\sum_{k=1}^{3} a_{1jk} L_k, \quad j = 1, 2, 3. \tag{5}$$

Since

$$a_1 = \begin{Vmatrix} 0 & 0 & 0 \\ 0 & 0 & -1 \\ 0 & 1 & 0 \end{Vmatrix},$$

this means that

$$[A_1, L_1] = 0, \quad [A_1, L_2] = L_3, \quad [A_1, L_3] = -L_2. \tag{6}$$

Similarly, letting $g = a_2(t) = 1+a_2t+ \dots$ and $g = a_3(t) = 1+ + a_3t+ \dots$, we find that

$$[A_2, L_1] = -L_3, \quad [A_2, L_2] = 0, \quad [A_2, L_3] = L_1, \tag{7}$$

and

$$[A_3, L_1] = L_2, \qquad [A_3, L_2] = -L_1, \qquad [A_3, L_3] = 0. \tag{8}$$

Conversely, let L_1, L_2, L_3 be closed linear operators in R, satisfying the following conditions:

(1) R contains a dense subspace $\mathfrak{D}$, on which all the L_j and A_j are defined and which is invariant with respect to all the operators L_j, A_j and T_g, $g \in G_0$;

(2) the closures of the operators L_j, considered only on finite sums of vectors $E_{jj}^k x$, $x \in \mathfrak{D}$, coincide with the original operators L_j;

(3) the operators A_j and L_j satisfy the relations (6–8) on $\mathfrak{D}$.

Then the equation

$$L_1 \frac{\partial \psi}{\partial x_1} + L_2 \frac{\partial \psi}{\partial x_2} + L_3 \frac{\partial \psi}{\partial x_3} + i\kappa\psi = 0 \tag{9}$$

is invariant with respect to the transformations $g \in G_0$.

For the proof we consider the expression

$$\psi_j(t) = \sum_{k=1}^{3} a_{1jk}(t) A_1(t) L_k A_1(-t)\psi, \tag{10}$$

where $\psi \in \mathfrak{D}$; differentiating this with respect to t and taking into account the fact that

$$\frac{da_1(t)}{dt} = a_1(t) a_1, \qquad \frac{dA_1(t)\xi}{dt} = A_1(t) A_1 \xi = A_1 A_1(t)\xi \text{ for } \xi \in \mathfrak{D},$$

we obtain

$$\frac{d\psi_j}{dt} = \sum_{k=1}^{3} \sum_{\nu=1}^{3} a_{1j\nu}(t) a_{1\nu k} A_1(t) L_k A_1(-t)\psi$$

$$+ \sum_{\nu=1}^{3} a_{1j\nu}(t) A_1(t) A_1 L_\nu A_1(-t)\psi - \sum_{\nu=1}^{3} a_{1j\nu}(t) A_1(t) L_\nu A_1 A_1(-t)\psi$$

$$= A_1(t) \left\{ \sum_{\nu=1}^{3} a_{1j\nu}(t) \left[\sum_{k=1}^{3} a_{1\nu k} L_k + A_1 L_\nu - L_\nu A_1 \right] \right\} A_1(-t)\psi;$$

but the expression in the square brackets is equal to zero by virtue of relation (5), equivalent to relations (6). This means that $\psi_j(t) = \text{const.} = \psi_j(0) = L_j\psi$; hence:

$$\sum_{k=1}^{3} a_{1jk}(t)\, A_1(t) L_k A_1(-t)\psi = L_j\psi.$$

This means that condition (4) Subsection 3 is satisfied when $g = a_1(t)$, i.e. that equation (9) is invariant with respect to the transformations $g = a_1(t)$. Analogously, using relations (7) and (8), one can show that it is invariant with respect to the transformations $g = a_2(t)$, $g = a_3(t)$, and this means also with respect to all possible products of these transformations. But the whole group G_0 is exhausted by these products (see Section 1 Subsection 4); hence, equation (9) is invariant with respect to all the transformations $g \in G_0$.

Thus, our problem reduces to finding the general form of the operators L_1, L_2, L_3, satisfying conditions (1–3).

5. General form of the operators L_1, L_2, L_3

Let us introduce, as in § 4, Subsection 6 the operators

$$H_+ = iA_1 - A_2, \quad H_- = iA_1 + A_2, \quad H_3 = iA_3; \tag{1}$$

moreover, we set

$$M_+ = iL_1 - L_2, \quad M_- = iL_1 + L_2, \quad M_3 = iL_3. \tag{2}$$

Then conditions (6–8) Subsection 4 take the form†

$$[H_+, M_+] = [H_-, M_-] = [H_3, M_3] = 0, \tag{3}$$

$$[H_+, M_3] = -M_+, [H_-, M_3] = M_-, \tag{4}$$

$$[H_+, M_-] = -[H_-, M_+] = 2M_3, \tag{5}$$

$$[M_+, H_3] = -M_+, [M_-, H_3] = M_-. \tag{6}$$

† We note that relations (3–6) are analogous to relations (5) and (7–9) § 8, Subsection 1 for the operators F_+, F_-, F_3; the difference lies in the fact that now there are no relations analogous to relations (6) § 8, Subsection 1.

Instead of the given representation $g \to T_g$ of the group G it will be convenient to consider the corresponding representation $u \to T_u$ of the unitary group $\mathfrak{U}$. We consider the operators E^k_{jl} and the subspaces $\mathfrak{M}^k_j$ in R, corresponding to this representation. From the reasoning at the beginning of Subsection 4 it follows that one may assume that $\mathfrak{D}$ is invariant with respect to all the operators E^k_{jl}.

In fact, *if* $\eta = \int f(u) T_u \xi \, du$, then $E^k_{jl}\eta = \int f_1(u) T_u \xi \, du$, where $f_1(u) = (2k+1) \int \overline{c^k_{jl}(u_1)} f(u_1^{-1} u) du$, so that $f_1(u)$ is infinitely differentiable on $\mathfrak{U}$, if $f(u)$ is infinitely differentiable on $\mathfrak{U}$. Therefore, in correspondence with the decomposition of the space R into the direct sum of the spaces $\mathfrak{M}^k_j$, every linear operator A in $\mathfrak{D}$ can be represented in the form of a matrix $\|A^{kk_1}_{jj_1}\|$ of operators $A^{kk_1}_{jj_1}$ from $\mathfrak{M}^{k_1}_{j_1}$ to $\mathfrak{M}^k_j$ (see Appendix VI); here the operator $A^{kk_1}_{jj_1}$ is defined by means of the formula

$$A^{kk_1}_{jj_1} x = E^k_{jj} A x \quad \text{when} \quad x \in E^{k_1}_{j_1 j_1} \mathfrak{D} = \mathfrak{M}^{k_1}_{j_1} \cap \mathfrak{D}. \tag{7}$$

In particular, the operators H_+, H_-, H_3, M_+, M_-, M_3 can be represented thus in the form of matrices, which we denote by $\|\overset{+}{H}{}^{kk_1}_{jj_1}\|$, $\|\overset{-}{H}{}^{kk_1}_{jj_1}\|$, $\|\overset{3}{H}{}^{kk_1}_{jj_1}\|$, $\|\overset{+}{M}{}^{kk_1}_{jj_1}\|$, $\|\overset{-}{M}{}^{kk_1}_{jj_1}\|$, $\|\overset{3}{M}{}^{kk_1}_{jj_1}\|$ respectively. Our task consists of finding the matrices of the operators M_+, M_-, M_3; first it will be necessary to find the matrices of the operators H_+, H_-, H_3.

As a preliminary we note that

$$H_+ E^k_{jj} = \alpha^k_{j+1} E^k_{j+1,j}, \quad H_- E^k_{jj} = \alpha^k_j E^k_{j-1,j}, \quad H_3 E^k_{jj} = j E^k_{jj}, \tag{8}$$

where

$$\alpha^k_j = \sqrt{[(k+j)(k-j+1)]}. \tag{9}$$

Here the symbols $\alpha^k_{k+1} E^k_{k+1,k}$ and $\alpha^k_{-k} E^k_{-k-1,-k}$ must be interpreted as operators equal to zero.

In fact, let x_{-k} be an arbitrary vector in $\mathfrak{M}^k_{-k}$; we set

$$x_j = E^k_{j,-k} x_{-k}, \quad j = -k+1, \dots, k.$$

By virtue of formulae (2a) § 6, Subsection 6 we then have:

$$T_u x_j = T_u E^k_{j,-k} x_{-k} = \sum_{p=-k}^{k} c^k_{pj}(u) E^k_{p,-k} x_{-k} = \sum_{p=-k}^{k} c^k_{pj}(u) x_p, \tag{10}$$

in particular

$$T_\gamma x_p = c_{pp}(\gamma) x_p = e^{2i\omega p} x_p \quad \text{when} \quad \gamma = \begin{Vmatrix} e^{-i\omega} & 0 \\ 0 & e^{i\omega} \end{Vmatrix}.$$

This means that the x_p are weight vectors of an irreducible representation S_k, and so can differ only by numerical factors from the vectors ξ_p of the canonical basis: $\xi_p = \alpha_p x_p$. On the other hand, we have also

$$T_u \xi_j = \sum_{p=-k}^{k} c_{pj}^k(u) \xi_p, \quad \text{i.e.} \quad \alpha_j T_u x_j = \sum_{p=-k}^{k} c_{pj}^k(u) \alpha_p x_p.$$

Comparing this last formula with (10) and taking into account the linear independence of the functions $c_{pj}^k(u)$, we deduce that all the numbers α_j are equal to one another. But then formulae (16), (17) § 4 Subsection 6 give

$$H_+ x_j = \alpha_{j+1}^k x_{j+1}, \quad H_- x_j = \alpha_j^k x_{j-1}, \quad H_3 x_j = j x_j,$$

i.e.

$$H_+ E_{j,-k}^k x_{-k} = \alpha_{j+1}^k E_{j+1,-k}^k x_{-k}, \quad H_- E_{j,-k}^k x_{-k} = \alpha_j^k E_{j-1,-k}^k x_{-k},$$
$$H_3 E_{j,-k}^k x_{-k} = j E_{j,-k}^k x_{-k}.$$

Letting here $x_{-k} = E_{-k,j}^k x$, $x \in \mathfrak{D}$, we obtain formulae (8). These formulae mean that†

$$\overset{+}{H}{}_{jj_1}^{kk_1} = \begin{cases} 0 & \text{when} \quad k \neq k_1, \\ 0 & \text{when} \quad k = k_1, \quad j \neq j_1 + 1, \\ \alpha_{j_1+1}^{k_1} E_{j_1+1,j_1}^{k_1} & \text{when} \quad k = k_1, \quad j = j_1 + 1, \end{cases} \tag{11}$$

$$\overset{-}{H}{}_{jj_1}^{kk_1} = \begin{cases} 0 & \text{when} \quad k \neq k_1, \\ 0 & \text{when} \quad k = k_1, \quad j \neq j_1 - 1, \\ \alpha_{j_1}^{k_1} E_{j_1-1,j_1}^{k_1} & \text{when} \quad k = k_1, \quad j = j_1 - 1; \end{cases} \tag{12}$$

$$\overset{3}{H}{}_{jj_1}^{kk_1} = \begin{cases} 0 & \text{when} \quad k \neq k_1 \quad \text{or} \quad j \neq j_1, \\ j\mathbf{1} & \text{when} \quad k = k_1 \quad \text{and} \quad j = j_1. \end{cases} \tag{13}$$

Now we make of relations (3–6). The relation $[H_3, M_3] = 0$ means that $\overset{3}{M}{}_{jj_1}^{kk_1} j_1 - j \overset{3}{M}{}_{jj_1}^{kk_1} = 0$; hence,

$$\overset{3}{M}{}_{jj_1}^{kk_1} = 0 \quad \text{when} \quad j \neq j_1. \tag{14}$$

† In formula (13), $\mathbf{1} = E_{j_1 j_1}^{k_1}$ is the identity operator in $\mathfrak{M}_{j_1}^{k_1}$.

Further, the relation $[M_+, H_3] = -M_+$ means that

$$\overset{+}{M}{}^{kk_1}_{jj_1} j_1 - j\overset{+}{M}{}^{kk_1}_{jj_1} = -\overset{+}{M}{}^{kk_1}_{jj_1};$$

hence,

$$\overset{+}{M}{}^{kk_1}_{jj_1} = 0 \quad \text{when} \quad j \neq j_1+1. \tag{15}$$

Analogously, from the relation $[M_-, H_3] = M_-$ it follows that

$$\overset{-}{M}{}^{kk_1}_{jj_1} = 0 \quad \text{when} \quad j \neq j_1-1. \tag{16}$$

Now we apply the relation $[H_+, M_+] = 0$ (see (3)). By virtue of (11), this relation can be written in the form

$$\sum_{j_2=-k}^{k} \overset{+}{H}{}^{kk}_{jj_2} \overset{+}{M}{}^{kk_1}_{j_2 j_1} = \sum_{j_2=-k_1}^{k_1} \overset{+}{M}{}^{kk_1}_{jj_2} \overset{+}{H}{}^{k_1 k_1}_{j_2 j_1}. \tag{17}$$

Hence it follows that

$$\overset{+}{M}{}^{kk_1}_{jj_1} = 0 \quad \text{when} \quad |k-k_1| \geqslant 2. \tag{18}$$

In fact, let, for example, $k_1 \geqslant k+2$; we set in (17) $j_1 = -k-2$. Since $j_2 \geqslant -k$ on the left side of (17) then, by virtue of (15), $\overset{+}{M}{}^{kk_1}_{j_2,-k-2} = 0$ for all j_2, so that the left side of relation (17) is equal to zero; but the right hand side is equal to $\alpha^{k_1}_{-k-1} \overset{+}{M}{}^{kk_1}_{j,-k-1} \times$ $\times\, E^{k_1}_{-k-1,-k-2}$, by (II). Since $\alpha^{k_1}_{-k-1} \neq 0$, we deduce that for $j = -k$,

$$\overset{+}{M}{}^{kk_1}_{-k,-k-1} E^{k_1}_{-k-1,-k-2} = 0.$$

Multiplying both sides of this equation on the right by $E^{k_1}_{-k-2,-k-1}$, we obtain:

$$\overset{+}{M}{}^{kk_1}_{-k,-k-1} = \overset{+}{M}{}^{kk_1}_{-k,-k-1} E^{k_1}_{-k-1,-k-1} = 0. \tag{19}$$

Now we set $j_1 = -k-1$, $j = -k+1$ in (17); this equation then takes the form

$$\overset{+}{H}{}^{kk}_{-k+1,-k} \overset{+}{M}{}^{kk_1}_{-k,-k-1} = \alpha^{k_1}_{-k} \overset{+}{M}{}^{kk_1}_{-k+1,-k} E^{k_1}_{-k,-k-1}.$$

Taking (19) into account, we again deduce from this that $\overset{+}{M}{}^{kk_1}_{-k+1,-k}$ $= 0$. Further letting $j_1 = -k, \ldots, k-2$ successively, we arrive at the conclusion that $\overset{+}{M}{}^{kk_1}_{j+1,j} = 0$ when $j = -k-1, -k, \cdots, k-1$. Combining this result with (15), we obtain that $M^{kk_1}_{jj_1} = 0$ when $k_1 \geqslant k+2$. If however $k \geqslant k_1+2$, then, taking $j = k_1+2, k_1+1, \ldots, -k_1+2$ in (17) successively we prove similarly that (18) holds also for $k \geqslant k_1+2$.

Let $|k-k_1| \leqslant 1$. In (17) we set $j = k$; we obtain:

$$\overset{+}{H}{}^{kk}_{k,k-1}\overset{+}{M}{}^{kk_1}_{k-1,k-2} = \overset{+}{M}{}^{kk_1}_{k,k-1}\overset{+}{H}{}^{k_1k_1}_{k-1,k-2},$$

i.e., by virtue of (11),

$$\alpha^k_k E^k_{k,k-1}\overset{+}{M}{}^{kk_1}_{k-1,k-2} = \alpha^{k_1}_{k-1}\overset{+}{M}{}^{kk_1}_{k,k-1}E^{k_1}_{k-1,k-2}. \tag{20}$$

Multiplying both sides of (20) on the left by $E^k_{k-1,k}$ and taking into account the fact that

$$E^k_{k-1,k}E^k_{k,k-1}\overset{+}{M}{}^{kk_1}_{k-1,k-2} = E^k_{k-1,k-1}\overset{+}{M}{}^{kk_1}_{k-1,k-2} = \overset{+}{M}{}^{kk_1}_{k-1,k-2},$$

we conclude that

$$\overset{+}{M}{}^{kk_1}_{k-1,k-2} = \frac{\alpha^{k_1}_{k-1}}{\alpha^k_k}E^k_{k-1,k}\overset{+}{M}{}^{kk_1}_{k,k-1}E^{k_1}_{k-1,k-2}. \tag{21}$$

Analogously, letting in (17) $j = k-1$, we find

$$\overset{+}{M}{}^{kk_1}_{k-2,k-3} = \frac{\alpha^{k_1}_{k-2}}{\alpha^k_{k-1}}E^k_{k-2,k-1}\,\overset{+}{M}{}^{kk_1}_{k-1,k-2}E^{k_1}_{k-2,k-3}; \tag{22}$$

hence, by virtue of (21):

$$\overset{+}{M}{}^{kk_1}_{k-2,k-3} = \frac{\alpha^{k_1}_{k-2}\alpha^{k_1}_{k-1}}{\alpha^k_{k-1}\alpha^k_k}E^k_{k-2,k-1}E^k_{k-1,k}\overset{+}{M}{}^{kk_1}_{k,k-1}E^{k_1}_{k-1,k-2}E^{k_1}_{k-2,k-3},$$

i.e.

$$\overset{+}{M}{}^{kk_1}_{k-2,k-3} = \frac{\alpha^{k_1}_{k-2}\alpha^{k_1}_{k-1}}{\alpha^k_{k-1}\alpha^k_k}E^k_{k-2,k}\overset{+}{M}{}^{kk_1}_{k,k-1}E^{k_1}_{k-1,k-3}. \tag{23}$$

Repeating this reasoning, we arrive at the general formula

$$\overset{+}{M}{}^{kk_1}_{j,j-1} = \frac{\alpha^{k_1}_j\alpha^{k_1}_{j+1}\cdots\alpha^{k_1}_{k-1}}{\alpha^k_{j+1}\alpha^k_{j+2}\cdots\alpha^k_k}E^k_{j,k}\overset{+}{M}{}^{kk_1}_{k,k-1}E^{k_1}_{k-1,j-1}$$

$$\text{when} \quad |k-k_1| \leqslant 1, \quad -k_1+1 \leqslant j \leqslant k. \tag{24}$$

Hence, by virtue of (9)†

$$\overset{+}{M}{}^{k,\,k+1}_{j,\,j-1} = \sqrt{\left[\frac{(k-j+1)(k-j+2)}{2}\right]}\,E^{k}_{j,k}\overset{+}{M}{}^{k,\,k+1}_{k,\,k-1}E^{k+1}_{k-1,\,j-1} \tag{25}$$

when $-k \leqslant j \leqslant k$,

$$\overset{+}{M}{}^{kk}_{j,\,j-1} = \sqrt{\left[\frac{(k+j)(k-j+1)}{2k}\right]}\,E^{k}_{j,k}\overset{+}{M}{}^{kk}_{k,\,k-1}E^{k}_{k-1,\,j-1} \tag{26}$$

when $-k+1 \leqslant j \leqslant k$,

$$\overset{+}{M}{}^{k,\,k-1}_{j,\,j-1} = \sqrt{\left[\frac{(k+j)(k+j-1)}{2k(2k-1)}\right]}\,E^{k}_{j,k}\overset{+}{M}{}^{k,\,k-1}_{k,\,k-1}E^{k-1}_{k-1,\,j-1} \tag{27}$$

when $-k+2 \leqslant j \leqslant k$

and $\overset{+}{M}{}^{kk_1}_{jj_1} = 0$ for the remaining values of the indices k, k_1, j, j_1.

Similarly using the relation $[H_-, M_-] = 0$, we obtain

$$\overset{-}{M}{}^{kk_1}_{jj_1} = 0 \quad \text{when} \quad |k-k_1| \geqslant 2 \tag{28}$$

and

$$\overset{-}{M}{}^{kk_1}_{j,j+1} = \frac{\alpha^{k_1}_{j+1}\alpha^{k_1}_{j}\dots\alpha^{k_1}_{-k+2}}{\alpha^{k}_{j}\alpha^{k}_{j-1}\dots\alpha^{k}_{-k+1}}\;E^{k}_{j,-k}\overset{-}{M}{}^{kk_1}_{-k,-k+1}E^{k_1}_{-k+1,\,j+1} \tag{29}$$

when $|k-k_1| \leqslant 1,\ -k \leqslant j \leqslant k_1-1$;

hence

$$\overset{-}{M}{}^{k,\,k+1}_{j,\,j+1} = \sqrt{\left[\frac{(k+j+1)(k+j+2)}{2}\right]}\,E^{k}_{j,-k}\overset{-}{M}{}^{k,\,k+1}_{-k,-k+1}E^{k+1}_{-k+1,\,j+1} \tag{30}$$

when $-k \leqslant j \leqslant k$,

$$\overset{-}{M}{}^{kk}_{j,\,j+1} = \sqrt{\left[\frac{(k+j+1)(k-j)}{2k}\right]}\,E^{k}_{j,-k}\overset{-}{M}{}^{k,k}_{-k,\,-k+1}E^{k}_{-k+1,\,j+1} \tag{31}$$

when $-k \leqslant j \leqslant k-1$,

$$\overset{-}{M}{}^{k,\,k-1}_{j,\,j+1} = \sqrt{\left[\frac{(k-j)(k-j-1)}{2k(2k-1)}\right]}\,E^{k}_{j,-k}\overset{-}{M}{}^{k,\,k-1}_{-k,-k+1}E^{k-1}_{-k+1,\,j+1} \tag{32}$$

when $-k \leqslant j \leqslant k-2$.

---

† When $k = 0$ the operators $\overset{+}{M}{}^{kk}_{j,j-1}, \overset{+}{M}{}^{k,k-1}_{j,j-1}$ do not exist and formulae (26), (27) lose their meaning; an analogous remark must be made regarding formulae (31), (32), (37), (38), (40), (41), (49), (50).

Further, from relations (5) we conclude that

$$\overset{3}{M}{}^{kk_1}_{jj_1} = 0 \quad \text{when} \quad |k-k_1| \geqslant 2 \tag{33}$$

and that when $|k-k_1| \leqslant 1$, $\max \{-k, -k_1\} \leqslant j \leqslant \min \{k, k_1\}$,

$$\overset{+}{H}{}^{kk}_{j,j-1}\overset{-}{M}{}^{kk_1}_{j-1,j} - \overset{-}{M}{}^{kk_1}_{j,j+1}\overset{+}{H}{}^{k_1k_1}_{j+1,j} = 2\overset{3}{M}{}^{kk_1}_{jj}, \tag{34}$$

$$-\overset{-}{H}{}^{kk}_{j,j+1}\overset{+}{M}{}^{kk_1}_{j+1,j} + \overset{+}{M}{}^{kk_1}_{j,j-1}\overset{-}{H}{}^{k_1k_1}_{j-1,j} = 2\overset{3}{M}{}^{kk_2}_{jj}. \tag{35}$$

If here $|j+1|$ or $|j-1|$ is greater than k or k_1, then the corresponding summand in (34), (35) must be considered equal to zero. Substituting in (34), (35) instead of $\overset{+}{H}{}^{kk}_{j,j-1}$, $\overset{-}{H}{}^{k_1k_1}_{j-1,j}$, $\overset{-}{M}{}^{kk_1}_{j-1,j}$, $\overset{+}{M}{}^{kk_1}_{j+1,j}$ their expressions from formulae (11), (12), (25–27), (30–32), we obtain after simple calculations

$$\overset{3}{M}{}^{k,k+1}_{jj} = -\sqrt{\left[\frac{(k+j+1)(k-j+1)}{2}\right]}E^k_{j,-k}\overset{-}{M}{}^{k,k+1}_{-k,-k+1}E^{k+1}_{-k+1,j}, \tag{35}$$

$$-k \leqslant j \leqslant k,$$

$$\overset{3}{M}{}^{kk}_{jj} = \frac{j}{\sqrt{(2k)}}E^k_{j,-k}M^{kk}_{-k,-k+1}E^k_{-k+1,j}, \qquad -k \leqslant j \leqslant k, \tag{37}$$

$$\overset{3}{M}{}^{k,k-1}_{jj} = \sqrt{\left[\frac{(k+j)(k-j)}{2k(2k-1)}\right]}E^k_{j,-k}\overset{-}{M}{}^{k,k-1}_{-k,-k+1}E^{k-1}_{-k+1,j}, \tag{38}$$

$$-k+1 \leqslant j \leqslant k-1,$$

$$\overset{3}{M}{}^{k,k+1}_{jj} = \sqrt{\left[\frac{(k+j+1)(k-j+1)}{2}\right]}E^k_{jk}\overset{+}{M}{}^{k,k+1}_{k,k-1}E^{k+1}_{k-1,j}, \tag{39}$$

$$-k \leqslant j \leqslant k,$$

$$\overset{3}{M}{}^{kk}_{jj} = \frac{j}{\sqrt{(2k)}}E^k_{jk}\overset{+}{M}{}^{kk}_{k,k-1}E^k_{k-1,j}, \qquad -k \leqslant j \leqslant k, \tag{40}$$

$$\overset{3}{M}{}^{k,k-1}_{jj} = -\sqrt{\left[\frac{(k+j)(k-j)}{2k(2k-1)}\right]}E^k_{jk}\overset{+}{M}{}^{k,k-1}_{k,k-1}E^{k-1}_{k-1,j}, \tag{41}$$

$$-k+1 \leqslant j \leqslant k-1.$$

Hence

$$E^k_{j,-k}\overset{-}{M}{}^{k,k+1}_{-k,-k+1}E^{k+1}_{-k+1,j} = -E^k_{jk}\overset{+}{M}{}^{k,k+1}_{k,k-1}E^{k+1}_{k-1,j}, \tag{42}$$

$$E^k_{j,-k}\overset{-}{M}{}^{kk}_{-k,-k+1}E^k_{-k+1,j} = E^k_{jk}\overset{+}{M}{}^{kk}_{k,k-1}E^k_{k-1,j}, \tag{43}$$

$$E^k_{j,-k}\overset{-}{M}{}^{k,k-1}_{-k,-k+1}E^{k-1}_{-k+1,j} = -E^k_{jk}\overset{+}{M}{}^{k,k-1}_{k,k-1}E^{k-1}_{k-1,j}. \tag{44}$$

Multiplying both sides of these equations on the right by $E^{k+1}_{j,-k+1}$, $E^k_{j,-k+1}$, $E^{k-1}_{j,-k+1}$ respectively, and on the left by $E^k_{-k,j}$, we arrive at the equations:

$$\overset{-}{M}{}^{k,k+1}_{-k,-k+1} = -E^k_{-k,k}\overset{+}{M}{}^{k,k+1}_{k,k-1}E^{k+1}_{k-1,-k+1}, \tag{45}$$

$$\overset{-}{M}{}^{kk}_{-k,-k+1} = E^k_{-k,k}\overset{+}{M}{}^{kk}_{k,k-1}E^k_{k-1,-k+1}, \tag{46}$$

$$\overset{-}{M}{}^{k,k-1}_{-k,-k+1} = -E^k_{-k,k}\overset{+}{M}{}^{k,k-1}_{k,k-1}E^{k-1}_{k-1,-k+1}, \tag{47}$$

and substitution in (30–32) gives:

$$\overset{-}{M}{}^{k,k+1}_{j,j+1} = -\sqrt{\left[\frac{(k+j+1)(k+j+2)}{2}\right]}E^k_{jk}\overset{+}{M}{}^{k,k+1}_{k,k-1}E^{k+1}_{k-1,j+1}, \tag{48}$$

$$-k \leqslant j \leqslant k,$$

$$\overset{-}{M}{}^{kk}_{j,j+1} = \sqrt{\left[\frac{(k+j+1)(k-j)}{2k}\right]}E^k_{jk}\overset{+}{M}{}^{kk}_{k,k-1}E^k_{k-1,j+1}, \tag{49}$$

$$-k \leqslant j \leqslant k-1$$

$$\overset{-}{M}{}^{k,k-1}_{j,j+1} = -\sqrt{\left[\frac{(k-j)(k-j-1)}{2k(2k-1)}\right]}E^k_{jk}\overset{+}{M}{}^{k,k-1}_{k,k-1}E^{k-1}_{k-1,j+1}, \tag{50}$$

$$-k \leqslant j \leqslant k-2.$$

By direct substitution of these expressions we can prove that relations (4) are also satisfied; hence, formulae (25–27), (39–41) and (48–50) give a general form for the operators M_+, M_- and M_3. Now we find expressions for the operators $M_+E^k_{jj}$, $M_-E^k_{jj}$, $M_3E^k_{jj}$.

Let $x \in \mathfrak{D}$; we set $x_j^k = E_{jj}^k x$. By definition of the operators $\overset{+}{M}{}_{j'}^{k'k}$, $E_{j'j'}^{k'} M_+ x_j^k = \overset{+}{M}{}_{j'j}^{k'k} x_j^k$, and so

$$M_+ x_j^k = \sum_{k',j'} \overset{+}{M}{}_{j'j}^{k'k} x_j^k = \overset{+}{M}{}_{j+1,j}^{k-1,k} x_j^k + \overset{+}{M}{}_{j+1,j}^{kk} x_j^k + \overset{+}{M}{}_{j+1,j}^{k+1,k} x_j^k,$$

i.e.

$$M_+ E_{jj}^k x = \overset{+}{M}{}_{j+1,j}^{k-1,k} E_{jj}^k x + \overset{+}{M}{}_{j+1,j}^{kk} E_{jj}^k x + \overset{+}{M}{}_{j+1,j}^{k+1,k} E_{jj}^k x$$

for all $x \in \mathfrak{D}$. By virtue of formulae (25–27), this means that

$$\begin{aligned} M_+ E_{jj}^k = {} & \sqrt{\left[\frac{(k-j-1)(k-j)}{2}\right]} E_{j+1,k-1}^{k-1} \overset{+}{M}{}_{k-1,k-2}^{k-1,k} E_{k-2,j}^k \\ & + \sqrt{\left[\frac{(k+j+1)(k-j)}{2k}\right]} E_{j+1,k}^k \overset{+}{M}{}_{k,k-1}^{kk} E_{k-1,j}^k \\ & + \sqrt{\left[\frac{(k+j+2)(k+j+1)}{(2k+2)(2k+1)}\right]} E_{j+1,k+1}^{k+1} \overset{+}{M}{}_{k+1,k}^{k+1,k} E_{k,j}^k . \end{aligned}$$

As before, this equation must be understood in the sense that the operators on the left and right sides coincide on $\mathfrak{D}$. Computing $M_- E_{jj}^k$ and $M_3 E_{jj}^k$, similarly and taking formula (2) into account, and also condition (3) on page 328 and introducing the notations:

$$\left.\begin{aligned} P_k = -\frac{1}{\sqrt{(2k)}} \overset{+}{M}{}_{k,k-1}^{kk} E_{k-1,k}^k, \quad Q_k = \frac{1}{\sqrt{2}} \overset{+}{M}{}_{k-1,k-2}^{k-1,k} E_{k-2,k}^k, \\ D_k = \frac{1}{\sqrt{[2k(2k-1)]}} \overset{+}{M}{}_{k,k-1}^{k,k-1}, \end{aligned}\right\} \tag{51}$$

we arrive at the following theorem:

THEOREM 1. *An equation of the form*

$$L_1 \frac{\partial \psi}{\partial x_1} + L_2 \frac{\partial \psi}{\partial x_2} + L_3 \frac{\partial \psi}{\partial x_3} + i\kappa\psi = 0$$

is an invariant equation corresponding to a given representation $g \to T_g$ *of the group* G_0 *if and only if* L_1, L_2, L_3 *are the closures of the linear operators* $\hat{L}_1$, $\hat{L}_2$, $\hat{L}_3$, *defined by the formulae*:

$$\hat{L}_1 = \frac{1}{2i}(M_+ + M_-), \quad \hat{L}_2 = \frac{1}{2}(M_- - M_+), \quad \hat{L}_3 = \frac{1}{i} M_3, \tag{52}$$

$$M_+E^{kk}_{jj} = \sqrt{[(k-j-1)(k-j)]}\, E^{k-1}_{j+1,k-1} Q_k E^k_{k,j}$$
$$-\sqrt{[(k+j+1)(k-j)]}\, E^k_{j+1,k} P_k E^k_{k,j}$$
$$+\sqrt{[(k+j+2)(k+j+1)]}\, E^{k+1}_{j+1,k+1} D_{k+1} E^k_{kj}, \quad (53)$$

$$M_-E^k_{jj} = -\sqrt{[(k+j-1)(k+j)]}\, E^{k-1}_{j-1,k-1} Q_k E^k_{k,j}$$
$$-\sqrt{[(k+j)(k-j+1)]}\, E^k_{j-1,k} P_k E^k_{k,j}$$
$$-\sqrt{[(k-j+2)(k-j+1)]}\, E^{k+1}_{j-1,k+1} D_{k+1} E^k_{kj}, \quad (54)$$

$$M_3E^k_{jj} = \sqrt{[(k+j)(k-j)]} E^{k-1}_{j,k-1} Q_k E^k_{k,j} - jE^k_{jk} P_k E^k_{k,j}$$
$$-\sqrt{[(k+j+1)(k-j+1)]}\, E^{k+1}_{j,k+1} D_{k+1} E^k_{kj}, \quad (55)$$

where Q_k, P_k, D_{k+1} *are arbitrary operators from* $\mathfrak{M}^k_k$ *to* $\mathfrak{M}^{k-1}_{k-1}$, $\mathfrak{M}^k_k$, $\mathfrak{M}^{k+1}_{k+1}$ *respectively whose domains of definition contain* $\mathfrak{M}^k_k \cap \mathfrak{D}$ *and satisfy the conditions*:

$$Q_k(\mathfrak{M}^k_k \cap \mathfrak{D}) \subset \mathfrak{M}^{k-1}_{k-1} \cap \mathfrak{D}, \quad P_k(\mathfrak{M}^k_k \cap \mathfrak{D}) \subset \mathfrak{M}^k_k \cap \mathfrak{D},$$
$$D_{k+1}(\mathfrak{M}^k_k \cap \mathfrak{D}) \subset \mathfrak{M}^{k+1}_{k+1} \cap \mathfrak{D},$$

and such that the closures L_1, L_2, L_3 *exist.*

Formulae (53–55) mean that

$$\overset{+}{M}{}^{k-1,k}_{j+1,j} = \sqrt{[(k-j-1)(k-j)]}\, E^{k-1}_{j+1,k-1} Q_k E^k_{kj}, \quad (56)$$

$$\overset{+}{M}{}^{kk}_{j+1,j} = -\sqrt{[(k+j+1)(k-j)]}\, E^k_{j+1,kk} P E^k_{kj}, \quad (57)$$

$$\overset{+}{M}{}^{k+1,k}_{j+1,j} = \sqrt{[(k+j+2)(k+j+1)]}\, E^{k+1}_{j+1,k+1} D_{k+1} E^k_{kj}, \quad (58)$$

$$\overset{-}{M}{}^{k-1,k}_{j-1,j} = -\sqrt{[(k+j-1)(k+j)]}\, E^{k-1}_{j-1,k-1} Q_k E^k_{kj}, \quad (59)$$

$$\overset{-}{M}{}^{kk}_{j-1,j} = -\sqrt{[(k+j)(k-j+1)]}\, E^k_{j-1,k} P_k E^k_{kj}, \quad (60)$$

$$\overset{-}{M}{}^{k+1,k}_{j-1,j} = -\sqrt{[(k-j+2)(k-j+1)]}\, E^{k+1}_{j-1,k+1} D_{k+1} E^k_{kj}, \quad (61)$$

$$\overset{3}{M}{}^{k-1,k}_{jj} = \sqrt{[(k+j)(k-j)]}\, E^{k-1}_{j,k-1} Q_k E^k_{kj}, \quad (62)$$

$$\overset{3}{M}{}^{kk}_{jj} = -jE^k_{jk} P_k E^k_{kj}, \quad (63)$$

$$\overset{3}{M}{}^{k+1,k}_{jj} = -\sqrt{[(k+j+1)(k-j+1)]}\, E^{k+1}_{j,k+1} D_{k+1} E^k_{kj}. \quad (64)$$

Formulae (53–64) were derived on the assumption that $k \neq 0$. However, it is easy to verify immediately that these formulae remain valid also for $k = 0$, where, by virtue of relations (15), (16) and (34), it is necessary to take $P_0 = 0$, and in correspondence with this the symbols $\overset{+}{M}{}^{00}_{j+1,j}, \overset{-}{M}{}^{00}_{j-1,j}, \overset{3}{M}{}^{00}_{jj}$ are all equal to zero.

Now we suppose that a basis ξ^k_p can be chosen in each of the spaces $\mathfrak{M}^k_k \cap \mathfrak{D}$ so that every vector $x \in \mathfrak{M}^k_k$ is represented uniquely as the sum of a series which is convergent in the norm: $x = \sum_p \lambda_p \xi^k_p$; moreover, we suppose that each operator P_k, Q_k, D_{k+1} is represented in such a basis in the form of numerical matrices $\| P^k_{pq} \|, \| Q^k_{pq} \|, \| D^{k+1}_{pq} \|$, so that

$$Q_k \xi^k_p = \sum_q Q^k_{qp} \xi^{k-1}_q, \quad P_k \xi^k_p = \sum_q P^k_{qp} \xi^k_q, \quad D_{k+1} \xi^k_p = \sum_q D^{k+1}_{ıp} \xi^{k+1}_q.$$

Then we can introduce a basis in each subspace $\mathfrak{M}^k_j$, letting $\xi^k_{jp} = E^k_{jk} \xi^k_p$; in fact, from the relations

$$E^k_{jk} \mathfrak{M}^k_k = E^k_{jk} E^k_{kk} R = E^k_{jk} R = \mathfrak{M}^k_j,$$

$$E^k_{kj} \mathfrak{M}^k_{jk} = E^k_{kj} E^k_{jk} R = E^k_{kk} R = \mathfrak{M}^k_k$$

(see I Section 6 Subsection 6) it follows that E^k_{jk}, E^k_{kj} are bounded mutually inverse operators, mapping $\mathfrak{M}^k_k$ on $\mathfrak{M}^k_j$ and $\mathfrak{M}^k_j$ on $\mathfrak{M}^k_k$ respectively.

It is evident that in these bases the operators $E^{k-1}_{j+1,k-1} Q_k E^k_{kj'}$, $E^k_{j+1,k} P_k E^k_{kj'}$, $E^{k+1}_{j+1,k+1} D_{k+1} E^k_{kj'}$ are represented by the same matrices $\|Q^k_{pq}\|, \|P^k_{pq}\|, \|D^{k+1}_{pq}\|$. All these bases together generate a basis $\{\xi^k_{jp}\}$ of the whole space R of the representation. In this basis the operators M_+, M_-, M_3 are represented by the numerical matrices:

$$\| \overset{+}{M}{}^{kk_1}_{jj_1pq} \|, \quad \| \overset{-}{M}{}^{kk_1}_{jj_1pq} \|, \quad \| \overset{3}{M}{}^{kk_1}_{jj_1pq} \|,$$

where, by virtue of formulae (56–64):

$$\overset{+}{M}{}^{k-1,k}_{j+1,j,p,q} = \sqrt{[(k-j-1)(k-j)]} Q^k_{pq}, \tag{65}$$

$$\overset{+}{M}{}^{kk}_{j+1,j,p,q} = -\sqrt{[(k+j+1)(k-j)]} P^k_{pq}, \tag{66}$$

$$\overset{+}{M}{}^{k+1,k}_{j+1,j,p,q} = \sqrt{[(k+j+2)(k+j+1)]}\, D^{k+1}_{pq}, \tag{67}$$

$$\overset{-}{M}{}^{k-1,k}_{j-1,j,p,q} = -\sqrt{[(k+j-1)(k+j)]}\, Q^{k}_{pq}, \tag{68}$$

$$\overset{-}{M}{}^{kk}_{j-1,j,p,q} = -\sqrt{[(k+j)(k-j+1)]}\, P^{k}_{pq}, \tag{69}$$

$$\overset{-}{M}{}^{k+1,k}_{j-1,j,p,q} = -\sqrt{[(k-j+2)(k-j+1)]}\, D^{k+1}_{pq}, \tag{70}$$

$$\overset{3}{M}{}^{k-1,k}_{jj,p,q} = \sqrt{[(k+j)(k-j)]}\, Q^{k}_{pq}, \tag{71}$$

$$\overset{3}{M}{}^{kk}_{jj,p,q} = -jP^{k}_{pq}, \tag{72}$$

$$\overset{3}{M}{}^{k+1,k}_{jj,p,q} = -\sqrt{[(k+j+1)(k-j+1)]}\, D^{k+1}_{pq}, \tag{73}$$

and all the remaining matrix elements are equal to zero.

Since every finite-dimensional space has a basis possessing the properties indicated above, these formulae hold in particular for every representation $g \to T_g$ of the group G_0, for which all the $\mathfrak{M}^k_j$ are finite-dimensional, in particular for every finite-dimensional representation of the group G_0.

An invariant equation corresponding to a given representation $g \to T_g$ is called *decomposable* if:

(1) the space of the representation R is the closed direct sum of two of its closed subspaces $R' \neq (0)$, $R'' \neq (0)$;

(2) the representation $g \to T_g$ is the direct sum of two representations $g \to T'_g$, $g \to T''_g$ in the spaces R' and R'';

(3) the subspaces $\mathfrak{D}'$, $\mathfrak{D}''$, corresponding to these representations, are invariant with respect to the operators L_1, L_2, L_3, defining the given invariant equation.

In the contrary case the invariant equation is called *indecomposable.*

If the equation is decomposable, then, considering the operators L_1, L_2, L_3 only on $\mathfrak{D}'$ or only on $\mathfrak{D}''$ and closing the operators obtained in R' and R'' respectively, we arrive at two invariant equations, corresponding to the representations $g \to T'_g$ and $g \to T''_g$. In this case we will say that the given invariant equation is *decom-*

posed into two invariant equations. In the finite-dimensional case this means that, by a proper choice of basis in R (namely, one composed of bases of R' and R''), the given invariant system of equations is decomposed into two systems, of which one contains only the components of the unknown vector-valued function ψ in the basis of R', and the other only the components of the unknown vector-valued function ψ in the basis of R''.

In the finite-dimensional case one can also give a condition for the decomposition of an equation in terms of the operators P_k, Q_k, D_{k+1}. Let the given finite-dimensional equation (i.e. one corresponding to a finite-dimensional representation) be decomposable. The subspace $\mathfrak{M}_j^k$ in this case is the direct sum of the subspaces $\mathfrak{M}_j'^k$, $\mathfrak{M}_j''^k$, corresponding to the representations $g \to T_g'$, $g \to T_g''$, and the operators P_k, Q_k, D_{k+1} are the direct sums of the corresponding operators P_k', P_k'', Q_k', Q_k'', D_{k+1}', D_{k+1}''; in this case we will say that *the operators Q_k, P_k, D_{k+1} form a decomposable system.* Conversely, let Q_k, P_k, D_{k+1} form a decomposable system. We set $\mathfrak{M}_j'^k = E_{jk}^k \mathfrak{M}_k'^k$, $\mathfrak{M}_j''^k = E_{jk}^k \mathfrak{M}_k''^k$ and we denote by R', R'' the subspaces of R which are the direct sums of the subspaces $\mathfrak{M}_j'^k$, $\mathfrak{M}_j''^k$ respectively; clearly, R is the direct sum of the subspaces R' and R''. By virtue of property (2a) § 6, Subsection 6 of the operators E_{jl}^k the subspaces R', R'' are invariant with respect to the operators of $g \to T_g$.

Let $g \to T_g'$ and $g \to T_g''$ be the restrictions of the representation $g \to T_g$ on R' and R'' respectively; then the given representation $g \to T_g$ is the direct sum of the representations $g \to T_g'$, $g \to T_g''$. Finally, by virtue of formulae (53–55), condition (3) is also satisfied, and so the given equation is decomposable.

Thus, *a finite-dimensional equation, invariant with respect to the group of rotations of three-dimensional space, is decomposable if and only if the corresponding operators Q_k, P_k, D_{k+1} form a decomposable system.*

This proposition extends to infinite-dimensional equations, corresponding to a *unitary* representation of the group $\mathfrak{G}_0$; here all the direct sums of subspaces and operators considered will be orthogonal direct sums.

§ 18. Equations Invariant with Respect to Proper Lorentz Transformations

1. General linear representations of the proper Lorentz group in infinitesimal form

Until now we have been concerned only with *completely irreducible* representations of the proper Lorentz group $\mathfrak{G}_+$. In order to find the general form of equations invariant with respect to the transformations $g \in \mathfrak{G}_+$, we need the general form of arbitrary, not necessarily completely irreducible, representations of the group $\mathfrak{G}_+$, in infinitesimal form.

We recall (see § 8, Subsection 1), that the infinitesimal operators H_+, H_-, H_3, F_+, F_-, F_3 of any linear representation $g \to T_g$ of the group $\mathfrak{G}_+$ satisfy the relations

$$[H_+, H_3] = -H_+, \quad [H_-, H_3] = H_-, \quad [H_+, H_-] = 2H_3, \tag{1}$$

$$[H_+, F_+] = [H_-, F_-] = [H_3, F_3] = 0, \tag{2}$$

$$[F_+, F_3] = H_+, \quad [F_-, F_3] = -H_-, \quad [F_+, F_-] = -2H_3, \tag{3}$$

$$[H_+, F_3] = -F_+, \quad [H_-, F_3] = F_-, \tag{4}$$

$$[H_+, F_-] = -[H_-, F_+] = 2F_3, \tag{5}$$

$$[F_+, H_3] = -F_+, \quad [F_-, H_3] = F_-. \tag{6}$$

These equations must be understood in the sense that their left and right hand sides coincide on some subspace $\mathfrak{D}$ dense in R, to which all the operators H_+, H_-, H_3, F_+, F_-, F_3 are applicable and which is invariant with respect to these operators and the operators T_g, E^k_{jl} of the given representation (see § 7, Subsection 3 and § 13, Subsection 5). But the relations (2) and (4–6) coincide with the relations (3–6) § 17, Subsection 5 (with M_+, M_-, M_3 instead of F_+, F_-, F_3); hence the results of § 17, Subsection 5 are applicable to them. The representation $g \to T_g$ can also be considered as a representation $a \to T_a$ of the group $\mathfrak{A}$ (see § 9, Subsection 2); considering the operators T_a only when $a = u \in \mathfrak{U}$, we obtain a representation $u \to T_u$ of the group $\mathfrak{U}$. We construct by means of this representation $u \to T_u$ the operators E^k_{jl}. With the aid of these operators E^k_{jj} we introduce, as in § 17, Subsection 5, the matrices $\|\overset{+}{H}{}^{kk_1}_{jj_1}\|$, $\|\overset{-}{H}{}^{kk_1}_{jj_1}\|$, $\|\overset{3}{H}{}^{kk_1}_{jj_1}\|$, $\|\overset{+}{F}{}^{kk_1}_{jj_1}\|$, $\|\overset{-}{F}{}^{kk_1}_{jj_1}\|$, $\|\overset{3}{F}{}^{kk_1}_{jj_1}\|$ of the operators H_+, H_-, H_3, F_+, F_-, F_3; from the results of § 17, Subsection 5 it follows that

$$\overset{+}{H}{}^{kk_1}_{jj_1} = \begin{cases} 0 & \text{when} \quad k \neq k_1, \\ 0 & \text{when} \quad k = k_1, \quad j \neq j_1+1, \\ \alpha^{k_1}_{j_1+1} E^{k_1}_{j_1+1, j_1} & \text{when} \quad k = k_1, \quad j = j_1+1; \end{cases} \tag{7}$$

$$\overset{-}{H}{}^{kk_1}_{jj_1} = \begin{cases} 0 & \text{when} \quad k \neq k_1, \\ 0 & \text{when} \quad k = k_1, \quad j \neq j_1-1, \\ \alpha^{k_1}_{j_1} E^{k_1}_{j_1-1, j_1} & \text{when} \quad k = k_1, \quad j = j_1-1; \end{cases} \tag{8}$$

$$\overset{3}{H}{}^{kk_1}_{jj_1} = \begin{cases} 0 & \text{when} \quad k \neq k_1 \quad \text{or} \quad j \neq j_1, \\ j\mathbf{1} & \text{when} \quad k = k_1 \quad \text{and} \quad j = j_1; \end{cases} \tag{9}$$

$$\overset{+}{F}{}^{kk_1}_{jj_1} = 0, \quad \overset{-}{F}{}^{kk_1}_{jj_1} = 0, \quad \overset{3}{F}{}^{kk_1}_{jj_1} = 0 \quad \text{when} \quad |k-k_1| \geqslant 2, \tag{10}$$

$$\overset{+}{F}{}^{kk_1}_{jj_1} = 0 \quad \text{when} \quad j \neq j_1+1, \quad \overset{-}{F}{}^{kk_1}_{jj_1} = 0 \quad \text{when} \quad j \neq j_1-1,$$

$$\overset{3}{F}{}^{kk_1}_{jj_1} = 0 \quad \text{when} \quad j \neq j_1, \tag{11}$$

$$\overset{+}{F}{}^{k,k+1}_{j,j-1} = \sqrt{[(k-j+1)(k-j+2)]}\, E^k_{jk} Q_{k+1} E^{k+1}_{k+1,j-1}, \; -k \leqslant j \leqslant k, \tag{12}$$

$$\overset{+}{F}{}^{kk}_{j,j-1} = \sqrt{[(k+j)(k-j+1)]}\, E^k_{jk} P_k E^k_{k,j-1}, \; -k+1 \leqslant j \leqslant k, \tag{13}$$

$$\overset{+}{F}{}^{k,k-1}_{j,j-1} = \sqrt{[(k+j)(k+j-1)]}\, E^k_{jk} D_k E^{k-1}_{k-1,j-1}, \; -k+2 \leqslant j \leqslant k, \tag{14}$$

$$\overset{-}{F}{}^{k,k+1}_{j,j+1} = -\sqrt{[(k+j+1)(k+j+2)]}\, E^k_{jk} Q_{k+1} E^{k+1}_{k+1,j+1}, \; -k \leqslant j \leqslant k, \tag{15}$$

$$\overset{-}{F}{}^{kk}_{j,j+1} = -\sqrt{[(k+j+1)(k-j)]}\, E^k_{jk} P_k E^k_{k,j+1}, \; -k \leqslant j \leqslant k-1, \tag{16}$$

$$\overset{-}{F}{}^{k,k-1}_{j,j+1} = -\sqrt{[(k-j)(k-j-1)]} E^k_{jk} D_k E^{k-1}_{k-1,j+1}, \; -k \leqslant j \leqslant k-2, \tag{17}$$

$$\overset{3}{F}{}^{k,k+1}_{jj} = \sqrt{[(k+j+1)(k-j+1)]}\, E^k_{jk} Q_{k+1} E^{k+1}_{k+1,j}, \; -k \leqslant j \leqslant k, \tag{18}$$

$$\overset{3}{F}{}^{kk}_{jj} = -jE^k_{jk} P_k E^k_{kj}, \qquad -k \leqslant j \leqslant k, \tag{19}$$

$$\overset{3}{F}{}_{jj}^{k,k-1} = -\sqrt{[(k+j)(k-j)]}\,E^k_{jk}D_kE^{k-1}_{k-1,j},\quad -k+1 \leqslant j \leqslant k-1, \tag{20}$$

where Q_k, P_k, D_{k+1} are some operators from $\mathfrak{M}^k_k$ to $\mathfrak{M}^{k-1}_{k-1}$, $\mathfrak{M}^k_k$, $\mathfrak{M}^{k+1}_{k+1}$ respectively, here defined on $\mathfrak{M}^k_k \cap \mathfrak{D}$ and satisfying the conditions

$$\left.\begin{array}{c} Q_k(\mathfrak{M}^k_k\cap\mathfrak{D})\subset\mathfrak{M}^{k-1}_{k-1}\cap\mathfrak{D},\ P_k(\mathfrak{M}^k_k\cap\mathfrak{D})\subset\mathfrak{M}^k_k\cap\mathfrak{D}, \\ D_{k+1}(\mathfrak{M}^k_k\cap\mathfrak{D})\subset\mathfrak{M}^{k+1}_{k+1}\cap\mathfrak{D}. \end{array}\right\} \tag{21}$$

So far we have not made use of relations (3). We consider the first of these: $[F_+, F_3] = H_+$. This means that

$$\overset{+}{F}{}^{k,k-1}_{j,j-1}\overset{3}{F}{}^{k-1,k_1}_{j-1,j-1} + \overset{+}{F}{}^{k,k}_{j,j-1}\overset{3}{F}{}^{kk_1}_{j-1,j-1} + \overset{+}{F}{}^{k,k+1}_{j,j-1}\overset{3}{F}{}^{k+1,k_1}_{j-1,j-1}$$
$$- \overset{3}{F}{}^{k,k-1}_{jj}\overset{+}{F}{}^{k-1,k_1}_{j,j-1} - \overset{3}{F}{}^{kk}_{jj}\overset{+}{F}{}^{kk_1}_{j,j-1} - \overset{3}{F}{}^{k,k+1}_{jj}\overset{+}{F}{}^{k+1,k_1}_{j,j-1} = \overset{+}{H}{}^{kk_1}_{j,j-1};$$

by virtue of (10), this equation differs from the identity $0 = 0$ only when $k_1 = k-2,\ k-1,\ k,\ k+1,\ k+2$, in which cases it becomes the relations:

$$\overset{+}{F}{}^{k,k-1}_{j,j-1}\overset{3}{F}{}^{k-1,k-2}_{j-1,j-1} - \overset{3}{F}{}^{k,k-1}_{jj}\overset{+}{F}{}^{k-1,k-2}_{j,j-1} = 0, \tag{22}$$

$$\overset{+}{F}{}^{k,k-1}_{j,j-1}\overset{3}{F}{}^{k-1,k-1}_{j-1,j-1} + \overset{+}{F}{}^{k,k}_{j,j-1}\overset{3}{F}{}^{k,k-1}_{j-1,j-1} - \overset{3}{F}{}^{k,k-1}_{jj}\overset{+}{F}{}^{k-1,k-1}_{j,j-1}$$
$$- \overset{3}{F}{}^{kk}_{jj}\overset{+}{F}{}^{k,k-1}_{j,j-1} = 0, \tag{23}$$

$$\overset{+}{F}{}^{k,k-1}_{j,j-1}\overset{3}{F}{}^{k-1,k}_{j-1,j-1} + \overset{+}{F}{}^{k,k}_{j,j-1}\overset{3}{F}{}^{k,k}_{j-1,j-1} + \overset{+}{F}{}^{k,k+1}_{j,j-1}\overset{3}{F}{}^{k+1,k}_{j-1,j-1}$$
$$- \overset{3}{F}{}^{k,k-1}_{jj}\overset{+}{F}{}^{k-1,k}_{j,j-1} - \overset{3}{F}{}^{kk}_{jj}\overset{+}{F}{}^{kk}_{j,j-1} - \overset{3}{F}{}^{k,k+1}_{jj}\overset{+}{F}{}^{k+1,k}_{j,j-1} = \alpha^k_j E^k_{j,j-1}, \tag{24}$$

$$\overset{+}{F}{}^{k,k}_{j,j-1}\overset{3}{F}{}^{k,k+1}_{j-1,j-1} + \overset{+}{F}{}^{k,k+1}_{j,j-1}\overset{3}{F}{}^{k+1,k+1}_{j-1,j-1} - \overset{3}{F}{}^{kk}_{jj}\overset{+}{F}{}^{k,k+1}_{j,j-1}$$
$$- \overset{3}{F}{}^{k,k+1}_{jj}\overset{+}{F}{}^{k+1,k+1}_{j,j-1} = 0, \tag{25}$$

$$\overset{+}{F}{}^{k,k+1}_{j,j-1}\overset{3}{F}{}^{k+1,k+2}_{j-1,j-1} - \overset{3}{F}{}^{k,k+1}_{jj}\overset{+}{F}{}^{k+1,k+2}_{j,j-1} = 0 \tag{26}$$

respectively. By an immediate substitution from formulae (12), (14), (18) and (20) we can prove that relations (22) and (26) are satisfied identically.

Further, substituting in (23–25) instead of $\overset{+}{F}{}^{kk_1}_{j,j-1}$, $\overset{3}{F}{}^{kk_1}_{jj}$ their expressions from formulae (12–14) and (18–20) and simplifying, we obtain:

$$-(k-1)E^k_{jk}D_kP_{k-1}E^{k-1}_{k-1,j-1}+(k+1)E^k_{jk}P_kD_kE^{k-1}_{k-1,j-1} = 0, \quad (27)$$

$$(2k-1)E^k_{jk}D_kQ_kE^k_{k,j-1}-E^k_{jk}P^2_kE^k_{k,j-1}$$
$$-(2k+3)E^k_{jk}Q_{k+1}D_{k+1}E^k_{k,j-1} = E^k_{j,j-1}, \quad (28)$$

$$-kE^k_{jk}P_kQ_{k+1}E^{k+1}_{k+1,j-1}+(k+2)E^k_{jk}Q_{k+1}P_{k+1}E^{k+1}_{k+1,j-1} = 0. \quad (29)$$

Multiplying both sides of these equations on the left by E^k_{kj}, and on the right by $E^{k-1}_{j-1,k-1}$, $E^k_{j-1,k}$, $E^{k+1}_{j-1,k+1}$ respectively, we conclude that

$$-(k-1)D_kP_{k-1}+(k+1)P_kD_k = 0, \quad (30)$$

$$(2k-1)D_kQ_k-P^2_k-(2k+3)Q_{k+1}D_{k+1} = E^k_{kk}, \quad (31)$$

$$-kP_kQ_{k+1}+(k+2)Q_{k+1}P_{k+1} = 0. \quad (32)$$

Conversely, the relations (27–29) are obtained from relations (30–32) by multiplying on the left by E^k_{jk}, and on the right respectively by $E^{k-1}_{k-1,j-1}$, $E^k_{k,j-1}$, $E^{k+1}_{k+1,j-1}$.

An analogous substitution in the remaining two relations: $[F_-, F_3] = -H_-$, $[F_+, F_-] = -2H_3$, leads to the same formulae (30–32).

We arrive at the following theorem:

THEOREM 2. *The infinitesimal operators of a linear representation $g \to T_g$ of the proper Lorentz group are given by the formulae:*

$$H_+E^k_{jj} = \sqrt{[(k-j)(k+j+1)]}\,E^k_{j+1,j}, \quad (33)$$

$$H_-E^k_{jj} = \sqrt{[(k+j)(k-j+1)]}\,E^k_{j-1,j}, \quad (34)$$

$$H_3E^k_{jj} = jE^k_{jj}, \quad (35)$$

$$F_+E^{kk}_{jj} = \sqrt{[(k-j-1)(k-j)]}\,E^{k-1}_{j+1,k-1}Q_kE^k_{k,j}$$
$$-\sqrt{[(k+j+1)(k-j)]}\,E^k_{j+1,k}P_kE^k_{kj}$$
$$+\sqrt{[(k+j+2)(k+j+1)]}\,E^{k+1}_{j+1,k+1}D_{k+1}E^k_{kj}, \quad (36)$$

$$F_-E_{jj}^{kk} = -\sqrt{[(k+j-1)(k+j)]}\,E_{j-1,k-1}^{k-1}\,Q_k E_{k,j}^{k}$$
$$-\sqrt{[(k+j)(k-j+1)]}\,E_{j-1,k}^{k} P_k E_{kj}^{k}$$
$$-\sqrt{[(k-j+2)(k-j+1)]}\,E_{j-1,k+1}^{k+1} D_{k+1} E_{kj}^{k}, \qquad (37)$$

$$F_3 E_{jj}^{k} = \sqrt{[(k+j)(k-j)]}\,E_{j,k-1}^{k-1}\,Q_k E_{k,j}^{k} - jE_{jk}^{k} P_k E_{k,j}^{k}$$
$$-\sqrt{[(k+j+1)(k-j+1)]}\,E_{j,k+1}^{k+1} D_{k+1} E_{kj}^{k}, \qquad (38)$$

where P_k *is an operator in* $\mathfrak{M}_k^k$, Q_k *is an operator from* $\mathfrak{M}_k^k$ to $\mathfrak{M}_{k-1}^{k-1}$, D_{k+1} *is an operator from* $\mathfrak{M}_k^k$ *to* $\mathfrak{M}_{k+1}^{k+1}$, *satisfying the relations*:

$$-(k-1)\,D_k P_{k-1} + (k+1)\,P_k D_k = 0, \qquad (39)$$

$$(2k-1)\,D_k Q_k - (2k+3)\,Q_{k+1} D_{k+1} - P_k^2 = E_{kk}^k, \qquad (40)$$

$$-kP_k Q_{k+1} + (k+2)\,Q_{k+1} P_{k+1} = 0, \qquad (41)$$

$$Q_k(\mathfrak{M}_k^k \cap \mathfrak{D}) \subset \mathfrak{M}_{k-1}^{k-1} \cap \mathfrak{D}, \quad P_k(\mathfrak{M}_k^k \cap \mathfrak{D}) \subset \mathfrak{M}_k^k \cap \mathfrak{D},$$
$$D_{k+1}(\mathfrak{M}_k^k \cap \mathfrak{D}) \subset \mathfrak{M}_{k+1}^{k+1} \cap \mathfrak{D}. \qquad (42)$$

We leave open the following more complex question: in what cases are the operators H_+, H_-, H_3, F_+, F_-, F_3, defined by these formulae in fact infinitesimal operators of some representation of the proper Lorentz group, and also the question of the general form of the operators P_k, Q_k, D_{k+1}, satisfying conditions (39–41). We limit ourselves only to the following remarks:

Remark 1. We set

$$\hat{P}_k = k(k+1)P_k, \quad \hat{Q}_k = (2k+1)(2k-1)\,Q_k; \qquad (43)$$

then relations (39–41) can be rewritten in the form

$$D_k P_{k-1} - \hat{P}_k D_k = 0, \qquad (44)$$

$$D_k\hat{Q}_k - \hat{Q}_{k+1}D_{k+1} - \left[\frac{1}{k^2} - \frac{1}{(k+1)^2}\right]\hat{P}_k^2 = (2k+1)E_{kk}^k, \qquad (45)$$

$$\hat{P}_k\hat{Q}_{k+1} - \hat{Q}_{k+1}\hat{P}_{k+1} = 0. \qquad (46)$$

From (44) we deduce that

$$\hat{P}_k D_k D_{k-1} = D_k \hat{P}_{k-1} D_{k-1} = D_k D_{k-1} \hat{P}_{k-2}$$

and in general when $\nu+1 \leqslant k$

$$\hat{P}_k D_k D_{k-1} \dots D_{\nu+1} = D_k D_{k-1} \dots D_{\nu+1} \hat{P}_\nu. \tag{47}$$

Analogously

$$\hat{P}_k^2 D_k D_{k-1} \dots D_{\nu+1} = D_k D_{k-1} \dots D_{\nu+1} \hat{P}_\nu^2. \tag{48}$$

We set, further:

$$\left.\begin{aligned} Q_{k\mu\nu} &= D_k D_{k-1} \dots D_{\mu+1} D_\mu \hat{Q}_\mu D_\mu D_{\mu-1} \dots D_{\nu+1} \\ &\quad \text{when} \quad \nu+1 \leqslant \mu \leqslant k-1, \\ Q_{k\nu\nu} &= D_k D_{k-1} \dots D_{\nu+1} D_\nu \hat{Q}_\nu; \\ Q_{kk\nu} &= D_k Q_k D_k D_{k-1} \dots D_{\nu+1}; \end{aligned}\right\} \tag{49}$$

multiplying both sides of relation (45) (with μ instead of k) namely

$$D_\mu \hat{Q}_\mu - \hat{Q}_{\mu+1} D_{\mu+1} - \left[\frac{1}{\mu^2} - \frac{1}{(\mu+1)^2}\right] \hat{P}_\mu^2 = (2\mu+1) E_{\mu\mu}^\mu$$

on the right by $D_\mu D_{\mu-1} \dots D_{\nu+1}$, and on the left by $D_k D_{k-1} \dots$ $\dots D_{\mu+1}$, we obtain:

$$Q_{k\mu\nu} - Q_{k,\mu+1,\nu} - \left[\frac{1}{\mu^2} - \frac{1}{(\mu+1)^2}\right] D_k D_{k-1} \dots D_{\nu+1} \hat{P}_\nu^2$$
$$= (2\mu+1) D_k D_{k-1} \dots D_{\nu+1}.$$

Adding these equations term by term for $\mu = \nu, \nu+1, \dots, k-1$, we arrive at the relation

$$Q_{k\nu\nu} - Q_{kk\nu} - \left(\frac{1}{\nu^2} - \frac{1}{k^2}\right) D_k D_{k-1} \dots D_{\nu+1} \hat{P}_\nu^2 = (k^2 - \nu^2) D_k D_{k-1} \dots$$
$$\dots D_{\nu+1};$$

hence

$$Q_{kk\nu} = Q_{k\nu\nu} - \frac{k^2-\nu^2}{k^2\nu^2} D_k D_{k-1} \dots D_{\nu+1} (\hat{P}_\nu^2 + k^2\nu^2 1),$$

i.e.

$$D_k \hat{Q}_k D_k D_{k-1} \dots D_{\nu+1}$$
$$= D_k D_{k-1} \dots D_{\nu+1} \left[D_\nu \hat{Q}_\nu - \frac{k^2-\nu^2}{k^2\nu^2} (\hat{P}_\nu^2 + k^2\nu^2 1) \right]. \tag{50}$$

Finally, multiplying both sides of (46) on the right by D_{k+1} and making use of relation (44), we obtain:

$$\hat{P}_k \hat{Q}_{k+1} D_{k+1} = \hat{Q}_{k+1} \hat{P}_{k+1} D_{k+1} = \hat{Q}_{k+1} D_{k+1} \hat{P}_k,$$

i.e. $\hat{P}_k$ and $\hat{Q}_{k+1} D_{k+1}$ commute; by virtue of (45), it follows from this that $\hat{P}_k^2$ and $D_k \hat{Q}_k$ also commute.

Let k_0 be the least of all the k for which $E^k_{kk} \neq 0$. Then $D_{k_0} = 0$, and formula (50) with $v = k_0$, $k_0 \neq 0$, takes the form

$$D_k \hat{Q}_k D_k D_{k-1} \dots D_{k_0+1} = -\frac{k^2-k_0^2}{k^2 k_0^2} D_k D_{k-1} \dots$$
$$\dots D_{k_0+1}(\hat{P}^2_{k_0} + k^2 k_0^2 1). \qquad (51a)$$

If, however, $k_0 = 0$, then (see page 343) $P_{k_0} = 0$, and so $\hat{P}_k D_k D_{k-1} \dots D_{k_0+1} = 0$. Hence, repeating the reasoning in the derivation of formula (50) for this case, we conclude that when $k_0 = 0$,

$$D_k \hat{Q}_k D_k D_{k-1} \dots D_{k_0+1} = -k^2 D_k D_{k-1} \dots D_{k_0+1}. \qquad (51b)$$

We denote by $\mathfrak{N}_{kv}$ the domain of variation of the operator $D_k D_{k-1} \dots D_{v+1}$, and by $\mathfrak{N}_{kv}$ the set of all vectors $x \in \mathfrak{M}^k_k \cap \mathfrak{D}$, for which $D_k D_{k-1} \dots D_{v+1} x = 0$. Clearly,

$$\mathfrak{N}_{kk_0} \subset \mathfrak{N}_{k,k_0+1} \subset \dots \subset \mathfrak{N}_{k,k-1}, \qquad (52)$$

$$\mathfrak{N}_{v+1,v} \subset \mathfrak{N}_{v+2,v} \subset \mathfrak{N}_{v+3,v} \subset \dots. \qquad (53)$$

From relations (47) and (50) it follows that $\mathfrak{N}_{kv}$ must be invariant with respect to the operators $\hat{P}_v$ and $D_v \hat{Q}_v$. In fact, if $x \in \mathfrak{N}_{kv}$, then from (47) we conclude that

$$D_k D_{k-1} \dots D_{v+1} \hat{P}_v x = \hat{P}_k D_k D_{k-1} \dots D_{v+1} x = 0,$$

hence, also $\hat{P}_v x \in \mathfrak{N}_{kv}$. This means that $\mathfrak{N}_{kv}$ is invariant with respect to $\hat{P}_v$. The invariance of $\mathfrak{N}_{kv}$ with respect to $D_v \hat{Q}_v$ is proved similarly.

Conversely, when this condition of invariance is satisfied equations (47) and (50) define $\hat{P}_k$ and $D_k \hat{Q}_k$ uniquely on $\mathfrak{N}_{kv}$, if $\hat{P}_v$ and $D_v \hat{Q}_v$

are already known. In fact, we define $\hat{P}_k$ on the vectors $y = D_k D_{k-1} \dots D_{\nu+1}\, x \in \mathfrak{N}_{k\nu}$, by

$$\hat{P}_\nu y = D_k D_{k-1} \dots D_{\nu+1} \hat{P}_\nu x.$$

By this formula $\hat{P}_k$ is defined on $\mathfrak{N}_{k\nu}$ uniquely, i.e. if $y = D_k D_{k-1} \dots D_{\nu+1} x_1 = D_k D_{k-1} \dots D_{\nu+1} x_2$, then also $D_k D_{k-1} \dots D_{\nu+1} \hat{P}_\nu x_1 = D_k D_{k-1} \dots D_{\nu+1} \hat{P}_\nu x_2$; this follows from the fact that $x_1 - x_2 \in \mathfrak{N}_{k\nu}$, so that

$$\hat{P}_\nu(x_1 - x_2) \in \mathfrak{N}_{k\nu}.$$

In the same way $D_k \hat{Q}_k$ is defined on $\mathfrak{N}_{k\nu}$.

In particular taking $\nu = k_0$, we define (for given D_{k_0} and $\hat{P}_{k_0}$) operators $\hat{P}_k$ on $\mathfrak{N}_{kk_0}$. However, $\mathfrak{N}_{k,k_0}$ cannot exhaust the whole of $\mathfrak{M}_k^k \cap \mathfrak{D}$, and then $\hat{P}_k$ can be defined on the vectors $x \bar{\in} \mathfrak{N}_{kk_0}$ in a manner independent of $\hat{P}_{k_0}$. This happens for instance if the given representation $g \to T_g$ is the direct sum of two representations $g \to T_g'$ and $g \to T_g''$ with different values of k_0. If these values are k_0' and $k_0'' > k_0'$, then the situation indicated above will occur when $k = k_0''$, $\nu = k_0'$.

Remark 2. We denote by $\mathfrak{M}$ the set of all finite sums $x_1 + x_2 + \dots + x_n$, where $x_j \in \mathfrak{M}_{kj}^{kj}$, and we define the operators $\hat{P}$, $\hat{Q}$, D, Λ', Λ'' in $\mathfrak{M}$ setting

$$P(x_1 + \dots + x_n) = \hat{P}_{k_1} x_1 + \dots + \hat{P}_{k_n} x_n,$$

$$\hat{Q}(x_1 + \dots + x_n) = \hat{Q}_{k_1} x_1 + \dots + \hat{Q}_{k_n} x_n,$$

$$D(x_1 + \dots + x_n) = D_{k_1} x_1 + \dots + D_{k_n} x_n,$$

$$\Lambda'(x_1 + \dots + x_n) = \lambda'_{k_1} x_1 + \dots + \lambda'_{k_n} x_n,$$

$$\Lambda''(x_1 + \dots + x_n) = \lambda''_{k_1} x_1 + \dots + \lambda''_{k_n} x_n,$$

where

$$\lambda'_k = \frac{1}{k^2} - \frac{1}{(k+1)^2}, \quad \lambda''_k = 2k+1;$$

it is easy to verify that relations (44–46) can then be rewritten in the form

$$\hat{P}D = D\hat{P}, \quad D\hat{Q} - \hat{Q}D - \Lambda'\hat{P}^2 = \Lambda'', \quad \hat{P}\hat{Q} = \hat{Q}\hat{P}.$$

2. Some special cases of representations of the group $\mathfrak{G}_+$

The representation $g \to T_g$ of the group $\mathfrak{G}_+$ is called *a multiple of the irreducible* representation $S_c^{k_0}$ of this group (see end of § 15),

$$P_k = \frac{ik_0 c}{k(k+1)} \cdot \mathbf{1}, \tag{1}$$

$$Q_k = \frac{i}{k} \sqrt{\left[\frac{(k^2-k_0^2)(k^2-c^2)}{4k^2-1}\right]} U_k, \tag{2}$$

$$D_k = \frac{i}{k} \sqrt{\left[\frac{(k^2-k_0^2)(k^2-c^2)}{4k^2-1}\right]} U_k^{-1}, \tag{3}$$

if where U_k is a linear operator from $\mathfrak{M}_k^k$ to $\mathfrak{M}_{k-1}^{k-1}$, mapping $\mathfrak{M}_k^k$ on $\mathfrak{M}_{k-1}^{k-1}$ isometrically.

Such operators U_k exist only when all the non-zero subspaces $\mathfrak{M}_k^k$, $k = k_0, k_0+1, \ldots$, are isometric to each other. In the case of finite-dimensional $\mathfrak{M}_{k_0}^{k_0}$ this means that all the non-zero subspaces $\mathfrak{M}_j^k$ have the same dimension, coinciding with the dimension of the subspace $\mathfrak{M}_{k_0}^{k_0}$. If $\mathfrak{M}_{k_0}^{k_0}$ has finite-dimension n, then we will say that the given representation $g \to T_g$ is an n-fold multiple† of the representation $S_c^{k_0}$. By an immediate substitution it is easy to convince oneself that the operators A_k, C_k, D_k, defined by formulae (1–3), satisfy the relations (39–41) Subsection 1.

We will indicate a very general method of constructing a representation which is a multiple of a given representation.

Let, for instance, $S_c^{k_0} = \mathfrak{S}_{m,\rho}$ and let R_0 be a fixed Banach space. We will take as the space R of the representation the set of all measurable vector-valued functions $f = f(u)$ with values in R_0, satisfying the conditions:

$$f(\gamma u) = e^{im\omega} f(u) \quad \text{when} \quad \gamma = \begin{Vmatrix} e^{-i\omega} & 0 \\ 0 & e^{i\omega} \end{Vmatrix}, \tag{4}$$

$$\int |f(u)|^2 \, du < \infty. \tag{5}$$

Defining the operations in R in the usual way, and the norm by means of the formula $|f| = \sqrt{[\int |f(u)|^2 du]}$, we convert R into a

† In this connection see § 6, Subsection 6.

normed, in fact a complete, space; its completeness is proved in the same way as the completeness of the space $L^2(a, b)$.

Further, we define in R the operators T_a, letting

$$T_a f(u) = \frac{\alpha(ua)}{\alpha(u\bar{a})} f(u\bar{a}) \tag{6}$$

where $\alpha(a) = |a_{22}|^{-m+i\rho-2}\, a_{22}^m$.

Thus, the representation $a \to T_a$ is defined by the same formulae as the representation $\mathfrak{S}_{m,\rho}$ with the difference that $f(u)$ is now not a numerical function, but a vector-valued function.

We consider all possible vector-valued functions from R of the form $f(u) = \phi(u) f_0$, where $\phi(u)$ is a numerical valued function, and f_0 is a fixed normalized vector from R_0. These vector-valued functions form a closed subspace R_{f_0} in R, invariant with respect to the operators T_a, and the correspondence $\phi(u) f_0 \to \phi(u)$ is an isometric mapping of the subspace R_{f_0} on L_2^m $(\mathfrak{U})$; in this mapping the operators T_a, considered only on R_{f_0}, go into operators of the representation $\mathfrak{S}_{m,\rho}$. Hence we deduce (see Theorem 8 § 11, Subsection 4 and § 11, Subsection 6) that $\mathfrak{M}_j^k$ is the set of all vector-valued functions $c_{\nu j}^k(u) f$, $f \in R_0$, where $\nu = \frac{1}{2}m$, and that formulae (1–3) hold for the operators A_k, C_k, D_k; here the operators U_k are given by the following formula (see the remark in §11, Subsection 4)

$$U_k(\kappa_{\nu\rho}^k c_{\nu k}^k(u) f) = \kappa_{\nu\rho}^{k-1} c_{\nu,k-1}^{k-1}(u) f. \tag{7}$$

We obtain another interesting example of a representation of the group $\mathfrak{G}_+$ if we take the direct sum of representations (see § 6, Subsections 6) which are multiples of irreducible representations.

Of course, the linear representations of the group $\mathfrak{G}_+$ are not exhausted by these representations; the problem of investigating other possibilities mentioned here is of great significance.

3. The concept of an equation invariant with respect to proper Lorentz transformations

Let $g \to T_g$ be some representation of the group $\mathfrak{G}_+$, R the space of this representation, and $\mathfrak{D}$ the set defined in Subsection 1.

We consider the equation

$$L_1\frac{\partial\psi}{\partial x_1} + L_2\frac{\partial\psi}{\partial x_2} + L_3\frac{\partial\psi}{\partial x_3} + L_4\frac{\partial\psi}{\partial x_4} + i\kappa\psi = 0, \tag{1}$$

where ψ is the required vector-valued function of x_1, x_2, x_3, x_4 with values from $\mathfrak{D}$, κ a real number distinct from zero, and L_1, L_2, L_3, L_4 are given closed operators in R, possessing the following properties:

(1) L_j, $j = 1, 2, 3, 4$, are defined on $\mathfrak{D}$, and $\mathfrak{D}$ is invariant with respect to each of the operators L_j;

(2) the closures of the operators L_j, considered only on finite sums of vectors of the form $E_{jj}^k x$, $x \in \mathfrak{D}$, coincide with the original operators L_j.

Such an equation (1) is called *invariant with respect to the transformations of the group* $\mathfrak{G}_+$, if it is not altered by any transformation $g \in \mathfrak{G}_+$ of the point (x_1, x_2, x_3, x_4) and a simultaneous transformation T_g of the vector ψ for all vector-valued functions $\psi(x_1, x_2, x_3, x_4)$ with values from $\mathfrak{D}$, having continuous partial derivatives of the second order with respect to x_1, x_2, x_3, x_4.

Repeating the reasoning of § 17, Subsection 3, we deduce that a necessary and sufficient condition for the invariance of equation (1) is the validity of the equations†

$$\sum_{k=1}^{4} g_{jk} T_g L_k T_g^{-1} = L_j, \quad j = 1, 2, 3, 4, \tag{2}$$

for all $g \in \mathfrak{G}_+$.

In (2) we set $g = a(t)$, where $a(t)$ is one of the one-parameter groups $a_j(t)$, $b_j(t)$, $j = 1, 2, 3$ (see § 7, Subsection 1), and we rewrite the resulting equation in the form

$$\sum_{k=1}^{4} a_{jk}(t) T_{a(t)} L_k = L_j T_{a(t)}.$$

† As before, all equations between operators are here understood in the sense that their left and right sides coincide on all vectors x from $\mathfrak{D}$.

Differentiating both sides of this equation with respect to t at $t = 0$ and taking into account the fact that the operators L_j are closed, we conclude that

$$AL_j - L_jA = -\sum_{k=1}^{4} a_{jk} L_k, \tag{3}$$

where $a = \|a_{jk}\|$ is the infinitesimal matrix of the one-parameter group $a(t)$, and A is an infinitesimal operator of the one-parameter group of operators $A(t) = T_{a(t)}$.

Conversely, if relations (3) are satisfied when $a(t) = a_j(t)$ and $a(t) = b_j(t)$, $j = 1, 2, 3$, then, reasoning in the same way as in § 17, Subsection 4, we deduce that relations (2) are satisfied, i.e. that equation (1) is invariant with respect to the transformations of the group $\mathfrak{G}_+$. Hence, condition (3) is necessary and sufficient for the invariance of equation (1) with respect to the transformations of the group $\mathfrak{G}_+$.

4. The general form of an equation invariant with respect to the transformations of the group $\mathfrak{G}_+$

In condition (3) Subsection (3) we set $a = b_\nu$, $\nu = 1, 2, 3$ and $j = 4$; making use of the formulae for the matrix elements of the operators b_j (see (16–18) § 7, Subsection 1), we obtain:

$$L_\nu = [L_4, B_\nu], \quad \nu = 1, 2, 3. \tag{1}$$

Therefore it is sufficient to find L_4; the operators L_1, L_2, L_3 are then determined from relations (1).

Now setting $a = b_\nu$, $\nu = 1, 2, 3$, and $j = 1, 2, 3$ in condition (3) Subsection 3 we obtain:

$$[L_j, B_\nu] = \begin{cases} 0 & \text{when } j \neq \nu, \\ L_4 & \text{when } j = \nu. \end{cases} \tag{2}$$

Finally, when $a = a_\nu$, $\nu = 1, 2, 3$, condition (3) Subsection 3 gives:

$$[L_4, A_\nu] = 0, \quad \nu = 1, 2, 3, \tag{3}$$

$$[L_1, A_1] = [L_2, A_2] = [L_3, A_3] = 0, \tag{4}$$

$$[L_1, A_2] = L_3, \quad [L_1, A_3] = -L_2, \tag{5}$$

$$[L_2, A_1] = -L_3, \quad [L_2, A_3] = L_1, \tag{6}$$

$$[L_3, A_1] = L_2, \quad [L_3, A_2] = -L_1. \tag{7}$$

It is easy to verify directly that relations (4–7) follow from (1), (3) and the relations between A_ν and B_ν (see (1–6) § 7, Subsection 4).†

From (1) when $\nu = 3$ and (2) when $j = \nu = 3$ we deduce that

$$[[L_4, B_3], B_3] = L_4. \tag{8}$$

Therefore we will first find the operator L_4, satisfying relations (3) and (8).

Again introducing the operators

$$H_+ = iA_1 - A_2, \quad H_- = iA_1 + A_2, \quad H_3 = iA_3, \quad F_3 = iB_3,$$

we can rewrite these relations in the form

$$[L_4, H_+] = 0, \quad [L_4, H_-] = 0, \quad [L_4, H_3] = 0;$$

$$[[L_4, F_3], F_3] = -L_4.$$

As before (see § 17, Subsection 5 and Subsection 1) we introduce, the matrices $\|\overset{+}{H}{}^{kk_1}_{jj_1}\|$, $\|\overset{-}{H}{}^{kk_1}_{jj_1}\|$, $\|\overset{3}{H}{}^{kk_1}_{jj_1}\|$, $\|\overset{3}{F}{}^{kk_1}_{jj_1}\|$ of the operators H_+, H_-, H_3, F_3 and we will seek L_4 also in the form of a matrix $\|L^{kk_1}_{jj_1}\|$.

By virtue of (9) Subsection 1, the relation $[L_4, H_3] = 0$ means that $j_1 L^{kk_1}_{jj_1} = j L^{kk_1}_{jj_1}$ and so

$$L^{kk_1}_{jj_1} = 0 \quad \text{when} \quad j_1 \neq j. \tag{9}$$

Further, by virtue of (7) and (8) Subsection 1, the relations $[L_4, H_+] = 0$ and $[L_4, H_-] = 0$ mean respectively that

$$\alpha^{k_1}_{j_1+1} L^{kk_1}_{j,j_1+1} E^{k_1}_{j_1+1,j_1} = \alpha^k_j E^k_{j,j-1} L^{kk_1}_{j-1,j_1}, \tag{10}$$

$$\alpha^{k_1}_{j_1} L^{kk_1}_{j,j_1-1} E^{k_1}_{j_1-1,j_1} = \alpha^k_{j+1} E^k_{j,j+1} L^{kk_1}_{j+1,j_1}. \tag{11}$$

---

† For instance, when $\nu = 1, 2, 3$

$$[L_\nu, A_\nu] = [[L_4, B_\nu], A_\nu] = -[[B_\nu, A_\nu], L_4] - [[A_\nu, L_4], B_\nu] = 0;$$

$$[L_1, A_2] = [[L_4, B_1], A_2] = -[[B_1, A_2], L_4] - [[A_2, L_4], B_1] = -[B_3, L_4] = L_3$$

and so on. Here we make use of the easily proved relation:

$$[[A, B], C] + [[B, C], A] + [[C, A], B] = 0.$$

By virtue of (9), relations (10) and (11) are satisfied identically when $\neq j_1+1$, respectively when $j \neq j_1-1$.

Letting $j_1+1 = j$ in (10), and $j_1 - 1 = j$ in (11), we obtain:

$$\alpha_j^{k_1} L_{jj}^{kk_1} E_{j,j-1}^{k_1} = \alpha_j^k E_{j,j-1}^k L_{j-1,j-1}^{kk_1}, \tag{12}$$

$$\alpha_{j+1}^{k_1} L_{jj}^{kk_1} E_{j,j+1}^{k_1} = \alpha_{j+1}^k E_{j,j+1}^k L_{j+1,j+1}^{kk_1}, \tag{13}$$

or, replacing $j+1$ by j in (13):

$$\alpha_j^{k_1} L_{j-1,j-1}^{kk_1} E_{j-1,j}^{k_1} = \alpha_j^k E_{j-1,j}^k L_{jj}^{kk_1}. \tag{14}$$

Multiplying both sides of (12) on the right by $E_{j-1,j}^{k_1}$, and both sides of (14) on the left by $E_{j,j-1}^k$, we obtain:

$$\left.\begin{aligned} \alpha_j^{k_1} L_{jj}^{kk_1} &= \alpha_j^k E_{j,j-1}^k L_{j-1,j-1}^{kk_1} E_{j-1,j}^{k_1}, \\ \alpha_j^k L_{jj}^{kk_1} &= \alpha_j^{k_1} E_{j,j-1}^k L_{j-1,j-1}^{kk_1} E_{j-1,j}^{k_1}. \end{aligned}\right\} \tag{15}$$

Hence

$$(\alpha_j^k)^2 E_{j,j-1}^k L_{j-1,j-1}^{kk_1} E_{j-1,j}^{k_1} = (\alpha_j^{k_1})^2 E_{j,j-1}^k L_{j-1,j-1}^{kk_1} E_{j-1,j}^{k_1},$$

i.e.

$$\begin{aligned} &(k+j)(k-j+1) E_{j,j-1}^k L_{j-1,j-1}^{kk_1} E_{j-1,j}^{k_1} \\ &\qquad = (k_1+j)(k_1-j+1) E_{j,j-1}^k L_{j-1,j-1}^{kk_1} E_{j-1,j}^{k_1}. \end{aligned}$$

When $k \neq k_1$ this is possible only when

$$E_{j,j-1}^k L_{j-1,j-1}^{kk_1} E_{j-1,j}^{k_1} = 0.$$

Multiplying both sides of the equation on the left by $E_{j-1,j}^k$, and on the right by $E_{j,j-1}^{k_1}$, we deduce that† $L_{j-1,j-1}^{kk_1} = 0$ when $k \neq k_1$. Thus the operator $L_{jj_1}^{kk_1}$ can be distinct from zero only when $j_1 = j$ and $k_1 = k$.

From (15) when $k_1 = k$ we find that $L_{jj}^{kk} = E_{j,j-1}^k L_{j-1,j-1}^{kk} \times \times E_{j-1,j}^k$ and so

$$L_{j-1,j-1}^{kk} = E_{j-1,j}^k L_{jj}^{kk} E_{j,j-1}^k.$$

Hence

$$L_{k-1,k-1}^{kk} = E_{k-1,k}^k L_{kk}^{kk} E_{k,k-1}^k;$$

$$\begin{aligned} L_{k-2,k-2}^{kk} &= E_{k-2,k-1}^k L_{k-1,k-1}^{kk} E_{k-1,k-2}^k \\ &= E_{k-2,k-1}^k E_{k-1,k}^k L_{kk}^{kk} E_{k,k-1}^k E_{k-1,k-2}^k = E_{k-2,k}^k L_{kk}^{kk} E_{k,k-2}^k. \end{aligned}$$

---

† When $j - 1 = k$ or $j - 1 = k_1$ this follows immediately from (9), (12) and (14).

Repeating this reasoning and introducing the notation

$$L^{kk}_{kk} = \Lambda_k,$$

we obtain:

$$L^{kk}_{jj} = E^k_{j,k}\Lambda_k E^k_{k,j}.$$

Thus, finally

$$L^{kk_1}_{jj_1} = \begin{cases} 0 & \text{when} \quad j \neq j_1 \quad \text{or} \quad k \neq k_1, \\ E^k_{jk}\Lambda_k E^k_{kj} & \text{when} \quad j_1 = j \quad \text{and} \quad k_1 = k. \end{cases} \tag{16}$$

Now we apply the relation $[[L_4, F_3], F_3] = -L_4$.

Let $\|M^{kk_1}_{jj_1}\|$ be the matrix of the operator $[L_4, F_3]$ with respect to the same subspaces $\mathfrak{M}^k_j$. From formulae (38) Subsection 1 and (16) it follows that

$$M^{kk_1}_{jj_1} = 0 \quad \text{when} \quad |k-k_1| \geqslant 2 \quad \text{and when} \quad j_1 \neq j,$$

$$M^{k,k-1}_{jj} = \sqrt{[(k+j)(k-j)]}\, E^k_{jk}(D_k\Lambda_{k-1} - \Lambda_k D_k)E^{k-1}_{k-1,j}, \tag{17}$$

$$M^{kk}_{jj} = jE^k_{jk}(P_k\Lambda_k - \Lambda_k P_k)E^k_{kj}, \tag{18}$$

$$M^{k,k+1}_{jj} = \sqrt{[(k+j+1)(k-j+1)]}\, E^k_{jk}(\Lambda_k Q_{k+1} - Q_{k+1}\Lambda_{k+1})E^{k+1}_{k+1,j}. \tag{19}$$

On the other hand, the relation $[[L_4, F_3], F_3] = -L_4$ means that

$$M^{k,k+1}_{jj}\overset{3}{F}{}^{k+1,k+2}_{jj} - \overset{3}{F}{}^{k,k+1}_{jj}M^{k+1,k+2}_{jj} = 0, \tag{20}$$

$$M^{kk}_{jj}\overset{3}{F}{}^{k,k+1}_{jj} + M^{k,k+1}_{jj}\overset{3}{F}{}^{k+1,k+1}_{jj} - \overset{3}{F}{}^{kk}_{jj}M^{k,k+1}_{jj} - \overset{3}{F}{}^{k,k+1}_{jj}M^{k+1,k+1}_{jj} = 0, \tag{21}$$

$$M^{k,k-1}_{jj}\overset{3}{F}{}^{k-1,k}_{jj} + M^{kk}_{jj}\overset{3}{F}{}^{kk}_{jj} + M^{k,k+1}_{jj}\overset{3}{F}{}^{k+1,k}_{jj} - \overset{3}{F}{}^{k,k-1}_{jj}M^{k-1,k}_{jj} - \overset{3}{F}{}^{kk}_{jj}M^{kk}_{jj} - \overset{3}{F}{}^{k,k+1}_{jj}M^{k+1,k}_{jj} = -L^{kk}_{jj}, \tag{22}$$

$$M^{kk}_{jj}\overset{3}{F}{}^{k,k-1}_{jj} + M^{k,k-1}_{jj}\overset{3}{F}{}^{k-1,k-1}_{jj} - \overset{3}{F}{}^{kk}_{jj}M^{k,k-1}_{jj} - \overset{3}{F}{}^{k,k-1}_{jj}M^{k-1,k-1}_{jj} = 0, \tag{23}$$

$$M^{k,k-1}_{jj}\overset{3}{F}{}^{k-1,k-2}_{jj} - \overset{3}{F}{}^{k,k-1}_{jj}M^{k-1,k-2}_{jj} = 0. \tag{24}$$

Now making use of formulae (38) Subsection 1 and (17–19) we obtain, after simple manipulation,

$$(\Lambda_k Q_{k+1} - Q_{k+1}\Lambda_{k+1})Q_{k+2} - Q_{k+1}(\Lambda_{k+1}Q_{k+2} - Q_{k+2}\Lambda_{k+2}) = 0, \quad (25)$$

$$\begin{aligned}(P_k\Lambda_k - \Lambda_k P_k)\,Q_{k+1} - (\Lambda_k Q_{k+1} - Q_{k+1}\Lambda_{k+1})\,P_{k+1}\\ + P_k(\Lambda_k Q_{k+1} - Q_{k+1}\Lambda_{k+1}) - Q_{k+1}(P_{k+1}\Lambda_{k+1} - \Lambda_{k+1}P_{k+1}) = 0,\end{aligned} \quad (26)$$

$$\begin{aligned}(k^2-j^2)(D_k\Lambda_{k-1} - \Lambda_k D_k)\,Q_k - j^2(P_k\Lambda_k - \Lambda_k P_k)\,P_k\\ -(k+j+1)(k-j+1)(\Lambda_k Q_{k+1} - Q_{k+1}\Lambda_{k+1})\,D_{k+1}\\ +(k^2-j^2)\,D_k(\Lambda_{k-1}Q_k - Q_k\Lambda_k) + j^2 P_k(P_k\Lambda_k - \Lambda_k P_k)\\ -(k+j+1)(k-j+1)\,Q_{k+1}(D_{k+1}\Lambda_k - \Lambda_{k+1}D_{k+1}) = -\Lambda_k,\end{aligned} \quad (27)$$

$$\begin{aligned}(P_k\Lambda_k - \Lambda_k P_k)\,D_k + (D_k\Lambda_{k-1} - \Lambda_k D_k)\,P_{k-1} - P_k(D_k\Lambda_{k-1} - \Lambda_k D_k)\\ - D_k(P_{k-1}\Lambda_{k-1} - \Lambda_{k-1}P_{k-1}) = 0,\end{aligned} \quad (28)$$

$$(D_k\Lambda_{k-1} - \Lambda_k D_k)\,D_{k-1} - D_k(D_{k-1}\Lambda_{k-2} - \Lambda_{k-1}D_{k-1}) = 0. \quad (29)$$

Subtracting relations (27), corresponding to two different values of j, we deduce that

$$\begin{aligned}P_k(P_k\Lambda_k - \Lambda_k P_k) - (P_k\Lambda_k - \Lambda_k P_k)\,P_k\\ = (D_k\Lambda_{k-1} - \Lambda_k D_k)\,Q_k + D_k(\Lambda_{k-1}Q_k - Q_k\Lambda_k)\\ -(\Lambda_k Q_{k+1} - Q_{k+1}\Lambda_{k+1})\,D_{k+1} - Q_{k+1}(D_{k+1}\Lambda_k - \Lambda_{k+1}D_{k+1}),\end{aligned} \quad (30)$$

and substitution in (27) gives:

$$\begin{aligned}k^2[(D_k\Lambda_{k-1} - \Lambda_k D_k)\,Q_k + D_k(\Lambda_{k-1}Q_k - Q_k\Lambda_k)] - (k+1)^2\,[(\Lambda_k Q_{k+1}\\ - Q_{k+1}\Lambda_{k+1})D_{k+1} + Q_{k+1}(D_{k+1}\Lambda_k - \Lambda_{k+1}D_{k+1})] = -\Lambda_k.\end{aligned} \quad (31)$$

By means of analogous calculations we convince ourselves of the fact that substitution in the remaining conditions of (2) leads to the same relations (25–31).

Thus we have proved

THEOREM 3. *Every equation*

$$\mathbf{L}_1\frac{\partial\psi}{\partial x_1} + \mathbf{L}_2\frac{\partial\psi}{\partial x_2} + \mathbf{L}_3\frac{\partial\psi}{\partial x_3} + \mathbf{L}_4\frac{\partial\psi}{\partial x_4} + i\kappa\psi = 0,$$

invariant with respect to the transformations of the proper Lorentz group $\mathfrak{G}_+$ *and corresponding to a given representation* $g \to T_g$ *of this group, is given by the formulae*

$$L_\nu = [L_4, B_\nu], \quad \nu = 1, 2, 3,$$

where L_4 *is the operator defined by formula* (16), *and* Λ_k *are operators satisfying the relations* (25–31).

Now we consider the special case when the given representation $g \to T_g$ of the group $\mathfrak{G}_+$ is the direct sum of the representations $g \to T_g^{(\alpha)}$ (where α runs through some set of indices A), which are multiples of irreducible representations S_c^k. In this case each of the subspaces $\mathfrak{M}_k^k$ is the direct sum of the subspaces $\mathfrak{M}_k^{k\alpha}$, corresponding to the representations $g \to T_g^{(\alpha)}$, in correspondence with which each of the operators P_k, Q_k, D_k is represented in the form of a matrix $\|P_k^{\alpha\beta}\|$, $\|Q_k^{\alpha\beta}\|$, $\|D_k^{\alpha\beta}\|$, $\alpha, \beta \in A$, where

$$P_k^{\alpha\beta} = 0, \quad Q_k^{\alpha\beta} = 0, \quad D_k^{\alpha\beta} = 0 \quad \text{when} \quad \beta \neq \alpha, \tag{32}$$

$$P_k^{\alpha\alpha} = \frac{ik_{0\alpha}c_\alpha}{k(k+1)} \cdot 1, \quad k \geqslant k_{0\alpha}, \tag{33}$$

$$Q_k^{\alpha\alpha} = \frac{i}{k}\sqrt{\left[\frac{(k^2-k_{0\alpha}^2)(k^2-c_\alpha^2)}{4k^2-1}\right]}U_{k\alpha}, \quad k \geqslant k_{0\alpha}+1, \tag{34}$$

$$D_k^{\alpha\alpha} = \frac{i}{k}\sqrt{\left[\frac{(k^2-k_{0\alpha}^2)(k^2-c_\alpha^2)}{4k^2-1}\right]}U_{k\alpha}^{-1}, \quad k \geqslant k_{0\alpha}+1, \tag{35}$$

where $U_{k\alpha}$ is a linear operator from $\mathfrak{M}_k^{k\alpha}$ to $\mathfrak{M}_{k-1}^{k-1,\alpha}$, mapping $\mathfrak{M}_k^{k\alpha}$ on $\mathfrak{M}_{k-1}^{k-1,\alpha}$ isometrically. Here it will be convenient to consider $P_k^{\alpha\alpha}$ also for $k < k_{0\alpha}$ and $Q_k^{\alpha\alpha}$, $D_k^{\alpha\alpha}$ for $k \leqslant k_{0\alpha}$, regarding them as equal to zero for such values of k.

Further, every operator $\Lambda_{jj_1}^{kk_1}$ is represented in the form of a matrix $\|\Lambda_{jj_1}^{kk_1\alpha\beta}\|$ of operators from $\mathfrak{M}_{j_1}^{k_1\beta}$ into $\mathfrak{M}_j^{k\alpha}$, in particular, the operators Λ_k are represented in the form of matrices $\|\Lambda_k^{\alpha\beta}\|$ of operators from $\mathfrak{M}_k^{k\beta}$ into $\mathfrak{M}_j^{k\alpha}$.

From condition (16) we deduce at once that the operator $\Lambda_{jj_1}^{kk_1\alpha\beta}$ can be distinct from zero only when $j_1 = j$, $k_1 = k$, hence, only in the case when $k_1 = k \geqslant \max\,(k_{0\alpha}, k_{0\beta})$ and $k_{0\alpha}, k_{0\beta}$ are both integral or both semi-integral numbers. Moreover, by virtue of (32), conditions (25), (26), (28–31) can be written in this matrix notation in the form

$$(\Lambda_k^{\alpha\beta} Q_{k+1}^{\beta\beta} - Q_{k+1}^{\alpha\alpha} \Lambda_{k+1}^{\alpha\beta}) Q_{k+2}^{\beta\beta} - Q_{k+1}^{\alpha\alpha} (\Lambda_{k+1}^{\alpha\beta} Q_{k+2}^{\beta\beta} - Q_{k+2}^{\alpha\alpha} \Lambda_{k+2}^{\alpha\beta}) = 0, \tag{36}$$

$$\begin{aligned}(P_k^{\alpha\alpha}\Lambda_k^{\alpha\beta} - \Lambda_k^{\alpha\beta}P_k^{\beta\beta}) Q_{k+1}^{\beta\beta} - (\Lambda_k^{\alpha\beta} Q_{k+1}^{\beta\beta} - Q_{k+1}^{\alpha\alpha}\Lambda_{k+1}^{\alpha\beta}) P_{k+1}^{\beta\beta} \\ + P_k^{\alpha\alpha}(\Lambda_k^{\alpha\beta} Q_{k+1}^{\beta\beta} - Q_{k+1}^{\alpha\alpha}\Lambda_{k+1}^{\alpha\beta}) \\ - Q_{k+1}^{\alpha\alpha}(P_{k+1}^{\alpha\alpha}\Lambda_{k+1}^{\alpha\beta} - \Lambda_{k+1}^{\alpha\beta} P_{k+1}^{\beta\beta}) = 0,\end{aligned} \tag{37}$$

$$\begin{aligned}(P_k^{\alpha\alpha}\Lambda_k^{\alpha\beta} - \Lambda_k^{\alpha\beta}P_k^{\beta\beta}) D_k^{\beta\beta} + (D_k^{\alpha\alpha}\Lambda_{k-1}^{\alpha\beta} - \Lambda_k^{\alpha\beta} D_k^{\beta\beta}) P_{k-1}^{\beta\beta} \\ - P_k^{\alpha\alpha}(D_k^{\alpha\alpha}\Lambda_{k-1}^{\alpha\beta} - \Lambda_k^{\alpha\beta} D_k^{\beta\beta}) \\ - D_k^{\alpha\alpha}(P_{k-1}^{\alpha\alpha}\Lambda_{k-1}^{\alpha\beta} - \Lambda_{k-1}^{\alpha\beta} P_{k-1}^{\beta\beta}) = 0,\end{aligned} \tag{38}$$

$$(D_k^{\alpha\alpha}\Lambda_{k-1}^{\alpha\beta} - \Lambda_k^{\alpha\beta} D_k^{\beta\beta}) D_{k-1}^{\beta\beta} - D_k^{\alpha\alpha}(D_{k-1}^{\alpha\alpha}\Lambda_{k-2}^{\alpha\beta} - \Lambda_{k-1}^{\alpha\beta} D_{k-1}^{\beta\beta}) = 0, \tag{39}$$

$$\begin{aligned}P_k^{\alpha\alpha}(P_k^{\alpha\alpha}\Lambda_k^{\alpha\beta} - \Lambda_k^{\alpha\beta}P_k^{\beta\beta}) - (P_k^{\alpha\alpha}\Lambda_k^{\alpha\beta} - \Lambda_k^{\alpha\beta}P_k^{\beta\beta}) P_k^{\beta\beta} \\ = (D_k^{\alpha\alpha}\Lambda_{k-1}^{\alpha\beta} - \Lambda_k^{\alpha\beta} D_k^{\beta\beta}) Q_k^{\beta\beta} + D_k^{\alpha\alpha}(\Lambda_{k-1}^{\alpha\beta} Q_k^{\beta\beta} - Q_k^{\alpha\alpha}\Lambda_k^{\alpha\beta}) \\ - (\Lambda_k^{\alpha\beta} Q_{k+1}^{\beta\beta} - Q_{k+1}^{\alpha\alpha}\Lambda_{k+1}^{\alpha\beta}) D_{k+1}^{\beta\beta} - Q_{k+1}^{\alpha\alpha}(D_{k+1}^{\alpha\alpha}\Lambda_k^{\alpha\beta} - \Lambda_{k+1}^{\alpha\beta} D_{k+1}^{\beta\beta}),\end{aligned} \tag{40}$$

$$\begin{aligned}k^2[(D_k^{\alpha\alpha}\Lambda_{k-1}^{\alpha\beta} - \Lambda_k^{\alpha\beta} D_k^{\beta\beta}) Q_k^{\beta\beta} + D_k^{\alpha\alpha}(\Lambda_{k-1}^{\alpha\beta} Q_k^{\beta\beta} - Q_k^{\alpha\alpha}\Lambda_k^{\alpha\beta})] \\ - (k+1)^2[(\Lambda_k^{\alpha\beta} Q_{k+1}^{\beta\beta} - Q_{k+1}^{\alpha\alpha}\Lambda_{k+1}^{\alpha\beta}) D_{k+1}^{\beta\beta} + Q_{k+1}^{\alpha\alpha}(D_{k+1}^{\alpha\alpha}\Lambda_k^{\alpha\beta} \\ - \Lambda_{k+1}^{\alpha\beta} D_{k+1}^{\beta\beta})] = -\Lambda_k^{\alpha\beta}.\end{aligned} \tag{41}$$

Now we will prove that

$$\Lambda_k^{\alpha\beta} = 0 \quad \text{when} \quad |k_{0\alpha} - k_{0\beta}| \geqslant 2. \tag{42}$$

Let, for instance, $k_{0\alpha} \leqslant k_{0\beta} - 2$. In (36) taking $k = k_{0\beta} - 2$, we obtain:

$$Q_{k-1}^{\alpha\alpha} Q_k^{\alpha\alpha} \Lambda_k^{\alpha\beta} = 0 \quad \text{when} \quad k = k_{0\beta}. \tag{43}$$

If here $Q_{k-1}^{\alpha\alpha} \neq 0$, $Q_k^{\alpha\alpha} \neq 0$, then, by virtue of (34), relation (43) is possible only when $\Lambda_k^{\alpha\beta} = 0$ where $k = k_{0\beta}$. Now letting $k = k_{0\beta} - 1$ in (36) and supposing that $Q_k^{\alpha\alpha} \neq 0$ when $k = k_{0\beta} - 1$, $k_{0\beta}$, $k_{0\beta}+1$, we deduce that $\Lambda_k^{\alpha\beta} = 0$ also when $k = k_{0\beta}+1$.

Repeating this argument, we see that $\Lambda_k^{\alpha\beta} = 0$ for all $k \geqslant k_{0\beta}$, for which $Q_k^{\alpha\alpha} \neq 0$ and $Q_{k-1}^{\alpha\alpha} \neq 0$.

Only the two following cases are possible:
(a) all $Q_k^{\alpha\alpha} \neq 0$ when $k \geqslant k_{0\beta} - 1$; then $\Lambda_k^{\alpha\beta} = 0$ for all k;
(b) there exist values $k \geqslant k_{0\beta} - 1$, for which $Q_k^{\alpha\alpha} = 0$.

Let k_1+1 be the least of the values such that $Q_k^{\alpha\alpha} \neq 0$, and so $\Lambda_k^{\alpha\beta} = 0$ when $k \leqslant k_1$. But in this case the representation $g \to T_g^{(\alpha)}$ is a multiple of a *finite-dimensional* irreducible representation, in which not all $k > k_1$ occur (see Theorem 2 § 8, Subsection 3). Hence, in this case also $\Lambda_k^{\alpha\beta} = 0$ for all k. Thus the assertion is proved for the case $k_{0\alpha} \leqslant k_{0\beta} - 2$.

The case $k_{0\beta} \leqslant k_{0\alpha} - 2$ is considered analogously, where instead of relation (36) it is necessary to use relation (39).

Now substituting in relations (36–41) instead of $P_k^{\alpha\alpha}$, $Q_k^{\alpha\alpha}$, $D_k^{\alpha\alpha}$ their expressions from formulae (33–35) and introducing the notations:

$$\lambda_{k\alpha} = \sqrt{[(k^2-k_{0\alpha}^2)(k^2-c_\alpha^2)]}, \quad \xi_\alpha = k_{0\alpha} c_\alpha, \quad \eta_\alpha = k_{0\alpha}^2 + c_\alpha^2, \tag{44}$$

we obtain:

$$\lambda_{k+1,\beta}\lambda_{k+2,\beta}\Lambda_k^{\alpha\beta} U_{k+1,\beta} U_{k+2,\beta} - 2\lambda_{k+1,\alpha}\lambda_{k+2,\beta} U_{k+1,\alpha}\Lambda_{k+1}^{\alpha\beta} U_{k+2,\beta} + \lambda_{k+1,\alpha}\lambda_{k+2,\alpha} U_{k+1,\alpha} U_{k+2,\alpha}\Lambda_{k+2}^{\alpha\beta} = 0, \tag{45}$$

$$[(\xi_\alpha - \xi_\beta)(k+1) + \xi_\alpha]\lambda_{k+1,\beta}\Lambda_k^{\alpha\beta} U_{k+1,\beta} - [(\xi_\alpha - \xi_\beta)(k+1) + \xi_\beta]\lambda_{k+1,\alpha} U_{k+1,\alpha}\Lambda_{k+1}^{\alpha\beta} = 0, \tag{46}$$

$$[(\xi_\alpha - \xi_\beta)k - \xi_\alpha]\lambda_{k\beta}\Lambda_k^{\alpha\beta} U_{k\beta}^{-1} - [(\xi_\alpha - \xi_\beta)k - \xi_\beta]\lambda_{k\alpha} U_{k\alpha}^{-1}\Lambda_{k-1}^{\alpha\beta} = 0, \tag{47}$$

$$2\lambda_{k\alpha}\lambda_{k-1,\beta} U_{k\alpha}^{-1}\Lambda_{k-1}^{\alpha\beta} U_{k-1,\beta}^{-1} - \lambda_{k\beta}\lambda_{k-1,\beta}\Lambda_k^{\alpha\beta} U_{k\beta}^{-1} U_{k-1,\beta}^{-1} - \lambda_{k\alpha}\lambda_{k-1,\alpha} U_{k\alpha}^{-1} U_{k-1,\alpha}^{-1}\Lambda_{k-2}^{\alpha\beta} = 0, \tag{48}$$

$$\left[\frac{(\xi_\alpha - \xi_\beta)^2}{k^2(k+1)^2} + \frac{\lambda_{k\beta}^2}{k^2(4k^2-1)} + \frac{\lambda_{k\alpha}^2}{k^2(4k^2-1)} + \frac{\lambda_{k+1,\beta}^2}{(k+1)^2[4(k+1)^2-1]} + \frac{\lambda_{k+1,\alpha}^2}{(k+1)^2[4(k+1)^2-1]}\right]\Lambda_k^{\alpha\beta} - 2\frac{\lambda_{k\alpha}\lambda_{\alpha\beta}}{k^2(4k^2-1)} U_{k\alpha}^{-1}\Lambda_{k-1}^{\alpha\beta} U_{k\beta} - 2\frac{\lambda_{k+1,\alpha}\lambda_{k+1,\beta}}{(k+1)^2[4(k+1)^2-1]} U_{k+1,\alpha}\Lambda_{k+1}^{\alpha\beta} U_{k+1,\beta}^{-1} = 0, \tag{49}$$

$$\left[1+\frac{\lambda_{k\beta}^2}{4k^2-1}+\frac{\lambda_{k\alpha}^2}{4k^2-1}+\frac{\lambda_{k+1,\beta}^2}{4(k+1)^2-1}+\frac{\lambda_{k+1,\alpha}^2}{4(k+1)^2-1}\right]\Lambda_k^{\alpha\beta}$$

$$=2\frac{\lambda_{k\alpha}\lambda_{k\beta}}{4k^2-1}U_{k\alpha}^{-1}\Lambda_{k-1}^{\alpha\beta}U_{k\beta}+2\frac{\lambda_{k+1,\alpha}\lambda_{k+1,\beta}}{4(k+1)^2-1}U_{k+1,\alpha}\Lambda_{k+1}^{\alpha\beta}U_{k+1,\beta}^{-1}. \quad (50)$$

In (47) we replace k by $k+1$, multiply the resulting equation on the right by $U_{k+1,\beta}$ and on the left by $U_{k+1,\alpha}$, and use the result together with (46) to eliminate $U_{k+1,\alpha}\Lambda_{k+1}^{\alpha\beta}$.

After simple calculations we arrive at the relation

$$\{[(\xi_\alpha-\xi_\beta)^2(\eta_\alpha-\eta_\beta)+\xi_\alpha^2-\xi_\beta^2](k+1)^2-[(\xi_\alpha-\xi_\beta)^2(\xi_\alpha^2-\xi_\beta^2) \\ +\xi_\beta^2\eta_\alpha-\xi_\alpha^2\eta_\beta]\}\Lambda_k^{\alpha\beta}=0. \quad (51)$$

Further, we multiply both sides of (50) by $-1/k^2$ and add the equation so obtained to equation (49); we get:

$$\{[\lambda_{k+1,\alpha}^2+\lambda_{k+1,\beta}^2+(k+1)^2-(\xi_\alpha-\xi_\beta)^2] \\ +2[(k+1)^3-(k+1)(\xi_\alpha-\xi_\beta)^2]\}\Lambda_k^{\alpha\beta} \\ -2\lambda_{k+1,\alpha}\lambda_{k+1,\beta}U_{k+1,\alpha}\Lambda_{k+1}^{\alpha\beta}U_{k+1,\beta}^{-1}=0. \quad (52)$$

Analogously, multiplying both sides of (50) by $-1/(k+1)^2$, adding the equation so obtained to equation (49) and then replacing k by $k+1$, we find after simple manipulations

$$-2\lambda_{k+1,\alpha}\lambda_{k+1,\beta}\Lambda_k^{\alpha\beta}+\{[\lambda_{k+1,\alpha}^2+\lambda_{k+1,\beta}^2+(k+1)^2-(\xi_\alpha-\xi_\beta)^2] \\ -2[(k+1)^3-(\xi_\alpha-\xi_\beta)^2(k+1)]\}U_{k+1,\alpha}\Lambda_{k+1}^{\alpha\beta}U_{k+1,\beta}^{-1}=0. \quad (53)$$

Now eliminating $\Lambda_{k+1}^{\alpha\beta}$ from (46) and (52), (46) and (53), (52) and (53), we arrive at the relations:

$$\{(k+1)[(\eta_\alpha-\eta_\beta)(\xi_\alpha-\xi_\beta)-(\xi_\alpha+\xi_\beta)] \\ +[2(\xi_\alpha-\xi_\beta)^3+\eta_\beta\xi_\beta+\eta_\alpha\xi_\beta-2\eta_\beta\xi_\alpha-\xi_\beta]\}\Lambda_k^{\alpha\beta}=0, \quad (54)$$

$$\{(k+1)[(\eta_\alpha-\eta_\beta)(\xi_\alpha-\xi_\beta)-(\xi_\alpha+\xi_\beta)] \\ +[2(\xi_\alpha-\xi_\beta)^3+\xi_\alpha-(\eta_\alpha+\eta_\beta)\xi_\alpha+2\eta_\alpha\xi_\beta]\}\Lambda_k^{\alpha\beta}=0, \quad (55)$$

$$\{[(\eta_\alpha-\eta_\beta)^2-2(\eta_\alpha+\eta_\beta)+1+4(\xi_\alpha-\xi_\beta)^2](k+1)^2 \\ +4[(\eta_\beta\xi_\alpha-\eta_\alpha\xi_\beta)(\xi_\alpha-\xi_\beta)-(\xi_\alpha-\xi_\beta)^4+\xi_\alpha\xi_\beta]\}\Lambda_k^{\alpha\beta} = 0. \tag{56}$$

If $\Lambda_k^{\alpha\beta} \neq 0$, then from (51) and (54–56) we deduce that

$$[(\xi_\alpha-\xi_\beta)^2(\eta_\alpha-\eta_\beta)+\xi_\alpha^2-\xi_\beta^2](k+1)^2-[(\xi_\alpha-\xi_\beta)^2(\xi_\alpha^2-\xi_\beta^2) \\ +\xi_\beta^2\eta_\alpha-\xi_\alpha^2\eta_\beta] = 0, \tag{57}$$

$$(k+1)[(\eta_\alpha-\eta_\beta)(\xi_\alpha-\xi_\beta)-(\xi_\alpha+\xi_\beta)]+[2(\xi_\alpha-\xi_\beta)^3 \\ +\eta_\beta\xi_\beta+\eta_\alpha\xi_\beta-2\eta_\beta\xi_\alpha-\xi_\beta] = 0, \tag{58}$$

$$(k+1)[(\eta_\alpha-\eta_\beta)(\xi_\alpha-\xi_\beta)-(\xi_\alpha+\xi_\beta)]+[2(\xi_\alpha-\xi_\beta)^3 \\ +\xi_\alpha-(\eta_\alpha+\eta_\beta)\xi_\alpha+2\eta_\alpha\xi_\beta] = 0, \tag{59}$$

$$[(\eta_\alpha-\eta_\beta)^2-2(\eta_\alpha+\eta_\beta)+1+4(\xi_\alpha-\xi_\beta)^2](k+1)^2 \\ +4[(\eta_\beta\xi_\alpha-\eta_\alpha\xi_\beta)(\xi_\alpha-\xi_\beta)-(\xi_\alpha-\xi_\beta)^4+\xi_\alpha\xi_\beta] = 0. \tag{60}$$

Subtracting (59) from (58), we find that

$$(\eta_\alpha-\eta_\beta)(\xi_\alpha-\xi_\beta)-(\xi_\alpha+\xi_\beta) = 0, \tag{61}$$

and comparison with (57) gives

$$(\xi_\alpha-\xi_\beta)^2(\xi_\alpha^2-\xi_\beta^2)+\xi_\beta^2\eta_\alpha-\xi_\alpha^2\eta_\beta = 0. \tag{62}$$

We saw above that $\Lambda_k^{\alpha\beta} \neq 0$ only when $k_{0\beta} = k_{0\alpha}+1$, $k_{0\beta} = k_{0\alpha}-1$, $k_{0\beta} = k_{0\alpha}$.

We consider these cases separately:

(1) $k_{0\beta} = k_{0\alpha}+1$. Letting $k+1 = k_{0\beta}$, $k = k_{0\alpha}$ in (46), we obtain;

$$[(\xi_\alpha-\xi_\beta)k_{0\beta}+\xi_\beta]\lambda_{k_{0\beta},\alpha}\, U_{k_{0\beta},\alpha}\Lambda_{k_{0\beta}}^{\alpha\beta} = 0.$$

Hence, if $\Lambda_{k_{0\beta}}^{\alpha\beta} \neq 0$, then $[(\xi_\alpha-\xi_\beta)k_{0\beta}+\xi_\beta]\lambda_{k_{0\beta},\alpha} = 0$. Here we can assume that $\lambda_{k_{0\beta},\alpha} \neq 0$, because otherwise the $k_{0\beta}$ do not all occur in the representation $g \to T_g^{(\alpha)}$ and $\Lambda_{k_{0\beta}}^{\alpha\beta} = 0$. Therefore $(\xi_\alpha-\xi_\beta)k_{0\beta}+\xi_\beta = 0$, i.e. $(k_{0\alpha}c_\alpha-k_{0\beta}c_\beta)k_{0\beta}+k_{0\beta}c_\beta = 0$. Since $k_{0\beta} = k_{0\alpha}+1 > 0$, we conclude from this that $k_{0\alpha}c_\alpha-k_{0\beta}c_\beta+c_\beta = 0$, i.e. $k_{0\alpha}c_\alpha-k_{0\alpha}c_\beta = 0$. Hence, either $k_{0\alpha} = 0$, or $c_\alpha = c_\beta$.

Let $k_{0\alpha} = 0$, and hence $k_{0\beta} = 1$.

Substituting these values in (61) and making use of the notation (44) we obtain:

$$c_\beta(c_\alpha^2 - c_\beta^2) = 0.$$

Hence, either $c_\alpha^2 = c_\beta^2$, or $c_\beta = 0$.

Because $k_{0\alpha} = 0$, then c_α and $-c_\alpha$ define equivalent representations, and we can assume in the first case that $c_\beta = c_\alpha$.

Now we suppose that $c_\beta = 0$. Then from (60) we see that $(c_\alpha^2 - 1)^2 - 2(c_\alpha^2 + 1) + 1 = 0$, i.e. $c_\alpha^4 - 4c_\alpha^2 = 0$. Hence, either $c_\alpha = 0$, or $c_z = \pm 2$. But in the second case substitution in (52) when $k = 1$ gives $\Lambda_1^{\alpha\beta} = 0$, so that $\Lambda_{k_{0\beta}}^{\alpha\beta} = \Lambda_1^{\alpha\beta} = 0$.

Hence, in either case $\Lambda_{k_{0\beta}}^{\alpha\beta} = 0$, if $c_\beta \neq c_\alpha$. But if $\Lambda_{k_{0\beta}}^{\alpha\beta} = 0$, then, letting $k = k_{0\beta} - 1, k_{0\beta}, \ldots$, successively in (36), we find that $\Lambda_k^{\alpha\beta} = 0$ for all k. Thus if $\Lambda_k^{\alpha\beta} \neq 0$ and $k_{0\beta} = k_{0\alpha} + 1$, then $c_\beta = c_\alpha$. If here $c_\alpha \neq 0$, then relation (46) gives

$$\Lambda_{k+1}^{\alpha\beta} = \sqrt{\left[\frac{(k+k_{0\alpha}+2)(k+1-k_{0\alpha})}{(k+k_{0\alpha}+1)(k-k_{0\alpha})}\right]}\, U_{k+1,\alpha}^{-1} \Lambda^{\alpha\beta} U_{k+1,\beta},$$

and repeated application of this formula leads to the equation

$$\Lambda_k^{\alpha\beta} = \sqrt{[(k+k_{0\alpha}+1)(k-k_{0\alpha})]}\, U_{k,\alpha}^{-1} \ldots U_{k_{0\alpha}+2,\alpha}^{-1} \Lambda^{\alpha\beta} U_{k_{0\alpha}+2,\beta} \ldots U_{k\beta},$$

$$k \geqslant k_{0\alpha} + 2, \tag{63}$$

where

$$\Lambda^{\alpha\beta} = \frac{1}{\sqrt{[2k_{0\alpha}+2]}} \Lambda_{k_{0\alpha}+1}^{\alpha\beta} \tag{64}$$

is an operator from $\mathfrak{M}_{k_{0\alpha}+1}^{k_{0\alpha}+1,\beta}$ into $\mathfrak{M}_{k_{0\alpha}+1}^{k_{0\alpha}+1,\alpha}$, defined on $\mathfrak{D} \cap \mathfrak{M}_{k_{0\alpha}+1}^{k_{0\alpha}+1,\beta}$ and mapping $\mathfrak{D} \cap \mathfrak{M}_{k_{0\alpha}+1}^{k_{0\alpha}+1,\beta}$ into $\mathfrak{D} \cap \mathfrak{M}_{k_{0\alpha}+1}^{k_{0\alpha}+1,\alpha}$.

If however $c_\alpha = 0$, then substitution in relation (52) leads to the same formula (63).

Conversely, by an immediate substitution one can convince oneself that when $k_{0\beta} = k_{0\alpha} + 1$, $c_\beta = c_\alpha$ the operators $\Lambda_k^{\alpha\beta}$, defined by formula (63), satisfy all the relations (45–50).

(2) $k_{0\beta} = k_{0\alpha} - 1$. Reasoning as in case (1) (where instead of relation (46) it is necessary to apply relation (47)), we find that

$\Lambda_k^{\alpha\beta}$ can be distinct from zero only when $c_\beta = c_\alpha$ and that in this case

$$\Lambda_k^{\alpha\beta} = \sqrt{[(k+k_{0\alpha})(k-k_{0\alpha}+1)]}\, U_{k,\alpha}^{-1} \dots U_{k_{0\alpha}+1,\alpha}^{-1} \Lambda^{\alpha\beta} U_{k_{0\alpha}+1,\beta} \dots U_{k\beta},$$
$$k \geqslant k_{0\alpha}+1, \tag{65}$$

where

$$\Lambda^{\alpha\beta} = \frac{1}{\sqrt{(2k_{0\alpha})}} \Lambda_{k_{0\alpha}}^{\alpha\beta}; \tag{66}$$

(3) $k_{0\beta} = k_{0\alpha}$. Substitution in relation (61) gives

$$k_{0\alpha}[(c_\alpha^2 - c_\beta^2)(c_\alpha - c_\beta) - (c_\alpha + c_\beta)] = 0,$$

so that the only possible cases are:

3(α) $(c_\alpha - c_\beta)^2 = 1$,
3(β) $c_\alpha + c_\beta = 0$,
3(γ) $k_{0\alpha} = 0$.

We examine these cases separately.

Let $(c_\alpha - c_\beta)^2 = 1$. Applying formula (46) when $k_{0\alpha} \neq 0$ and (52) when $k_{0\alpha} = 0$, we find that for $c_\alpha - c_\beta = 1$, $k \geqslant k_{0\alpha}+1$

$$\Lambda_k^{\alpha\beta} = \sqrt{[(k+c_\alpha)(k+1-c_\alpha)]} \times$$
$$\times U_{k,\alpha}^{-1} \dots U_{k_{0\alpha}+1,\alpha}^{-1} \Lambda^{\alpha\beta} U_{k_{0\alpha}+1,\beta} \dots U_{k,\beta}, \tag{67}$$

where

$$\Lambda^{\alpha\beta} = \frac{1}{\sqrt{[(k_{0\alpha}+c_\alpha)(k_{0\alpha}+1-c_\alpha)]}} \Lambda_{k_{0\alpha}}^{\alpha\beta}, \tag{68}$$

and when $c_\alpha - c_\beta = -1$, $k \geqslant k_{0\alpha}+1$

$$\Lambda_k^{\alpha\beta} = \sqrt{[(k+1+c_\alpha)(k-c_\alpha)]} \times$$
$$\times U_{k,\alpha}^{-1} \dots U_{k_{0\alpha}+1,\alpha}^{-1} \Lambda^{\alpha\beta} U_{k_{0\alpha}+1,\beta} \dots U_{k,\beta}, \tag{69}$$

where

$$\Lambda^{\alpha\beta} = \frac{1}{\sqrt{[(k_{0\alpha}-c_\alpha)(k_{0\alpha}+1+c_\alpha)]}} \Lambda_{k_{0\alpha}}^{\alpha\beta}. \tag{70}$$

Conversely, by an immediate substitution one can show that when $k_{0\alpha} = k_{0\beta}$ and $(c_\alpha - c_\beta)^2 = 1$ the operators $\Lambda_k^{\alpha\beta}$, defined by formulae (67) and (69), satisfy all the relations (45–50).

In the derivation of formulae (67) and (69) we have in fact assumed that $(k_{0\alpha}+c_\alpha)(k_{0\alpha}+1-c_\alpha) \neq 0$, respectively $(k_{0\alpha}-c_\alpha)(k_{0\alpha}+1+c_\alpha) \neq 0$. It is easy, to show however, that these formulae remain valid also in the remaining cases. Let, for instance, $c_\alpha = -k_{0\alpha}$. Then formula (67) holds when $k \geqslant k_{0\alpha}+1$, if one sets

$$\Lambda^{\alpha\beta} = \frac{1}{\sqrt{[(k_{0\alpha}+1+c_\alpha)(k_{0\alpha}+2-c_\alpha)]}} U_{k_{0\alpha}+1,\alpha} \Lambda^{\alpha\beta}_{k_{0\alpha}+1} U^{-1}_{k_{0\alpha}+1,\beta}.$$

The remaining cases are considered analogously.

Now let $c_\alpha+c_\beta = 0$. Then relation (60) takes the form

$$(4k_{0\alpha}^2-1)(4c_\alpha^2-1)[(k+1)^2-4k_{0\alpha}^2c_\alpha^2] = 0,$$

so that either $c_\alpha^2 = \frac{1}{4}$, or $k_{0\alpha}^2 = \frac{1}{4}$.

In the first case $c_\alpha = \pm\frac{1}{2}$, $c_\beta = \mp\frac{1}{2}$; hence , $c_\alpha - c_\beta = \pm 1$, and we arrive at case 3(α).

In the second case $k_{0\alpha} = k_{0\beta} = \frac{1}{2}$. In order to include this case in the general scheme, let us agree also to admit negative values of k_0, considering here that the pairs (k_0, c) and $(-k_0, -c)$ describe one and the same representation (see the footnote on page 307. Then we can assume that $c_\beta = c_\alpha$, $k_{0\alpha} = \frac{1}{2}$, $k_{0\beta} = -\frac{1}{2}$, $k_{0\alpha} - k_{0\beta} = 1$, and include in the same treatment this case and case (2).

Finally, let $k_{0\alpha} = 0$, and hence also $k_{0\beta} = 0$. Relation (60) then takes the form

$$(c_\alpha^2 - c_\beta^2)^2 - 2(c_\alpha^2 + c_\beta^2) + 1 = 0.$$

Solving this equation for c_β^2, we find that $c_\beta^2 = (c_\alpha \pm 1)^2$; since $k_{0\beta} = 0$ and the pairs $(0, c_\beta)$, $(0, -c_\beta)$ define one and the same representation, we can assume that $c_\beta = c_\alpha \pm 1$, and include in the same treatment this case and case 3(α).

We have therefore proved the following theorem:

THEOREM 4. *Let $g \to T_g$ be a representation of the proper Lorentz group $\mathfrak{G}_+$, which is the direct sum of representations $g \to T_g^{(\alpha)}$ which are multiples of irreducible representations, and let $\Lambda_k \sim \|\Lambda_k^{\alpha\beta}\|$ be the corresponding form of the operators Λ_k defining some invariant* *equation corresponding to the representation* $g \to T_g$. *Then the operator* $\Lambda_k^{\alpha\beta}$ *can be distinct from zero only in the following cases:*

(1) $$k_{0\alpha}-k_{0\beta} = \pm 1, \quad c_{0\alpha} = c_{0\beta};$$

(2) $$k_{0\alpha} = k_{0\beta}; \quad c_{0\alpha}-c_{0\beta} = \pm 1.$$

Here we have

$$\left.\begin{aligned} \Lambda_k^{\alpha\beta} &= \sqrt{[(k+k_{0\alpha}+1)(k-k_{0\alpha})]}\times \\ &\qquad \times U_{k\alpha}^{-1} \dots U_{k_{0\alpha}+2,\alpha}^{-1}\Lambda^{\alpha\beta}U_{k_{0\alpha}+2,\beta}\dots U_{k\beta}, \\ &\qquad k \geqslant k_{0\alpha}+2, \\ \Lambda_{k_{0\alpha}+1} &= \sqrt{[2k_{0\alpha}+2]}\Lambda^{\alpha\beta}, \end{aligned}\right\} \tag{71a}$$

if $k_{0\alpha}-k_{0\beta} = -1$, $c_\alpha = c_\beta$;

$$\left.\begin{aligned} \Lambda_k^{\alpha\beta} &= \sqrt{[(k+k_{0\alpha})(k-k_{0\alpha}+1)]}\times \\ &\qquad \times U_{k,\alpha}^{-1} \dots U_{k_{0\alpha}+1,\alpha}^{-1}\Lambda^{\alpha\beta}U_{k_{0\alpha}+1,\beta}\dots U_{k\beta}, \\ &\qquad k \geqslant k_{0\alpha}+1, \\ \Lambda_{k_{0\alpha}}^{\alpha\beta} &= \sqrt{[2k_{0\alpha}]}\Lambda^{\alpha\beta}, \end{aligned}\right\} \tag{71b}$$

if $k_{0\alpha}-k_{0\beta} = 1$, $c_\alpha=c_\beta$;

$$\left.\begin{aligned} \Lambda_k^{\alpha\beta} &= \sqrt{[(k+c_\alpha)(k+1-c_\alpha)]}\times \\ &\qquad \times U_{k\alpha}^{-1} \dots U_{k_{0\alpha}+1,\alpha}^{-1}\Lambda^{\alpha\beta}U_{k_{0\alpha}+1,\beta}\dots U_{k\beta}, \\ &\qquad k \geqslant k_{0\alpha}+1, \\ \Lambda_{k_{0\alpha}}^{\alpha\beta} &= \sqrt{[(k_{0\alpha}+c_\alpha)(k_{0\alpha}+1-c_\alpha)]}\Lambda^{\alpha\beta}, \end{aligned}\right\} \tag{71c}$$

if $k_{0\alpha} = k_{0\beta}$, $c_\alpha - c_\beta = 1$;

$$\left.\begin{aligned} \Lambda_k^{\alpha\beta} &= \sqrt{[(k+1+c_\alpha)(k-c_\alpha)]}\times \\ &\qquad \times U_{k\alpha}^{-1} \dots U_{k_{0\alpha}+1,\alpha}^{-1}\Lambda^{\alpha\beta}U_{k_{0\alpha}+1,\beta}\dots U_{k\beta}, \\ &\qquad k \geqslant k_{0\alpha}+1, \\ \Lambda_{k_{0\alpha}}^{\alpha\beta} &= \sqrt{[(k_{0\alpha}-c_\alpha)(k_{0\alpha}+1+c_\alpha)]}\Lambda_{k_{0\alpha}}^{\alpha\beta}, \end{aligned}\right\} \tag{71d}$$

if $k_{0\alpha} = k_{0\beta}$, $c_\alpha - c_\beta = -1$, *and* $\Lambda^{\alpha\beta}$ *is some operator from* $\mathfrak{M}_\nu^{\nu\beta}$ *to* $\mathfrak{M}_\nu^{\nu\alpha}$, *where* $\nu = k_{0\alpha}+1$ *in the first case and* $\nu = k_{0\alpha}$ *in the remaining three cases.*

The preceding formulae can be given in a more simple form if each of the subspaces $\mathfrak{M}_\nu^{\nu\alpha}$ has a basis $\{e_\tau\}$, consisting of elements of the set $\mathfrak{D} \cap \mathfrak{M}_\nu^{\nu\alpha}$ and each operator $\Lambda^{\alpha\beta}$ is given in this basis by a numerical matrix $\|\Lambda^{\alpha\beta\tau\tau'}\|$.

Applying the operators $U_{\nu+1,\alpha}$, $U_{\nu+2,\alpha}$, $U_{\nu+3,\alpha}$, ..., to the vector e_τ we then obtain a basis in each subspace $\mathfrak{M}_k^{k\alpha}$. To each operator $\Lambda_k^{\alpha\beta}$ will correspond relative to these bases a numerical matrix, whose elements we denote $\Lambda_k^{\alpha\beta\tau\sigma}$. Formulae (71) here take the form

$$\Lambda_k^{\alpha\beta\tau\sigma} = \sqrt{[(k+k_{0\alpha}+1)(k-k_{0\alpha})]}\Lambda^{\alpha\beta\tau\sigma}, \quad k \geqslant k_{0\alpha}+1, \tag{72a}$$

if $k_{0\alpha} - k_{0\beta} = -1$, $c_\alpha = c_\beta$;

$$\Lambda_k^{\alpha\beta\tau\sigma} = \sqrt{[(k+k_{0\alpha})(k-k_{0\alpha}+1)]}\Lambda^{\alpha\beta\tau\sigma}, \quad k \geqslant k_{0\alpha}, \tag{72b}$$

if $k_{0\alpha} - k_{0\beta} = 1$, $c_\alpha = c_\beta$;

$$\Lambda_k^{\alpha\beta\tau\sigma} = \sqrt{[(k+c_\alpha)(k+1-c_\alpha)]}\Lambda^{\alpha\beta\tau\sigma}, \quad k \geqslant k_{0\alpha}, \tag{72c}$$

if $k_{0\alpha} = k_{0\beta}$, $c_\alpha - c_\beta = 1$;

$$\Lambda_k^{\alpha\beta\tau\sigma} = \sqrt{[(k+1+c_\alpha)(k-c_\alpha)]}\Lambda^{\alpha\beta\tau\sigma}, \quad k \geqslant k_{0\alpha}, \tag{72d}$$

if $k_{0\alpha} = k_{0\beta}$, $c_\alpha - c_\beta = -1$, where $\Lambda^{\alpha\beta\tau\sigma}$ are some complex numbers.

Finally, one can obtain a further simplification if one considers the pair (α, τ) as a single index: $\nu = (\alpha, \tau)$, and one sets $k_{0\alpha} = k_{0\nu}$, $c_\alpha = c_\nu$. Here one and the same pair $(k_{0\nu}, c_\nu)$ can correspond to different indices ν. Formulae (72) then take the form

$$\Lambda_k^{\nu\mu} = \sqrt{[(k+k_{0\nu}+1)(k-k_{0\nu})]}\Lambda^{\nu\mu}, \quad k \geqslant k_{0\nu}+1, \tag{73a}$$

if $k_{0\nu} - k_{0\mu} = -1$, $c_\nu = c_\mu$;

$$\Lambda_k^{\nu\mu} = \sqrt{[(k+k_{0\nu})(k-k_{0\nu}+1)]}\Lambda^{\nu\mu}, \quad k \geqslant k_{0\nu}, \tag{73b}$$

if $k_{0\nu} - k_{0\mu} = 1$, $c_\nu = c_\mu$;

$$\Lambda_k^{\nu\mu} = \sqrt{[(k+c_\nu)(k+1-c_\nu)]}\Lambda^{\nu\mu}, \quad k \geqslant k_{0\nu}, \tag{73c}$$

if $k_{0\nu} = k_{0\mu}$, $c_\nu - c_\mu = 1$;

$$\Lambda_k^{\nu\mu} = \sqrt{[(k+1+c_\nu)(k-c_\nu)]}\Lambda^{\nu\mu}, \quad k \geqslant k_{0\nu}, \tag{73d}$$

if $k_{0\nu} = k_{0\mu}$, $c_\nu - c_\mu = -1$ and $\Lambda_k^{\nu\mu} = 0$ in all the remaining cases. Here the $\Lambda^{\nu\mu}$ are some complex numbers.

We will say that two representations $a \to T_a^{(\nu_1)}$, $a \to T_a^{(\nu_2)}$ are *linked*, and we will write $\nu_1 \rightleftarrows \nu_2$, if $\Lambda^{\nu_1\nu_2} \neq 0$; by virtue of the preceding results, the representations $a \to T_a^{(\nu_1)}$, $a \to T_a^{(\nu_2)}$ can be linked only when either $k_{0\nu_1} - k_{0\nu_2} = \pm 1$, $c_{\nu_1} - c_{\nu_2} = 0$, or $k_{0\nu_1} - k_{0\nu_2} = 0$, $c_{\nu_1} - c_{\nu_2} = \pm 1$.

One of the important and hitherto unsolved problems is the description of all indecomposable invariant equations corresponding to a given representation of the group $\mathfrak{G}_+$. Here an indecomposable equation is defined in the same way as for the group of rotations of three-dimensional space (see § 17, Subsection 5).

In § 15, Subsection 15 and 16 we saw that every completely irreducible representation of the group $\mathfrak{G}_+$ can be realized in a Hilbert space. Suppose that the given representation $g \to T_g$ of the group $\mathfrak{G}_+$ is the orthogonal direct sum of the completely irreducible representations $g \to T_g^{(\nu)}$ in the Hilbert spaces R_ν. It follows from formulae (73) that, *in the case of an indecomposable invariant equation corresponding to such a representation $g \to T_g$ of the group $\mathfrak{G}_+$, any two representations $g \to T_g^{(\nu_1)}$, $g \to T_g^{(\nu_2)}$ must be joined by a chain of successively linked representations and, consequently, each pair $(k_{0\nu}, c_\nu)$ must have the form $k_{0\nu} = k_{0\nu}^0 + m$, $c_\nu = c_\nu^0 + n$, where m, n are whole numbers, and $(k_{0\nu}^0, c_\nu^0)$ is one of these pairs.*

§ 19. Equations Invariant with Respect to Transformations of the Complete Lorentz Group

1. General linear representations of the complete Lorentz group in infinitesimal form

The problem of describing the linear representations $g \to T_g$ of the complete Lorentz group $\mathfrak{G}_0$ is equivalent to that of describing their restrictions to $\mathfrak{G}_+$, i.e. the linear representation $a \to T_a$ of the group $\mathfrak{A}$ and the operator $S = T_s$, satisfying the conditions

$$\left.\begin{aligned} S^2 = 1, \quad ST_u &= T_u S \quad \text{for all} \quad u \in \mathfrak{U}, \\ ST_\varepsilon S &= T_{\varepsilon^{-1}} \quad \text{for all} \quad \varepsilon \in E \end{aligned}\right\} \tag{1}$$

(see § 16, Subsection 2). Returning from the group $\mathfrak{A}$ to the proper Lorentz group $\mathfrak{G}_+$, we can write the last two conditions in the form

$$ST_g = T_g S \quad \text{for all } g \in G_0 \tag{2}$$

and

$$ST_{b_3(t)} = T_{b_3(-t)} S \quad \text{for all real } t. \tag{3}$$

Letting $g = a_k(t)$, $k = 1, 2, 3$, in (2) and differentiating, with respect to t, both sides of the resulting relation and relation (3) at $t = 0$, we deduce that

$$[S, A_k] = 0, \quad k = 1, 2, 3, \quad SB_3 + B_3 S = 0, \tag{4}$$

and so, going over to the operators H_+, H_-, H_3, F_+, F_-, F_3 (see (1–3) § 8, Subsection 1), we have:

$$[S, H_+] = [S, H_-] = [S, H_3] = 0, \tag{5}$$

$$SF_3 + F_3 S = 0. \tag{6}$$

Consequently, our problem consists in finding the general form of an operator S, satisfying conditions (5) and (6). In correspondence with the decomposition of the space of the representation R by the subspaces $\mathfrak{M}_j^k$, the operator S can be represented in the form of a matrix of operators $\|S_{jj_1}^{kk_1}\|$. From relations (5) it follows that

$$S_{jj_1}^{kk_1} = \begin{cases} 0 & \text{when} \quad k_1 \neq k \quad \text{or} \quad j_1 \neq j, \\ E_{jk}^k S_k E_{kj}^k & \text{when} \quad k_1 = k \quad \text{and} \quad j_1 = j, \end{cases} \tag{7}$$

where S_k is an operator in $\mathfrak{M}_k^k$ (see the proof of the analogous assertion for L_4 in § 18, Subsection 4).

Now we apply relation (6), which, by virtue of (7) and formula (38) § 18, Subsection 1 means that

$$E_{jk}^k S_k E_{kj}^k \sqrt{[(k+1+j)(k+1-j)]}\, E_{jk}^k Q_{k+1} E_{k+1,j}^{k+1}$$
$$+\sqrt{[(k+1+j)(k+1-j)]}\, E_{jk}^k Q_{k+1} E_{k+1,j}^{k+1} E_{j,k+1}^{k+1} S_{k+1} E_{k+1,j}^{k+1} = 0,$$

$$E_{jk}^k S_k E_{kj}^k (-jE_{jk}^k P_k E_{kj}^k) + (-jE_{jk}^k P_k E_{kj}^k) E_{jk}^k S_k E_{kj}^k = 0,$$

$$E_{jk}^k S_k E_{kj}^k (-\sqrt{[(k+j)(k-j)]}\, E_{jk}^k D_k E_{k-1,j}^{k-1})$$
$$+(-\sqrt{[(k+j)(k-j)]} E_{jk}^k D_k E_{k-1,j}^{k-1}) E_{j,k-1}^{k-1} S_{k-1} E_{k-1,j}^{k-1} = 0,$$

and these equations are equivalent to the relations:

$$S_k Q_{k+1} + Q_{k+1} S_{k+1} = 0, \quad S_k P_k + P_k S_k = 0,$$
$$S_k D_k + D_k S_{k-1} = 0.$$

In this way is proved

THEOREM 5. *Every linear representation of the complete Lorentz group is given by some linear representation of the proper Lorentz group (hence, by some operators E^k_{jl}, P_k, Q_k, D_k) and an operator $S = T_s$, having a matrix $\|S^{kk_1}_{jj_1}\|$ of the form*

$$S^{kk_1}_{jj_1} = \begin{cases} 0 & \text{when} \quad k_1 \neq k \quad \text{or} \quad j_1 \neq j, \\ E^k_{jk} S_k E^k_{kj} & \text{when} \quad k_1 = k \quad \text{and} \quad j_1 = j, \end{cases}$$

where the S_k are operators in $\mathfrak{M}^k_k$, satisfying the conditions:

$$S_k Q_{k+1} + Q_{k+1} S_{k+1} = 0, \quad S_k P_k + P_k S_k = 0,$$
$$S_k D_k + D_k S_{k-1} = 0. \tag{8}$$

Now we consider the case when the corresponding representation $g \to T_g$ of the proper Lorentz group is the direct sum of representations which are multiples of irreducible representations, so that the operators P_k, Q_k, D_k, defining the representation $g \to T_g$, are given by the formulae (32–35) § 18, Subsection 4.

Let $\|S^{kk_1\alpha\beta}_{jj_1}\|$, $\|S^{\alpha\beta}_k\|$ be the corresponding matrices of the operators $S^{kk_1}_{jj_1}$, S_k. From (7) we deduce that

$$S^{\alpha\beta}_k = 0 \quad \text{when} \quad k < k_{0\alpha} \quad \text{or} \quad k < k_{0\beta}. \tag{9}$$

Rewriting conditions (8) in matrix form and using formulae (32–35) § 18, Subsection 4, we find after simple transformations,

$$\sqrt{\{[(k+1)^2 - k^2_{0\beta}][(k+1)^2 - c^2_\beta]\}}\, S^{\alpha\beta}_k U_{k+1,\beta}$$
$$+\sqrt{\{[(k+1)^2 - k_{0\alpha}][(k+1)^2 - c^2_\alpha]\}}\, U_{k+1,\alpha} S^{\alpha\beta}_{k+1} = 0, \tag{10}$$
$$(k_{0\alpha} c_\alpha + k_{0\beta} c_\beta) S^{\alpha\beta}_k = 0, \tag{11}$$
$$\sqrt{\{[(k+1)^2 - k^2_{0\alpha}][(k+1)^2 - c^2_\alpha]\}}\, S^{\alpha\beta}_k U_{k+1,\beta}$$
$$+\sqrt{\{[(k+1)^2 - k^2_{0\beta}][(k+1)^2 - c^2_\beta]\}}\, U_{k+1,\alpha} S^{\alpha\beta}_{k+1} = 0. \tag{12}$$

Hence, if $S^{\alpha\beta}_k \neq 0$, then, firstly,

$$k_{0\alpha} c_\alpha + k_{0\beta} c_\beta = 0. \tag{13}$$

Moreover, considering (10) and (12) as homogeneous systems of equations in the $S_k^{\alpha\beta}U_{k+1,\beta}$, $U_{k+1,\alpha}S_{k+1}^{\alpha\beta}$, we deduce that the determinant of this system must be equal to zero wherever $S_k^{\alpha\beta} \neq 0$:

$$[(k+1)^2-k_{0\beta}^2][(k+1)^2-c_\beta^2] - [(k+1)^2-k_{0\alpha}^2][(k+1)^2-c_\alpha^2] = 0.$$

Hence

$$(k+1)^2(k_{0\alpha}^2+c_\alpha^2-k_{0\beta}^2-c_\beta^2) + k_{0\beta}^2 c_\beta^2 - k_{0\alpha}^2 c_\alpha^2 = 0;$$

consequently, using (13) we have:

$$k_{0\alpha}^2+c_\alpha^2 = k_{0\beta}^2+c_\beta^2. \tag{14}$$

From (13) and (14) it follows that

$$(k_{0\alpha}+c_\alpha)^2 = (k_{0\beta}-c_\beta)^2, \quad (k_{0\alpha}-c_\alpha)^2 = (k_{0\beta}+c_\beta)^2,$$

so that one of the following four cases occurs

$$k_{0\alpha}+c_\alpha = k_{0\beta}-c_\beta, \qquad k_{0\alpha}-c_\alpha = k_{0\beta}+c_\beta,$$

$$k_{0\alpha}+c_\alpha = k_{0\beta}-c_\beta, \qquad k_{0\alpha}-c_\alpha = -k_{0\beta}-c_\beta,$$

$$k_{0\alpha}+c_\alpha = -k_{0\beta}+c_\beta, \qquad k_{0\alpha}-c_\alpha = k_{0\beta}+c_\beta,$$

$$k_{0\alpha}+c_\alpha = -k_{0\beta}+c_\beta, \qquad k_{0\alpha}-c_\alpha = -k_{0\beta}-c_\beta,$$

which give in turn:

$$k_{0\beta} = k_{0\alpha}, \qquad c_\beta = -c_\alpha, \tag{15a}$$

$$k_{0\beta} = c_\alpha, \qquad c_\beta = -k_{0\alpha}, \tag{15b}$$

$$k_{0\beta} = -c_\alpha, \qquad c_\beta = k_{0\alpha}, \tag{15c}$$

$$k_{0\alpha} = k_{0\beta} = 0, \qquad c_\beta = c_\alpha. \tag{15d}$$

Here the equation $k_{0\alpha} = k_{0\beta} = 0$ in case (15d) follows from the relation $k_{0\beta} = -k_{0\alpha}$ and the fact that the numbers $k_{0\alpha}$, $k_{0\beta}$ are non-negative.

First we consider case (15b). Let $k_{0\alpha} < k_{0\beta}$; since $c_\alpha^2 = k_{0\beta}^2$, the representation $g \to T_g^{(\alpha)}$ is a multiple of a finite-dimensional representation, which involves only those k satisfying the inequality

$k_{0\alpha} \leqslant k < k_{0\beta}$; hence, $S_k^{\alpha\beta} = 0$, by virtue of (9). Similarly $S_k^{\alpha\beta} = 0$ when $k_{0\alpha} > k_{0\beta}$. If, however, $k_{0\alpha} = k_{0\beta}$, then it follows from (15b) that $c_\beta = -c_\alpha$, and we arrive at case (15a).

Similarly, it can be proved in case (15c) that $\Lambda_k^{\alpha\beta} \neq 0$ only when $k_{0\alpha} = k_{0\beta}$, $c_\beta = -c_\alpha$, so that this case also is reduced to case (15a).

In each of the cases (15a) and (15d) the square roots in (10) are equal, and so

$$S_{k+1}^{\alpha\beta} = -U_{k+1,\alpha}^{-1} S_k^{\alpha\beta} U_{k+1,\beta}.$$

Hence

$$S_k^{\alpha\beta} = (-1)^{k-k_{0\alpha}} U_{k\alpha}^{-1} U_{k-1,\alpha}^{-1} \dots U_{k_{0\alpha}+1,\alpha}^{-1} S^{\alpha\beta} U_{k_{0\alpha}+1,\beta} \dots U_{k-1,\beta} U_{k\beta}, \tag{16}$$

where $S^{\alpha\beta} = S_{k_{0\alpha}}^{\alpha\beta}$ remains arbitrary.

Hence there holds

THEOREM 6. *Let $g \to T_g$ be a representation of the complete Lorentz group and let the restriction of this representation to the proper Lorentz group be the direct sum of representations $g \to T_g^{(\alpha)}$, which are multiples of irreducible representations. Then the operator $S = T_s$, corresponding to the reflection s, is given by the formulae:*

$$S \sim \|S_{jj_1}^{kk_1}\|, \quad S_{jj_1}^{kk_1} = \begin{cases} 0 & \text{when } k_1 \neq k \text{ or } j_1 \neq j, \\ E_{jk}^k S_k E_{kj}^k & \text{when } k_1 = k, \quad j_1 = j, \end{cases}$$

$$S_k = \|S_k^{\alpha\beta}\|, \quad S_k^{\alpha\beta} = (-1)^{k-k_{0\alpha}} U_{k\alpha}^{-1} \dots U_{k_{0\alpha}+1,\alpha}^{-1} S^{\alpha\beta} U_{k_{0\alpha}+1,\beta} \dots U_{k\beta};$$

here the $S^{\alpha\beta}$ can be distinct from zero only in the cases

$$k_{0\alpha} = k_{0\beta}, \quad c_\alpha = -c_\beta \quad \text{when} \quad k_{0\alpha} \neq 0$$

and

$$k_{0\alpha} = k_{0\beta} = 0, \quad c_\beta = \pm c_\alpha;$$

moreover, the $S^{\alpha\beta}$ satisfy the condition

$$\sum_\gamma S^{\alpha\gamma} S^{\gamma\beta} = \begin{cases} 1 & \text{when} \quad \beta = \alpha, \\ 0 & \text{when} \quad \beta \neq \alpha. \end{cases}$$

2. A description of the equations invariant with respect to the complete Lorentz group

Let $g \to T_g$ be a linear representation of the complete Lorentz group $\mathfrak{G}_0$, and R the space of this representation. By means of the restriction of this representation to the proper Lorentz group $\mathfrak{G}_+$ we construct the corresponding set $\mathfrak{D}$ (see the remark in § 13 Subsection 5). This set is invariant with respect to the operator $S = T_s$, because

$$S \int x(g) T_g \xi dg = \int x(g) T_{sg} \xi dg$$

$$= \int x(g) T_{sgs} S \xi dg = \int x^{\wedge}(g) T_g S \xi dg,$$

where $x^{\wedge}(g) = x(sgs)$ (see § 16, Subsection 2).

We consider an equation of the form

$$\sum_{k=1}^{4} L_k \frac{\partial \psi}{\partial x_k} + i\kappa\psi = 0, \tag{1}$$

where ψ is a vector function with values from $\mathfrak{D}$, and κ is a real number.

Equation (1) is called *an invariant equation with respect to the complete Lorentz group* $\mathfrak{G}_0$, corresponding to a given representation $g \to T_g$ of this group, if it remains unaltered under any transformation $g \in \mathfrak{G}_0$ of the coordinates x_1, x_2, x_3, x_4 and a simultaneous application to ψ of the operator T_g.

Clearly this means that:

(1) equation (1) is an invariant equation with respect to the proper Lorentz group $\mathfrak{G}_+$, corresponding to the restriction to $\mathfrak{G}_+$ of the given representation $g \to T_g$;

(2) equation (1) remains unaltered by the reflection $x_1' = -x_1$, $x_2' = -x_2$, $x_3' = -x_3$, $x_4' = x_4$ and a simultaneous application to ψ of the operator S.

From condition (1) it follows that the operators L_k, $k = 1, 2, 3, 4$, are given by formulae (1), (16), (25–31) § 18, Subsection 4. It is easy to see that condition (2) yields

$$SL_k S^{-1} = -L_k, \quad k = 1, 2, 3, \tag{2}$$

and

$$SL_4 S^{-1} = L_4. \tag{3}$$

But by (4) and (5) § 8, Subsection 4, by (4) Subsection 1 and by the formulae $L_k = [L_4, B_k]$, $k = 1, 2, 3$, condition (2) is a consequence of condition (3). Therefore it is sufficient to subject L_4 to the additional condition (3).

Using formulae (16) § 18, Subsection 4, we deduce that this condition is equivalent to the condition $S_k \Lambda_k = \Lambda_k S_k$.

Hence we have

THEOREM 7. *Let $g \to T_g$ be a linear representation of the complete Lorentz group $\mathfrak{G}_0$, and let S_k be operators in $\mathfrak{M}_k^k$ defining the operator $S = T_s$ in this representation. Then an invariant equation, corresponding to the representation $g \to T_g$, is an invariant equation corresponding to the restriction of this representation to the proper Lorentz group $\mathfrak{G}_+$, for which the operators Λ_k satisfy the condition*

$$S_k \Lambda_k = \Lambda_k S_k. \tag{4}$$

Now we suppose that the given representation $g \to T_g$ of the group $\mathfrak{G}_0$ is the direct sum (possibly of an uncountable number) of completely irreducible representations $g \to T_g^{(\alpha)}$ of this group, where equivalent representations can correspond to different indices α. According to the results of § 16, every such representation corresponds to a pair of numbers (ν, ρ), where ν is an integral or semi-integral number, and ρ is a complex number; moreover, the restriction to $\mathfrak{G}_+$ of such a representation is a completely irreducible representation $\mathfrak{S}_{m,\rho}$, $m = 2\nu$ when $\nu = 0$ or $\rho = 0$, and is the direct sum of the representations $\mathfrak{S}_{m,\rho}$, $\mathfrak{S}_{-m,\rho}$ when $\nu \neq 0$ and $\rho \neq 0$. Hence the restriction to the group $\mathfrak{G}_+$ of the given representation $g \to T_g$ is also the direct sum of completely irreducible representations of this group. We introduce instead of the index α two indices α, $\dot{\alpha}$ and we denote by $\mathfrak{S}_{m\alpha,\rho\alpha}$, $\mathfrak{S}_{m\dot{\alpha},\rho\dot{\alpha}}$ the representations of the group $\mathfrak{G}_+$, into which is decomposed the restriction to $\mathfrak{G}_+$ of the representation $g \to T_g^{(\alpha)}$. Thus, it is necessary to take $\dot{\alpha} = \alpha$ when $m_\alpha = 0$ or $\rho_\alpha = 0$ and $\dot{\alpha} \neq \alpha$ otherwise. In correspondence with these we denote by $\xi_{p\alpha}^k$ and $\xi_{p\dot{\alpha}}^k$ the canonical bases of the representations $\mathfrak{S}_{m\alpha,\rho\alpha}$ and $\mathfrak{S}_{m\dot{\alpha}\rho\dot{\alpha}}$; then all possible $\xi_{p\alpha}^k$, $\xi_{p\dot{\alpha}}^k$ form a basis in the R of the original representation. For convenience let us agree to denote by one letter τ the index α or $\dot{\alpha}$; moreover, we set

$$\dot{\tau} = \begin{cases} \dot{\alpha} & \text{when} \quad \tau = \alpha, \\ \alpha & \text{when} \quad \tau = \dot{\alpha}; \end{cases}$$

clearly, $\ddot{\tau} = \tau$. Then it is possible to introduce for the basis vectors $\xi^k_{p\alpha}$, $\xi^k_{p\dot{\alpha}}$ one notation $\xi^k_{p\tau}$. The matrix elements of the operators L_4 and S in this basis are denoted by $l^{kk'}_{pp'\tau\tau'}$, $S^{kk'}_{pp'\tau\tau'}$.

By virtue of formulae (16) § 18, Subsection 4 and (7) Subsection 1, each of the numbers $l^{kk'}_{pp'\tau\tau'}$, $S^{kk'}_{pp'\tau\tau'}$ can be distinct from zero only when $k' = k$ and $p' = p$; moreover, the elements $l^{kk}_{pp\tau\tau'}$ do not depend on p and can be distinct from zero only when $k_{0\tau} - k_{0\tau'} = \pm 1$ and $c_\tau = c_{\tau'}$ or when $k_{0\tau} = k_{0\tau'}$ and $c_\tau - c_{\tau'} = \pm 1$, and the elements $S^{kk}_{pp\tau\tau'}$ do not depend on p and can be distinct from zero only when $k_{0\tau} = k_{0\tau'}$ and $c_\tau = -c_{\tau'}$ or when $k_{0\tau} = k_{0\tau'} = 0$ and $c_\tau = c_{\tau'}$ (see Theorem 4 § 18, Subsection 4 and Theorem 6 Subsection 1).

Thus, we can set $l^{kk}_{pp\tau\tau'} = l^k_{\tau\tau'}$, $S^{kk}_{pp\tau\tau'} = S^k_{\tau\tau'}$; then by virtue of formulae (73) § 18, Subsection 4 and (11), (12), (22), (23), (31), (32) § 16, Subsection 6:

$$\left. \begin{aligned} l^k_{\tau\tau'} = \sqrt{[(k+k_{0\tau}+1)(k-k_{0\tau})]}\, l_{\tau\tau'} \quad & \text{when} \quad k \geqslant k_{0\tau}+1, \\ k_{0\tau}-k_{0\tau'} = -1, \quad & c_\tau = c_{\tau'}, \end{aligned} \right\} \tag{5a}$$

$$\left. \begin{aligned} l^k_{\tau\tau'} = \sqrt{[(k+k_{0\tau})(k-k_{0\tau}+1)]}\, l_{\tau\tau'} \quad & \text{when} \quad k \geqslant k_{0\tau}, \\ k_{0\tau}-k_{0\tau'} = 1, \quad & c_\tau = c_{\tau'}, \end{aligned} \right\} \tag{5b}$$

$$\left. \begin{aligned} l^k_{\tau\tau'} = \sqrt{[(k+c_\tau)(k+1-c_\tau)]}\, l_{\tau\tau'} \quad & \text{when} \quad k \geqslant k_{0\tau}, \\ k_{0\tau} = k_{0\tau'}, \quad & c_\tau - c_{\tau'} = 1, \end{aligned} \right\} \tag{5c}$$

$$\left. \begin{aligned} l^k_{\tau\tau'} = \sqrt{[(k+1+c_\tau)(k-c_\tau)]}\, l_{\tau\tau'} \quad & \text{when} \quad k \geqslant k_{0\tau}, \\ k_{0\tau} = k_{0\tau'}, \quad & c_\tau - c'_\tau = -1, \end{aligned} \right\} \tag{5d}$$

$$S^k_{\tau\tau'} = 0 \quad \text{when} \quad \tau' \neq \dot{\tau} \tag{6}$$

and†

$$S^k_{\tau\dot{\tau}} = (-1)^{[k]} \quad \text{in the case of the representations } D^+_{0\rho}, D^+_{\nu 0}, \tag{7a}$$

† We recall that $\dot{\tau} = \tau$ in cases (7a), (7b).

$S^k_{\dot{\tau}\tau} = (-1)^{[k]+1}$ in the case of the representations $D^-_{0\rho}$, $D^-_{\nu 0}$, (7b)

$S^k_{\dot{\tau}\tau} = (-1)^{[k]}$ in the case of the representations $D_{\nu\rho}$, $\nu \neq 0$, $\rho \neq 0$. (7c)

Now we make use of condition (4). In terms of the matrix elements it means that

$$\sum_{\tau''} S^k_{\tau\tau''} l^k_{\tau''\tau'} = \sum_{\tau''} l^k_{\tau\tau''} S^k_{\tau''\tau'},$$

or, by virtue of (6):

$$S^k_{\tau\dot{\tau}} l^k_{\dot{\tau}\tau'} = l^k_{\tau\dot{\tau}'} S^k_{\dot{\tau}'\tau'}. \tag{8}$$

Substituting here for $S^k_{\tau\dot{\tau}}$, $S^k_{\dot{\tau}'\tau'}$, $l^k_{\dot{\tau}\tau'}$, $l^k_{\tau\dot{\tau}'}$ their expressions from formulae (5) and (7), we deduce that

$$l_{\dot{\tau}\dot{\tau}'} = l_{\tau\tau'} \quad \text{when} \quad \dot{\tau} \neq \tau, \quad \dot{\tau}' \neq \tau' \tag{9}$$

and

$$l_{\dot{\tau}\dot{\tau}'} = \pm l_{\tau\tau'} \quad \text{when} \quad \dot{\tau} = \tau, \dot{\tau}' \neq \tau' \quad \text{or when} \quad \dot{\tau} \neq \tau, \dot{\tau}' = \tau'. \tag{10}$$

In relation (10) the sign + is taken if the representation for which $\dot{\tau} = \tau$ or $\dot{\tau}' = \tau'$ is of the type $D^+_{0\rho}$ or $D^+_{\nu 0}$, and the sign – when this representation is of the type $D^-_{0\rho}$ or $D^-_{\nu 0}$. If however $\dot{\tau} = \tau$ and $\dot{\tau}' = \tau'$, then eitger $l_{\tau\tau'} = 0$, or relation (8) is satisfied automatically.

We have now proved the following theorem:

THEOREM 8. *Let the representation $g \to T_g$ of the complete Lorentz group $\mathfrak{G}_0$ be the direct sum of completely irreducible representations $g \to T^{(\alpha)}_g$ of this group and let $\mathfrak{S}_{m\alpha,\rho\alpha}$, $\mathfrak{S}_{m\dot{\alpha},\rho\dot{\alpha}}$ be the representations into which is decomposed the restriction to the proper Lorentz group $\mathfrak{G}_+$ of the representation $g \to T^{(\alpha)}_g$. Let, further, $\xi^k_{p\tau}$ be the canonical basis of the representation $\mathfrak{S}_{m\tau\rho\tau}$, where τ denotes α or $\dot{\alpha}$. Then in the basis $\{\xi^k_{p\tau}\}$ the matrix $\|l^{kk'}_{pp'\tau\tau'}\|$ of every operator L_4, which defines an invariant equation corresponding to the representation $g \to T_g$, satisfies the conditions:*

(1) *$l^{kk'}_{pp'\tau\tau'} = 0$ when $k' \neq k$ or $p' \neq p$;*

(2) *$l^{kk}_{pp\tau\tau'} = l^k_{\tau\tau'}$ does not depend on p;*

(3) *$l^k_{\tau\tau'}$ can be distinct from zero only when $k_{0\tau} - k_{0\tau'} = \pm 1$*

and $c_\tau = c_{\tau'}$ *or* $k_{0\tau} = k_{0\tau'}$ *and* $c_\tau - c_{\tau'} = \pm 1$, *where*

$$l^k_{\tau\tau'} = \sqrt{[(k+k_{0\tau}+1)(k-k_{0\tau})]}\, l_{\tau\tau'} \quad \textit{when} \quad k \geqslant k_{0\tau}+1,$$
$$k_{0\tau}-k_{0\tau'} = -1, \quad c_\tau = c_{\tau'};$$

$$l^k_{\tau\tau'} = \sqrt{[(k+k_{0\tau})(k-k_{0\tau}+1)]}\, l_{\tau\tau'} \quad \textit{when} \quad k \geqslant k_{0\tau},$$
$$k_{0\tau}-k_{0\tau'} = 1, \quad c_\tau = c_{\tau'};$$

$$l^k_{\tau\tau'} = \sqrt{[(k+c_\tau)(k+1-c_\tau)]}\, l_{\tau\tau'} \quad \textit{when} \quad k \geqslant k_{0\tau},$$
$$k_{0\tau} = k_{0\tau'}, \quad c_\tau - c_{\tau'} = 1;$$

$$l^k_{\tau\tau'} = \sqrt{[(k+1+c_\tau)(k-c_\tau)]}\, l_{\tau\tau'} \quad \textit{when} \quad k \geqslant k_{0\tau},$$
$$k_{0\tau} = k_{0\tau'}, \quad c_\tau - c_{\tau'} = -1;$$

(4) *if one sets* $\dot\tau = \dot\alpha$ *when* $\tau = \alpha$ *and* $\dot\tau = \alpha$ *when* $\tau = \dot\alpha$, *then* $l_{\dot\tau\dot\tau'} = l_{\tau\tau'}$ *when* $\dot\tau \neq \tau$ *and* $\dot\tau' \neq \tau'$; $l_{\dot\tau\dot\tau'} = \pm l_{\tau\tau'}$, *when* $\dot\tau = \tau$ *and* $\dot\tau' \neq \tau'$ *or when* $\dot\tau \neq \tau$ *and* $\dot\tau' = \tau'$; *here the sign* + *occurs when the representation, for which* $\dot\tau = \tau$, *respectively* $\dot\tau' = \tau'$, *is a representation of the type* $D^+_{0\rho}$ *or* $D^+_{\nu 0}$, *and the sign — when this representation is a representation of the type* $D^-_{0,\rho}$ *or* $D^-_{\nu,0}$.

§ 20. Equations Derived from an Invariant Lagrangian Function

1. Invariant bilinear forms

A bilinear form in a vector space R is any numerical function $\phi(\xi, \eta)$ of $\xi, \eta \in R$, satisfying the conditions $\phi(\lambda_1\xi_1+\lambda_2\xi_2, \eta) = \lambda_1\phi(\xi_1, \eta)+\lambda_2\phi(\xi_2, \eta)$, $\phi(\xi, \lambda_1\eta_1+\lambda_2\eta_2) = \lambda_1\phi(\xi, \eta_1)+\lambda_2\phi \times (\xi, \eta_2)$ for all vectors $\xi, \eta \in R$ and all numbers λ_1, λ_2. A bilinear form $\phi(\xi, \eta)$ is called *Hermitian*, if

$$\phi(\eta, \xi) = \overline{\phi(\xi, \eta)} \quad \text{for all} \quad \xi, \eta \in R; \tag{1}$$

a Hermitian bilinear form $\phi(\xi, \eta)$ is called *non-degenerate*, if the equation $\phi(\xi, \eta) = 0$ for all $\eta \in R$ is possible only when $\xi = 0$.

A bilinear form in a normed space is called continuous, if from $|\xi_n - \xi| \to 0$, $|\eta_n - \eta| \to 0$ it follows that $\phi(\xi_n, \eta_n) \to \phi(\xi, \eta)$.

In what follows we will consider only Hermitian non-degenerate continuous bilinear forms and the term *bilinear form* will mean:

Hermitian, non-degenerate, continuous bilinear form. Moreover, for simplicity of notation we will drop the letter ϕ and denote the bilinear form simply by (ξ, η).

Let $a \to T_a$ be a representation of the group $\mathfrak{A}$ in the normed space R, which is the direct sum of completely irreducible representations $a \to T_a^{(\tau)}$.

The spaces R_τ of these representations can be assumed Hilbert spaces (see § 15, Subsection 15 and 16); for simplicity of presentation, we will suppose in all that follows that the given representation, $a \to T_a$ is the orthogonal direct sum of the representations $a \to T_a^{(\tau)}$ in the Hilbert space $R = \sum_\tau \oplus R_\tau$.

A bilinear form (ξ, η) on R is said to be *invariant with respect to the representation* $a \to T_a$, if

$$(T_a\xi, T_a\eta) = (\xi, \eta) \quad \text{for all} \quad a \in \mathfrak{A} \quad \text{and all} \quad \xi, \eta \in R. \tag{2}$$

Thus, if $a \to T_a$ is a *unitary* representation of the group $\mathfrak{A}$ in the Hilbert space R, then, with the same definition of a unitary representation, the scalar product (ξ, η) will be a bilinear form, invariant with respect to this representation.

We will now discuss the sort of conditions which ensure that a given representation $a \to T_a$ of the group $\mathfrak{A}$ possesses an invariant bilinear form. By virtue of what has been said above, every *unitary* representation of the group $\mathfrak{A}$ has such a form; however, non-unitary representations possessing these properties will also be of interest to us. We denote by $\xi_{p\tau}^k$ the vectors of the canonical basis of the representation $a \to T_a^{(\tau)}$ and we suppose that there exists a bilinear form (ξ, η) on R, invariant with respect to the representation $a \to T_a$, so that

$$(T_a\xi, T_a\eta) = (\xi, \eta) \quad \text{for all} \quad \xi, \eta \in R. \tag{3}$$

Letting $a = \tilde{a}_k(t)$ and $a = \tilde{b}_k(t)$ (see (1), (2) § 9, Subsection 4), we obtain:

$$(A_k(t)\xi, A_k(t)\eta) = (\xi, \eta), \quad k = 1, 2, 3, \tag{4}$$

$$(B_k(t)\xi, B_k(t)\eta) = (\xi, \eta), \quad k = 1, 2, 3. \tag{5}$$

Applying (4) and (5) with $\xi, \eta \in \mathfrak{D}$ (see the remark in § 13, Subsection 5) and differentiating the equation obtained with respect to t at $t = 0$, we deduce that

$$(A_k\xi, \eta) + (\xi, A_k\eta) = 0, \tag{6}$$

$$(B_k\xi, \eta) + (\xi, B_k\eta) = 0 \tag{7}$$

for all $\xi, \eta \in \mathfrak{D}$.

We denote by $\mathfrak{D}'$ the set of all finite linear combinations of the vectors $\xi^k_{p\tau}$ of the canonical basis (see § 19, Subsection 2); from the construction of the set $\mathfrak{D}$ (see the remark in § 13, Subsection 5) it follows that $\mathfrak{D}' \subset \mathfrak{D}$. Hence, relations (6) and (7) hold for all $\xi, \eta \in \mathfrak{D}'$. Conversely, let, for instance, relation (6) hold for all $\xi, \eta \in \mathfrak{D}'$. By virtue of formulae (51–55) § 8, Subsection 3 the set $\mathfrak{D}'$ is invariant with respect to the operators A_k, B_k; therefore also $(A_kA_k\xi, \eta) = -(A_k\xi, A_k\eta) = (\xi, A_kA_k\eta)$, i.e. $(A_k^2\xi, \eta) = (\xi, A_k^2\eta)$. Repeating this reasoning, we deduce that $(A_k^n\xi, \eta) = (-1)^n(\xi, A_k^n\eta)$ for all $\xi, \eta \in \mathfrak{D}'$ and all $n = 0, 1, 2, \ldots$; but then, taking into account the continuity of the bilinear form (ξ, η), we have:

$$\left(\sum_{n=0}^{\infty} \frac{t^n}{n!} A_k^n\xi, \eta\right) = \left(\xi, \sum_{n=0}^{\infty} \frac{(-t)^n}{n!} A_k^n\eta\right),$$

i.e. (see Appendix IX):

$$(A_k(t)\xi, \eta) = (\xi, A_k(-t)\eta)$$

for all $\xi, \eta \in \mathfrak{D}'$. Because $\mathfrak{D}'$ is dense in R, the operators $A_k(t)$ are bounded and the form (ξ, η) is continuous, then the preceding equation holds for all $\xi, \eta \in R$. We set $\zeta = A_k(-t)\eta$; then $\eta = A_k(t)\zeta$, and the equation obtained can be rewritten in the form (4), i.e.

$$(A_k(t)\xi, A_k(t)\zeta) = (\xi, \zeta)$$

for all $\xi, \zeta \in R$. Analogously it follows from (7) that

$$(B_k(t)\xi, B_k(t)\eta) = (\xi, \eta) \quad \text{for all} \quad \xi, \eta \in R.$$

Thus, if conditions (6) and (7) are satisfied for all $\xi, \eta \in \mathfrak{D}'$, then the form (ξ, η) is invariant with respect to the operators

$$A_k(t) = T_{\tilde{a}_k(t)}, \quad B_k(t) = T_{\tilde{b}_k(t)};$$

but then it is invariant also with respect to all possible products of these operators, i.e. with respect to all operators T_a, because every matrix a is a product of matrices $\tilde{a}_k(t)$, $\tilde{b}_k(t)$.

Hence, *conditions* (6) *and* (7) *with* $\xi, \eta \in \mathfrak{D}'$ *are necessary and sufficient for the invariance of the form* (ξ, η).

Going over in the conditions (6) and (7) from the operators A_k, B_k to the operators H_3, H_+, H_-, F_3, F_+, F_- and taking into account the Hermitian nature of the form (ξ, η), we deduce that these conditions are equivalent to the conditions:

$$(H_3\xi, \eta) - (\xi, H_3\eta) = 0, \tag{8}$$

$$(H_+\xi, \eta) - (\xi, H_-\eta) = 0, \tag{9}$$

$$(F_3\xi, \eta) - (\xi, F_3\eta) = 0, \tag{10}$$

$$(F_+\xi, \eta) - (\xi, F_-\eta) = 0 \tag{11}$$

where $\xi, \eta \in \mathfrak{D}'$.

But condition (11) is a consequence of conditions (8–10) and the relations $[H_+, F_3] = -F_+$, $[H_-, F_3] = F_-$; therefore it is sufficient to satisfy conditions (8–10).

Moreover, it is sufficient that conditions (8–10) be satisfied for the vectors $\xi^k_{p\tau}$ of the canonical basis; then they will also be satisfied for all finite linear combinations of these vectors, i.e. for all ξ, $\eta \in \mathfrak{D}'$.

We set

$$\alpha^{kk'}_{pp'\tau\tau'} = (\xi^k_{p\tau}, \xi^{k'}_{p'\tau'}); \tag{12}$$

by virtue of the Hermitian nature of the form (ξ, η) (see condition (1)), we have

$$\alpha^{k'k}_{p'p\tau'\tau} = \overline{\alpha^{kk'}_{pp'\tau\tau'}}. \tag{13}$$

Because the form (ξ, η) is continuous, and every vector $\xi \in R$ is represented in the form of the sum of a series $\sum \lambda^k_{p\tau}\xi^k_{p\tau}$ (in which there are only a finite or countable number of summands distinct from zero), then the form (ξ, η) is completely determined by the numbers $\alpha^{kk'}_{pp'\tau\tau'}$. Thus we have

$$\xi = \sum \lambda^k_{p\tau}\xi^k_{p\tau}, \quad \eta = \sum \mu^k_{p\tau}\xi^k_{p\tau}$$

$$(\xi, \eta) = \sum \alpha^{kk'}_{pp'\tau\tau'}\lambda^k_{p\tau}\bar{\mu}^{k'}_{p'\tau'}.$$

Letting $\xi = \xi^k_{p\tau}$, $\eta = \xi^{k'}_{p'\tau'}$ in (8) and using formula (16) § 4, Subsection 6 for H_3, we obtain:

$$p\alpha^{kk'}_{pp'\tau\tau'} - p'\alpha^{kk'}_{pp'\tau\tau'} = 0;$$

from this we deduce that

$$\alpha^{kk'}_{pp'\tau\tau'} = 0 \quad \text{when} \quad p' \neq p. \tag{14}$$

Now in (9) we set $\xi = \xi^k_{p\tau}$, $\eta = \xi^{k'}_{p'\tau'}$; from formula (16) § 4, Subsection 6 for H_+ and H_- we conclude that the equation obtained is satisfied identically when $p' \neq p+1$, and when $p' = p+1$ it coincides with the relation

$$\sqrt{[(k+p+1)(k-p)]}\,\alpha^{kk'}_{p+1,p+1,\tau\tau'} = \sqrt{[(k'+p+1)(k'-p)]}\,\alpha^{kk'}_{pp\,\tau\tau'}. \tag{15}$$

Going over to the complex conjugate numbers on both sides of (15), reversing the roles of k, τ and k', τ' and then using relation (13), we deduce that also

$$\sqrt{[(k'+p+1)(k'-p)]}\,\alpha^{kk'}_{p+1,p+1,\tau\tau'} = \sqrt{[(k+p+1)(k-p)]}\,\alpha^{kk'}_{pp\,\tau\tau'}. \tag{16}$$

Consequently, if $\alpha^{kk'}_{pp\,\tau\tau'} \neq 0$, then it must happen that

$$(k+p+1)(k-p)-(k'+p+1)(k'-p) = 0,$$

i.e. $(k-k')\,(k+k'+1) = 0$. But $k \geqslant 0$, $k' \geqslant 0$; therefore from the last equation we conclude that $k' = k$.

Thus:

$$\alpha^{kk'}_{pp\,\tau\tau'} = 0 \quad \text{when} \quad k' \neq k. \tag{17}$$

Now letting $k' = k$ in (15) and cancelling by $\sqrt{[(k+p+1)(k-p)]}$ on both sides of the resulting equation, we deduce that

$$\alpha^{kk}_{p+1,p+1,\tau\tau'} = \alpha^{kk}_{pp\,\tau\tau'},$$

i.e. $\alpha^{kk}_{pp\,\tau\tau'}$ does not depend on p, and we have

$$\alpha^{kk}_{pp\,\tau\tau'} = \alpha^k_{\tau\tau'}. \tag{18}$$

Thus:

$$\alpha^{kk}_{pp'\tau\tau'} = \begin{cases} 0 & \text{when} \quad k' \neq k \quad \text{or} \quad p' \neq p. \\ \alpha^k_{\tau\tau'} & \text{when} \quad k' = k \quad \text{and} \quad p' = p. \end{cases} \tag{19}$$

Now we use relation (10), again taking $\xi = \xi^k_{p\tau}$, $\eta = \xi^{k'}_{p'\tau'}$; by virtue of formula (54) § 8, Subsection 3 for F_3, the equation obtained is satisfied identically when $p' \neq p$ and $|k-k'| \geqslant 2$, and when $p' = p$ and $k' = k-1$, k, $k+1$ it becomes the following three conditions:

$$\sqrt{[(k^2-k_0^2)(k^2-c^2)]}\,\alpha^{k-1}_{\tau\tau'} = \sqrt{[(k^2-k_0'^2)(k^2-c'^2)]}\,\alpha^k_{\tau\tau'}, \tag{20}$$

$$k_0 c\alpha^k_{\tau\tau'} = -k_0'\bar{c}'\alpha^k_{\tau\tau'}, \tag{21}$$

$$\sqrt{\{[(k+1)^2-k_0^2][(k+1)^2-c^2]\}}\,\alpha^{k+1}_{\tau\tau'} = \sqrt{\{[(k+1)^2-k_0'^2][(k+1)^2-c'^2]\}}\,\alpha^k_{\tau\tau}, \tag{22}$$

where the notation is $k_0 = k_{0\tau}$, $c = c_\tau$, $k_0' = k_{0\tau'}$, $c' = c_\tau$. Replacing $k+1$ by k in (22), we see that $\alpha^k_{\tau\tau'} \neq 0$ only when

$$k_0 c + k_0'\bar{c}' = 0. \tag{23}$$

$$(k^2-k_0'^2)(k^2-\bar{c}'^2)-(k^2-k_0^2)(k^2-c^2) = 0. \tag{24}$$

Eliminating the brackets in (24) and using (23), we find that

$$k_0^2+c^2 = k_0'^2+\bar{c}'^2. \tag{25}$$

From equations (23) and (25), as in § 19, Subsection 1, we conclude that

$$k_0' = k_0, \quad c' = -\bar{c} \quad \text{when} \quad k_0 \neq 0 \tag{26a}$$

and

$$k_0' = k_0 = 0, \quad c' = -\bar{c} \quad \text{or}$$

$$k_0' = k_0 = 0 \quad \text{and} \quad c' = \bar{c} \quad \text{when} \quad k_0 = 0. \tag{26b}$$

Thus, $\alpha^k_{\tau\tau'}$ *can be distinct from zero only when conditions* (26) *are satisfied.*

But since the form (ξ, η) is non-degenerate, we have $(\xi^k_{p\tau}, \eta) \neq 0$ for some $\eta \in R$. Expanding η in terms of the elements of the basis: $\eta = \sum \beta^{k'}_{p'\tau'}\xi^{k'}_{p'\tau'}$, and using the continuity of the form (ξ, η), we see that

$$\sum \bar{\beta}^{k'}_{p'\tau'}(\xi^k_{p\tau}, \xi^{k'}_{p'\tau'}) \neq 0$$

and so

$$(\xi^k_{p\tau}, \xi^{k'}_{p'\tau'}) \neq 0 \tag{27}$$

for some p', k', τ'. By virtue of (19), this is possible only when $p' = p$, $k' = k$, and then condition (27) gives $\alpha^k_{\tau\tau'} \neq 0$.

Now using conditions (26), we arrive at the following conclusion:

I. *For the existence of a non-degenerate bilinear form it is necessary that there should be, in the decomposition of the representation* $a \to T_a$ *into completely irreducible representations* $a \to T_a^{(\tau)}$, *for each representation* $a \to T_a^{(\tau)}$ *a representation* $a \to T_a^{(\tau')}$ *such that*

$$k_{0\tau'} = k_{0\tau} \quad \text{and} \quad c_{\tau'} = -\bar{c}_\tau \quad \text{when} \quad k_{0\tau} \neq 0, \tag{28a}$$

$$k_{0\tau'} = k_{0\tau} = 0 \quad \text{and} \quad c_{\tau'} = -\bar{c}_\tau$$

or

$$k_{0\tau'} = k_{0\tau} = 0 \quad \text{and} \quad c_{\tau'} = \bar{c}_\tau \quad \text{when} \quad k_{0\tau} = 0. \tag{28b}$$

Let us agree to denote by one letter β the pair (k_0, c); here we will not distinguish the pairs (k_0, c) and $(-k_0, -c)$, in so far as they define equivalent representations. Further we denote by T_β the set of all indices τ, for which the representations $a \to T_a^{(\tau)}$ are defined by the pair β, so that all the representations $a \to T_a^{(\tau)}$, $\tau \in T_\beta$, are equivalent to one another.

Suppose that a given representation possesses an invariant bilinear form (ξ, η), and consider the following cases:

(a) $k_0 \neq 0$ *and* c *is not pure imaginary*. We denote the pair $(k_0, -\bar{c})$ by β^*; then $\beta^* \neq \beta$ and the sets T_β, T_{β^*} do not intersect. Clearly $\beta^{**} = \beta$. By virtue of I, one can establish a one-one correspondence $\tau \longleftrightarrow \tau^*$ between the elements of the sets T_β, T_{β^*} in such a way that

$$\alpha^k_{\tau\tau^*} \neq 0. \tag{29}$$

Because $\alpha^k_{\tau'\tau} = \overline{\alpha^k_{\tau\tau'}}$, we can assume here that $\tau^{**} = \tau$. Moreover,

$$\alpha^k_{\tau\tau'} = 0 \quad \text{when} \quad \tau \in T_\beta \quad \text{and} \quad \tau' \bar{\in} T_{\beta^*}. \tag{30}$$

(b) $k_0 = 0$, *c is neither real nor pure imaginary*, so that $\beta = (0, c)$. We set $\beta^* = (0, -\bar{c}) = (0, \bar{c})$; then again $\beta^* \neq \beta$, $\beta^{**} = \beta$. Therefore the sets T_β, T_{β^*} do not intersect and again one can establish a one-one correspondence $\tau^* \longleftrightarrow \tau$ so that $\tau^{**} = \tau$ and condition (29) is satisfied; here again condition (30) will be satisfied.

(c) *$k_0 \neq 0$ and c is pure imaginary, or $k = 0$ and c is real or pure imaginary.* Again we set $\beta^* = (k_0, -\bar{c})$. In this case $\beta^* = \beta$, and so $T_{\beta^*} = T_\beta$. By virtue of I in this case, there must exist a one-one mapping $\tau \longleftrightarrow \tau^*$ of the set T_β on itself such that $\tau^{**} = \tau$ and $\alpha_{\tau\tau^*} \neq 0$. Here

$$\alpha_{\tau\tau'} = 0 \quad \text{when} \quad \tau \in T_\beta \quad \text{and} \quad \tau' \bar{\in} T_\beta. \tag{31}$$

Now let one of the conditions (28a), (28b) be satisfied for some index τ'; then, cancelling in (22), we obtain:

$$\alpha_{\tau\tau'}^{k+1} = \pm \alpha_{\tau\tau'}^{k},$$

where the sign $\pm$ depends on the value of the argument in the square roots in formula (22). Hence, letting $\alpha_{\tau\tau'} = \alpha_{\tau\tau'}^{k_0}$, we have:

$$\alpha_{\tau\tau'}^{k} = \varepsilon_k \alpha_{\tau\tau'}, \quad \text{where} \quad \varepsilon_k = \pm 1, \quad \varepsilon_{k_0} = 1; \tag{32}$$

in particular,

$$\alpha_{\tau\tau^*}^{k} = \varepsilon_k \alpha_{\tau\tau^*}. \tag{32a}$$

If the condition of proposition I is satisfied, then it is easy to construct a bilinear form invariant with respect to the given representation $a \to T_a$; it is sufficient to set

$$\alpha_{pp'\tau\tau'}^{kk'} = \begin{cases} 0 & \text{when} \quad k' \neq k, \quad p' \neq p, \quad \tau' \neq \tau^*, \\ \varepsilon_k & \text{when} \quad k' = k, \quad p' = p, \quad \tau' = \tau^*. \end{cases}$$

The corresponding bilinear form is given by the formula

$$\begin{gathered} (\xi, \eta) = \sum \varepsilon_k \lambda_{p\tau}^k \bar{\mu}_{p\tau^*}^k \quad \text{when} \quad \xi = \sum \lambda_{p\tau}^k \xi_{p\tau}^k, \\ \eta = \sum \mu_{p\tau}^k \xi_{p\tau}^k, \end{gathered} \tag{33}$$

where the series on the right side of (33) converges by virtue of the convergence of the series $\Sigma|\lambda_{p\tau}^k|^2$, $\Sigma|\mu_{p\tau}^k|^2$. The continuity of this form (ξ, η) follows easily from its bilinearity and the inequality

$$|(\xi, \eta)|^2 \leqslant \sum |\lambda_{p\tau}^k|^2 \sum |\mu_{p\tau^*}^k|^2 = |\xi|^2 |\eta|^2.$$

Moreover, this form is not degenerate, since if $(\xi, \eta) = 0$ for all η then, letting $\eta = \xi_{p\tau^*}^k$, in (33) we see that $\varepsilon_k \alpha_{p\tau}^k = 0$, and so $\alpha_{p\tau}^k = 0$ for all k, p, τ, i.e. $\xi = 0$.

Thus the following theorem has been proved:

THEOREM 9. *Let $a \to T_a$ be a representation of the group $\mathfrak{A}$ in the Hilbert space R, which is the orthogonal direct sum of its completely irreducible representations $a \to T_a^{(\tau)}$. Then in order that R should possess a bilinear form invariant with respect to the representation $a \to T_a$, it is necessary and sufficient that for every representation $a \to T_a^{(\tau)}$ there should exist a representation $a \to T_a^{(\tau^*)}$, satisfying the conditions*

$$k_{0\tau^*} = k_{0\tau}, \qquad c_{\tau^*} = -\bar{c}_\tau \quad \text{when} \quad k_{0\tau} \neq 0$$

or

$$k_{0\tau^*} = k_{0\tau} = 0, \quad c_{\tau^*} = \pm\bar{c}_\tau \quad \text{when} \quad k_{0\tau} = 0.$$

If, in particular, the representation $a \to T_a$ is itself completely irreducible, then $\tau^* = \tau$, and we arrive at the following result:

II. *For a completely irreducible representation $a \to T_a$ of the group $\mathfrak{A}$ an invariant bilinear form exists if and only if c is pure imaginary and hence $a \to T_a$ is unitary (see* II § 11, *Subsection* 6), *or $k_0 = 0$ and c is real.*

Until now we have considered bilinear forms invariant with respect to a representation $a \to T_a$ of the group $\mathfrak{A}$, or, which is the same thing, a representation of the proper Lorentz group $\mathfrak{G}_+$.

Analogously one can introduce the concept of a bilinear form invariant with respect to a representation $g \to T_g$ of the complete Lorentz group $\mathfrak{G}_0$. In fact, a bilinear form (ξ, η) $\xi, \eta \in R$, is called *invariant with respect to a representation $g \to T_g$ of the complete Lorentz group $\mathfrak{G}_0$* in the space R, if

$$(T_g\xi, T_g\eta) = (\xi, \eta) \quad \text{for all} \quad g \in \mathfrak{G}. \tag{34}$$

If $a \to T_a$ is the corresponding representation of the group and $T_s = S$, then, clearly, condition (34) is equivalent to the following two conditions:

$$(T_a\xi, T_a\eta) = (\xi, \eta) \quad \text{for all} \quad a \in \mathfrak{A} \tag{35}$$

and

$$(S\xi, S\eta) = (\xi, \eta). \tag{36}$$

Condition (35) means that the form (ξ, η) is invariant with respect to the representation $a \to T_a$ of the group $\mathfrak{A}$.

We now seek to ensure the existence of a bilinear form, invariant with respect to a given representation. Here we assume that R is a *Hilbert space* and that the given representation $g \to T_g$ of the group $\mathfrak{G}_0$ is the orthogonal direct sum of its completely irreducible representations; then the restriction of this representation to the group $\mathfrak{G}_+$ is also the orthogonal direct sum of completely irreducible representations $a \to T_a^{(\tau)}$ of the group $\mathfrak{A}$.

An invariant form (ξ, η) with respect to the representation $g \to T_g$ is also an invariant form with respect to its restriction $a \to T_a$; hence, this representation must satisfy the condition of Theorem 9. The corresponding numbers $\alpha_{pp'\tau\tau'}^{kk'}$ are given by formulae (19) and (32). But, moreover, it must satisfy condition (36); by virtue of formulae (7) § 19, Subsection 2,[†] for the operator S this condition gives

$$\alpha_{\dot{\tau}\dot{\tau}'}^{k} = \alpha_{\tau\tau'}^{k},$$

which is equivalent to the condition

$$\alpha_{\dot{\tau}\dot{\tau}'} = \alpha_{\tau\tau'}.$$

We have proved the following proposition:

III. *Let $g \to T_g$ be a representation of the group $\mathfrak{G}_0$ in the Hilbert space R, which is the orthogonal direct sum of its completely irreducible representations. In order that in R there should exist a bilinear form (ξ, η) invariant with respect to this representation, it is necessary that such a form should exist for the restriction of this representation to the group $\mathfrak{A}$. A form (ξ, η) invariant with respect to this restriction will also be invariant with respect to the original representation $g \to T_g$ if and only if the numbers $\alpha_{\tau\tau'}$, defining this form, satisfy the condition*

$$\alpha_{\dot{\tau}\dot{\tau}'}^{k} = \alpha_{\tau\tau'}^{k} \tag{37a}$$

and, consequently, the condition

$$\alpha_{\dot{\tau}\dot{\tau}'} = \alpha_{\tau\tau'}. \tag{37b}$$

If, in particular, the numbers c_τ are real, for all the representations $a \to T_a^{(\tau)}$, into which this restriction is decomposed, then one can set $\tau^* = \tau$; hence:

† See also § 16, Subsection 6.

IV. *If for the representation $g \to T_g$ of the group $\mathfrak{G}_0$ all the numbers c_τ are real, then there exists a bilinear form, invariant with respect to this representation.* In the case of a *finite-dimensional* representation of the group $\mathfrak{G}_0$ all the numbers c_τ are real (see Theorem 2 § 8, Subsection 3), and so:

V. *For every finite-dimensional representation of the complete Lorentz group $\mathfrak{G}_0$ there exists an invariant bilinear form.* In some cases one can simplify the coefficients $\alpha_{\tau\tau'}$ by means of a transition to a new basis; we will show how to perform such a simplification. We consider first the case of a bilinear form invariant with respect to representations of the proper Lorentz group.

We denote by $\mathfrak{N}_\beta$ the closed linear hull of the vectors $\xi^{ko}_{ko\tau}$, $\tau \in T_\beta$; then $\mathfrak{N}_\beta \perp \mathfrak{N}_{\beta^*}$, if $\beta^* \neq \beta$ and $\mathfrak{N}_\beta = \mathfrak{N}_{\beta^*}$ when $\beta^* = \beta$.

As we saw above, the first case holds if $k_0 \neq 0$, Re $c \neq 0$ or $k_0 = 0$, but Re $c \neq 0$ and Im $c \neq 0$, and the second case holds if $k_0 \neq 0$ and Re $c = 0$, or $k_0 = 0$, and Re $c = 0$, or Im $c = 0$.

Since (ξ, η) is a continuous Hermitian bilinear form, there exists a bounded Hermitian operator H in R such that†

$$(\xi, \eta) = \langle H\xi, \eta\rangle \quad \text{for all} \quad \xi, \eta \in R, \tag{38}$$

where $\langle \xi, \eta\rangle$ denotes the scalar product in R. Here

$$H\xi \neq 0 \quad \text{for} \quad \xi \neq 0, \tag{39a}$$

because the form (ξ, η) is not degenerate.

We consider first the case $\beta^* \neq \beta$, so that $\mathfrak{N}_\beta \perp \mathfrak{N}_{\beta^*}$.

Let A denote an operator defined only on $\mathfrak{N}_\beta$ and equal to H on $\mathfrak{N}_\beta$.

The domain of variation of the operator A lies in $\mathfrak{N}_{\beta^*}$ and is dense in $\mathfrak{N}_{\beta^*}$.

In fact, by virtue of (30), when $\tau' \overline{\in} T_{\beta^*}$ and $\tau \in T_\beta$

$$\langle A\xi^{ko}_{ko\tau}, \xi^{k}_{p\tau'}\rangle = \langle H\xi^{ko}_{ko\tau}, \xi^{k'}_{p\tau'}\rangle = (\xi^{ko}_{ko\tau}, \xi^{k'}_{p\tau'}) = 0,$$

and so $A\xi^{ko}_{po\tau} \in \mathfrak{N}_{\beta^*}$. Since $\mathfrak{N}_\beta$ is the closed linear hull of the vectors $\xi^{ko}_{ko\tau}$, $\tau \in T_\beta$, then also $A\xi \in \mathfrak{N}_{\beta^*}$ for all $\xi \in \mathfrak{N}_\beta$. Similarly

$$H\eta \in \mathfrak{N}_\beta \quad \text{whenever} \quad \eta \in \mathfrak{N}_{\beta^*}. \tag{39b}$$

† See Appendix VII.

If the vectors $A\xi$, $\xi \in \mathfrak{N}_\beta$ form a non-dense set in $\mathfrak{N}_{\beta*}$, then there exists a vector $\eta \neq 0$ in $\mathfrak{N}_{\beta*}$, orthogonal to all the $A\xi$, $\xi \in \mathfrak{N}_\beta$, i.e. $\langle A\xi, \eta\rangle = 0$ for all $\xi \in \mathfrak{N}_\beta$. But then also $\langle \xi, H\eta\rangle = \langle A\xi, \eta\rangle = 0$ for all $\xi \in \mathfrak{N}_\beta$, i.e. $H_\eta \perp \mathfrak{N}_\beta$. By virtue of (39b) and (39a), this is possible only when $H\eta = 0$, hence, $\eta = 0$.

In this way it is proved that the vectors $A\xi$, $\xi \in \mathfrak{N}_\beta$, form a dense set in $\mathfrak{N}_{\beta*}$. But in that case $A = WH_0$, where H_0 is a positive definite bounded Hermitian operator in $\mathfrak{N}_\beta$, and W is an operator from $\mathfrak{N}_\beta$ to $\mathfrak{N}_{\beta*}$, mapping $\mathfrak{N}_\beta$ on $\mathfrak{N}_{\beta*}$ isometrically (see Appendix VIII). Since $A\xi = WH_0\xi \neq 0$ for all $\xi \neq 0$, $\xi \in \mathfrak{N}_\beta$, then also

$$H_0\xi \neq 0 \quad \text{for all} \quad \xi \neq 0, \quad \xi \in \mathfrak{N}_\beta. \tag{39c}$$

Now we make the following additional assumption:

(A) $\mathfrak{N}^\beta$ *contains a complete orthogonal system of eigenvectors of the operator* H_0.

We can take this system as the basis $\xi^{ko}_{ko\tau}$, with respect to which a given finite representation is again decomposed into the representations $a \to T^{(\tau)}_a$ (see § 18, Subsection 2). The vectors $W\xi^{ko}_{ko\tau}$ then form a complete orthogonal system in $\mathfrak{N}_{\beta*}$, and we can take them as the basis $\xi^{ko}_{ko\tau*}$ in $\mathfrak{N}_{\beta*}$. In this way a one-one correspondence $\tau \longleftrightarrow \tau^*$ is established between the sets T_β and $T_{\beta*}$; it is easy to see that if one changes the roles of β and β^*, then W goes into W^{-1}, and H_0 into WH_0W^{-1}, and so $\tau^{**} = \tau$.

Let λ_τ be an eigenvalue of the operator H_0, corresponding to the eigenvector $\xi^{ko}_{ko\tau}$; since H_0 is a positive definite operator (see also (39c)), then $\lambda_\tau > 0$. Here for $\tau \in T_\beta$, $\tau' \in T_{\beta*}$

$$\alpha_{\tau\tau'} = (\xi^{ko}_{ko\tau}, \xi^{ko}_{ko\tau'}) = \langle A\xi^{ko}_{ko\tau}, \xi^{ko}_{ko\tau'}\rangle = \langle WH_0\xi^{ko}_{ko\tau}, W\xi^{ko}_{ko\tau'*}\rangle$$

$$= \langle H_0\xi^{ko}_{ko\tau}, \xi^{ko}_{ko\tau'*}\rangle = \lambda_\tau\langle \xi^{ko}_{ko\tau}, \xi^{ko}_{ko\tau'*}\rangle = \begin{cases} 0 & \text{when} \quad \tau' \neq \tau^*, \\ \lambda_\tau & \text{when} \quad \tau' = \tau^*. \end{cases}$$

Now choosing as coordinate vectors $\lambda_\tau^{-\frac{1}{2}}\xi^{ko}_{ko\tau}$, $\lambda_\tau^{-\frac{1}{2}}\xi^{ko}_{ko\tau*}$ instead of $\xi^{ko}_{ko\tau}$, $\xi^{ko}_{ko\tau*}$ (this being accompanied by an unimportant change of the scalar product in R), we obtain:

$$\alpha_{\tau\tau'} = \begin{cases} 0 & \text{when} \quad \tau' \neq \tau^*, \\ 1 & \text{when} \quad \tau' = \tau^*. \end{cases}$$

Thus:

VI. *if $\beta^* \neq \beta$ and if condition (A) is satisfied then one can choose qases $\{\xi^{k_0}_{k_0\tau}\}$, $\{\xi^{k_0}_{k_0\tau'}\}$ for $\mathfrak{N}_\beta$ and $\mathfrak{N}_{\beta*}$ and define a correspondence $\tau \longleftrightarrow \tau^*$ in such a way that*

$$\alpha_{\tau\tau'} = \begin{cases} 0 & \text{when} \quad \tau' \neq \tau^*, \\ 1 & \text{when} \quad \tau' = \tau^*. \end{cases} \tag{40}$$

Now we consider the case when $\beta^* = \beta$, hence, $\mathfrak{N}_{\beta*} = \mathfrak{N}_\beta$. Reasoning as in the preceding case, we deduce that $\mathfrak{N}_\beta$ is invariant with respect to H and, hence:

$$(\xi, \eta) = \langle H\xi, \eta\rangle = 0 \quad \text{when} \quad \xi \in \mathfrak{N}_\beta, \quad \eta \perp \mathfrak{N}_\beta. \tag{41}$$

Let B be an operator in $\mathfrak{N}_\beta$, equal to H on $\mathfrak{N}_\beta$, with regard to which we make the following assumption:

(B) *In $\mathfrak{N}_\beta$ there exists a complete orthogonal system of eigenvectors of the operator B.*

We choose these eigenvectors as the vectors $\xi^{k_0}_{k_0\tau}$, $\tau \in T_\beta$, and we set $\tau^* = \tau$. Let λ_τ be an eigenvalue of the operator B, corresponding to the eigenvector $\xi^{k_0}_{k_0\tau}$. Because B is a Hermitian operator and the form $(\xi, \eta) = \langle B\xi, \eta\rangle$ is not degenerate in $\mathfrak{N}_\beta$, then λ_τ is a real number, distinct from zero. Here

$$\alpha_{\tau\tau'} = (\xi^{k_0}_{k_0\tau}, \xi^{k_0}_{k_0\tau'}) = \langle B\zeta^{k_0}_{k_0\tau}, \xi^{k_0}_{k_0\tau'}\rangle = \lambda_\tau\langle \xi^{k_0}_{k_0\tau}, \xi^{k_0}_{k_0\tau'}\rangle$$
$$= \begin{cases} 0 & \text{when} \quad \tau' \neq \tau, \\ \lambda_\tau & \text{when} \quad \tau' = \tau. \end{cases}$$

Now choosing as the coordinate vectors $|\lambda_\tau|^{-\frac{1}{2}}\xi^{k_0}_{k_0\tau}$ instead of $\xi^{k_0}_{k_0\tau}$, we obtain:

$$\alpha_{\tau\tau'} = \begin{cases} 0 & \text{when} \quad \tau' \neq \tau, \\ \pm 1 & \text{when} \quad \tau' = \tau, \end{cases}$$

where the sign $+$ is taken if $\lambda_\tau > 0$, and the sign $-$ if $\lambda_\tau < 0$. Hence:

VII. *If $\beta^* = \beta$ and if condition (B) is satisfied, then one can choose a basis $\xi^{k_0}_{k_0\tau}$ in $\mathfrak{N}_\beta$ so that*

$$\alpha_{\tau\tau'} = \begin{cases} 0 & \text{when} \quad \tau' \neq \tau, \\ \pm 1 & \text{when} \quad \tau' = \tau. \end{cases} \tag{42}$$

We note that *conditions* (A) *and* (B) *are known to be satisfied if the corresponding subspace* $\mathfrak{N}_\beta$ *is finite-dimensional, i.e. if the representations* $a \to T_a^{(\tau)}$, *corresponding to a given pair* $\beta = (k_0, c)$, *are contained only a finite number of times in the given representation* $g \to T_g$. In particular, these conditions are satisfied if the given representation is the direct sum of a *finite* number of completely irreducible representations and, hence, for every finite-dimensional representation.

Now we pass to the case of a representation of the complete Lorentz group. Let V denote a unitary operator in R, defined by the formula

$$V\xi^k_{p\tau} = \xi^k_{p\dot{\tau}}. \tag{43}$$

Condition (37a) means that the form (ξ, η) must be invariant with respect to the operator V:

$$(V\xi, V\eta) = (\xi, \eta). \tag{44}$$

This means that $\langle HV\xi, V\eta\rangle = \langle H\xi, \eta\rangle$, i.e. $\langle V^{-1}HV\xi, \eta\rangle = \langle H\xi, \eta\rangle$ for all $\xi, \eta \in R$, and so $V^{-1}HV = H$. Hence

$$HV = VH, \tag{45}$$

i.e. the operators H and V must commute.

Now let us admit no transitions to new basis vectors $\xi^k_{p\tau}$, but only such as commute with the operator V.

Making use of this circumstance, and also the condition $HV = VH$ and repeating the preceding reasoning, we arrive at the following result.

VIII. *Let conditions* (*A*) *and* (*B*) *be satisfied for a bilinear form invariant with respect to a representation of the complete Lorentz group* $\mathfrak{G}_0$. *Then one can choose a basis* $\xi^k_{p\tau}$ *in* R *so that*

$$\alpha_{\tau\tau'} = \begin{cases} 0 & \text{when} \quad \tau' \neq \tau^*, \\ 1 & \text{when} \quad \tau' = \tau^* \quad \text{and} \quad \tau^* \neq \tau, \\ 1 \text{ or } -1 & \text{when} \quad \tau' = \tau^* \quad \text{and} \quad \tau^* = \tau. \end{cases}$$

2. Lagrangian functions

Let $g \to T_g$ be a representation of the proper Lorentz group $\mathfrak{G}_+$ in the space R, and (ξ, η) a bilinear form invariant with respect to this representation. A *Lagrangian function*, corresponding to the representation $g \to T_g$ and the form (ξ, η) is any function of the form

$$L = \frac{1}{2i} \sum_{k=1}^{4} \left[\left(A_k \frac{\partial \psi}{\partial x_k}, \psi \right) - \left(\psi, A_k \frac{\partial \psi}{\partial x_k} \right) \right] + \kappa(\psi, \psi), \qquad (1)$$

where κ is a real number, $\psi = \psi(x_1, x_2, x_3, x_4)$ is a vector-valued function with values from $\mathfrak{D}$ (see the remark in § 13, Subsection 5), and the A_k are linear operators satisfying the following conditions:

(1) the operators A_k are defined on $\mathfrak{D}$, and $\mathfrak{D}$ is invariant with respect to the operators A_k, $k = 1, 2, 3, 4$;

(2) there exist closed operators A_k^* also defined everywhere on $\mathfrak{D}$ such that

$$(A_k \xi, \eta) = (\xi, A_k^* \eta) \quad \text{for all} \quad \xi, \eta \in \mathfrak{D}, \qquad (2)$$

and $\mathfrak{D}$ is invariant with respect to the operators A_k^*;

(3) the closures of the operators $\frac{1}{2}(A_k + A_k^*)$ considered only on finite sums of vectors of the form $E_{jj}^k \xi$, $\xi \in \mathfrak{D}$, exist and coincide with the original operators $\frac{1}{2}(A_k + A_k^*)$;

$$(4) \ \sum_{k=1}^{4} g_{jk} T_g A_k T_g^{-1} = A_j, \quad j = 1, 2, 3, 4 \text{ for all } g \in \mathfrak{G}_+ \qquad (3)$$

and on all vectors $\xi \in \mathfrak{D}$.

Condition (4) means that the function L remains invariant under any proper Lorentz transformation

$$x_j' = \sum_{k=1}^{4} g_{ik} x_k, \quad j = 1, 2, 3, 4$$

and a simultaneous application to ψ of the operator T_g (see §17, Subsection 3 and § 18, Subsection 3).

The notion of a Lagrangian function corresponding to a representation $g \to T_g$ of the complete Lorentz group $\mathfrak{G}_0$ and a form

(ξ, η), invariant with respect to this representation, is defined in the same way.

Given a Lagrangian function one can obtain an invariant equation corresponding to the representation $g \to T_g$, by seeking the stationary values of the integral

$$\iiint L \mathrm{d}x_1 \mathrm{d}x_2 \mathrm{d}x_3 \mathrm{d}x_4 .$$

Constructing the Euler–Lagrange equation in the usual way, we obtain

$$\frac{1}{2}\sum_{k=1}^{4} (A_k + A_k^*) \frac{\partial \psi}{\partial x_k} + i\kappa\psi = 0. \tag{4}$$

It follows from the invariance of the Lagrangian function that equation (4) is an invariant equation corresponding to the representation $g \to T_g$, where $L_k = \frac{1}{2}(A_k + A_k^*)$. From this it follows that

$$(L_k \xi, \eta) = (\xi, L_k \eta), \quad k = 1, 2, 3, 4 \quad \text{for all} \quad \xi, \eta \in \mathfrak{D}. \tag{5}$$

Conversely, if the invariant equation

$$\sum_{k=1}^{4} L_k \frac{\partial \psi}{\partial x_k} + i\kappa\psi = 0 \tag{6}$$

satisfies condition (5) then, letting $A_k = L_k$ in (1), we obtain a Lagrangian function, for which equation (6) is the Euler–Lagrange equation.

Thus:

I. *The invariant equation* (6) *arises from some Lagrangian function if and only if there exists an invariant bilinear form* (ξ, η), *for which the operators* L_k *satisfy the condition* $(L_k \xi, \eta) = (\xi, L_k \eta)$, $k = 1, 2, 3, 4$ *for all* $\xi, \eta \in \mathfrak{D}$.

Condition (5) can be simplified in the following way.

From condition (5) it follows that the numbers $(L_k \xi, \xi)$, $k = 1, 2, 3, 4$, are real for any $\xi \in \mathfrak{D}$; for letting $\eta = \xi$ in (5), we have:

$$(L_k \xi, \xi) = (\xi, L_k \xi) = \overline{(L_k \xi, \xi)}.$$

Conversely, assume that the numbers $(L_k\xi, \xi)$, $k = 1, 2, 3, 4$, are real for any $\xi \in \mathfrak{D}$. Then taking the imaginary part on both sides of the equations

$$(L_k(\xi+\eta), \xi+\eta) = (L_k\xi, \xi)+(L_k\xi, \eta)+(L_k\eta, \xi)+(L_k\eta, \eta),$$
$$(L_k(\xi+i\eta), \xi+i\eta) = (L_k\xi, \xi)-i(L_k\xi, \eta)+i(L_k\eta, \xi)+(L_k\eta, \eta),$$

we obtain:

$$\operatorname{Im}(L_k\xi, \eta)+\operatorname{Im}(L_k\eta, \xi) = 0,$$
$$\operatorname{Re}(L_k\xi, \eta)-\operatorname{Re}(L_k\eta, \xi) = 0.$$

Hence

$$(L_k\xi, \eta) = \overline{(L_k\eta, \xi)} = (\xi, L_k\eta).$$

Further, the reality of the expressions $(L_k\xi, \xi)$, $k = 1, 2, 3$, follows from the reality of the expression $(L_4\xi, \xi)$.

In fact, since $L_k = [L_4, B_k]$, $k = 1, 2, 3$, and $(B_k\xi, \eta)+(\xi, B_k\eta) = 0$ (see (1) § 18, Subsection 4 and (7) Subsection 1), then when $k = 1, 2, 3$, $\xi \in \mathfrak{D}$,

$$(L_k\xi, \xi) = (L_4B_k\xi, \xi)-(B_kL_4\xi, \xi)$$
$$= (B_k\xi, L_4\xi)+(L_4\xi, B_k\xi) = (B_k\xi, L_4\xi)+\overline{(B_k\xi, L_4\xi)};$$

however, the last expression is a real number.

Thus:

II. *The invariant equation* (6) *arises from a Lagrangian function if and only if there exists an invariant form* (ξ, η) *such that* $(L_4\xi, \xi)$ *is real for all* $\xi \in \mathfrak{D}$.

We discuss invariant equations satisfying this last condition.

Instead of this condition we can require that $(L_4\xi, \eta) = (\xi, L_4\eta)$ for all $\xi, \eta \in \mathfrak{D}$; on the other hand, by virtue of condition (2) § 18, Subsection 3, this equation will be satisfied if

$$(L_4\xi^k_{p\tau}, \xi^{k'}_{p'\tau'}) = (\xi^k_{p\tau}, L_4\xi^{k'}_{p'\tau'})$$

for all $p, k, \tau, p', k', \tau'$. By virtue of the formulae for L_4 and the coefficients $\alpha^{kk'}_{pp'\tau\tau'}$ (see § 19, Subsection 2 and (19) Subsection 1), this reduces to the condition

$$\sum_{\tau''} l^k_{\tau''\tau}\alpha^k_{\tau''\tau'} = \sum_{\tau''} \overline{l^k_{\tau''\tau'}}\alpha^k_{\tau\tau''}.$$

THEOREM 10. *The invariant equation*

$$\sum_{k=1}^{4} L_k \frac{\partial \psi}{\partial x_k} + \kappa\psi = 0,$$

corresponding to the representation $g \to T_g$, arises from some Lagrangian function if and only if there exists a bilinear form (ξ, η) invariant with respect to the representation $g \to T_g$ and satisfying the condition

$$\sum_{\tau''} l^k_{\tau''\tau} \alpha^k_{\tau''\tau'} = \sum_{\tau''} \overline{l^k_{\tau''\tau'} \alpha^k_{\tau\tau''}}, \tag{7}$$

where $l^k_{\tau\tau'}$ and $\alpha^k_{\tau\tau'}$ are numbers defining the operator L_4 and the form (ξ, η) respectively.

If conditions (A) and (B) Subsection 1 are satisfied, then with a proper choice of basis vectors (see (32a) and (40), (42) Subsection 1) condition (7) takes the more simple form:

$$l^k_{\tau'^*\tau} = \pm \overline{l^k_{\tau^*\tau'}}. \tag{8}$$

In the case of a finite-dimensional invariant equation (i.e. an equation corresponding to a finite-dimensional representation), all the c_τ are real, all the square roots $\sqrt{[(k^2 - k_0^2)(k^2 - c^2)]}$ are pure imaginary, and we can take their arguments equal to $\frac{1}{2}\pi$. Then formula (32) Subsection 1 takes the form

$$\alpha^k_{\tau\tau'} = (-1)^k \alpha_{\tau\tau'};$$

hence, with a proper choice of basis

$$\alpha^k_{\tau\tau'} = \begin{cases} (-1)^k & \text{when} \quad \tau' = \tau^* \quad \text{and} \quad \tau^* \neq \tau, \\ \pm(-1)^k & \text{when} \quad \tau' = \tau^* \quad \text{and} \quad \tau^* = \tau, \\ 0 & \text{when} \quad \tau' \neq \tau^* \end{cases} \tag{9a}$$

in the case of an equation invariant with respect to transformations of the group $\mathfrak{G}_+$, and

$$\alpha^k_{\tau\tau'} = \begin{cases} \pm(-1)^k & \text{when} \quad \tau' = \tau^*, \\ 0 & \text{when} \quad \tau' \neq \tau^* \end{cases} \tag{9b}$$

in the case of an equation invariant with respect to transformations of the group $\mathfrak{G}_0$; here the sign $\pm$ in formulae (9) depends only on τ and does not depend on k.

Combining formulae (9) with conditions (8) § 19, Subsection 2 and (7), we deduce that in the case of a finite-dimensional equation invariant with respect to transformations of the group $\mathfrak{G}_+$;

$$l^k_{\tau'\tau} = \overline{l^k_{\tau^*\tau'^*}} \quad \text{when} \quad \tau \neq \tau^* \quad \text{and} \quad \tau' \neq \tau'^*, \tag{10a}$$

$$l^k_{\tau'\tau} = \pm l^k_{\tau^*\tau'^*} \quad \text{when} \quad \tau = \tau^* \quad \text{or} \quad \tau' = \tau'^*, \tag{10b}$$

and in the case of a finite-dimensional equation invariant with respect to transformations of the group $\mathfrak{G}_0$:

$$l^k_{\tau'\tau} = \pm \overline{l^k_{\tau\tau'}} = \pm l^k_{\tau'^*\tau^*}; \tag{10c}$$

here the $\pm$ in formulae (10) does not depend on k.

Hence we deduce:

III. *In an indecomposable finite-dimensional equation, corresponding to a representation of the complete Lorentz group, which can be obtained from an invariant Lagrangian function, for every index* τ *there exists an index* τ' *such that* $l^k_{\tau'\tau} \neq 0$ *and, hence* $l^k_{\tau\tau'} \neq 0$, *for some* k.

In fact, otherwise it would follow from (10) that $l^k_{\tau'\tau} = l^k_{\tau\tau'} = l^{k\,*}_{\tau'\tau} = l^k_{\tau^*\tau'} = 0$ for all τ'; from this and from (9) it would then follow that the equation is decomposable (see Subsection 3 below).

3. The definition of rest mass and spin

In relativistic quantum mechanics it is assumed that every particle can be described by an indecomposable invariant equation, corresponding to some representation of the complete Lorentz group $\mathfrak{G}_0$, and moreover such an equation as is obtainable from some Lagrangian function. Here, an equation arising from an invariant Lagrangian function is considered decomposable only when the equation itself and the bilinear form (, η) defining the Lagrangian function both decompose; the latter condition requires that $(\xi, \eta) = 0$ whenever $\xi \in R_1$, $\eta \in R_2$, where R_1 and R_2 are the subspaces realizing the decomposition.

Every solution of the equation describing a particle represents a wave-function, which gives a possible state of the particle. In particular, *the state of rest*† is the state described by a solution of this equation of the form

$$\psi(x_1, x_2, x_3, x_4) = \psi_0 e^{-ipx_4}, \tag{1}$$

where ψ_0 does not depend on x_1, x_2, x_3, x_4.

Substituting this expression in equation (6) Subsection 2, we deduce that

$$pL_4\psi_0 - \kappa\psi_0 = 0,$$

i.e. the vector ψ_0 must be an eigenvector of the operator L_4, corresponding to the eigenvalue $\lambda = \kappa/p$. Thus, $p = \kappa/\lambda$, where λ is some eigenvalue of the operator L_4 distinct from zero. But, as is well known,

$$m = \frac{\hbar}{c}p,$$

where m is the mass of the particle in a given state, c is the speed of light in a vacuum, and

$$\hbar = \frac{h}{2\pi}, \qquad h = 6\cdot 55 \times 10^{-27} \text{ erg/sec}$$

(h is the so-called Planck constant; see, for instance, Refs. [24b] and [1]). Therefore the possible values of the mass, corresponding to all possible states of rest, are given by the formula

$$m_j = \frac{\kappa\hbar}{c\lambda_j}, \qquad j = 1, 2, \ldots, \tag{2}$$

† A wave-function of the form $\psi = \psi_0\, e^{i(p_1x_1 + p_2x_2 + p_3x_3 - px_4)}$, i.e. a plane wave, describes the state of particle with definite momentum (p_1, p_2, p_3) and energy p. If the momentum is equal to zero, we obtain (1), i.e. the state of rest.

where λ_j is an eigenvalue† of the operator L_4 distinct from zero. But, according to formulae (16) § 18, Subsection 4, the operator L_4 is given by the matrix $L^{kk'}_{pp'}$, where

$$L^{kk'}_{pp'} = \begin{cases} 0 & \text{when} \quad k' \neq k \quad \text{or} \quad p' \neq p, \\ E^k_{pk} \Lambda_k E^k_{kp} & \text{when} \quad k' = k \quad \text{and} \quad p' = p. \end{cases} \tag{3}$$

This means that every subspace $\mathfrak{M}^k_p$ is invariant with respect to the operator L_4 and on $\mathfrak{M}^k_p$ the operator L_4 coincides with $E^k_{pk}\Lambda_k E^k_{kp}$. But E^k_{pk} and E^k_{kp} are mutually inverse isometric mappings of $\mathfrak{M}^k_k$ on $\mathfrak{M}^k_p$ and $\mathfrak{M}^k_p$ on $\mathfrak{M}^k_k$ respectively; therefore the operators L_4 and Λ_k have the same eigenvalues, where every eigenvalue of the operator Λ_k appears $2k+1$ times as an eigenvalue of the operator L_4, because there are this many operators $E^k_{pk}\Lambda_k E^k_{kp}$ isometric to the operator Λ_k.

Here if ψ_0 is an eigenvector of the operator L_4 corresponding to the eigenvalue λ, then the equation $L_4\psi_0 = \lambda\psi_0$ implies also that $L_4 E^k_{pp}\psi_0 = \lambda E^k_{pp}\psi_0$, so that the vector $E^k_{pp}\psi_0$, if it is not equal to zero, is also an eigenvector of the operator L_4, corresponding to the eigenvalue λ, and moreover belonging to the subspace $\mathfrak{M}^k_p$; the vector ψ_0 is itself the sum of a series converging in the norm of such eigenvectors $E^k_{pp}\psi_0$. In the case when the eigenvector ψ_0 belongs to the subspace $\mathfrak{M}^k$, the corresponding state of rest is called a *state with spin k*; if, moreover, $\psi_0 \in \mathfrak{M}^k_p$, then the state of rest is called a *state with spin k and projective spin p*. The values of the mass at rest, corresponding to such states, are defined by the non-zero eigenvalues of the operator Λ_k.

Now we assume that the given representation $g \to T_g$ is the orthogonal direct sum of a *finite number*, namely n, of completely irreducible representations $g \to T^{(\alpha)}_g$, among which there are infinite-dimensional representations. In such a case all the sub-spaces $\mathfrak{M}^k_k$ will be finite-dimensional. Hence, for all k the operators Λ_k will be represented by matrices of finite-order, whose elements $l^k_{\tau\tau'}$ are calculated by means of formulae (5) § 19, Subsection 2. By virtue of these formulae, the coefficients of the characteristic equation

† It is usually assumed that the whole spectrum of the operator L_4 consists of eigenvalues distinct from zero. In such a case *the invariant equation is called an equation without additional conditions.*

of every such operator Λ_k will be square roots† of polynomials in k; therefore the eigenvalues of the operators Λ_k, being roots of the characteristic equation, form an unbounded set. The only exceptional case will be when all the coefficients of the characteristic equations of the operators Λ_k, beginning with some k, do not depend on k; in this case the eigenvalues of the operators Λ_k will coincide for all k, beginning with some k.

Hence, using formula (2), we arrive at the following result:

If the given representation $g \to T_g$ is the direct sum of a finite number of completely irreducible representations, among which occur infinite-dimensional representations, then either there exist masses at rest of a particle, corresponding to a given spin k, which tend to zero for increasing k (the general case), or all the masses at rest remain constant, beginning with some k (the exceptional case).

4. Conditions of definiteness of density of charge and energy

Let

$$\sum_{k=1}^{4} L_k \frac{\partial \psi}{\partial x_k} + i\kappa\psi = 0 \tag{1}$$

be the equation of a particle, corresponding to some Lagrangian function, let $g \to T_g$ be the corresponding representation, and (ξ, η) the corresponding bilinear invariant form. It is easy to see that for any solution ψ of equation (1) the numbers

$$s_k = \frac{\varepsilon}{\hbar c}(L_k \psi, \psi)$$

(where ε is the charge of the particle) are components of a four-dimensional vector s (i.e. they are transformed by Lorentz transformations as the components of a vector), and the numbers

$$T_k^j = \frac{1}{2i}\left\{\left(L_k \frac{\partial \psi}{\partial x_j}, \psi\right) - \left(\psi, L_k \frac{\partial \psi}{\partial x_j}\right)\right\}$$

† One can show that in reality these coefficients will be simply polynomials in k.

are the components of a four-dimensional tensor T of the second rank. The vector s is called the *vector of current*, and the tensor T *the energy momentum tensor* (for details see, for instance, Refs. [24a] and [1]). In particular, the expression

$$\rho = s_4 = \frac{\varepsilon}{\hbar c}(L_4\psi, \psi) \tag{2}$$

is called the *density of charge*, and

$$W = -T_4^4 = -\frac{1}{2i}\left[\left(L_4\frac{\partial\psi}{\partial x_4}, \psi\right) - \left(\psi, L_4\frac{\partial\psi}{\partial x_4}\right)\right] \tag{3}$$

is called the *density of energy* in the state ψ.

The density of charge is called definite if it keeps one and the same sign in all states of the particle; analogously the density of energy is called *definite* if it keeps one and the same sign in all states of the particle. Here we do not exclude the case when the density of charge or the density of energy vanishes in some states. In particular, the density of charge and density of energy are called *positive definite* if they are non-negative in all states of the particle.

THEOREM 11. *Let there be given an indecomposable invariant equation, obtained from an invariant Lagrangian function, and let the corresponding representation $g \to T_g$ of the group $\mathfrak{G}_0$ be the direct sum of completely irreducible representations, and $g \to T_g^{(\tau)}$ be the completely irreducible representations of the group $\mathfrak{G}_+$, into which the restriction of the representation $g \to T_g$ to $\mathfrak{G}_+$ is decomposed.*

Then:

(1) *If for only one of the pairs (and hence for all the pairs) $\beta = (k_0, c)$, defining the representations $g \to T_g^{(\tau)}$, the number c is non-real and* Re *c is neither an integral nor a semi-integral number, then neither the density of charge nor the density of energy can be definite.*

(2) *If for only one of the pairs (and hence for all the pairs) $\beta = (k_0, c)$, defining the representations $g \to T_g^{(\tau)}$, the number c is*

non-real, then in the case of integral Re c *the density of charge cannot be definite, and in the case of semi-integral* Re c *the density of energy cannot be definite.*

(3) *If for only one of the pairs (and hence for all the pairs)* $\beta = (k_0, c)$, *defining the representations* $g \to T_g^{(\tau)}$, c *is a real non-integral and non-semi-integral number, then when* k_0 *is integral the density of charge cannot be definite, and when* k_0 *is semi-integral the density of energy cannot be definite.*

(4) *If for only one of the pairs (and hence for all the pairs)* $\beta = (k_0, c)$, *defining the representations* $g \to T_g^{(\tau)}$ *both* k_0 *and* c *are integers, then there cannot be definiteness of charge, and if both* k_0 *and* c *are semi-integers, then there cannot be definiteness of energy.*†

Proof. (1) Let $\beta_0 = (k_{00}, c_0)$ be one of the pairs defining the representations $g \to T_g^{(\tau)}$. We separate the set of all indices τ into two classes T_1 and T_2; in the class T_1 we place those indices τ, for which $\beta = (k_{00}+m, c_0+n)$, and in T_2 those indices τ, for which $\beta = (k_{00}+m, -\bar{c}_0+n)$, where in both cases m and n are integers. The set T_1 does not intersect T_2, because if $c_0+n_1 = -\bar{c}_0+n_2$, then Re $c_0 = \frac{1}{2}(n_2-n_1)$ is an integral or semi-integral number contrary to the nature of c_0. Let R^+ be the direct sum of all the R_τ, $\tau \in T_1$, and R^- the direct sum of all the R_τ, $\tau \in T_2$. Then $R = R^+ \oplus R^-$, so that every vector $\xi \in R$ is represented in a unique way in the form $\xi = \xi^+ + \xi^-$. The representations $g \to T_g^{(\tau_1)}$, $g \to T_g^{(\tau_2)}$ cannot be linked if $\tau_1 \in T_1$ and $\tau_2 \in T_2$. Therefore the original invariant equation is decomposed into two invariant equations:

$$\sum_{j=1}^{4} L_j \frac{\partial \psi^+}{\partial x_j} + i\kappa\psi^+ = 0, \tag{4a}$$

$$\sum_{j=1}^{4} L_j \frac{\partial \psi^-}{\partial x_j} + i\kappa\psi^- = 0, \tag{4b}$$

† We note that apart from the cases enumerated in this theorem there is only one other possibility, namely when one of the numbers of the pair (k_0, c) is integral and the other semi-integral. The example quoted above (see example B) Subsection 6) shows that in this case there are equations for which the charge and energy are both definite.

where ψ^+, ψ^- are vector-valued functions with values in R^+, R^- respectively, and every solution ψ of the original equation is represented in the form $\psi = \psi^+ + \psi^-$, where ψ^+, ψ^- are solutions of equations (4a), (4b) respectively. Nevertheless, the original equation cannot be considered decomposable. In fact, if $\tau \in T_1$, then $\tau^* \in T_2$; therefore $(\xi^+, \xi^+) = (\xi^-, \xi^-) = 0$ for any vectors $\xi^+ \in R^+$, $\xi^- \in R^-$, and for every vector $\xi^+ \in R^+$ there exists a vector $\xi^- \in R^-$ such that $(\xi^+, \xi^-) \neq 0$. But if $\xi^+ \in R^+$, $\xi^- \in R^-$, then also $L_j \xi^+ \in R^+$ and $L_j \xi^- \in R^-$; therefore also

$$(L_j \xi^+, \xi^+) = (\xi^+, L_j \xi^+) = (L_j \xi^-, \xi^-) = (\xi^-, L_j \xi^-) = 0.$$

Hence we deduce that if $\psi = \psi^+ + \psi^-$

$$\rho = \varepsilon\{(L_4 \psi^+, \psi^-) + (L_4 \psi^-, \psi^+)\}, \tag{5}$$

$$W = -\frac{1}{2i}\left\{\left(L_4 \frac{\partial \psi^+}{\partial x_4}, \psi^-\right) + \left(L_4 \frac{\partial \psi^-}{\partial x_4}, \psi^+\right) - \left(\psi^+, L_4 \frac{\partial \psi^-}{\partial x_4}\right) - \left(\psi^-, L_4 \frac{\partial \psi^+}{\partial x_4}\right)\right\}. \tag{6}$$

But these expressions change sign in the transition from $\psi^+ + \psi^-$ to $\psi^+ - \psi^-$ and so density of charge and density of energy cannot be definite. In this way the theorem is proved in case (1).

(2) Again let $\beta_0 = (k_{00}, c_0)$ be one of the pairs defining the representations $g \to T_g^{(\tau)}$. We separate the set of all indices τ into two classes T_1, T_2; in the class T_1 we place those indices which correspond to the pairs $(k_{00}+m, c_0+n)$ with even $m+n$, and in the class T_2 those indices τ corresponding to the pairs $(k_{00}+m, c_0+n)$ with odd $m+n$. Again let R^+ be the direct sum of all the R_τ, $\tau \in T_1$, and R^- the direct sum of all the R_τ, $\tau \in T_2$, so that $R = R^+ \oplus R^-$. The representation $g \to T_g^{(\tau)}$, corresponding to the pair $\beta = (k_{00}+m, c_0+n)$, can be linked only with the representations corresponding to the pairs $(k_{00}+m, c_0+n\pm 1)$, $(k_{00}+m\pm 1, c_0+n)$, and so, when $\tau_1 \in T_1$ the representation $g \to T_g^{(\tau_1)}$ can be linked only with representations $g \to T_g^{(\tau_2)}$, $\tau_2 \in T_2$.

Hence, if $\xi^+ \in R^+$, $\xi^- \in R^-$, then $L_j\xi^+ \in R^-$, $L_j\xi^- \in R^+$, and so the original invariant equation is represented in the form of a system of equations

$$\sum_{j=1}^{4} L_j \frac{\partial \psi^+}{\partial x_j} + i\kappa\psi^- = 0, \quad \sum_{j=1}^{4} L_j \frac{\partial \psi^-}{\partial x_j} + i\kappa\psi^+ = 0, \tag{7}$$

where ψ^+ is a vector-valued function with values in R^+, and ψ^- is a vector-valued function with values in R^-.

We set $\operatorname{Re} c = c'$, $\operatorname{Im} c = c''$; if $\beta = (k_0, c) = (k_0, c' + ic'')$,

$$\text{then } \beta^* = (k_0, -c' + ic'') = (k_0, c - 2c'),$$

hence, if c' is an integer, then the indices τ, τ^* either both belong to T_1, or both to T_2; if, however, c' is a semi-integer, then one of the indices τ, τ^* belongs to T_1, and the other to T_2. Therefore for $\xi^+ \in R^+$, $\xi^- \in R^-$,

$$(\xi^+, \xi^-) = (\xi^-, \xi^+) = 0 \quad \text{when } c' \text{ is an integer,}$$
$$(\xi^+, \xi^+) = (\xi^-, \xi^-) = 0 \quad \text{when } c' \text{ is a semi-integer.}$$

In particular,

$$(L_j\xi^-, \xi^-) = (L_j\xi^+, \xi^+) = 0 \quad \text{when } c' \text{ is an integer,}$$
$$(L\xi^+, \xi^-) = (L_j\xi^-, \xi^+) = 0 \quad \text{when } c' \text{ is a semi-integer.}$$

But in such a case the solution $\psi = \psi^+ + \psi^-$ of the system (7) corresponds to the density of charge and density of energy defined by formulae (5) and (6) when c' is an integer, and by the formulae:

$$\rho = \varepsilon\{(L_4\psi^+, \psi^+) + (L_4\psi^-, \psi^-)\}, \tag{8}$$

$$W = -\frac{1}{2i}\left\{\left(L_4\frac{\partial \psi^+}{\partial x_4}, \psi^+\right) + \left(L_4\frac{\partial \psi^-}{\partial x_4}, \psi^-\right) - \left(\psi^+, L_4\frac{\partial \psi^+}{\partial x_4}\right) - \left(\psi^-, L_4\frac{\partial \psi^-}{\partial x_4}\right)\right\} \tag{9}$$

when c' is a semi-integer. On the other hand, together with the function

$$\psi = \psi^+(x_1, x_2, x_3, x_4) + \psi^-(x_1, x_2, x_3, x_4)$$

the function

$$\psi_1 = \psi^+(-x_1, -x_2, -x_3, -x_4) - \psi^-(-x_1, -x_2, -x_3, -x_4)$$

is also a solution of the system (7); however, in the transition from ψ to ψ_1 the expression for ρ in formula (5) and the expression for W in formula (9) change sign. Hence, the density of charge cannot be definite when c' is an integer, and the density of energy cannot be definite when c' is a semi-integer.

(3) We make the same partition into the sets T_1, T_2 and the same decomposition $R = R_1 \oplus R_2$ as in case (2). If $\beta = (k_0, c)$, then $\beta^* = (k_0, -c) = (-k_0, c) = (k_0 - 2k_0, c)$. Hence, if k_0 is an integer, then either τ and τ^* belong to T_1, or both τ and τ^* belong to T_2; if, however, k_0 is a semi-integer, then one of the indices τ, τ^* belongs to T_1, and the other to T_2. Thus the argument proceeds as in case (2).

(4) In this case one can write:

$$(k_{00}+m, c_0+n) = (-k_{00}-m, -c_0-n)$$
$$= (k_{00}-2k_{00}-m, c_0-2c_0-n) = (k_{00}+m', c_0+n'),$$

where $m' = -m-2k_{00}$, $n' = -2c_0-n$; hence, in this case the numbers m, n are defined by a given pair uniquely. But, by virtue of the relation $m'+n' = -(m+n)-2(k_{00}+c_0)$, $m'+n'$ differs from $m+n$ by an even number, because $2(k_{00}+c_0)$ is even; hence, the partition into the sets T_1 and T_2, performed for case (2), can here be performed in a unique way, after which the reasoning remains the same as in case (2), and the theorem is completely proved.

If, in particular, the given representation $g \to T_g$ of the group $\mathfrak{G}_0$ is finite-dimensional, then for every representation $g \to T_g^{(\tau)}$ the numbers k_0, c are either both integers or both semi-integers, i.e. case (4) holds. Thus, as a special case of the theorem one obtains the following theorem of PAULI† Ref. [30]:

---

† Theorem 11, generalizing Pauli's theorem, is due to I. M. GELFAND and A. M. YAGLOM [14b].

For every particle, described by a finite-dimensional equation, the density of charge cannot be definite in the case of integral spin, and the density of energy cannot be definite in the case of semi-integral spin. Hence, for such a particle the density of charge and density of energy cannot be both definite simultaneously.

Now we will discuss conditions under which density of charge or density of energy will be definite. Clearly, it is sufficient to find conditions of positive definiteness of density of charge or energy, because the case of negative definite densities of charge or energy is reduced to this case by the transition from L_4 to $-L_4$. For simplicity of presentation we assume further that the eigenvectors of the operators L_4 form a complete system in R.

Let $\{\xi_\alpha\}$ be a complete system of eigenvectors of the operator L_4, and λ_α the corresponding eigenvalues. Moreover, we will take $\varepsilon > 0$.

We consider a solution of equation (1) of the form

$$\psi = \sum_\alpha c_\alpha e^{-ip_\alpha x_4} \xi_\alpha, \tag{10}$$

in which the sum extends over a finite number of indices α such that $\lambda_\alpha \neq 0$, and

$$p_\alpha = \frac{\kappa}{\lambda_\alpha}. \tag{11}$$

Substituting these expressions in formula (2), we find that the expression $(L_4\psi, \psi)$ must be non-negative for all vectors ψ of the form (10). Since $L_4 \xi_\alpha = 0$, if $\lambda_\alpha = 0$, then $(L_4\psi, \psi) \geqslant 0$ also for such vectors ψ of the form (10) which contain summands with $\lambda_\alpha = 0$. But by this condition the vectors ξ_α form a complete system in R, and the closure of the operator L_4, considered only on finite linear combinations of the vectors ξ_α, coincides with the original operator L_4. Therefore

$$(L_4\xi, \xi) \geqslant 0 \tag{12}$$

for all vectors ξ from the domain of definition of the operator L_4. Conversely, if this condition is satisfied, then by virtue of formula (2) the density of charge will be non-negative in all states ψ.

Thus:

I. *If the operator L_4 possesses a complete system of eigenvectors, then the density of charge is positive definite if and only if $(L_4\,\xi, \xi) \geqslant 0$ for all vectors ξ from the domain of definition of the operator L_4.* Now we turn to the density of energy. By virtue of the invariance of equation (1), non-negativeness of the density of energy will occur, if it occurs for solutions of equation (1) not depending on x_1, x_2, x_3. But, applying the Fourier transform with respect to x_4, we deduce that every such solution can be represented as the limit of a sum of the form (10); therefore it is sufficient to know when the density of energy will be non-negative for these sums. On the other hand, for such sums

$$L_4\frac{\partial\psi}{\partial x_4} = -iL_4\Big(\sum_\alpha c_\alpha e^{-ip_\alpha x_4}p_\alpha\xi_\alpha\Big) = -i\sum_\alpha c_\alpha e^{-ip_\alpha x_4}p_\alpha\lambda_\alpha\xi_\alpha$$
$$= -i\kappa\sum_\alpha c_\alpha e^{-ip_\alpha x_4}\xi_\alpha,$$

and so

$$\left(L_4\frac{\partial\psi}{\partial x_4}, \psi\right) = -i\kappa\sum_{\alpha,\beta} c_\alpha\bar{c}_\beta e^{-ip_\alpha x_4}e^{ip_\beta x_4}(\xi_\alpha, \xi_\beta)$$
$$= -i\kappa\sum_{\alpha,\beta} c_\alpha\bar{c}_\beta e^{-ip_\alpha x_4}e^{ip_\beta x_4}\frac{1}{\lambda_\alpha\bar{\lambda}_\beta}(L_4\xi_\alpha, L_4\xi_\beta).$$

Letting

$$\mu_\alpha = c_\alpha e^{-ip_\alpha x_4}\frac{1}{\lambda_\alpha}, \quad \xi = \sum_\alpha \mu_\alpha\xi_\alpha,$$

we see that

$$\left(L_4\frac{\partial\psi}{\partial x_4}, \psi\right) = -i\kappa(L_4\xi, L_4\xi),$$

and similarly

$$\left(\psi, L_4\frac{\partial\psi}{\partial x_4}\right) = i\kappa(L_4\xi, L_4\xi).$$

Substituting these expressions in formula (3), we find that the density of energy will be positive definite if and only if

$$(L_4\xi, L_4\xi) \geqslant 0 \tag{13}$$

for all finite sums $\xi = \sum_\alpha \mu_\alpha \xi_\alpha$, in which $\lambda_\alpha \neq 0$. But, as before, condition (13) is also satisfied for all finite sums $\xi = \sum_\alpha \mu_\alpha \xi_\alpha$, because $L_4 \xi_\alpha = 0$ when $\lambda_\alpha = 0$. Reasoning again as in the cnsoderation of the density of charge, we conclude that condition (i3) must be satisfied for all vectors ξ from the domain of definition of the operator L_4.

Hence:

II. *If the operator L_4 possesses a complete system of einvectors, then the density of energy is positive definite if and only if $(L_4\xi, L_4\xi) \geqslant 0$ for all vectors ξ from the domain of definition of the operator L_4.*

5. The case of finite-dimensional equations

Now we discuss finite-dimensional equations (i. e. equations corresponding to a finite-dimensional representation $g \to T_g$) with positive definite density of charge or density of energy. Here, as in Subsection 4, we assume that the space of the representation R has a basis of eigenvectors of the operator L_4, so that the matrix of the operator L_4 in this basis is diagonal. Moreover, the discussion will be about invariant equations corresponding to a representation $g \to T_g$ of the *complete* Lorentz group $\mathfrak{G}_0$.

By virtue of VIII Subsection 1, one can decompose the corresponding representation $a \to T_a$ of the group $\mathfrak{A}$ into irreducible representations $a \to T_a^{(\tau)}$ and construct a one-one mapping $\tau \leftrightarrow \tau^*$ in such a way that $\tau^{**} = \tau$, the corresponding invariant bilinear form being

$$\alpha_{\tau\tau'}^k = \begin{cases} 0 & \text{when} \quad \tau' \neq \tau^*, \\ \pm 1 & \text{when} \quad \tau' = \tau^*. \end{cases} \tag{1}$$

First we consider conditions ensuring that the density of charge is non-negative. According to I Subsection 4, this will be the case if and only if

$$(L_4\xi, \xi) \geqslant 0 \quad \text{for all} \quad \xi \in R. \tag{2}$$

Suppose now that among the representations $a \to T_a^{(\tau)}$ there is a representation $a \to T_a^{(\tau_1)}$, corresponding to a pair $\beta_1 = (k_0, c)$, where $k_0 \neq \frac{1}{2}$. Then there must exist also a representation $a \to T_a^{(\tau_2)}$, for which $\beta_2 = (k_0 \pm 1,\ c)$ or $\beta_2 = (k_0,\ c \pm 1)$ and $l^k_{\tau_2\tau_1} \neq 0$, and this means also $l^k_{\tau_1\tau_2} \neq 0$ for some k(see Theorem 4 § 18, Subsection 4 and III Subsection 2). Here $\tau_2 \neq \tau_1{}^*$, because $k_0 \neq \frac{1}{2}$, and so c cannot be a semi-integer; hence, $\alpha^k_{\tau_1\tau_2} = 0$ and $l^k_{\tau_1^*\tau_1} = l^k_{\tau_2\tau_2^*} = 0$. Then, letting $\xi = \mu_1 \xi^k_{k\tau_1} + \mu_2 \xi^k_{k\tau_2}$, we have:

$$(L_4 \xi,\ \xi) = \pm l^k_{\tau_2\tau_1} \mu_1 \bar{\mu}_2 \pm l^{k*}_{\tau_1\tau_2^*} \bar{\mu}_1 \mu_2,$$

and this expression cannot be non-negative for all μ_1, μ_2. Hence, all the representations $a \to T_a^{(\tau)}$ correspond to a pair $\beta = (\frac{1}{2},\ c)$. We will prove that here necessarily $|c| = \frac{3}{2}$. We assume the contrary; let $|c| > \frac{3}{2}$ for some representation $a \to T_a^{(\tau)}$ and let $a \to T_a^{(\tau_1)}$ be a representation for which $l_{\tau\tau_1} \neq 0$. If $\tau^* \neq \tau_1$, then, as before, we deduce that $(L_4\xi,\ \xi)$ can take negative values. We therefore consider the case $l_{\tau\tau^*} \neq 0$. By hypothesis, $k_0 = \frac{1}{2}$, $|c| > \frac{3}{2}$, and so the index k takes at least two different values, namely $\frac{1}{2}$, $\frac{3}{2}$, where, by virtue of formulae (9) Subsection 2 and (5) § 19, Subsection 2, $\alpha^k_{\tau\tau^*} = \pm(-1)^k$, and $l^k_{\tau^*\tau}$, $l^{k-1}_{\tau^*\tau}$ differ by a positive factor, which we denote ω_k. Letting $\xi = \mu_1 \xi^{k-1}_{p\tau} + \mu_2 \xi^k_{p\tau}$, we have:

$$\begin{aligned}(L_4\xi,\ \xi) &= |\mu_1|^2 l^{k-1}_{\tau^*\tau} \alpha^{k-1}_{\tau^*\tau} + |\mu_2|^2 l^k_{\tau^*\tau} \alpha^k_{\tau^*\tau} \\ &= \pm(-1)^{k-1} l^{k-1}_{\tau^*\tau}(|\mu_1|^2 - \omega_k |\mu_2|^2),\end{aligned}$$

and this expression cannot be non-negative for all μ_1, μ_2.

Thus, the representations $a \to T_a^{(\tau)}$ correspond only to the pairs $(\frac{1}{2},\ \frac{3}{2})$ $(\frac{1}{2},\ -\frac{3}{2})$ or, which is the same thing, the pairs $(\frac{1}{2},\ \frac{3}{2})$, $(-\frac{1}{2},\ \frac{3}{2})$; because the original representation $g \to T_g$ is a representation of the complete Lorentz group $\mathfrak{G}_0$, then both pairs occur the same number of times, i.e. the representation $g \to T_g$ is a multiple of the representation $\hat{D}_{\frac{1}{2},\frac{3}{2}}$ (see the remark at the end of § 16, Subsection 6).

We will prove that the representation $\hat{D}_{\frac{1}{2},\frac{3}{2}}$ cannot be contained in $g \to T_g$ more than once, i.e. that the given representation $g \to T_g$ coincides with $\hat{D}_{\frac{1}{2},\frac{3}{2}}$. Let T_1 be the set of all indices τ, corresponding to the pair $(\frac{1}{2},\ \frac{3}{2})$, and T_2 the set of all indices τ, corresponding to the pair $(-\frac{1}{2},\ \frac{3}{2})$; we denote by R_1 the closed linear hull of all the vectors $\xi^{\frac{1}{2}}_{\frac{1}{2}\tau}$, $\tau \in T_1$, and by R_2 the closed linear hull of all the vectors $\xi^{\frac{1}{2}}_{\frac{1}{2}\tau}$, $\tau \in T_2$. We define an isometric operator W from R_1 to R_2, letting $W\xi^{\frac{1}{2}}_{\frac{1}{2}\tau} = \pm\xi^{\frac{1}{2}}_{\frac{1}{2}\tau^*}$, where the sign $\pm$ is the same as in formula (42), Subsection 1. By virtue of VIII Subsection 1, the invariant bilinear form (ξ, η) will be given by the formulae

$$(\xi, \eta) = 0 \quad \text{when} \quad \xi \in R_1, \quad \eta \in R_1 \quad \text{or} \quad \xi \in R_2, \quad \eta \in R_2,$$
$$(\xi, \eta) = \langle \xi, W^*\eta \rangle \quad \text{when} \quad \xi \in R_1, \quad \eta \in R_2,$$
$$(\xi, \eta) = \langle \xi, W\eta \rangle \quad \text{when} \quad \xi \in R_2, \quad \eta \in R_1.$$

On the other hand, $(L_4\,\xi, \eta) = (\xi, L_4\eta)$; taking ξ, $\eta \in R_1$ and remembering that this implies $L_4\,\xi$, $L_4\,\eta \in R_2$, we obtain $\langle L_4\,\xi, W\eta \rangle = \langle \xi, W^*L_4\,\eta \rangle$, i.e. $\langle W^*\,L_4\,\xi, \eta \rangle = \langle \xi, W^*L_4\,\eta \rangle$. This means that W^*L_4 is a Hermitian operator in R_1, and so one can choose a basis ξ_τ for R_1 consisting of eigenvectors of the operator W^*L_4 in R_1; letting

$$\xi^{\frac{1}{2}}_{\frac{1}{2}\tau} = \xi_\tau, \quad \xi^{\frac{1}{2}}_{\frac{1}{2}\tau^*} = W\xi_\tau, \quad \tau \in T_1,$$

we obtain bases in R_1 and R_2, for which as before

$$\alpha_{\tau\tau'} = \begin{cases} 0 & \text{when} \quad \tau' \neq \tau^* \\ \pm 1 & \text{when} \quad \tau' = \tau^* \end{cases} \tag{3}$$

and

$$L_4\xi^{\frac{1}{2}}_{\frac{1}{2}\tau} = WW^*L_4\xi_\tau = \lambda_\tau W\xi_\tau = \lambda_\tau\xi^{\frac{1}{2}}_{\frac{1}{2}\tau^*},$$

where λ_τ is the eigenvalue of the operator W^*L_4, corresponding to its eigenvector ξ_τ. From this and from (10c) Subsection 2 we deduce that

$$l^{\frac{1}{2}}_{\tau\tau'} = l^{\frac{1}{2}}_{\tau'\tau} = 0 \quad \text{when} \quad \tau' \neq \tau^*. \tag{4}$$

But relations (3) and (4) mean that the equation decomposes, if the sets T_1 and T_2 contain more than one element; hence, by virtue of the indecomposability of the equation, the representation $g \to T_g$ coincides with $\hat{D}_{\frac{1}{2},\frac{3}{2}}$. Moreover, $l^{\frac{1}{2}}_{\tau^*\tau} = l^{\frac{1}{2}}_{\tau\tau^*} = (L_4\xi^{\frac{1}{2}}_{\frac{1}{2}\tau}, \xi^{\frac{1}{2}}_{\frac{1}{2}\tau^*})$ $= \langle L_4\xi^{\frac{1}{2}}_{\frac{1}{2}\tau}, W\xi^{\frac{1}{2}}_{\frac{1}{2}\tau}\rangle = \lambda_\tau \langle \xi^{\frac{1}{2}}_{\frac{1}{2}\tau^*}, \xi^{\frac{1}{2}}_{\frac{1}{2}\tau^*}\rangle = \lambda_\tau$, i.e. λ_τ is a real number.

Thus, the space R of the representation is four-dimensional, the spin k takes only one value ($\frac{1}{2}$), and the operator $\Lambda_{\frac{1}{2}}$ is given by a matrix of the form $\begin{Vmatrix} 0 & \lambda \\ \lambda & 0 \end{Vmatrix}$, where λ is some real number.

Dividing the whole equation by λ, we can assume that $\lambda = 1$ and, hence, that $\Lambda_{\frac{1}{2}}$ is given by the matrix $\begin{Vmatrix} 0 & 1 \\ 1 & 0 \end{Vmatrix}$.

Therefore the operator L_4 will be given in the basis $\xi^{\frac{1}{2}}_{-\frac{1}{2},\tau}$, $\xi^{\frac{1}{2}}_{-\frac{1}{2},\tau^*}$, $\xi^{\frac{1}{2}}_{\frac{1}{2}\tau}$, $\xi^{\frac{1}{2}}_{\frac{1}{2}\tau^*}$ by a matrix of the fourth order:

$$L_4 \sim \begin{Vmatrix} 0 & 1 & 0 & 0 \\ 1 & 0 & 0 & 0 \\ 0 & 0 & 0 & 1 \\ 0 & 0 & 1 & 0 \end{Vmatrix}.$$

For the determination of the matrices of the remaining operators L_k, $k = 1, 2, 3$, we use the formula $L_k = [L_4, B_k]$ (see (1) § 18, Subsection 4) and the formulae:

$$B_1 \sim \begin{Vmatrix} 0 & 0 & -\frac{1}{2} & 0 \\ 0 & 0 & 0 & \frac{1}{2} \\ \frac{1}{2} & 0 & 0 & 0 \\ 0 & -\frac{1}{2} & 0 & 0 \end{Vmatrix}, \quad B_2 \sim \begin{Vmatrix} 0 & 0 & \frac{i}{2} & 0 \\ 0 & 0 & 0 & -\frac{i}{2} \\ -\frac{i}{2} & 0 & 0 & 0 \\ 0 & \frac{i}{2} & 0 & 0 \end{Vmatrix}$$

$$B_3 \sim \begin{Vmatrix} \frac{1}{2} & 0 & 0 & 0 \\ 0 & -\frac{1}{2} & 0 & 0 \\ 0 & 0 & -\frac{1}{2} & 0 \\ 0 & 0 & 0 & \frac{1}{2} \end{Vmatrix}$$

(see (52–55) § 8, Subsection 3 when $k_0 = \frac{1}{2}$, $c = \pm\frac{3}{2}$ and (2), (3) § 8, Subsection 1). We obtain:

$$L_1 \sim \begin{Vmatrix} 0 & 0 & 0 & 1 \\ 0 & 0 & -1 & 0 \\ 0 & -1 & 0 & 0 \\ 1 & 0 & 0 & 0 \end{Vmatrix}, \quad L_2 \sim \begin{Vmatrix} 0 & 0 & 0 & -i \\ 0 & 0 & i & 0 \\ 0 & i & 0 & 0 \\ -i & 0 & 0 & 0 \end{Vmatrix},$$

$$L_3 \sim \begin{Vmatrix} 0 & -1 & 0 & 0 \\ 1 & 0 & 0 & 0 \\ 0 & 0 & 0 & 1 \\ 0 & 0 & -1 & 0 \end{Vmatrix}.$$

The corresponding equation

$$\sum_{\nu=1}^{4} L_\nu \frac{\partial\psi}{\partial x_\nu} + i\kappa\psi = 0$$

is the *Dirac equation.*

Thus:

Of all the finite-dimensional equations with diagonable operator L_4 only the Dirac equation has definite density of charge.

Now we pass to the investigation of finite-dimensional equations with definite density of energy. Let there be given such an equation and let $g \to T_g$ and (ξ, η) be the representation and the invariant form corresponding to this equation, and $a \to T_a^{(\tau)}$ the corresponding completely irreducible representations of the group $\mathfrak{A}$. By virtue of II Subsection 4, positive definiteness of density of energy occurs if and only if

$$(L_4\xi, L_4\xi) \geqslant 0 \quad \text{for all} \quad \xi \in R. \tag{5}$$

Assume that there exists a representation $a \to T_a^{(\tau)}$, for which $k_0 \neq 0$ and $|k_0| \neq 1$. Then it is easy to see that there exists no index τ', for which $l^k_{\tau*\tau'} \neq 0$ and $l^k_{\tau'\tau} \neq 0$. Hence,

$$(L_4\xi^k_{p\tau}, L_4\xi^k_{p\tau}) = (L_4^2\xi^k_{p\tau}, \xi^k_{p\tau}) = \alpha^k_{\tau*\tau}\sum_{\tau'} l^k_{\tau*\tau'}\, l^k_{\tau'\tau} = 0, \tag{6}$$

and, moreover, by (2), (10) Subsection 2 and III Subsection 2 we have

$$(L_4\xi^k_{p\tau}, L_4\xi^k_{p\tau*}) = (L_4^2\xi^k_{p\tau}, \xi^k_{p\tau*})$$

$$= \alpha^k_{\tau\tau*}\sum_{\tau'} l^k_{\tau\tau'}\, l^k_{\tau'\tau} = \pm\alpha^k_{\tau\tau'}\sum_{\tau'} |l^k_{\tau\tau'}|^2 \neq 0. \tag{7}$$

Therefore if $\xi = \mu_1\xi^k_{p\tau} + \mu_2\xi^k_{p\tau*}$ the expression

$$(L_4\xi, L_4\xi) = \mu_1\bar{\mu}_2(L_4\xi^k_{p\tau}, L_4\xi^k_{p\tau*}) + \bar{\mu}_1\mu_2(L_4\xi^k_{p\tau*}, L_4\xi^k_{p\tau})$$
$$+ |\mu_2|^2(L_4\xi^k_{p\tau*}, L_4\xi^k_{p\tau*})$$

cannot be non-negative for all μ_1, μ_2.

Thus, the representations $g \to T_g^{(\tau)}$ can correspond only to the pairs $(0, c)$, $(\pm 1, c)$, where for the pairs $(\pm 1, c)$ there must necessarily exist a scheme of linkages of the form $(-1, c) \rightleftarrows (0, c) \rightleftarrows (1, c)$.

If here $|c| > 2$, then, by virtue of formulae (5) § 19, Subsection 2 and (10), Subsection 2, the expressions

$$(L_4\xi^k_{p\tau}, L_4\xi^k_{p\tau*}) = \alpha^k_{\tau\tau*}\sum_{\tau'} l^k_{\tau\tau'} l^k_{\tau'\tau},$$

$$(L_4\xi^{k-1}_{p\tau}, L_4\xi^{k-1}_{p\tau*}) = \alpha^{k-1}_{\tau\tau*}\sum_{\tau'} l^{k-1}_{\tau\tau'} l^{k-1}_{\tau'\tau}$$

have opposite signs, and so $(L_4\,\xi, L_4\,\xi)$ cannot be non-negative for all $\xi \in R$.

Similarly if there exists a linkage of the form $(0, c) \rightleftarrows (0, c+1)$, where $c > 1$, then $(L_4\,\xi^k_{p\tau}, L_4\xi^k_{p\tau})$ and $(L_4\xi^{k-1}_{p\tau}, L_4\xi^{k-1}_{p\tau})$ will have opposite signs; hence, such a linkage is impossible, and for the equation considered only linkages of the type $(1, 2) \rightleftarrows (0, 2) \rightleftarrows (-1, 2)$ and $(0, 1) \rightleftarrows (0, 2)$ are possible. Hence we deduce that only representations corresponding to the pairs (1, 2) (−1, 2), (0, 2) and (0, 1) can be contained among the representations $a \to T^{(\tau)}_a$. But the representations corresponding to the pairs $\beta_0 = (0, 1)$, $\beta_1 = (0, 2)$, $\beta_2 = (1, 2)$ and $\beta_2^* = (-1, 2)$ cannot simultaneously occur among our representations $a \to T^{(\tau)}_a$, since if they did, $(L_4\,\xi^0_{0\tau_1}, L_4\,\xi^0_{0\tau_1})$ and $(L_4\,\overset{1}{\xi}_{p\tau_2}, L_4\,\overset{2}{\xi}_{p\tau_2})$ would have opposite signs. Moreover, each of these representations can occur among the representations $a \to T^{(\tau)}_a$ at most once, because otherwise the equation would be decomposable. Therefore for the equations considered only the following two schemes of linkages are possible:

(1) $(0, 1) \rightleftarrows (0, 2)$ and (2) $(1, 2) \rightleftarrows (0, 2) \rightleftarrows (-1, 2)$.

For these schemes the energy is positive definite for the following choice of the matrices of the operator (apart from transformations of the coordinates this is the only such choice):

(1) $$\left\| l^0_{\tau\tau'} \right\| = \left\| \begin{matrix} 0 & 1 \\ 1 & 0 \end{matrix} \right\|, \quad \left\| l^1_{\tau\tau'} \right\| = \left\| 0 \right\|,$$

(2) $$\left\| l^0_{\tau\tau'} \right\| = \left\| 0 \right\|, \quad \left\| l^1_{\tau\tau'} \right\| = \left\| \begin{matrix} 0 & 1 & 1 \\ 1 & 0 & 0 \\ 1 & 0 & 0 \end{matrix} \right\|.$$

In the first case the given equation is the Duffin equation [19] for a particle with spin 0, and in the second case it is the Duffin equation [19] for a particle with spin† 1. Hence, *of all finite-dimensional equations with operator* L_4 *reducible to diagonal form only the Duffin equation for a particle with spin* 0 *or* 1 *has positive definite energy.*

6. Examples of invariant equations

(*A*) *The equation for a particle with spin* $\frac{3}{2}$. Besides the equations considered in Subsection 5 other finite-dimensional invariant equations with definite density of charge or energy are possible; by virtue of the results of Subsection 5, the operator L_4 for such equations is not reducible to diagonal form.

We will consider as an example the case when the given representation $g \to T_g$ of the group $\mathfrak{G}_0$ is the direct sum of the two representations: $\hat{D}_{\frac{1}{2},\frac{3}{2}}$, $\hat{D}_{\frac{1}{2},\frac{5}{2}}$, and so contains four completely irreducible representations, corresponding to the pairs: $(\frac{1}{2}, \frac{3}{2})$, $(-\frac{1}{2}, \frac{3}{2})$, $(\frac{1}{2}, \frac{5}{2})$, $(-\frac{1}{2}, \frac{5}{2})$ which we number by the indices 1, $\dot{1}$, 3, $\dot{3}$ respectively. By virtue of Theorem 4 § 18, Subsection 4, the corresponding "scheme of linkages" must have the form

$$\begin{array}{ccc} \left(\frac{1}{2}, \frac{1}{2}\right) & \rightleftarrows & \left(\frac{1}{2}, \frac{5}{2}\right) \\ \downarrow\uparrow & & \downarrow\uparrow \\ \left(-\frac{1}{2}, \frac{3}{2}\right) & \rightleftarrows & \left(-\frac{1}{2}, \frac{5}{2}\right). \end{array}$$

Here the spin can take the values $\frac{1}{2}$ and $\frac{3}{2}$, and the operators $\Lambda_{\frac{1}{2}}$, $\Lambda_{\frac{3}{2}}$ are given by the matrices:

$$\Lambda_{\frac{1}{2}} \sim \begin{Vmatrix} 0 & c_{1\dot{1}} & c_{13} & 0 \\ c_{\dot{1}1} & 0 & 0 & c_{\dot{1}\dot{3}} \\ c_{31} & 0 & 0 & c_{3\dot{3}} \\ 0 & c_{\dot{3}\dot{1}} & c_{\dot{3}3} & 0 \end{Vmatrix}, \quad \Lambda_{\frac{3}{2}} \sim \begin{Vmatrix} 0 & 2c_{3\dot{3}} \\ 2c_{\dot{3}3} & 0 \end{Vmatrix}$$

(see formulae (5) § 19, Subsection 2).

† These equations can be rewritten componentwise in the form of systems of equations as follows:

$$(1) \quad \psi_j = \frac{\partial \psi_0}{\partial x_j}, \quad j = 1, 2, 3, 4; \sum_{j=1}^{4} \frac{\partial \psi_j}{\partial x_j} = \mu^2 \psi;$$

$$(2) \quad \psi_{jk} = \frac{\partial \psi_k}{\partial x_j} - \frac{\partial \psi_j}{\partial x_k}; \quad \sum_{\nu=1}^{4} \frac{\partial \psi_{j\nu}}{\partial x_\nu} + \mu^2 \psi_j = 0, \quad j, k = 1, 2, 3, 4$$

(see, for instance, [1], § 52).

For the coefficients of the invariant bilinear form there are only two possibilities:

$$\text{(a)} \quad \alpha_{1\dot{1}} = +1, \quad \alpha_{3\dot{3}} = +1,$$
$$\text{(b)} \quad \alpha_{1\dot{1}} = +1, \quad \alpha_{3\dot{3}} = -1,$$

which do not reduce to one another in the transition to a new basis.

Making use of conditions (9) § 19, Subsection 2 and (7) Subsection 2, we find that the equation corresponding to the given representation can be obtained from a Lagrangian function only in one of the following two cases:

$$\text{(a)}\ c_{1\dot{1}} = \overline{c_{\dot{1}1}} = \overline{c_{1\dot{1}}}, \quad c_{13} = \overline{c_{\dot{3}\dot{1}}},$$
$$c_{\dot{1}\dot{3}} = \overline{c_{31}}, \quad c_{3\dot{3}} = \overline{c_{\dot{3}3}} = \overline{c_{3\dot{3}}},$$
$$\text{(b)}\ c_{1\dot{1}} = \overline{c_{\dot{1}1}} = \overline{c_{1\dot{1}}}, \quad c_{13} = -\overline{c_{\dot{3}\dot{1}}},$$
$$c_{\dot{1}\dot{3}} = -\overline{c_{31}}, \quad c_{3\dot{3}} = \overline{c_{\dot{3}3}} = \overline{c_{3\dot{3}}}.$$

These coefficients can be simplified still further by means of a transition to a new basis:

$$\xi'^k_{p1} = e^{i\theta_1}\xi^k_{p1}, \quad \xi'^k_{p\dot{1}} = e^{i\theta_1}\xi^k_{p\dot{1}},$$
$$\xi'^k_{p3} = e^{i\theta_3}\xi^k_{p3}, \quad \xi'^k_{p\dot{3}} = e^{i\theta_3}\xi^k_{p\dot{3}}.$$

Here the elements $c_{1\dot{1}}$ and $c_{3\dot{3}}$ are not altered, and $c_{1\dot{3}}$ goes into $c'_{1\dot{3}} = c_{1\dot{3}}\, e^{i(\theta_1-\theta_3)}$. Choosing $\theta_1-\theta_3$ properly, we can arrange that the coefficients $c_{1\dot{3}}$ become real and non-negative. Then dividing the whole equation by $2c_{3\dot{3}}$ (which is equivalent to a change of the constant κ), we obtain the following matrices for the operators $\Lambda_{\frac{1}{2}}, \Lambda_{\frac{3}{2}}$:

$$\text{(a)}\ \Lambda_{\frac{1}{2}} \sim \begin{Vmatrix} 0 & \alpha & \beta & 0 \\ \alpha & 0 & 0 & \beta \\ \beta & 0 & 0 & \frac{1}{2} \\ 0 & \beta & \frac{1}{2} & 0 \end{Vmatrix}, \qquad \Lambda_{\frac{3}{2}} \sim \begin{Vmatrix} 0 & 1 \\ 1 & 0 \end{Vmatrix},$$

$$\text{(b)}\ \Lambda_{\frac{1}{2}} \sim \begin{Vmatrix} 0 & \alpha & \beta & 0 \\ \alpha & 0 & 0 & \beta \\ -\beta & 0 & 0 & \frac{1}{2} \\ 0 & -\beta & \frac{1}{2} & 0 \end{Vmatrix}, \qquad \Lambda_{\frac{3}{2}} \sim \begin{Vmatrix} 0 & 1 \\ 1 & 0 \end{Vmatrix},$$

where α is real, and β is a real non-negative number.

Hence it is seen that the eigenvalues of the operator L_4, corresponding to spin $\frac{3}{2}$ are equal to ± 1. The eigenvalues corresponding to spin $\frac{1}{2}$, will be determined in cases (a) and (b) from the characteristic equations:

$$\text{(a)} \quad \lambda^4 - \left(\alpha^2 + \frac{1}{4} + 2\beta^2\right)\lambda^2 + \left(\frac{\alpha}{2} - \beta^2\right)^2 = 0,$$

$$\text{(b)} \quad \lambda^4 - \left(\alpha^2 + \frac{1}{4} - 2\beta^2\right)\lambda^2 + \left(\frac{\alpha}{2} + \beta^2\right)^2 = 0.$$

Clearly, in case (a) the roots $\pm\lambda_1$, $\pm\lambda_2$ of this equation are real, and in case (b) they are real only when

$$\alpha^2 + \tfrac{1}{4} \geqslant 2\beta^2, \qquad |\alpha - \tfrac{1}{2}| \geqslant 2\beta.$$

The equations thus obtained describe a particle, which can be in a state with spin $\frac{3}{2}$ and mass $m_{\frac{3}{2}} = \kappa\hbar/c$ and in two states with spin $\frac{1}{2}$ and mass respectively equal to

$$m_{\frac{1}{2},1} = \frac{\kappa\hbar}{c\lambda_1}, \quad m_{\frac{1}{2},2} = \frac{\kappa\hbar}{c\lambda_2}.$$

Since the given equation is a finite-dimensional equation for a particle with semi-integral spin, then, according to Pauli's theorem (see Subsection 4), the density of energy corresponding to this equation cannot be definite. Moreover, in case (a) the matrix of the operator L_4 is real and symmetric and, consequently, can be reduced to diagonal form. On the basis of the results of Subsection 5 we deduce from this that no one of the equations of type (a) can also have definite density of charge. However, in case (b) density of charge cannot be definite if the corresponding characteristic equation has simple roots. Thus, it remains to consider only those equations of type (b), for which the corresponding characteristic equation has multiple roots, i.e. to consider the following cases:

(1b) $\alpha = -\frac{1}{2}$, $\lambda_{1,2} = \sqrt{(\frac{1}{4} - \beta^2)}$, $\lambda_{3,4} = -\sqrt{(\frac{1}{4} - \beta^2)}$,

(2b) $\alpha = \frac{1}{2} \pm 2\beta$, $\lambda_{1,2} = \frac{1}{2} \pm \beta$, $\lambda_{3,4} = -(\frac{1}{2} \pm \beta)$,

(3b) $\alpha = -2\beta^2$, $\lambda_{1,2} = 0$, $\lambda_3 = \frac{1}{2} - 2\beta^2$, $\lambda_4 = -\frac{1}{2} + 2\beta^2$.

However, it is easy to see that in cases (1b) and (3b) when $\beta \neq \frac{1}{2}$ the matrix of the operator L_4 can be reduced to diagonal form. Hence, in these cases the density of charge will not be definite. However, in case (2b) the matrix of the operator L_4 is not reducible to diagonal form. When $\beta \neq \frac{1}{2}$ this equation will describe a particle which can be in states with spin $\frac{1}{2}$ and with spin $\frac{3}{2}$, where in the state with spin $\frac{1}{2}$, $(\psi, \psi) = (L_4\psi, \psi) = 0$, i.e. both charge and energy are equal to zero. If, consequently, one rejects equations having such "null" states, then it is necessary in case (2b) to set $\beta = \frac{1}{2}$, and we obtain a unique equation with definite charge, defined by the formulae:

$$\Lambda_{\frac{1}{2}} \sim \begin{Vmatrix} 0 & -\frac{1}{2} & \frac{1}{2} & 0 \\ -\frac{1}{2} & 0 & 0 & \frac{1}{2} \\ -\frac{1}{2} & 0 & 0 & \frac{1}{2} \\ 0 & -\frac{1}{2} & \frac{1}{2} & 0 \end{Vmatrix}, \quad \Lambda_{\frac{3}{2}} \sim \begin{Vmatrix} 0 & 1 \\ 0 & 1 \end{Vmatrix}.$$

All the eigenvalues of the operator L_4, corresponding to $k = \frac{1}{2}$, are equal to zero, and the corresponding equation is the Pauli–Fierz equation [37] for a particle with spin $\frac{3}{2}$.

(*B*) *Examples of infinite-dimensional equations.* First we describe the sort of infinite-dimensional equations which can correspond to one completely irreducible infinite-dimensional representation $a \to T_a$ of the group $\mathfrak{A}$. Because this representation must also be a representation of the complete Lorentz group, then the representation $a \to T_a$ must be defined by one of the pairs $(k_0, 0)$ or $(0, c)$; moreover, this representation must be linked with itself, which is possible only when† $k_0 = \frac{1}{2}$, respectively $c = \frac{1}{2}$.

Thus it is necessary to consider only the representations corresponding to the pairs $(\frac{1}{2}, 0)$ and $(0, \frac{1}{2})$; the corresponding representations of the complete Lorentz group will be

$$\hat{D}^{+}_{\frac{1}{2},0}, \quad \hat{D}^{-}_{\frac{1}{2},0} \quad \text{and} \quad \hat{D}^{+}_{0,\frac{1}{2}}, \quad \hat{D}^{-}_{0,\frac{1}{2}}.$$

† We recall that the pairs $(\frac{1}{2}, 0), (-\frac{1}{2}, 0)$ define one and the same representation, so that in the case of the pair $(\frac{1}{2}, 0)$ such a limkage is possible; an analogous situation exists for the pair $(0, \frac{1}{2})$.

In this case all the operators Λ_k are one-dimensional and, by virtue of formulae (5) § 19, Subsection 2, the operator Λ_k is an operator of multiplication by the number $k+\frac{1}{2}$.

Hence, the corresponding invariant equation has the form

$$\frac{1}{2}\frac{\partial}{\partial x_1}\{\sqrt{[(k+p+1)(k-p+1)]}\psi_k^{p+1}+\sqrt{[(k+p)(k-p)]}\psi_k^{p-1}\}$$
$$+\frac{1}{4}\left(\frac{\partial}{\partial x_2}+i\frac{\partial}{\partial x_3}\right)\{\sqrt{[(k+p+1)(k+p+2)]}\psi_{p+1}^{k+1}$$
$$-\sqrt{[(k-p-1)(k-p)]}\psi_{p+1}^{k-1}\}-\frac{1}{4}\left(\frac{\partial}{\partial x_2}-i\frac{\partial}{\partial x_3}\right)\times$$
$$\times\{\sqrt{[(k-p+1)(k-p+2)]}\psi_{p-1}^{k+1}-\sqrt{[(k+p-1)(k+p)]}\psi_{p-1}^{k+1}\}$$
$$+\frac{\partial}{\partial x_4}\left(k+\frac{1}{2}\right)\psi_p^k+i\kappa\psi_p^k=0$$

(see formulae (1) and (16) §18, Subsection 4); here $k=\frac{1}{2},\frac{3}{2},\frac{5}{2},\ldots$, in the case of a representation corresponding to the pair $(\frac{1}{2}, 0)$, and $k = 0, 1, 2, 3, \ldots$ in the case of a representation corresponding to the pair $(0, \frac{1}{2})$.

In so far as these representations are unitary, then one can take the scalar product as the invariant form (ξ, η).

Because all the eigenvalues of the operator L_4 are positive, and the scalar product is a positive definite bilinear form, $(L_4\,\xi, \xi)\geqslant 0$ and $(L_4\,\xi, L_4\,\xi)\geqslant 0$ for all vectors ξ from the domain of definition of the operator L_4.

Thus, for both invariant equations, corresponding to the representations $D^{\pm}_{\frac{1}{2},0}$, $D^{\pm}_{0,\frac{1}{2}}$, *both the density of charge and the density of energy are definite*. According to Pauli's theorem (Subsection 4), this is impossible for finite-dimensional representations.

As a second example we consider the invariant equation corresponding to the representation $D_{\frac{1}{2},\rho}$, where ρ is a real number. Because the representation $D_{\frac{1}{2},\rho}$ is unitary, one can again take the scalar product as the invariant bilinear form. The scheme of linkages here has the form $(\frac{1}{2}, c) \rightleftarrows (-\frac{1}{2}, c)$; hence, with a proper choice of basis the operators Λ_k are given by the matrices

$$\Lambda_k \sim \begin{Vmatrix} 0 & k+\frac{1}{2} \\ k+\frac{1}{2} & 0 \end{Vmatrix}.$$

Hence it is seen that the eigenvalues of the operator L_4 will be $\pm (k+\frac{1}{2})$, that the density of charge will not be definite, and the density of energy will be definite.

The results of §§ 17–20 belong basically to I. M. GELFAND, Z. Ya. SHAPIRO and A. M. YAGLOM [13 and 14]; finite-dimensional invariant equations, and also some special cases of infinite dimensional equations were considered previously in the works of BHABHA [3], GINSBURG and TAMM [15], IZMAILOV [21], POTIER [33], WILD [36], FIERZ and PAULI [37] and HARISH-CHANDRA [38b] (see also DUFFIN [19] and Le COUTEUR [25]). It has fallen to the author to bring into the exposition of §§ 17–20 a series of additions necessary for the formulation of these results in the infinite dimensional case.

APPENDIX

I

IF $w_p = u_p + iv_p$, $p = 1, 2, \ldots, n$ are analytic functions of the variables $z_p = x_p + iy_p$, then

$$\frac{D(u_1, v_1, u_2, v_2, \ldots, u_n, v_n)}{D(x_1, y_1, x_2, y_2, \ldots, x_n, y_n)} = \left|\frac{D(w_1, w_2, \ldots, w_n)}{D(z_1, z_2, \ldots, z_n)}\right|^2. \tag{1}$$

In fact, using the Cauchy–Riemann equations we have

$$\frac{D(u, v)}{D(x, y)} = \begin{vmatrix} \dfrac{\partial u}{\partial x} & \dfrac{\partial u}{\partial y} \\ \dfrac{\partial v}{\partial x} & \dfrac{\partial v}{\partial y} \end{vmatrix} = \left(\frac{\partial u}{\partial x}\right)^2 + \left(\frac{\partial u}{\partial y}\right)^2 = \left|\frac{dw}{dz}\right|^2, \tag{2}$$

so that the formula is valid for $m = 1$. Let it be valid for $n = m-1$; then its validity for $n = m$ follows from the formula

$$\frac{D(u_1, v_1, u_2, v_2, \ldots, u_m, v_m)}{D(x_1, y_1, x_2, y_2, \ldots, x_m, y_m)}$$

$$= \frac{D(u_1, v_1, u_2, v_2, \ldots, u_m, v_m)\, D(x_1, y_1, u_2, v_2, \ldots, u_m, v_m)}{D(x_1, y_1, u_2, v_2, \ldots, u_m, v_m)\, D(x_1, y_1, x_2, y_2, \ldots, x_m, y_m)}$$

$$= \frac{D(u_1, v_1)\, D(u_2, v_2, \ldots, u_m, v_m)}{D(x_1, y_1)\, D(x_2, y_2, \ldots, x_m, y_m)} = \left|\frac{D(w_1)}{D(z_1)}\right|^2 \left|\frac{D(w_2, \ldots, w_m)}{D(z_2, \ldots, z_m)}\right|^2$$

$$= \left|\frac{D(w_1, w_2, \ldots, w_m)}{D(z_1, z_2, \ldots, z_m)}\right|^2,$$

hence, formula (1) is valid for any n.

II

Every bounded operator A in L^2 (W), which commutes with all the operators of multiplication by an essentially bounded measurable function, is also an operator of multiplication by an essentially bounded measurable function.

Proof. Let $f_0(w)$ be an arbitrary positive function from $L^2(W)$. We set $Af_0(w) = \phi_0(w)$ and

$$\omega_0(w) = \frac{\phi_0(w)}{f_0(w)}. \tag{1}$$

Then for any essentially bounded measurable function $\phi(w) \in L^2(W)$, for which $\dfrac{\phi(w)}{f_0(w)}$ is also essentially bounded, we have

$$A\phi(w) = A\frac{\phi(w)}{f_0(w)}f_0(w) = \frac{\phi(w)}{f_0(w)}Af_0(w)$$
$$= \frac{\phi(w)}{f_0(w)}\phi_0(w) = \omega_0(w)\phi(w),$$

i.e. for all such functions $\phi(w)$:

$$A\phi(w) = \omega_0(w)\phi(w). \tag{2}$$

Since the functions $\phi(w)$ form a dense set in $L^2(W)$ and the operator A is bounded, then equation (2) holds for all functions $\phi(w)$ from $L^2(W)$.

III

Burnside's Theorem. *Every irreducible ring of operators in a finite-dimensional space R is the set of all linear operators in R.*

Proof. Let $\mathfrak{B}$ be an irreducible ring of operators in R. We will consider $\mathfrak{B}$ as a linear space and for any $B \in \mathfrak{B}$ we define an operator $\hat{B}$ in $\mathfrak{B}$ letting

$$\hat{B}X = BX \quad \text{for} \quad X \in \mathfrak{B}, \tag{1}$$

so that $\hat{B}$ is the operator of multiplication† by B. Clearly, the operators $\hat{B}$ form a ring which we denote by $\hat{\mathfrak{B}}$; this ring is, generally speaking, reducible in $\mathfrak{B}$.

Let $\mathfrak{M}_1$ be one of the minimal subspaces in $\mathfrak{B}$ distinct from (0), invariant with respect to all the operators of the ring $\hat{\mathfrak{B}}$, so that $\hat{\mathfrak{B}}$ is irreducible in $\mathfrak{M}_1$. Let X_0 be an operator from $\mathfrak{M}_1$ distinct from zero, and e a vector from R such that $X_0 e \neq 0$.

We denote by $\mathfrak{N}$ the set of all vectors of the form Xe, $X \in \mathfrak{M}_1$; then $\mathfrak{N}$ is a subspace in R, invariant with respect to all $B \in \mathfrak{B}$, because also $BX \in \mathfrak{M}_1$, and so $BXe \in \mathfrak{N}$. By virtue of the irreducibility of the ring $\mathfrak{B}$, we deduce from this that either $\mathfrak{N} = (0)$, or $\mathfrak{N} = R$. But the first case is impossible, because $X_0 e \neq 0$, therefore $\mathfrak{N} = R$, i.e. every vector $x \in R$ is represented in the form $x = Xe$ for some $X \in \mathfrak{M}_1$. The correspondence $x \to X$ between $x \in R$ and $X \in \mathfrak{M}_1$, thus established, is one-one. In fact, the set of all $X \in \mathfrak{M}_1$, for which $Xe = 0$, forms a subspace $\mathfrak{M}_0$ in $\mathfrak{M}_1$, invariant with respect to all $\hat{B} \in \hat{\mathfrak{B}}$ and distinct from $\mathfrak{M}_1$ (because $X_0 e \neq 0$); in view of the irreducibility of $\hat{\mathfrak{B}}$ in $\mathfrak{M}_1$ we deduce from this that $\mathfrak{M}_0 = (0)$, i.e. from $Xe = 0$, $X \in \mathfrak{M}_1$ it follows that

$$X = 0. \tag{2}$$

In particular, in $\mathfrak{M}_1$ there is exactly one operator $P_1 \in \mathfrak{M}_1$ such that $P_1 e = e$. By virtue of (2), it follows from the relation $(XP_1 - X)e = 0$ that

$$XP_1 = X \quad \text{for all} \quad X \in \mathfrak{M}_1; \tag{3}$$

in particular, $P_1^2 = P_1$. Hence we deduce that every operator $X \in \mathfrak{B}$ can be represented uniquely in the form

$$X = X_1 + Y, \tag{4}$$

where $X_1 \in \mathfrak{M}_1$, $YP_1 = 0$. In fact, if (4) holds, then, multiplying both of its sides on the right by P_1, we obtain:

$$XP_1 = X_1; \quad Y = X(1-P_1),$$

† This transition from B to $\hat{B}$ is called the *left regular representation* of the ring $\mathfrak{B}$.

hence, the decomposition (4) is unique. Conversely, the equation $X = XP_1 + X(\mathbf{1} - P_1)$ is a decomposition of the form (4).

Let $\mathfrak{B}_1$ be the set of all operators $Y = X(\mathbf{1} - P_1)$, $X \in \mathfrak{B}$; clearly, $\mathfrak{B}_1$ is a subspace of $\mathfrak{B}$, invariant with respect to all the operators $\hat{B} \in \hat{\mathfrak{B}}$. Choosing in it a minimal invariant subspace $\mathfrak{M}_2$ and repeating the preceding argument, we obtain an operator $P'_2 \in \mathfrak{M}_2$ such that $XP'_2 = X$ for all $X \in \mathfrak{M}_2$; in particular, $P'^2_2 = P'_2$. Hence we again deduce that every operator $Y \in \mathfrak{B}_1$ is represented in a unique way in the form $Y = X_2 + Z$, where $X_2 \in \mathfrak{M}_2$, $ZP'_2 = 0$; indeed, $X_2 = YP'_2$, $Z = Y(\mathbf{1} - P'_2)$. Substituting these expressions in (4), we obtain:

$$X = X_1 + X_2 + Z = XP_1 + X(\mathbf{1} - P_1)P'_2 + Z. \tag{5}$$

We set

$$P_2 = (\mathbf{1} - P_1)P'_2 = P'_2 - P_1 P'_2; \tag{6}$$

since $P'_2 \in \mathfrak{M}_2$, then $P'_2 P_1 = 0$; hence

$$P_2^2 = (\mathbf{1} - P_1)P'_2(\mathbf{1} - P_1)P'_2 = (\mathbf{1} - P_1)(P'_2 - P'_2 P_1)P'_2$$
$$= (\mathbf{1} - P_1)P'^2_2 = (\mathbf{1} - P_1)P'_2 = P_2,$$

and

$$P_1 P_2 = P_1(\mathbf{1} - P_1)P'_2 = 0, \quad P_2 P_1 = (\mathbf{1} - P_1)P'_2 P_1 = 0.$$

Here formula (5) becomes

$$X = XP_1 + XP_2 + Z,$$

where $Z = X(1 - P_1 - P_2)$, so that $ZP_1 = ZP_2 = 0$.

The set of all operators $Z = X(1 - P_1 - P_2)$, $X \in \mathfrak{B}$, again forms an invariant subspace, and if it is not equal to zero, one can again single out a minimal invariant subspace $\mathfrak{M}_3$. Because the whole space $\mathfrak{B}$ is finite-dimensional, then after a finite number of steps we obtain a decomposition of the form

$$X = XP_1 + XP_2 + \dots + XP_m, \tag{7}$$

valid for all $X \in \mathfrak{B}$, where

$$P_j P_k = \begin{cases} 0 & \text{when} \quad j \neq k, \\ P_k & \text{when} \quad j = k. \end{cases} \tag{8}$$

We set $P = P_1 + \dots + P_m$.

From (7) we deduce that $XP = X$ for all $X \in \mathfrak{B}$; in particular, $P^2 = P$. The set of all vectors $x \in R$, for which $Px = 0$, is a subspace in R, invariant with respect to all the operators $B \in \mathfrak{B}$; hence, it is either equal to the whole of R, or $= (0)$. But the first case would mean $Xx = XPx = 0$ for all $x \in R$, $X \in \mathfrak{B}$, i.e. that $\mathfrak{B} = (0)$. Excluding this trivial case, we arrive at the conclusion that $Px = 0$ only when $x = 0$. Because $P(\mathbf{1} - P)x = 0$ for all $x \in R$, then this is possible only when $P = \mathbf{1}$, i.e.

$$P_1 + \dots P_m = 1. \tag{9}$$

Now we consider the operators of the form P_jXP_j, $X \in \mathfrak{B}$; they clearly form a ring. The subspace $\tilde{\mathfrak{M}}_j$ of all vectors P_jx is invariant with respect to these operators; we will consider the operators P_jXP_j as operators in $\tilde{\mathfrak{M}}_j$. They form a ring of linear operators in $\tilde{\mathfrak{M}}_j$, where P_j is the identity operator in $\tilde{\mathfrak{M}}_j$. We will prove that all the operators P_jXP_j have the form λP_j, where λ is a number. For this we note that for fixed $P_jXP_j \neq 0$ the set of all operators YP_jXP_j, $Y \in \mathfrak{B}$, is a subspace $\mathfrak{M}_j'$ in $\mathfrak{M}_j = \mathfrak{B}P_j$, invariant with respect to all the operators $\hat{B} \in \hat{\mathfrak{B}}$ and $\neq (0)$, because $YP_jXP_j = P_jXP_j \neq 0$ when $Y = P_j$; in view of the fact that $\mathfrak{M}_j$ is minimal, we deduce from this that $\mathfrak{M}_j' = \mathfrak{M}_j$. In particular, there exists a $Y \in \mathfrak{B}$ such that $YP_jXP_j = P_j$, and so $(P_jYP_j)(P_jXP_j) = P_j$. This means that the operator P_jYP_j is inverse to P_jXP_j in the space $\tilde{\mathfrak{M}}_j$. Hence, every operator P_jXP_j distinct from zero has an inverse in $\tilde{\mathfrak{M}}_j$. We choose a number λ so that the determinant of the matrix of the operator $P_j(X - \lambda P_j)P_j$ in the space $\tilde{\mathfrak{M}}_j$ should be zero; then $P_j(X - \lambda P_j)P_j$ does not have an inverse in $\tilde{\mathfrak{M}}_j$; by the preceding remark this is possible only when $P_j(X - \lambda P_j)P_j = 0$.

Now let e_j be vectors in R, distinct from zero, and such that $P_je_j = e_j$. For fixed e_j the set of all vectors Xe_j, $X \in \mathfrak{B}$, is the whole space R (see page 424), therefore there exist operators $X_j \in \mathfrak{B}$ such that $X_je_j = e_1$. Similarly there exists operators $Y_j \in \mathfrak{B}$ such that $Y_je_1 = e_j$. We set

$$P_{1j} = P_1X_jP_j, \quad P_{j1} = P_jY_jP_1,$$

$$P_{jk} = P_{j1} P_{1k} \quad \text{when} \quad j, k \neq 1. \tag{10}$$

It is then easy to see that

$$P_{1j} e_j = e_1, \quad P_{j1} e_1 = e_j, \quad P_{jk} e_k = e_j. \tag{11}$$

Hence we deduce that $P_{jk} \neq 0$.

Moreover,

$$P_{jk} e_l = 0 \quad \text{when} \quad k \neq l, \tag{12}$$

because $P_{jk} e_l = P_{jk} P_k P_l e_l = 0$. We will prove that

$$P_{jk} P_{kj} = P_j. \tag{13}$$

For this we note that $P_{jk}P_{kj}$ is an operator of the form $P_j X P_j$, hence, $P_{jk}P_{kj} = \lambda P_j$ for some λ. Hence $P_{jk}P_{kj}e_j = \lambda P_j e_j$, i.e. $e_j = \lambda e_j$, so that $\lambda = 1$.

We consider the operators of the form $P_j X P_k P_{kj}$; they are also operators of the form $P_j Y P_j$, and so $P_j X P_k \cdot P_{kj} = \lambda_{kj} P_j$ for some λ_{kj}. Hence, by virtue of (13):

$$P_j X P_k = P_j X P_k P_{kj} P_{jk} = \lambda_{kj} P_j P_{jk} = \lambda_{kj} P_{jk};$$

consequently, by (9),

$$X = \sum_{j,k=1}^{m} P_j X P_k = \sum_{j,k=1}^{m} \lambda_{kj} P_{jk}, \quad \text{for all} \quad X \in \mathfrak{B}. \tag{14}$$

Now we consider the vectors $e_1, e_2, \ldots, e_m$. They are linearly independent; in fact, if

$$\alpha_1 e_1 + \alpha_2 e_2 + \ldots + \alpha_m e_m = 0,$$

then, applying the operator P_j, we obtain that $\alpha_j e_j = 0$, $\alpha_j = 0$. From formulae (11), (12) and (14) it follows that the subspace spanned by the vectors $e_1, \ldots, e_m$, is invariant with respect to all the operators $B \in \mathfrak{B}$ and so coincides with R; hence, $e_1, e_2, \ldots, e_m$ is a basis of R.

Now let A be an arbitrary linear operator in R and $\|a_{jk}\|_{j,k=1,\ldots,m}$ be the matrix of the operator A in the basis $e_1, e_2, \ldots, e_m$, so that $Ae_j = \sum_{k=1}^{m} a_{kj} e_k$.

We set

$$B = \sum_{j,k=1}^{m} a_{kj} P_{kj};$$

then $B \in \mathfrak{B}$ and, by virtue of (11) and (12):

$$Be_j = \sum_{k=1}^{m} a_{kj} e_k = Ae_j;$$

therefore $A = B \in \mathfrak{B}$, and $\mathfrak{B}$ consists of all linear operators in R.

IV

Representations of the complete ring of operators. The ring of all linear operators in a fixed finite-dimensional space R will be called *the complete ring of operators.*

THEOREM. *Every irreducible representation $B \to T_B$ of the complete ring of operators $\mathfrak{B}$, distinct from the null representation $B \to 0$, is equivalent to the identity representation $B \to B$.*

Proof. Let R be the space in which the operators of the ring $\mathfrak{B}$ act, X the space of the representation $B \to T_B$, and $e_1, e_2, \ldots, e_n$ a basis of R. We define a linear operator P_{jk} in R, letting

$$P_{jk}(\lambda_1 e_1 + \ldots + \lambda_n e_n) = \lambda_k e_j, \tag{1}$$

so that

$$P_{jk} e_k = e_j, \quad P_{jk} e_l = 0 \quad \text{when} \quad l \neq k.$$

It is easy to verify that

$$P_{jk} P_{lq} = \begin{cases} 0 & \text{when} \quad k \neq l, \\ P_{jq} & \text{when} \quad k = l \end{cases} \tag{2}$$

and that every linear operator B in R is represented in the form

$$B = \sum_{j,k=1}^{n} b_{jk} P_{jk}, \tag{3}$$

where b_{jk} is the matrix of the operator B in the basis $e_1, e_2, \ldots, e_n$. We set $Q_{jk} = T_{P_{jk}}$; since the correspondence $B \to T_B$ is a representation, then from (2) and (3) we deduce that

$$Q_{jk} Q_{lq} = \begin{cases} 0 & \text{when} \quad k \neq l, \\ Q_{jq} & \text{when} \quad k = l \end{cases} \tag{4}$$

and

$$T_B = \sum_{j,k=1}^{n} b_{jk} Q_{jk}. \tag{5}$$

Because the representation T_B is not zero, then at least one of the operators Q_{jk}, for instance $Q_{\alpha\beta}$, is distinct from zero; hence, there exists a vector e' such that $Q_{\alpha\beta}e' \neq 0$. We set

$$e'_j = Q_{j\beta} e', \quad j = 1, 2, \dots, n, \tag{6}$$

and we denote by $\mathfrak{M}$ the subspace in X spanned by the vectors e'_1, $e'_2, \dots, e'_n$. This subspace is distinct from zero, because $e'_\alpha = Q_{\alpha\beta}e' \neq$ $\neq 0$; moreover, by virtue of (4):

$$Q_{jk} e'_k = Q_{jk} Q_{k\beta} e' = Q_{j\beta} e' = e'_j, \tag{7a}$$

$$Q_{jk} e'_l = Q_{jk} Q_{l\beta} e' = 0 \quad \text{when} \quad l \neq k. \tag{7b}$$

From this and from (5) we deduce that the subspace $\mathfrak{M}$ is invariant with respect to all the operators T_B; in view of the irreducibility of the representation $B \to T_B$ this is possible only when $\mathfrak{M} = X$.

We note that the vectors $e'_1, e'_2, \dots, e'_n$ are linearly independent and, consequently, form a basis in X. In fact, if $\lambda_1 e'_1 + \dots + \lambda_n e'_n = 0$, then, applying to both sides of this equation the operator $Q_{\alpha k}$ and using relations (7), we obtain $\lambda_k e'_\alpha = 0$, hence, $\lambda_k = 0$ for all $k = 1, 2, \dots, n$. Formula (5) and relations (7) show that any operator $B \in \mathfrak{B}$ and the corresponding operator T_B have one and the same matrix relative to the bases $e_1, \dots, e_n$ and $e'_1, \dots, e'_n$ respectively; this means that the linear mapping

$$W(\lambda_1 e_1 + \dots + \lambda_n e_n) = \lambda_1 e'_1 + \dots + \lambda_n e'_n$$

of the space R on X transforms the identity representation $B \to B$ into the representation $B \to T_B$, i.e. that these representations are equivalent.

COROLLARY. *Let $b \to T_b^{(1)}$ and $b \to T_b^{(2)}$ be two finite-dimensional inequivalent irreducible representations of a ring $\mathfrak{B}$ in the spaces R_1 and R_2 respectively. Then for any two operators A_1 in R_1 and A_2 in R_2 there exists an element $b \in \mathfrak{B}$ such that*

$$T_b^{(1)} = A_1 \quad \text{and} \quad T_b^{(2)} = A_2. \tag{8}$$

Proof. It is sufficient to prove that there exist elements b_1, $b_2 \in \mathfrak{B}$ such that

$$T_{b_1}^{(1)} = A_1, \quad T_{b_1}^{(2)} = 0, \quad T_{b_2}^{(1)} = 0, \quad T_{b_2}^{(2)} = A_2.$$

Then the element $b = b_1 + b_2$ will satisfy conditions (8). We will prove the existence of the element b_1; the existence of the element b_2 is proved analogously.

We denote by $\mathfrak{B}^{(1)}$ the set of all operators $T_b^{(1)}$, $b \in \mathfrak{B}$, and by $\mathfrak{B}^{(2)}$ the set of all operators $T_b^{(2)}$, $b \in \mathfrak{B}$. According to Burnside's theorem (see Appendix III), $\mathfrak{B}^{(1)}$ and $\mathfrak{B}^{(2)}$ are complete rings of operators in R_1 and R_2 respectively.

Further denote by I the set of all operators $B = T_b^{(1)}$, $b \in \mathfrak{B}$, for which $T_b^{(2)} = 0$. The set I possesses the following properties:†

(1) if B_1, $B_2 \in I$, then also $\lambda_1 B_1 + \lambda_2 B_2 \in I$;

(2) if $B \in I$ and $C \in \mathfrak{B}^{(1)}$, then $CB \in I$ and $BC \in I$.

In fact, if B_1, B_2, $B \in I$ and $C \in \mathfrak{B}^{(1)}$, then

$$B_1 = T_{b_1}^{(1)}, \quad B_2 = T_{b_2}^{(1)}, \quad B = T_b^{(1)},$$

$$C = T_c^{(1)}, \quad \text{where} \quad b_1, b_2, b, c \in \mathfrak{B}$$

and

$$T_{b_1}^{(2)} = T_{b2}^{(2)} = T_b^{(2)} = 0;$$

therefore also

$$T_{\lambda_1 b_1 + \lambda_2 b_2}^{(2)} = \lambda_1 T_{b_1}^{(2)} + \lambda_2 T_{b_2}^{(2)} = 0,$$

$$T_{cb}^{(2)} = T_c^{(2)} T_b^{(2)} = 0, \quad T_{bc}^{(2)} = T_b^{(2)} T_c^{(2)} = 0.$$

We will prove first that $I \neq (0)$. Assume the contrary i.e. let $I = (0)$. This means that from $T_b^{(2)} = 0$ it follows that

$$T_b^{(1)} = 0. \tag{9}$$

To every operator $T_b^{(1)} \in \mathfrak{B}^{(1)}$ we assign the operator $T_b^{(2)} \in \mathfrak{B}^{(2)}$, corresponding to the same element b. The correspondence obtained $T_b^{(1)} \to T_b^{(2)}$ is single-valued. In fact, if $T_{b_1}^{(1)} = T_{b_2}^{(1)}$, then $T_{b_1 - b_2}^{(1)} = 0$; by (9), it follows from this that $T_{b_1 - b_2}^{(2)} = 0$, i e. $T_{b_1}^{(2)} = T_{b_2}^{(2)}$.

Since, moreover, the correspondences $b \to T_b^{(1)}$, $b \to T_b^{(2)}$ are representations of the ring $\mathfrak{B}$, then the correspondence $T_b^{(1)} \to T_b^{(2)}$

† A set possessing properties (1) and (2) is called a two-sided ideal in the ring $\mathfrak{B}$ (see, for instance, Ref. [7b] § 16).

s a representation of the ring $\mathfrak{B}^{(1)}$. But then on the basis of the preceding theorem this representation is equivalent to the identity representation $T_b^{(1)} \to T_b^{(1)}$, contrary to the condition that the representations $b \to T_b^{(1)}$ and $b \to T_b^{(2)}$ are inequivalent.

Thus, $I \neq (0)$. By virtue of properties (1) and (2), I is a linear subspace in $\mathfrak{B}^{(1)}$, invariant with respect to the operators $\hat{B}$ of left multiplication:

$$\hat{B}X = BX, \quad B \in \mathfrak{B}^{(1)}, \quad X \in \mathfrak{B}^{(1)}$$

(see Appendix III). Hence, reasoning as at the beginning of the proof of Burnside's Theorem (see Appendix III), we deduce that there is in I an operator $P \neq 0$ such that $P^2 = P$.

Let $\xi_0 \neq 0$ be a vector in R_1 such that $P\xi_0 \neq 0$. We choose a basis $e_1, e_2, \dots, e_n$ in R_1 in such a way that $e_1 = P\xi_0 \neq 0$, and, starting from this basis, we define operators P_{jk} in R_1 by means of formula (1). It is easy to see that $P_{1k} = PP_{1k}$; hence, by virtue of property (1) of the set I, $P_{1k} \in I$. But then from the relation $P_{jk} = P_{j1}P_{1k}$ we deduce that all the P_{jk} belong to I and, hence, by virtue of (3), in general all linear operators B in R_1 belong to I. By the definition of the set I, this means that for any linear operator B in R_1 there exists an element $b \in \mathfrak{B}$ such that $T_b^{(1)} = B$, $T_b^{(2)} = 0$, and the corollary is proved.

V

The graph of an operator; the closure of an operator. Let A be an operator from the Banach space R_1 to the Banach space R_2 and let $\mathfrak{D}$ be the domain of definition, and Δ the domain of variation of the operator A.

We denote by $R_1 \dot{+} R_2$ the set of all possible pairs $x = \{x_1, x_2\}$, $x_1 \in R_1$, $x_2 \in R_2$; one can turn this set into a linear, and indeed a normed, space, by defining the operations and a norm in $R_1 \dot{+} R_2$ by means of the formulae:

$$\alpha\{x_1, x_2\} = \{\alpha x_1, \alpha x_2\},$$
$$\{x_1, x_2\} + \{y_1, y_2\} = \{x_1 + y_1, x_2 + y_2\},$$
$$|x| = |\{x_1, x_2\}| = |x_1| + |x_2|.$$

It is easy to verify that this normed space is complete, i.e. it is a Banach space. We will call the space R_1+R_2 *the direct sum* of the spaces R_1, R_2.

Now we consider in R_1+R_2 all possible pairs of the form $\{x, Ax\}$, $x \in \mathfrak{D}$; this set of pairs is called the *graph* of the operator A.

Thus, the graph of an operator is a generalization of the usual graph of a numerical function, which is the set of all points $\{x, f(x)\}$, where x runs through the domain of definition of the function f.

The graph of an operator possesses the property that for the element x of a pair $\{x, y\}$, belonging to the graph, the element y is uniquely defined. Conversely, if the set $S \subset R_1+R_2$ possesses this property, then it can be considered as the graph of some operator A, letting $Ax = y$, if $\{x, y\} \in S$.

It is easy to see that the operator A is linear if and only if its graph is a subspace in R_1+R_2.

The operator A is called *closed* if its graph is a closed set in R_1+R_2.

Clearly, this definition is equivalent to the following: the operator A is closed if from the relations $x_n \in \mathfrak{D}$, $x_n \to x_0$, $Ax_n \to y_0$ it follows that $x_0 \in \mathfrak{D}$ and $Ax_0 = y_0$. It is clear also that every bounded linear operator is closed; the converse assertion is untrue: there exist unbounded closed operators.

Let $\mathfrak{B}_A$ be the graph of the operator A; the operator A is said to *admit closure* if the closure $\overline{\mathfrak{B}}_A$ of the graph $\mathfrak{B}_A$ is also the graph of some operator B. This operator B is then called the *closure* of the operator A and is denoted $\tilde{A}$. Thus according to this definition:

$$\mathfrak{B}_{\tilde{A}} = \overline{\mathfrak{B}}_A.$$

Clearly, the operator A admits closure if and only if the relations

$$x_n', x_n'' \in \mathfrak{D},\ x_n' \to x,\ x_n'' \to x,\ Ax_n' \to y',\ Ax_n'' \to y''$$

imply that $y' = y''$.

In the case of a linear operator A this condition can be replaced by the following condition: from $x_n' \in \mathfrak{D}$, $x_n' \to 0$, $Ax_n' \to y$ it follows that $y = 0$.

VI

The matrix description of an operator. Let there be given in the Banach space R a sequence† of bounded linear operators P_n, $n = 1, 2, 3, \ldots$, possessing the following properties

(1) $P_n^2 = P_n$;

(2) $P_n P_m = 0$ when $n \neq m$;

(3) the set of all finite linear combinations of all vectors of the form $P_n x$, $x \in R$, $n = 1, 2, \ldots$, is dense in R.

We denote by $\mathfrak{M}_n$ the set of all vectors $x \in R$, for which $P_n x = x$; reasoning as in § 6, Subsection 6, we deduce that the $\mathfrak{M}_n$ are linearly independent closed subspaces in R and that R is the closed direct sum of all the subspaces $\mathfrak{M}_n$.

Let $\mathfrak{D}$ be a fixed dense subspace in R, invariant with respect to every operator P_n. Then

$$P_n \mathfrak{D} = \mathfrak{M}_n \cap \mathfrak{D}, \tag{1}$$

and os $\mathfrak{M}_n \cap \mathfrak{D}$ is dense in $\mathfrak{M}_n$. In fact, if $x \in \mathfrak{D}$, then $P_n x \in \mathfrak{M}_n \cap \mathfrak{D}$; conversely, if $x \in \mathfrak{M}_n \cap \mathfrak{D}$, then $P_n x = x \in \mathfrak{M}_n \cap \mathfrak{D}$.

We consider all possible linear operators A in R, defined everywhere on $\mathfrak{D}$ and satisfying the condition $A\mathfrak{D} \in \mathfrak{D}$; in what follows all operators in R are supposed to satisfy this condition.

For a given operator A we define an operator A_{mn} from $\mathfrak{M}_n$ to $\mathfrak{M}_m$, letting

$$A_{mn} x = P_m A x \quad \text{when} \quad x \in \mathfrak{D} \cap \mathfrak{M}_n. \tag{2}$$

The operators A_{mn} form a matrix $\|A_{mn}\|$, which we will call *the matrix of the operator* A with respect to the subspaces $\mathfrak{M}_m$.

The correspondence $A \sim \|A_{mn}\|$ possesses the following obvious properties:

$$\alpha A \sim \|\alpha A_{mn}\|, \quad A + B \sim \|A_{mn} + B_{mn}\|, \tag{3}$$

if $A \sim \|A_{mn}\|$, $B \sim \|B_{mn}\|$. Moreover,

$$AB \sim \left\|\sum_p A_{mp} B_{pn}\right\|, \tag{4}$$

if at least one of the following conditions is satisfied:

---

† In reality, denumerability is not essential here, and one can replace the natural series by a set of indices of any power.

(a) for every $n = 1, 2, \ldots$ and all $x \in \mathfrak{D} \cap \mathfrak{M}_n$

$$Bx = \sum_q B_{qn} x, \tag{5}$$

where the sum in formula (5) consists of a finite number of summands;

(b) for every $n = 1, 2, \ldots$ and all $x \in \mathfrak{D}$

$$P_n A x = \sum_q A_{nq} P_q x, \tag{6}$$

where the sum in formula (6) consists of a finite number of summands. In fact, in case (a) if $x \in \mathfrak{M}_n \cap \mathfrak{D}$, we have

$$\begin{aligned}(AB)_{mn} x = P_m ABx = P_m A \sum_q B_{qn} x \\ = \sum_q P_m AB_{qn} x = \sum_q A_{mq} B_{qn} x,\end{aligned}$$

because $B_{qn} x \in \mathfrak{M}_q \cap \mathfrak{D}$; further in case (b), we have

$$(AB)_{mn} x = P_m ABx = \sum_q A_{mq} P_q Bx = \sum_q A_{mq} B_{qn} x.$$

We note that the infinitesimal operators of a representation of the group of rotations of three-dimensional space satisfy both conditions (a) and (b), and also those of a representation of the proper Lorentz group, if one takes as the operators P_n the corresponding operators E^k_{jj}, and as the set $\mathfrak{D}$ the set of all finite linear combinations of the vectors $T_x \xi$, $x \in X$ (see the remark I in §13, Subsection 5).

We consider, for example, the operator H_3; the remaining operators are treated similarly.

By virtue of (8) § 17, Subsection 5, $H_3 \xi = j\xi$ when $\xi \in \mathfrak{D} \cap \mathfrak{M}^k_j$, and so

$$E^k_{ll} H_3 \xi = \begin{cases} 0 & \text{when} \quad l \neq j, \\ j\xi & \text{when} \quad l = j. \end{cases}$$

Hence $H_3 \xi = \sum_{l,k'} E^{k'}_{ll} H \xi$, where the sum consists of only one summand, corresponding to the values $l = j$ and $k' = k$; hence, the operator H_3 satisfies condition (a). Further, for any $\xi \in \mathfrak{D}$, $\eta \in \mathfrak{D}$,

$$\begin{aligned}(E^k_{jj} H_3 \xi, \eta) = (H_3 \xi, \hat{E}^k_{jj} \eta) = (\xi, \hat{H}_3 \hat{E}^k_{jj} \eta) \\ = (\xi, j\hat{E}^k_{jj} \eta) = (jE^k_{jj} \xi, \eta)\end{aligned}$$

(see (9) and (11) §15, Subsection 1); because $\mathfrak{D}$ is dense in R', we deduce from this that $E_{jj}^{k}H_3\xi = jE_{jj}^{k}\xi$, and so $E_{jj}^{k}H_3\xi = \sum_{j',k'} E_{jj}^{k}H_3E_{j'j'}^{k'}\xi$, where the sum again consists of only one summand, corresponding to $j' = j$ and $k' = k$. Hence, H_3 also satisfies condition (b),

VII

Every continuous bilinear form (ξ, η) *in the Hilbert space* R *can be represented in the form* $(\xi, \eta) = \langle A\xi, \eta\rangle$, *where* A *is a bounded linear operator in* R, *and* $\langle , \rangle$ *denotes the scalar product in* R.

If, moreover, the form (ξ, η) *is Hermitian, then the operator* A *is Hermitian.*

Proof. First we will prove that the form (ξ, η) is bounded when $|\xi| = 1$, $|\eta| = 1$. Assume the contrary; then there exist sequences ξ_n, η_n such that $|\xi_n| = 1$, $|\eta_n| = 1$ and $|(\xi_n, \eta_n)| > n^2$. Letting $\xi_n' = \frac{1}{n}\xi_n$, $\eta_n' = \frac{1}{n}\eta_n$, we obtain that $|\xi_n'| \to 0$, $|\eta_n'| \to 0$ and $|(\xi_n', \eta_n')| > 1$, but this contradicts the continuity of the bilinear form.

Thus, $|(\xi, \eta)| \leqslant C$ when $|\xi| = 1$, $|\eta| = 1$, where C is some constant. Now letting $\xi' = \frac{1}{|\xi|}\xi$, $\eta' = \frac{1}{|\eta|}\eta$ for arbitrary vectors $\xi, \eta \in R$, we see that $|(\xi', \eta')| \leqslant C$, and so

$$|(\xi, \eta)| \leqslant C|\xi||\eta|. \tag{1}$$

From inequality (1) we deduce that for fixed η the formula $f(\xi) = (\xi, \eta)$ defines a bounded linear functional in R, and so (see § 6, Subsection 7) $f(\xi)$ is represented in the form

$$(\xi, \eta) = \langle \xi, \eta_1\rangle, \tag{2}$$

where

$$|\eta_1| \leqslant C|\eta|. \tag{3}$$

We define an operator B in R, letting $B\eta = \eta_1$. It is easy to see that B is linear and, by virtue of (3), bounded.

Relation (2) now takes the form:

$$(\xi, \eta) = \langle \xi, B\eta\rangle.$$

Letting $A = B^*$, we obtain $(\xi, \eta) = \langle A\xi, \eta\rangle$. If (ξ, η) is a Hermitian form, then

$$\langle \xi, A\eta\rangle = \overline{\langle A\eta, \xi\rangle} = \overline{(\eta, \xi)} = (\xi, \eta) = \langle A\xi, \eta\rangle,$$

hence the operator A is Hermitian.

VIII

Let A be a bounded† *linear operator from the Hilbert space R_1 to the Hilbert space R_2 with domain of definition R_1 and domain of variation dense in R_2, satisfying the condition*

$$A\xi \neq 0 \quad \text{when} \quad \xi \neq 0. \tag{1}$$

Then A can be represented in the form

$$A = WH, \tag{2}$$

where H is a positive definite Hermitian operator in R_1, and W is an isometric mapping of R_1 on R_2.

Proof. We define a bilinear form (ξ, η) in R_1, letting

$$(\xi, \eta) = \langle A\xi, A\eta\rangle, \ \xi, \eta \in R_1. \tag{3}$$

It is easy to see that (ξ, η) is a Hermitian form which is continuous by virtue of the boundedness of the operator A. Hence (see Appendix VII), it can be represented in the form

$$(\xi, \eta) = \langle A\xi, A\eta\rangle = \langle B\xi, \eta\rangle, \tag{4}$$

where B is a Hermitian operator in R_1. Here $\langle B\xi, \xi\rangle = \langle A\xi, A\xi\rangle \geqslant 0$, so that B is a positive definite operator. But in such a case there exists a positive definite Hermitian operator H in R such that‡ $B = H^2$.

† In reality this theorem is also valid for unbounded operators (see, for instance, Ref. [28e]); however, we need only consider bounded operators.

‡ In the case when B possesses a complete system of eigenvectors $e_1, e_2, \ldots$ (this is the only case we need), the operator H is defined by the formula $H\xi = \sum_k \sqrt{\lambda_k}(\xi, e_k)e_k$, where λ_k is the eigenvalue of the operator B corresponding to its eigenvector e_k. In the general case we have

$$H = \int_0^\infty \sqrt{\lambda}\, \mathrm{d}E_\lambda, \ldots$$

where E_λ is the spectral decomposition of the identity for the operator B (see Ref. [2]).

Formula (3) then takes the form

$$\langle A\xi, A\eta\rangle = \langle H^2\xi, \eta\rangle = \langle H\xi, H\eta\rangle. \tag{5}$$

We define an operator W from R_1 to R_2, letting

$$WH\xi = A\xi. \tag{6}$$

The definition is unique, because it follows from (5) (when $\eta = \xi$) that $A\xi = 0$, if $H\xi = 0$; moreover, we deduce from (5) that the operator W is isometric. The domain of definition of the operator W is Δ_H, and the domain of variation Δ_A, where Δ_H, Δ_A are the domains of variation of the operators H and A. By hypothesis, Δ_A is dense in R_2. We will prove that Δ_H is dense in R_1. It will then follow that the operator W may be extended by continuity to an isometric operator — which we again denote by W — mapping R_1 on R_2; thus (2) follows from (6).

But if Δ_H were not dense in R_1, then there exists a vector $\eta \in R_1$, $\eta \neq 0$ such that $\langle \eta, H\xi\rangle = 0$, i.e. $\langle H\eta, \xi\rangle = 0$ for all $\xi \in R_1$. Hence $H\eta = 0$ and, by virtue of (5), $A\eta = 0$; this however, contradicts condition (1).

IX

I. *For two representations of the group $\mathfrak{A}$ in one and the same space R let it be possible to choose the same set $\mathfrak{D}$ (see page 97) and let the one-parameter groups $A(t)$, $B(t)$ of these two representations satisfy the conditions*

$$\frac{dA(t)x}{dt} = A\cdot A(t)x = A(t)Ax,$$

$$\frac{dB(t)x}{dt} = A\cdot B(t)x = B(t)Ax \tag{1}$$

for all $x \in \mathfrak{D}$; then $A(t) = B(t)$.

Proof. We set $C(t) = A(-t)B(t)$. From the relation

$$\frac{\Delta C(t)x}{\Delta t} = \frac{\Delta A(-t)B(t)x}{\Delta t} + A(-t)\frac{\Delta B(t)x}{\Delta t}$$

$$+\Delta A(-t)\left[\frac{\Delta B(t)x}{\Delta t} - B(t)Ax\right] + \Delta A(-t)B(t)Ax$$

and condition (1) it follows that

$$\frac{\mathrm{d}C(t)x}{\mathrm{d}t} = -A(-t)AB(t)x+A(-t)AB(t)x = 0$$

for all $x \in \mathfrak{D}$. Hence, $C(t)x = C(0)x = x$ for all $x \in \mathfrak{D}$. Since $\mathfrak{D}$ is dense in R and the operator $C(t)$ is bounded, we deduce from this that $C(t) = 1$, and so $A(t) = B(t)$.

II. *If* $\xi = \xi_p^k$ *is one of the vectors of the canonical basis of the representation* $\mathfrak{S}_{m,\rho}$, *then*

$$A_k(t)\xi = \sum_{n=0}^{\infty} \frac{t^n}{n!} A_k^n \xi, \qquad k = 1, 2, 3, \tag{2}$$

$$B_1(t)\xi = \sum_{n=0}^{\infty} \frac{t^n}{n!} B_1^n \xi \quad \text{when} \quad |\sinh t| < 1 \quad \text{and} \quad |t| < \frac{\pi}{2}, \tag{3}$$

where the sums (2) *and* (3) *converge in the norm in* R.

Proof. The assertion with regard to $A_k(t)$ was essentially proved in IV § 4, Subsection 3. Therefore it is only necessary to prove formula (3). By virtue of (9) Subsection 4 in § 11 we have $\xi \in \mathfrak{M}_p^k$ and therefore $T_{x'} \xi \in \mathfrak{M}_p^k$ for all $x' = e_{pp}^k x$, $x \in \tilde{X}$ (see the remarks 1 and 2 in § 13 Subsection 4 and Subsection 5 in § 15). Now $\mathfrak{M}_p^k$ is finite dimensional (Theorem 8 in § 11 Subsection 4) and the $T_{x'}\xi$, $x \in \tilde{X}$ form in $\mathfrak{M}_p^k$ a dense linear set; hence there exists an $x' = e_{pp} x$, $x \in \tilde{X}$ such that $T_{x'} \xi = \xi$. On the other hand $x' \in \tilde{X}$ for $x \in \tilde{X}$; therefore equation (3) follows from remark 1 in § 13 Subsection 5.

REFERENCES

1. A. I. AKHIYEZER and V. B. BERESTETSKII, *Quantum electrodynamics* (Kvantovaya elektrodinamika), Moscow (1953).
2. N. I. AKHIYEZER and I. M. GLAZMAN, *The theory of linear operators in Hilbert space* (Teoriya lineinykh operatorov v Gil'bertovom prostranstve), Moscow (1950).
3. N. J. BHABHA, Relativistic wave equations for the elementary particles, *Rev. Mod. Physics*, **17**, 200–216 (1945).
4. V. BARGMANN, Irreducible unitary representations of the Lorentz group, *Ann. of Math.* (2) **48**, 568–640 (1947).
5. F. A. BEREZIN, (a) Laplace operators on semi-simple Lie groups, *Dokl. Akad. Nauk SSSR*, **107**, 9–12 (1956).
   (b) Laplace operators on semi-simple Lie groups, *Trudy Mosk. Matem. Ob-va* **6**, 371–463 (1957).
6. F. A. BEREZIN and I. M. GELFAND, Some remarks on the theory of functions on symmetric Riemann manifolds, *Trudy Mosk. Matem. Ob-va*, **5** (1956).
7. B. L. VAN DER WAERDEN, (a) *Die gruppentheoretische Methode in der Quantenmechanik*, Springer, Berlin (1932).
   (b) *Modern algebra*, Ungar, New York (1940).
8. A. WEIL, L'integration dans les groupes topologiques et ces applications *Actualites Sci. et Indust*. 869, Paris (1938).
9. N. Ya. VILENKIN, Bessel functions and representations of the group of Euclidean motions, *Uspekhi Matem. Nauk*, **9**, 69–112 (1956).
10. I. M. GELFAND, (a) On one-parameter groups of operators in a normed space, *Dokl. Akad. Nauk SSSR*, **25**, 711–716 (1939).
    (b) *Lectures on linear algebra* (Lektsii po lineinoi algebre), Moscow (1948), English translation, Interscience tract.
    (c) The centre of an infinitesimal group ring, *Matem. Sbornik*, 26(68), 103–112 (1950).
    (d) Spherical functions on symmetric Riemann spaces, *Dokl. Akad. Nauk SSSR*, **70**, 5–8 (1950).
11. I. M. GELFAND and M. I. GRAYEV, (a) On a general method of decomposition of the regular representation of a Lie group into irreducible representations, *Dokl. Akad. Nauk SSSR*, **92**:2, 221–224 (1953).
    (b) Analogue to Plancherel's formula for classical groups, *Trudy Mosk. Matem. Ob-va*, **4**, 375–408 (1955).

12. I. M. GELFAND and M. A. NAIMARK, (a) Unitary representations of the Lorentz group, *Journ. of Physics* X, 93–94 (1946).
(b) Unitary representations of the Lorentz group, *Izv. Akad. Nauk SSSR, ser. matem.*, **11**, 411–504 (1947).
(c) Normed rings with involutions and their representations, *Izv. Akad. Nauk SSSR, ser. matem.*, **12**, 445–480 (1948).
(d) The connection between unitary representations of a complex unimodular group and its unitary subgroup, *Izv. Akad. Nauk SSSR, ser. matem.*, **14**, 239–260 (1950).
(e) Unitary representations of the classical groups, *Trudy Matem. In-ta im.* V. A. STEKLOVA, **36**, 1–288 (1950).

13. I. M. GELFAND and Z. Ya. SHAPIRO, Representations of the group of rotations in three-dimensional space and their applications, *Uspekhi Matem. Nauk*, **7**, 3–117 (1952); English translation *Amer. Math. Soc. Translations*, (2) **2**, 207–316 (1956).

14. I. M. GELFAND, and A. M. YAGLOM, (a) General relativistic-invariant equations and infinite-dimensional representations of the Lorentz group, *Zhur. Eksper. i Teoret. Fiz.*, **18**, 703–733 (1948).
(b) Pauli's theorem for general relativistic–invariant equations, *Zhur. Eksper. i Teoret. Fiz.*, **18**, 1096–1104 (1948.).

15. V. L. GINZBURG and I. Ye. TAMM, On the theory of spin, *Zhur. Eksper. i Teoret. Fiz.* **17**, 227–237, (1947).

16. R. GODEMENT, A theory of spherical functions I, *Trans. Amer. Math. Soc.*, **73**, 496–556 (1952).

17. M. I. GRAYEV, On a general method of computing traces of infinite-dimensional unitary representations of real simple Lie groups, *Dokl. Akad. Nauk SSSR*, **103**: 3, 357–360 (1955).

18. P. A. M. DIRAC, Unitary representations of the Lorentz group, *Proc. Roy Soc.*, A **183**, 284–295 (1945).

19. R. J. DUFFIN, On the characteristic matrices of covariant systems, *Phys. Rev.* **54**, 1114 (1938).

20. N. V. YEFIMOV, *A short course in analytical geometry*, Moscow (1954), English translation in preparation by Pergamon Press.

21. S. IZMAILOV, On the quantum theory of particles possessing internal rotational degrees of freedom, *Zh. Eksper. i Teoret. Fiz.*, **17**, 629–647 (1947).

22. R. COURANT and D. HILBERT, *Methods of Mathematical Physics*, Vol. I, Interscience (1953).

23. A. G. KUROSH, *Theory of groups* (Teoriya grupp), Moscow (1948), English translation, Chelsea (1955).

24. L. D. LANDAU and E. M. LIFSHITZ, (a) *The theory of fields* (Teoriya polya), Moscow, (1948), English translation published as *The Classical Theory of Fields*, Pergamon Press (1959).

(b) *Quantum mechanics* (Kvantovaya mechanika), English translation published by Pergamon Press, (1960).

25. LE COUTEUR, The structure of linear relativistic wave equations, I, II, *Proc. Roy. Soc.* A, **202**, 288–300, 394–407 (1950).

26. L. A. LYUSTERNIK and V. I. SOBOLEV, *Elements of functional analysis*, (Elementy funktsional'nogo analiza), Moscow (1951), English translation, Constable.

27. L. LOOMIS, *An introduction to abstract harmonic analysis*, Van Nostrand, New York (1953).

28. M. A. NAIMARK, (a) Rings with involution, *Uspekhi Matem. Nauk.* **3**, 52–145 (1948), English translation, *Amer. Math. Soc. Translation* No. 25 (1950).
   (b) On the description of all unitary representations of the complex classical groups, I, II, *Matem. Sbornik* **35** (77), 317–356 (1954); **37** (79), 121–140 (1955).
   (c) On linear representations of the proper Lorentz group, *Dokl. Akad. Nauk SSSR*, **97**, 969–972 (1954).
   (d) Linear representations of the Lorentz group, *Uspekhi Matem. Nauk*, **9**, 19–93 (1954); English translation, *Amer. Math. Soc. Translation*, Series 2, **6** (1957).
   (e) *Normed rings*, Normirovannye kol'tsa, Moscow (1956), English translation, Noordhoff, Groningen.
   (f) On irreducible linear representations of the complete Lorentz group, *Dokl. Akad. Nauk SSSR*, **112**, 583–586 (1957).

29. V. NEMYTSKII, M. SLUDSKAYA and A. CHERKASOV, A *course in mathematical analysis* (Kurs matematicheskogo analiza), Vol. I, Moscow (1944).

30. V. PAULI, *Relativistic theory of elementary particles* (Relyativistskaya teoria elementarnykh chastits), Moscow, (1947).

31. I. G. PETROVSKII, *Lectures on the theory of integral equations* (Lektsii po teorii integral'nykh uravnenii), Moscow (1951), English translation, Graylock (1957).

32. L. S. PONTRYAGIN, *Continuous groups* (Nepreryvnye gruppy), Moscow, (1954), English translation, Princeton (1946).

33. R. POTIER, (a) Sur les systèmes d'equation aux dérivées partielles linéaires et du premier ordre, à quatre variables invariantes dans toute transformation de Lorentz, *C. R. Acad. Sci. Paris* **222**, 638–640 (1946).
   (b) Sur la définition du vecteur-courant en théorie des corpuscules. Cas du spin demi entier, *C. R. Acad. Sci. Paris*, **222**, 855–857 (1946).
   (c) Sur la définition et les propriétés du vecteur-courant associé à un corpuscule de spin quelconque, *C. R. Acad. Sci. Paris*, **222**, 1076–1079 (1946).

34. I. M. Ryzhik and I. S. Gradshtein, *Tables of integrals, sums, series and products* (Tablitsy integralov summ ryadov i proizvedenii), Moscow, (1951).

35. V. I. Smirnov, *A course of higher mathematics*, Vol. III, Moscow, (1958), Vol. IV, Moscow (1958), Vol. V, Moscow, (1960), English translations of all three volumes in preparation by Pergamon Press.

36. E. Wild, On first order wave equations for elementary particles without subsidiary conditions, *Proc. Roy. Soc.*, *A*, **191**, 253–268 (1947).

37. M. Fierz and W. Pauli, On relativistic wave equations for particles of arbitrary spin in an electromagnetic field, *Proc. Royal Soc.*, *A*, **173**, 211–232, (1939).

38. Harish-Chandra, (a) Infinite irreducible representations of the Lorentz group, *Proc. Roy. Soc. A*, **189**, 372–401 (1947).

(b) On relativistic wave equations, *Phys. Rev.*, **71**, 793–805, (1947).

(c) Plancherel formula for complex semi-simple Lie groups, *Proc. Nat. Acad. Sci.*, **37**, 813–818, (1951).

(d) The Plancherel formula for complex semi-simple Lie groups, *Trans. Amer. Math. Soc.*, **76**, 485–528 (1954).

INDEX

VOLUMES PUBLISHED IN THE SERIES IN PURE AND APPLIED MATHEMATICS

Vol. 1. WALLACE—*Introduction to Algebraic Topology*
Vol. 2. PEDOE—*Circles*
Vol. 3. SPAIN—*Analytical Conics*
Vol. 4. MIKHLIN—*Integral Equations*
Vol. 5. EGGLESTON—*Problems in Euclidean Space: Application o Convexity*
Vol. 6. WALLACE—*Homology Theory on Algebraic Varieties*
Vol. 7. NOBLE—*Methods Based on the Wiener–Hopf Technique for the Solution of Partial Differential Equations*
Vol. 8. MIKUSIŃSKI—*Operational Calculus*
Vol. 9. HEINE—*Group Theory in Quantum Mechanics*
Vol. 10. BLAND—*The Theory of Linear Viscoelasticity*
Vol. 11. KURTH—*Axiomatics of Classical Statistical Mechanics*
Vol. 12. FUCHS—*Abelian Groups*
Vol. 13. KURATOWSKI—*Introduction to Set Theory and Topology*
Vol. 14. SPAIN—*Analytical Quadrics*
Vol. 15. HARTMAN and MIKUSIŃSKI—*Theory of Lebesgue Measure and Integration*
Vol. 16. KULCZYCKI—*Non-Euclidean Geometry*
Vol. 17. KURATOWSKI—*Introduction to Calculus*
Vol. 18. GERONIMUS—*Polynomials Orthogonal on a Circle and Interval*
Vol. 19. ELSGOLC—*Calculus of Variations*
Vol. 20. ALEXITS—*Convergence Problems of Orthogonal Series*
Vol. 21. FUCHS and LEVIN—*Functions of a Complex Variable*, *Vol. II*
Vol. 22. GOODSTEIN—*Fundamental Concepts of Mathematics*
Vol. 23. KEENE—*Abstract Sets and Finite Ordinals*
Vol. 24. DITKIN and PRUDNIKOV—*Operational Calculus in Two Variables and its Applications*
Vol. 25. VEKUA—*Generalized Analytic Functions*
Vol. 26. AMIR-MOÉZ and FASS—*Elements of Linear Spaces*
Vol. 27. GRADSHTEIN—*Direct and Converse Theorems*
Vol. 28. FUCHS—*Partially Ordered Algebraic Systems*
Vol. 29. POSTNIKOV—*Foundations of Galois Theory*
Vol. 30. BERMANT—*Course of Mathematical Analysis, Part II*
Vol. 31. ŁUKASIEWICZ—*Elements of Mathematical Logic*